FEATURES AND BENEFITS
Core-Plus Mathematics, Course 2 TEACHER'S GUIDE PART A ©2008

Content and Organization

See page(s):

- Alignment to the NCTM Grades 9–12 Content Standards. — x
- Introduction and Organization of Course 2. — xi–xvii
- Access, Equity, and Differentiation. — xvi–xvii
- Implementing the Curriculum. — xvii–xxviii

Student and Teacher Friendly

- Engaging student-centered applications invite students to read and do more mathematics on their own. Read *Matrix Methods* and *There's No Business Like Shoe Business*. — 73, 75
- Lesson development organizes problems for students into easy-to-understand instructions. See *On a Roll*, Investigation 1. — 3–9
- Full color *Student Edition* page alongside *Teacher's Guide* page for easy reference. — 1–T1
- Effective *Teacher's Guide* design provides point-of-use support to make it easier for you to focus on managing students' progress in completing investigations. — T3–T9

Extensive and Varied Practice

- **Applications** tasks help students use and apply ideas from each lesson. — 16–19
- **Connections** tasks connect each lesson's topics with other mathematics students know. — 19–21
- **Reflections** tasks help students avoid developing misconceptions and help them rethink key ideas that were developed in the lesson. — 22–23
- **Extensions** tasks provide opportunities to explore further or more deeply important ideas developed in the lesson. — 23
- **Review** tasks help students maintain important skills. — 23–24

Test Preparation and Assessment

- **Think About This Situation** assesses students' prior knowledge before the start of the lesson. — 163
- **Summarizing the Mathematics** assesses students' ability to correctly articulate the mathematics developed after each investigation in the lesson. — 169
- **Check Your Understanding** assesses students' ability to solve problems based upon the mathematics developed in each investigation in the lesson. — 169
- **Looking Back** lessons help students review and practice key ideas that were developed in the unit. — 252–256

Technology

- *CPMP-Tools*™ expands student use of technology by including software tools for algebra, geometry, statistics, and discrete mathematics and time-saving access to selected lesson data sets. — xi
- *StudentWorks*™ **CD-ROM** includes the *Student Edition* and more on one convenient CD.
- *ExamView*® *Assessment Suite* **CD-ROM** is a powerful state-of-the art test generator that combines ease of use with enormous flexibility in creating customized assessments.
- *TeacherWorks*™ *Plus* **CD-ROM** is the latest in all-in-one planners and teaching resource center including the ability to edit many of your print resources.
- *Core-Plus Mathematics* Web site resources at **www.glencoe.com**.

Course **2**

Core-Plus Mathematics

Contemporary Mathematics in Context

2nd Edition

Christian R. Hirsch • James T. Fey • Eric W. Hart
Harold L. Schoen • Ann E. Watkins
with
Beth E. Ritsema • Rebecca K. Walker • Sabrina Keller
Robin Marcus • Arthur F. Coxford • Gail Burrill

McGraw Hill **Glencoe**

New York, New York   Columbus, Ohio   Chicago, Illinois   Woodland Hills, California

 **Glencoe**

The *McGraw·Hill* Companies

 This material is based upon work supported, in part, by the National Science Foundation under grant no. ESI 0137718. Opinions expressed are those of the authors and not necessarily those of the Foundation.

Send all inquiries to:
Glencoe/McGraw-Hill
8787 Orion Place
Columbus, OH 43240-4027

ISBN: 978-0-07-877259-7   **Core-Plus Mathematics**
MHID: 0-07-877259-1   *Contemporary Mathematics in Context*
                           Course 2 Teacher Edition, Part A

ISBN: 978-0-07-877260-3   **Core-Plus Mathematics**
MHID: 0-07-877260-5   *Contemporary Mathematics in Context*
                           Course 2 Teacher Edition, Part B

Printed in the United States of America.

3 4 5 6 7 8 9 10 079/043 16 15 14 13 12 11 10 09

Core-Plus Mathematics 2 Development Team

Senior Curriculum Developers

Christian R. Hirsch (Director)
Western Michigan University

James T. Fey
University of Maryland

Eric W. Hart
Maharishi University of Management

Harold L. Schoen
University of Iowa

Ann E. Watkins
California State University, Northridge

Contributing Curriculum Developers

Beth E. Ritsema
Western Michigan University

Rebecca K. Walker
Grand Valley State University

Sabrina Keller
Michigan State University

Robin Marcus
University of Maryland

Arthur F. Coxford (deceased)
University of Michigan

Gail Burrill
*Michigan State University
(First edition only)*

Principal Evaluator

Steven W. Ziebarth
Western Michigan University

Advisory Board

Diane Briars
Pittsburgh Public Schools

Jeremy Kilpatrick
University of Georgia

Robert E. Megginson
University of Michigan

Kenneth Ruthven
University of Cambridge

David A. Smith
Duke University

Mathematical Consultants

Deborah Hughes-Hallett
University of Arizona / Harvard University

Stephen B. Maurer
Swarthmore College

William McCallum
University of Arizona

Doris Schattschneider
Moravian College

Richard Scheaffer
University of Florida

Evaluation Consultant

Norman L. Webb
University of Wisconsin-Madison

Technical Coordinator

James Laser
Western Michigan University

Collaborating Teachers

Mary Jo Messenger
Howard County Public Schools, Maryland

Jacqueline Stewart
Okemos, Michigan

Graduate Assistants

Allison BrckaLorenz
Christopher Hlas
University of Iowa

Michael Conklin
University of Maryland

Dana Grosser
Anna Kruizenga
Nicole Lanie
Diane Moore
Western Michigan University

Undergraduate Assistants

Cassie Durgin
University of Maryland

Rachael Kaluzny
Jessica Tucker
Ashley Wiersma
Western Michigan University

Core-Plus Mathematics 2 Field-Test Sites

Core-Plus Mathematics 2 builds on the strengths of the 1st edition which was shaped by multi-year field tests in 36 high schools in Alaska, California, Colorado, Georgia, Idaho, Iowa, Kentucky, Michigan, Ohio, South Carolina, and Texas. Each revised text is the product of a three-year cycle of research and development, pilot testing and refinement, and field testing and further refinement. Special thanks are extended to the following teachers and their students who participated in the testing and evaluation of 2nd Edition Course 2.

Hickman High School
Columbia, Missouri
  Melissa Hundley
  Stephanie Krawczyk
  Cheryl Lightner
  Amy McCann
  Tiffany McCracken
  Ryan Pingrey
  Michael Westcott

Holland Christian High School
Holland, Michigan
  Tim Laverell
  Brian Lemmen
  Betsi Roelofs
  John Timmer
  Mike Verkaik

Jefferson Junior High School
Columbia, Missouri
  Lori Kilfoil

Malcolm Price Lab School
Cedar Falls, Iowa
  Megan Balong
  Dennis Kettner
  James Maltas

Oakland Junior High School
Columbia, Missouri
  Dana Sleeth

Riverside University High School
Milwaukee, Wisconsin
  Cheryl Brenner
  Dave Cusma
  Alice Lanphier
  Ela Kiblawi
  Ulices Sepulveda

Rock Bridge High School
Columbia, Missouri
  Nancy Hanson
  Emily Hawn
  Lisa Holt
  Betsy Launder
  Linda Shumate

Sauk Prairie High School
Prairie du Sac, Wisconsin
  Joel Amidon
  Shane Been
  Kent Jensen
  Joan Quenan
  Scott Schutt
  Mary Walz

Washington High School
Milwaukee, Wisconsin
  Anthony Amoroso

West Junior High School
Columbia, Missouri
  Katie Bihr

Overview of Course 2

UNIT 1 FUNCTIONS, EQUATIONS, AND SYSTEMS

Functions, Equations, and Systems reviews and extends student ability to recognize, describe, and use functional relationships among quantitative variables, with special emphasis on relationships that involve two or more independent variables.

Topics include direct and inverse variation and joint variation; power functions; linear equations in standard form; and systems of two linear equations with two variables, including solution by graphing, substitution, and elimination.

UNIT 2 MATRIX METHODS

Matrix Methods develops student understanding of matrices and ability to use matrices to represent and solve problems in a variety of real-world and mathematical settings.

Topics include constructing and interpreting matrices, row and column sums, matrix addition, scalar multiplication, matrix multiplication, powers of matrices, inverse matrices, properties of matrices, and using matrices to solve systems of equations.

UNIT 3 COORDINATE METHODS

Coordinate Methods develops student understanding of coordinate methods for representing and analyzing properties of geometric shapes, for describing geometric change, and for producing animations.

Topics include representing two-dimensional figures and modeling situations with coordinates, including computer-generated graphics; distance in the coordinate plane, midpoint of a segment, and slope; coordinate and matrix models of rigid transformations (translations, rotations, and line reflections), of size transformations, and of similarity transformations; animation effects.

Overview of Course 2

Overview of Course 2

UNIT 7 TRIGONOMETRIC METHODS

Trigonometric Methods develops student understanding of trigonometric functions and the ability to use trigonometric methods to solve triangulation and indirect measurement problems.

Topics include sine, cosine, and tangent functions of measures of angles in standard position in a coordinate plane and in a right triangle; indirect measurement; analysis of variable-sided triangle mechanisms; Law of Sines and Law of Cosines.

UNIT 8 PROBABILITY DISTRIBUTIONS

Probability Distributions further develops student ability to understand and visualize situations involving chance by using simulation and mathematical analysis to construct probability distributions.

Topics include Multiplication Rule, independent events, conditional probability, probability distributions and their graphs, waiting-time distributions, expected value, and rare events.

Contents

Contents

NCTM Standards

Core-Plus Mathematics and the instructional and assessment practices it promotes address the focal points of the National Council of Teachers of Mathematics' *Principles and Standards for School Mathematics*. By design, the **process standards** on Problem Solving, Reasoning and Proof, Communication, Connections, and Representation are an integral part of each lesson of every unit in the curriculum. The chart below correlates Course 2 units with the **content standards** for grades 9–12 in terms of focus (Ⓕ) and connections (Ⓒ).

Correlation of Course 2 to NCTM Standards

NCTM Grades 9–12 Content Standards	Unit 1 Functions, Equations, and Systems	Unit 2 Matrix Methods	Unit 3 Coordinate Methods	Unit 4 Regression and Correlation	Unit 5 Nonlinear Functions and Equations	Unit 6 Network Optimization	Unit 7 Trigonometric Methods	Unit 8 Probability Distributions
Number and Operations								
Understand numbers, ways of representing numbers, relationships among numbers, and number systems		Ⓒ	Ⓒ	Ⓒ	Ⓕ		Ⓒ	Ⓒ
Understand meanings of operations and how they relate to one another		Ⓒ	Ⓒ		Ⓒ		Ⓒ	Ⓒ
Compute fluently and make reasonable estimates		Ⓒ	Ⓒ	Ⓒ	Ⓒ		Ⓒ	
Algebra								
Understand patterns, relations, and functions	Ⓕ	Ⓒ		Ⓕ	Ⓕ		Ⓕ	Ⓒ
Represent and analyze mathematical situations and structures using algebraic symbols	Ⓕ	Ⓕ	Ⓒ	Ⓕ	Ⓕ		Ⓕ	Ⓒ
Use mathematical models to represent and understand quantitative relationships	Ⓕ	Ⓕ	Ⓒ	Ⓕ	Ⓕ	Ⓒ	Ⓕ	Ⓕ
Analyze change in various contexts	Ⓕ	Ⓒ		Ⓕ	Ⓕ		Ⓒ	Ⓒ
Geometry								
Analyze characteristics and properties of two- and three-dimensional geometric shapes and develop mathematical arguments about geometric relationships			Ⓕ			Ⓕ	Ⓕ	
Specify locations and describe spatial relationships using coordinate geometry and other representational systems			Ⓕ			Ⓒ	Ⓕ	
Apply transformations and use symmetry to analyze mathematical situations			Ⓕ	Ⓒ			Ⓒ	
Use visualization, spatial reasoning, and geometric modeling to solve problems	Ⓒ		Ⓕ	Ⓒ		Ⓕ	Ⓕ	Ⓒ
Measurement								
Understand measurable attributes of objects and the units, systems, and processes of measurement			Ⓒ	Ⓒ			Ⓕ	
Apply appropriate techniques, tools, and formulas to determine measurements			Ⓒ	Ⓒ			Ⓕ	Ⓒ
Data Analysis and Probability								
Formulate questions that can be addressed with data and collect, organize, and display relevant data to answer them		Ⓒ		Ⓕ			Ⓒ	Ⓒ
Select and use appropriate statistical methods to analyze data				Ⓕ			Ⓒ	Ⓒ
Develop and evaluate inferences and predictions that are based on data				Ⓕ			Ⓒ	Ⓕ
Understand and apply basic concepts of probability				Ⓒ			Ⓒ	Ⓕ

Overview

Introduction

The first three courses in *Core-Plus Mathematics* provide a significant common core of broadly useful mathematics for all students. They were developed to prepare students for success in college, in careers, and in daily life in contemporary society. Course 4 continues the preparation of students for success in college mathematics and statistics courses. The program builds upon the theme of mathematics as sense-making. Through investigations of real-life contexts, students develop a rich understanding of important mathematics that makes sense to them and which, in turn, enables them to make sense out of new situations and problems.

Each course in *Core-Plus Mathematics* shares the following mathematical and instructional features.

- ## Integrated Content

  Each year the curriculum advances students' understanding of mathematics along interwoven strands of algebra and functions, statistics and probability, geometry and trigonometry, and discrete mathematics. These strands are unified by fundamental themes, by common topics, and by mathematical habits of mind or ways of thinking. Developing mathematics each year along multiple strands helps students develop diverse mathematical insights and nurtures their differing strengths and talents.

- ## Mathematical Modeling

  The curriculum emphasizes mathematical modeling including the processes of data collection, representation, interpretation, prediction, and simulation. The modeling perspective permits students to experience mathematics as a means of making sense of data and problems that arise in diverse contexts within and across cultures.

- ## Access and Challenge

  The curriculum is designed to make mathematics accessible to more students, while at the same time challenging the most able students. Differences in students' performance and interest can be accommodated by the depth and level of abstraction to which core mathematics topics are pursued, by the nature and degree of difficulty of applications, and by providing opportunities for student choice of homework tasks and projects.

- ## Technology

  Numeric, graphic, and symbolic manipulation capabilities such as those found on many graphing calculators are assumed and appropriately used throughout the curriculum. The curriculum materials also include a suite of computer software called *CPMP-Tools* that provide powerful aids to learning mathematics and solving mathematical problems. (See pages xvii–xviii for further details.) This use of technology permits the curriculum and instruction to emphasize multiple representations (verbal, numerical, graphical, and symbolic) and to focus on goals in which mathematical thinking and problem solving are central.

- ## Active Learning

  Instructional materials promote active learning and teaching centered around collaborative investigations of problem situations followed by teacher-led whole-class summarizing activities that lead to analysis, abstraction, and further application of underlying mathematical ideas and principles. Students are actively engaged in exploring, conjecturing, verifying, generalizing, applying, proving, evaluating, and communicating mathematical ideas.

- ## Multi-dimensional Assessment

  Comprehensive assessment of student understanding and progress through both curriculum-embedded assessment opportunities and supplementary assessment tasks supports instruction and enables monitoring and evaluation of each student's performance in terms of mathematical processes, content, and dispositions.

Core-Plus Mathematics is designed to make mathematics accessible and more meaningful to more students. Developing mathematics along multiple strands nurtures the differing strengths and talents of students and simultaneously helps them to develop diverse mathematical insights. Developing mathematics from a modeling perspective permits students to experience mathematics as a means of making sense of data and problems that arise in diverse contexts within and across cultures. Engaging students in collaborating on tasks in small groups develops their ability to both deal with, and find commonality in, diversity of ideas. Using technology as a means for learning and doing mathematics enables students to develop versatile ways of dealing with realistic situations and reduces the manipulative skill filter which has prevented large numbers of students from continuing their study of significant mathematics. In addition, technology-produced graphics offer powerful new ways of visualizing mathematics across each of the strands.

Integrated Mathematics

Core-Plus Mathematics replaces the traditional Algebra-Geometry-Advanced Algebra/Trigonometry-Precalculus sequence of high school mathematics courses with a sequence of courses that features concurrent and connected development of important mathematics drawn from four strands.

Algebra and Functions

The Algebra and Functions strand develops student ability to recognize, represent, and solve problems involving relations among quantitative variables. Central to the development is the use of functions as mathematical models. The key algebraic models in the curriculum are linear, exponential, power, polynomial, logarithmic, rational, and trigonometric functions. Modeling with systems of equations, both linear and nonlinear, is developed. Attention is also given to symbolic reasoning and manipulation.

Geometry and Trigonometry

The primary goal of the Geometry and Trigonometry strand is to develop visual thinking and ability to construct, reason with, interpret, and apply mathematical models of patterns in visual and physical contexts. The focus is on describing patterns in shape, size, and location; representing patterns with drawings, coordinates, or vectors; predicting changes and invariants in shapes under transformations; and organizing geometric facts and relationships through deductive reasoning.

Statistics and Probability

The primary goal of the Statistics and Probability strand is to develop student ability to analyze data intelligently, to recognize and measure variation, and to understand the patterns that underlie probabilistic situations. The ultimate goal is for students to understand how inferences can be made about a population by looking at a sample from that population. Graphical methods of data analysis, simulations, sampling, and experience with the collection and interpretation of real data are featured.

Discrete Mathematics

The Discrete Mathematics strand develops student ability to solve problems using vertex-edge graphs, recursion, matrices, systematic counting methods (combinatorics), and voting methods. Key themes are discrete mathematical modeling, optimization, and algorithmic problem-solving.

Connected Strands

Each of these four strands of mathematics is developed within focused units connected by fundamental ideas such as symmetry, matrices, functions, data analysis, and curve-fitting. The strands also are connected across units by mathematical habits of mind such as visual thinking, recursive thinking, searching for and explaining patterns, making and checking conjectures, reasoning with multiple representations, inventing mathematics, and providing convincing arguments and proofs.

The strands are unified further by the fundamental themes of data, representation, shape, and change. Important mathematical ideas are frequently revisited through this attention to connections within and across strands, enabling students to develop a robust and connected understanding of mathematics.

Organization of Course 2

Course 2 consists of eight units. Each of the units is comprised of two to four multi-day lessons in which major ideas are developed through investigation of rich applied problems. Units vary in length from approximately two to six weeks.

Unit 1 *Functions, Equations, and Systems*	**Unit 5** *Nonlinear Functions and Equations*
Unit 2 *Matrix Methods*	**Unit 6** *Network Optimization*
Unit 3 *Coordinate Methods*	**Unit 7** *Trigonometric Methods*
Unit 4 *Regression and Correlation*	**Unit 8** *Probability Distributions*

The 2nd Edition of Course 2 builds on the strengths of the 1st Edition. It includes mathematical content which the developers believed is the most important mathematics all ninth-grade students should have the opportunity to learn. In particular, the content of the last units in the text are not viewed as optional as is often the case with traditional textbooks. Depending on the mathematics standards and content expectations for your state, you may wish to have students complete all Course 1 units before they embark on Course 2 of the *Core-Plus Mathematics* series.

Instructional Model

The manner in which students encounter mathematical ideas can contribute significantly to the quality of their learning and the depth of their understanding. *Core-Plus Mathematics* units are designed around multi-day lessons centered on big ideas. Each lesson includes 2–4 focused mathematical investigations that engage students in a four-phase cycle of classroom activities, described in the following paragraph—*Launch, Explore, Share and Summarize,* and *Apply*. This cycle is designed to engage students in investigating and making sense of problem situations, in constructing important mathematical concepts and methods, in generalizing and proving mathematical relationships, and in communicating, both orally and in writing, their thinking and the results of their efforts. Most classroom activities are designed to be completed by students working collaboratively in groups of two to four students.

LAUNCH class discussion

Think About This Situation

The lesson launch promotes a teacher-led discussion of a problem situation and of related questions to think about. This discussion sets the context for the student work to follow and helps to generate student interest. It also provides an opportunity for the teacher to assess student knowledge and to clarify directions for the investigation to follow.

EXPLORE group investigation

Investigation

Classroom activity then shifts to investigating focused problems and questions related to the launching situation by gathering data, looking for and explaining patterns, constructing models and meanings, and making and verifying conjectures. As students collaborate in pairs or small groups, the teacher circulates among students providing guidance and support, clarifying or asking questions, giving hints, providing encouragement, and drawing group members into the discussion to help groups collaborate more effectively. The investigations and related questions posed by students and teachers drive the learning.

SHARE AND SUMMARIZE class discussion

Summarize the Mathematics

This investigative work is followed by a teacher-led class discussion (referred to as Summarize the Mathematics) in which students summarize mathematical ideas developed in their groups, providing an opportunity to construct a shared understanding of important concepts, methods, and approaches. This discussion leads to a class summary of important ideas or to further exploration of a topic if competing perspectives remain. Varying points of view and differing conclusions that can be justified should be encouraged.

APPLY individual tasks

Check Your Understanding

Students are given a task to complete on their own to check and reinforce their initial understanding of concepts and methods.

Overview

Homework

In addition to the classroom investigations, *Core-Plus Mathematics* provides sets of On Your Own tasks, which are designed to engage students in applying, connecting, reflecting on, extending, and reviewing their evolving mathematical knowledge. On Your Own tasks are provided for each lesson in the materials and are central to the learning goals of each lesson. These tasks are intended primarily for individual work outside of class. Selection of homework tasks should be based on student performance and the availability of time and technology. Also, students should exercise some choice of tasks to pursue, and, at times should be given the opportunity to pose their own problems and questions to investigate. The chart below describes the types of tasks in a typical On Your Own set.

On Your Own: Homework Tasks	
Applications	These tasks provide opportunities for students to use and strengthen their understanding of the ideas they have learned in the lesson.
Connections	These tasks help students to build links between mathematical topics they have studied in the lesson and to connect those topics with other mathematics that they know.
Reflections	These tasks provide opportunities for students to re-examine their thinking about ideas in the lesson.
Extensions	These tasks provide opportunities for students to explore further or more deeply the mathematics they are learning.
Review	These tasks provide opportunities for just-in-time review and distributed practice of mathematical skills to maintain procedural fluency.

Additional Summarizing Activities

In *Core-Plus Mathematics*, students learn mathematics by doing mathematics. However, it is important that students prepare and maintain summaries of important concepts and methods that are developed. Students should create a Math Toolkit that organizes important class-generated ideas and selected Summarize the Mathematics responses as they complete investigations. Math Toolkit Prompts are provided in this *Teacher's Guide* to assist in identifying and summarizing key concepts and methods as they are developed by students.

In addition, the final lesson in each unit is a Looking Back lesson that helps students review and synthesize the key mathematical concepts and techniques developed in the unit. The Summarize the Mathematics questions in this lesson are focused on key ideas of the unit. The Check Your Understanding asks students to prepare a summary of the important concepts and skills developed in the unit. Templates to guide preparation of these unit summaries can be found in the *Unit Resource Masters*. Completed Unit Summaries should become part of students' Math Toolkits.

Students should retain their Math Toolkits as they continue on to Courses 3 and 4. In some districts, teachers collect these resources at the end of the school year and return them to students in the fall.

Multiple Approaches to Assessment

Assessing what students know and are able to do is an integral part of *Core-Plus Mathematics*. There are opportunities for assessment in each phase of the instructional cycle. Initially, as students pursue the investigations that comprise the curriculum, the teacher is able to informally assess student understanding of mathematical processes and content and their disposition toward mathematics. At the end of each investigation, a class discussion to Summarize the Mathematics provides an opportunity for the teacher to assess levels of understanding that various groups of students have reached as they share and explain their findings. Finally, the Check Your Understanding tasks and the tasks in the On Your Own sets provide further opportunities to assess the level of understanding of each individual student. Quizzes, in-class tests, take-home assessment tasks, and extended projects are included in the teacher resource materials.

A more detailed description of the complete assessment program is given on pages xxi–xv of this text and in *Implementing Core-Plus Mathematics*.

Practicing for Standardized Tests

Opportunities for additional review and practice are provided in eight Preparing for Standardized Tests practice sets included in the *Unit Resource Masters*. Each Practicing for Standardized Tests master presents 10 questions and a test-taking tip. The questions are presented in the form of test items similar to how they often appear in standardized tests such as state assessments tests, the Preliminary Scholastic Aptitude Test (PSAT), or the ACT PLAN. By using these practice sets, students can become familiar with the formats of standardized tests and develop effective test-taking strategies for performing well on such tests.

Access, Equity, and Differentiation

Several research studies have provided evidence that introducing activities through class discussion, teaching students to explain and justify, and making real-world contexts accessible to students promote greater access and equity in mathematics classrooms. (Boaler, J. "Learning from Teaching: Exploring the Relationship Between Reform Curriculum and Equity," *Journal for Research in Mathematics Education*, 2002, Vol. 33, No. 4, 239–258, and Brown, C.A., Stein, M.K., and Forman, E. A. "Assisting teachers and students to reform their mathematics classroom," *Education Studies in Mathematics*, 1996, 31–93). These practices that help promote equity are briefly discussed below.

Introducing Activities Through Class Discussions Group and class discussions of the aim of activities, the meaning of contexts, the challenging points within problems, and possible problem access points to which students might turn make tasks more evenly accessible to all students.

Teaching Students to Explain and Justify their Thinking Giving explicit attention to explaining thinking and evaluating what makes a good piece of work helps students improve their work.

Making Real-world Contexts Accessible Considering the constraints that real situations involve and connecting these situations with issues and topics in their own lives helps students view mathematics as something that will help them interpret their world.

Other Practices that Promote Equity Mixed-ability classes, a focus on problems solving, high expectations for all students, attention to a broad array of mathematical topics, and allowing students to restate problems in their own words also appear to help students from different racial, ethnic, and linguistic groups be more successful in mathematics.

Overview

Core-Plus Mathematics offers many opportunities for teachers to incorporate these practices into daily routines. One such built-in opportunity is the Think About This Situations (TATS) used to introduce lessons through discussions. Although no TATS questions are in the student text for individual investigations there are often suggestions in the *Teacher's Guide* for class launches of investigations. Since much of the mathematical content is based on real contexts, it is important that all students understand the contexts and draw on their own or a classmates background knowledge. Opportunities for students to explain and justify their thinking are built into all curriculum features. Look for opportunities to encourage the habit of mind of justifying one's thinking as students work individually and participate in small-group or class discussions.

The *Teacher's Guide* periodically includes notes that provide specific ideas for differentiation at point of use. Look for the margin notes.

Implementing the Curriculum

Considering mathematics topics and knowledge presented at each grade level and how that knowledge is built upon in succeeding grades is key to improving student learning. To support building the teacher expertise to effectively implement *Core-Plus Mathematics* the developers recommend that districts begin adoption with Course 1 and add a course level each year. Encourage teachers to progress from Course 1 to Course 4 in stages, so they can develop an understanding of the growth of mathematical ideas in the curriculum. Realize that teachers will need time and support to improve instruction for their students.

Additional advice related to successful implementation is on the Core-Plus Mathematics Project (CPMP) Web site at www.wmich.edu/cpmp under Implementation.

Planning for Instruction

The *Core-Plus Mathematics* curriculum is not only changing what mathematics all students have the opportunity to learn, but also changing how that learning occurs and is assessed. Active learning is most effective when accompanied with active teaching. Just as the student text is designed to actively engage students in doing mathematics, the teacher's resource materials are designed to support teachers in planning for instruction; in observing, listening, questioning, and facilitating student work, and orchestrating classroom discussion; and in managing the classroom.

The *Teacher's Guide* provides suggestions, based on the experiences of field-test teachers, for implementing this exciting new curriculum in your classroom. You probably will find new ideas that can at first be overwhelming. The developers highly recommend that teachers who are teaching *Core-Plus Mathematics* for the first time do so at least in pairs who share a common planning period.

Each of the items listed below is included in the *Teacher's Guide* for each unit.
- Unit Overview
- Objectives, suggested timeline, and materials needed
- Instructional notes and suggestions
- Suggested assignments for each homework set
- Solutions for investigations and homework tasks

Each *Unit Resource Masters* includes reproducible masters for teaching, student activities, technology tips, a unit summary, and practicing for standardized tests. Also included in each *Unit Resource Masters* is the assessment package for the unit as outlined on pages xxi–xxiv.

A first step toward planning the teaching of a unit is to review the scope and sequence of the unit. This review provides an overall feel for the goals and coherence of the unit. The *Scope and Sequence* guide shows where specific mathematical topics fit in the complete four-year curriculum. Working through the student investigations, if possible with a colleague, provides help in thinking about possible student responses and understanding mathematical ideas that may be unfamiliar.

In the *Teacher's Guide*, at the beginning of each unit, you will find a Planning Guide to assist in overall planning. This resource gives a quick overview of lessons, suggested assignments, materials needed, and pacing suggestions.

You will also find teaching notes for each lesson, including instructional suggestions and sample student responses to investigations and homework sets. Thinking about the range of possible responses and solutions to problems proves to be very helpful in facilitating student work.

Some teachers choose to post the homework assignment at the beginning of a lesson along with the due date—usually a day or two following planned completion of the lesson. Other teachers prefer to assign particular tasks at appropriate points during the course of the multiday investigation, and then assign the remaining tasks toward the end of the lesson. Review tasks can be assigned before the completion of the investigation. Note that all recommended assignments include provision for student choice of some tasks. This is but one of many ways in which this curriculum is designed to accommodate and support differences in students' interests and performance levels.

It is strongly recommended that student solutions to Connections tasks be discussed in class. These tasks help students organize and formalize the mathematics developed in context and connect it to other mathematics they have studied. Structuring the underlying mathematics and building connections are best accomplished by comparing and discussing student work and synthesizing key ideas within the classroom.

Some recommended assignments include Just-in-Time Review tasks. It is important that these tasks be assigned as indicated in the Planning Guide to help ensure understanding of ideas or procedures needed in the next investigation.

Technology in Course 2

In the 21st century, anyone who faces the challenge of learning mathematics or using mathematics to solve problems can draw on the resources of powerful information technology tools. Calculators and computers can help with calculations, drawing, and data analysis in mathematical explorations and solving mathematical problems.

Graphing Calculators: Graphing calculators with iteration capabilities are assumed for class work and homework. Computer algebra system (CAS) capabilities are desirable.

Overview

Computers: Periodically, it would be valuable to have one classroom computer for whole class discussions, 4–6 classroom computers for groups to use as stations during investigations, portable classroom sets of computers, or computer lab access. For some homework tasks, school or home computer availability is also desirable.

Computer software: The use of spreadsheet, interactive geometry, data analysis, and vertex-edge graph software, and computer algebra systems (CAS) is incorporated into Course 2 units. The curriculum materials include computer software called *CPMP-Tools* specifically designed to support student learning and problem solving.

The software toolkit includes four families of programs:

Algebra The software for work on algebra problems includes an electronic spreadsheet and a computer algebra system (CAS) that produces tables and graphs of functions, manipulates algebraic expressions, and solves equations and inequalities.

Geometry The software for work on geometry problems includes an interactive drawing program for constructing, measuring, and manipulating geometric figures and a set of custom tools for studying computer animation and geometric models of physical mechanisms.

Statistics The software for work on data analysis and probability problems provides tools for graphic display and analysis of data, simulation of probabilistic situations, and mathematical modeling of quantitative relationships.

Discrete Mathematics The software for work on graph theory problems provides tools for constructing, manipulating, and analyzing vertex-edge graphs.

In addition to the general purpose tools provided for work on tasks in each strand of *Core-Plus Mathematics*, *CPMP-Tools* includes files that provide electronic copies of most data sets essential for work on problems in each *Core-Plus Mathematics* course. When students see an opportunity to use computer tools for work on a particular investigation, they can select the *CPMP-Tools* menu corresponding to the content involved in the problem. Then they can select the sub-menu items corresponding to the required mathematical operations and data sets. Each unit overview in the Teacher's Guide provides general information related to *CPMP-Tools* use in the unit. Technology notes at point of use alert teachers to applicable software and specific data sets included in the software.

Materials Needed for Course 2

The following is a complete list of items used in the eight units of Course 2.
Each unit Planning Guide indicates the items used in that unit. (See Unit 1
pages T3A–T3B for specifications to build the ramp indicated below.)

Necessary

Balls	Stop watches
Ramp materials	Graph poster paper
Tape measures	Spaghetti
Protractors	Colored pencils
Rulers, centimeter and inches	Protractors
Yardsticks or meter sticks	Linkage strips that allow 12-cm and
Dice	16-cm sides

Optional:

Household products with known pH levels	Game of LIFE®
Game of Monopoly®	Decks of cards

Electronic Resources

The *Core-Plus Mathematics* student text, *Teacher's Guide*, and *Unit Resource Masters* are included for viewing and printing from the *Core-Plus Mathematics TeacherWorks Plus* CD-ROM. Custom tailoring of assessment items can be accomplished by using the *ExamView* Assessment Suites. *CPMP-Tools* is available on both the *StudentWorks* and *TeacherWorks Plus* CD-ROMs.

Orchestrating Lessons

Core-Plus Mathematics is designed to engage students in a four-phase cycle of classroom activities. The activities in Course 2, as in Course 1, often require both students and teachers to assume roles quite different than those in more traditional mathematics classrooms. Students successfully completing Course 1 should have become accustomed to these new roles. Although realistic problem solving and investigative work by students are the heart of the curriculum, how teachers orchestrate the launching of an investigation and the sharing and summarizing of results is critical to successful implementation.

Students enter the classroom with differing strengths, experience, and knowledge. These differences can be viewed as assets. Engaging the class in a free-flowing give-and-take discussion of how students think about the launch situations serves to connect lessons with the informal understandings of data, shape, change, and chance that students bring to the classroom. Try to maximize the participation of students in these discussions by emphasizing that their ideas and possible approaches are valued and important and that definitive answers are not necessarily expected at this time.

Overview

Once launched, an investigation may involve students working together collaboratively in small groups for a period of days punctuated occasionally by brief class discussion of questions students have raised. In this setting, the investigation becomes driven primarily by the instructional materials themselves. Rather than orchestrating class discussion, the teacher shifts to circulating among the groups and observing, listening, and interacting with students by asking guiding or probing questions. These small-group investigations lead to (re)invention of important mathematics that make sense to students. Sharing, and agreeing as a class, on the mathematical ideas that groups are developing is the purpose of the Summarizing the Mathematics (STM) in the instructional materials.

Class discussions at STMs are orchestrated somewhat differently than during the launch of a lesson. At this stage, mathematical ideas and methods still may be under development and may vary for individual groups. So class discussion should involve groups comparing their methods and results, analyzing their work, and arriving at conclusions agreed upon by the class.

Periodically, you will find samples of class discussions centered around Think About This Situation or Summarize the Mathematics questions at point of use. These sample discussions, called Promoting Mathematical Discourse, may provide some ideas for your class discussions. These sample discussions are indicated by  .

Assessment

Throughout the *Core-Plus Mathematics* curriculum, the term "assessment" is meant to include all instances of gathering information about students' levels of understanding and their disposition toward mathematics for purposes of making decisions about instruction. You may want to consult the extended section on assessment in *Implementing Core-Plus Mathematics*.

The dimensions of student performance that are assessed in this curriculum (see chart below) are consistent with the assessment recommendations of the National Council of Teachers of Mathematics in the *Assessment Standards for School Mathematics* (NCTM, 1995). They are more comprehensive than those of a typical testing program.

Assessment Dimensions		
Process	**Content**	**Disposition**
Problem Solving	Concepts	Beliefs
Reasoning	Applications	Perseverance
Communication	Mathematical Representation	Confidence
Connections	Procedures	Enthusiasm

Overview

Sources of Assessment Information

Several kinds of assessment are available to teachers using *Core-Plus Mathematics*. Some of these sources reside within the student text itself, some of them are student-generated, and some are materials designed specifically for assessment. Understanding the nature of these sources is a prerequisite for selecting assessment tools, establishing guidelines on how to score assessments, making judgments about what students know and are able to do, and assigning grades.

Curriculum Sources

Two features of the curriculum, questioning and observation by the teacher, provide fundamental and particularly useful ways of gathering formative assessment information. The student text uses questions to facilitate student understanding of new concepts, of how these concepts fit with earlier ideas and with one another, and of how they can be applied in problem situations. Whether students are working individually or in groups, the teacher is given a window to watch how the students think about and apply mathematics as they attempt to answer the questions posed in the curriculum materials. In fact, by observing how students respond to the curriculum-embedded questions, the teacher can assess student performance across all process, content, and attitude dimensions described in the chart on page xxi.

Specific features in the student material that focus on different ways students respond to questions are the Summarize the Mathematics, Check Your Understanding, and the On Your Own homework sets. Summarize the Mathematics features are intended to bring students together, usually after they have been working in small groups, so they may share and discuss the progress each group has made during a sequence of related activities. The questions in the Summarize the Mathematics are focused on the mathematical concepts and procedures developed in the investigation. They should help the teacher and the students identify and formalize the key ideas of the investigation. Each Summarize the Mathematics is intended to be treated as a whole-class discussion, so it should provide an opportunity for teachers to assess, informally, the levels of understanding that the various groups of students have reached.

Following each Summarize the Mathematics, the Check Your Understanding tasks are meant to be completed by students working individually. Student responses to these tasks provide an opportunity for teachers to assess the level of understanding of each student.

The tasks in the On Your Own homework sets serve many purposes, including post-investigation assessment. Each type of task in the On Your Own homework sets has a different instructional purpose. Applications tasks provide opportunities for students to demonstrate how well they understand and can use the ideas they learned in the investigations of the lesson. Work on Connections tasks demonstrates how well the students understand links between mathematical topics they studied in the lesson and their ability to connect those topics with other mathematics that they know. Reflections tasks provide insight into students' mathematical thinking and strategic competence. Extensions tasks reveal how well students are able to extend the present content beyond the level addressed in the investigations. The Review tasks allow for pre-assessment of students' understanding of ideas or procedures needed in the upcoming lessons and also provide information on how well students are retaining previously learned mathematics. The performance of students or groups of students on each of these types of tasks provides the teacher with further information to help assess each student's evolving ability to use, connect, and extend the mathematics of the lesson.

Finally, an opportunity for group self-assessment is provided in the last element of each unit, the Looking Back lesson. These tasks help students pull together and demonstrate what they have learned in the unit and at the same time provide helpful review and confidence-building for students.

Student-Generated Sources

Mathematics Toolkits Students should create a Math Toolkit that organizes important class-generated ideas and selected Summarize the Mathematics responses as they complete investigations. Constructing a Math Toolkit prompts are provided in the *Teacher's Guide* to assist in identifying key concepts and methods as they are developed by students.

Unit Summaries A summary template intended to help students organize and record the main ideas learned in the unit is provided in each *Unit Resource Masters*. The synthesis of ideas that occurs during completion of the "Looking Back" lesson and the final unit Summarize the Mathematics discussion should provide the background for student completion of the unit summary.

Assessment Resources

Each *Unit Resource Masters* includes lesson quizzes and unit assessments in the form of tests, take-home tasks, and projects. There are also banks of questions and projects from which you can form end of semester exams following the Unit 4 and Unit 8 assessment masters. Calculators are assumed in most cases and are intended to be available to students. Teacher discretion should be used regarding student access to their textbook and Math Toolkit for assessments. In general, if the goals to be assessed are problem solving and reasoning, while memory of facts and procedural skill are of less interest, resources may be allowed. However, if automaticity of procedures or unaided recall are being assessed, it is appropriate to prohibit resource materials.

The *ExamView* software can be used to modify the curriculum provided assessment items or to create formal assessments using a combination of curriculum supplied items and ones by the teacher.

Lesson Quizzes Two forms of a quiz covering the main ideas of each lesson are provided. These quizzes are comprised of problems meant to determine if students have developed understanding of the important concepts and procedures of each lesson. The two forms of each quiz are not necessarily equivalent, although they assess essentially the same mathematical ideas. Since many rich opportunities for assessing students are embedded in the curriculum itself, you may choose not to use a quiz at the end of every lesson.

Overview

Unit Tests Two forms of tests are provided for each unit and are intended to be completed in a 50-minute class period. The two forms of each test are not necessarily equivalent, although they assess essentially the same mathematical ideas. Teachers should preview the two versions carefully to be sure that the unit assessment aligns with the learning goals emphasized.

Take-Home Assessments Take-home assessment tasks are included for each unit. The students or the teacher should choose one or, at most, two of these tasks. These assessments, some of which are best done by students working in pairs or small groups, provide students with the opportunity to organize the information from the completed unit, to work with another student or group of students, to engage in in-depth problem solving, to grapple with new and more complex situations related to the mathematics of the unit, and to avoid the time pressure often generated by in-class exams. These problems may also require more extensive use of technology than is often available in the regular classroom during testing situations. You may wish to use these more in-depth problems as a replacement for a portion of an in-class end-of-unit exam.

Projects Assessment traditionally has been based on evaluating work that students have completed in a very short time period and under restricted conditions. Some assessment, however, should involve work done over a longer time period and with the aid of resources. Thus, assessment projects are included in unit assessments. These projects, which are intended to be completed by small groups of students, provide an opportunity for students to conduct an investigation that extends and applies the main ideas from the unit and to write a summary of their findings. Many of these might also allow for students to present their work in a variety of ways. You may have students who would rather prepare and present their work orally or visually using computers and/or video equipment. In this way, the projects can provide an opportunity for students to use their creativity while demonstrating their understanding of mathematics.

Midterm and Final Assessments A bank of assessment tasks, from which to construct midterm and final exams that fit your particular class needs and emphases, are provided in the Unit 4 and Unit 8 *Unit Resource Masters*. In addition to problems similar in form to those on the quizzes and tests, these assessment banks include several multiple-choice problems for each unit.

Extended assessment projects are also included with the end-of-year assessments. These projects are investigations that make use of many of the main ideas encountered in the curriculum. They require use of material from more than one unit. The projects are intended to be completed by small groups of students working over a period of time. You may wish to have different groups work on different projects and then give presentations or create posters of their work.

Portfolios The *Core-Plus Mathematics* assessment program provides many tasks that can be placed in students' portfolios, including reports of individual and group projects, Math Toolkits, teacher-completed observation checklists, unit assessments (especially the take-home tasks), and projects. See *Implementing Core-Plus Mathematics* for additional portfolio information.

Overview

Scoring Assessments

High expectations of the quality of students' written work will encourage students to reach their potential. Assigning scores to open-ended assessments and to observations of students' performance requires more subjective judgment by the teacher than does grading short-answer or multiple-choice tests. It is therefore not possible to provide a complete set of explicit guidelines for scoring open-ended assessment items and written or oral reports. However, some general guidelines may be helpful. When scoring student work on open-ended assessment tasks, the goal is to reward, in a fair and consistent way, the kinds of thinking and understanding that the task is meant to measure. To score open-ended assessment tasks, teachers should have a general rubric, or scoring scheme, with several response levels in mind; a specific rubric and anchor items. (See *Implementing Core-Plus Mathematics* for more details.) The general rubric is the foundation for scoring across a wide range of types of open-ended tasks. The following general rubric can be used for most assessment tasks provided with *Core-Plus Mathematics*.

General Scoring Rubric	
4 points	Contains complete response with clear, coherent, and unambiguous explanation; includes clear and simple diagram, if appropriate; communicates effectively to identified audience; shows understanding of question's mathematical ideas and processes; identifies all important elements of question; includes examples and counterexamples; gives strong supporting arguments
3 points	Contains good solid response with some, but not all, of the characteristics above; explains less completely; may include minor error of execution but not of understanding
2 points	Contains complete response, but explanation is muddled; presents incomplete arguments; includes diagrams that are inappropriate or unclear, or fails to provide a diagram when it would be appropriate; indicates some understanding of mathematical ideas, but in an unclear way; shows clear evidence of understanding some important ideas while also making one or more fundamental, specific errors
1 point	Omits parts of question and response; has major errors; uses inappropriate strategies
0 points	No response; frivolous or irrelevant response

Assigning Grades

Since the *Core-Plus Mathematics* approach and materials provide a wide variety of assessment information, the teacher will be in a good position to assign appropriate grades. With such a wide choice for assessment, a word of caution is appropriate. *It is easy to overassess students.* The developers believe it is best to vary assessment methods from lesson to lesson, and from unit to unit. If information on what students understand and are able to do is available from their homework and in-class work, it may not be necessary to take the time for a formal quiz after each lesson. Similarly, information from take-home assessments or project work may replace all or portions of an in-class test.

Deciding exactly how to weigh the various kinds of assessment information is a decision that the teacher will need to make and communicate clearly to students.

Managing Classroom Activities

Active Learning and Collaborative Work

The *Core-Plus Mathematics* curriculum materials are designed to promote active, collaborative learning and group work for two important reasons. First, a collaborative environment fosters students' ability to make sense of mathematics and develop deep mathematical understandings. Collaborative learning is an effective method for engaging all the students in the learning process, particularly students who have been under represented in mathematics classes. Second, practice in collaborative learning in the classroom is practice for real life: students develop and exercise the same skills in the classroom that they need in their lives at home, in the community, and in the workplace.

Value of Individuals

Perhaps the most fundamental belief underlying the use of collaborative learning is that every student is viewed as a valuable resource and contributor. In other words, every student participates in group work and is given the opportunity and time to voice ideas and opinions. Implementing this concept is not easy nor does it happen automatically. In order to set a tone that will promote respect for individuals and their contributions, classroom norms should be established. Teachers should initiate a discussion and together write all the student formulated classroom rules for both individual and group behavior. The positively stated rules of behavior should be posted in the classroom and every member of the learning community should be held responsible for adhering to them.

Importance of Social Connections

Even in classrooms in which the rules for showing respect have been clearly established, experience has shown that students still cannot talk with one another about mathematics (or social studies, or literature, or any other subject) if they do not first have positive social connections.

One way to develop this kind of common base is through team-building activities. These short activities may be used at the beginning of the year to help students get acquainted with the whole class, and may be used during the year whenever new groups are formed to help groupmates know one another better. Team-building activities help students learn new and positive things about classmates with whom they may have attended classes for years, but have not known in depth. The time taken for these quick team builders pays off later in helping students feel comfortable enough to work with the members of their group.

Need for Teaching Social Skills

Experience also has shown that social skills are critical to the successful functioning of any small group. Because there is no guarantee that students of any particular age will have the social skills necessary for effective group work, it often is necessary to teach these skills to build a collaborative learning environment.

These social skills are specific skills, not general goals. Examples of specific social skills that the teacher can teach in the classroom include responding to ideas respectfully, keeping track of time, disagreeing in an agreeable way,

Overview

involving everyone, and following directions. Though goals such as cooperating and listening are important, they are too general to teach.

One of the premises of collaborative learning is that by developing the appropriate skills through practice, anyone in the class can learn to work in a group with anyone else. Learning to work in groups is a continuous process, however, and the process can be helped by decisions that the teacher makes.

One method of teaching social skills is to begin by selecting a specific skill and then having the class brainstorm to develop a script for practicing that skill. Next, the students practice that skill during their group work. Finally, in what is called the processing, the students discuss within their groups how well they performed the assigned social skill. Effective teaching of social skills requires practicing and processing; merely describing a specific social skill is not enough. The *Teacher's Guide* includes specific collaborative skills to practice and processing prompts for student self-assessment.

The culture and teaching-learning norms created within the classroom are crucial to the success of this curriculum. It is important to inculcate in students a sense of inquiry and responsibility for their own learning. Without this commitment, active, collaborative learning by students cannot be effective. Some students seem satisfied with the rationale that collaboration is important in workplace. Others may need to understand that the struggle of verbalizing their thinking, listening to others' thinking, questioning themselves and other group members, and coming to an agreement increases their understanding and retention of the mathematics while contributing to the formation of important thinking skills or habits of mind.

Issues of helping students to work collaboratively will become less pressing as both you and your students experience this type of learning. *Implementing Core-Plus Mathematics* provides additional information related to the challenge of facilitating collaborative work including support to help teachers make decisions about group size, composition, method of selection, the duration of groups and dealing with student absences. This resource also offers a number of practical suggestions from *Core-Plus Mathematics* teachers on effectively pacing instruction in a student-centered classroom.

Additional Resources

Implementing Core-Plus Mathematics contains expanded information on:
- the scope and sequence of Courses 1–4,
- managing classroom activities,
- differentiation built into the program,
- the assessment program,
- communication with parents, and
- mathematics program evaluation.

You will find it useful to have the implementation guide available for reference throughout the school year.

Math Link articles related to *Core-Plus Mathematics* written by developers and teachers are available on the *Core-Plus Mathematics* Project Web site at www.wmich.edu/cpmp under Publications. These articles were written based on first edition experiences, but in many cases are still applicable to the second edition materials.

Topics include:

- selecting and implementing *Core-Plus Mathematics*,
- effectively using collaborative groups,
- the four-year mathematics program,
- options for acceleration paths to AP Calculus or AP Statistics,
- meeting the needs of ELL and LEP students,
- college placement,
- the International Baccalaureate Program, and
- achievement in Science.

Annotated Bibliography Available on the CPMP Web site under Publications are references to articles, book chapters, dissertations, papers presented at conferences, and field-test reports based on the program. Some of these resources can be downloaded.

Professional Development Opportunities A variety of professional development opportunities are provided by Glencoe and the Core-Plus Mathematics Project. Workshops are listed on the CPMP Web site www.wmich.edu/cpmp under Implementation. Experienced *Core-Plus Mathematics* teacher-consultants can be contracted to provide onsite inservice. Contact your Glencoe sales representative or the CPMP office (cpmp@wmich.edu) for provider names.

Parent Support Information and resources for parents including helping with homework, research supporting *Core-Plus Mathematics*, evidence of success, and frequently asked questions is available at www.wmich.edu/cpmp/parentresource/index.html.

UNIT 1

FUNCTIONS, EQUATIONS, AND SYSTEMS

Mathematical problems that arise in science, government, business, sports, and the arts usually involve combinations of several variables and several conditions relating those variables.

For example, karate students often try to demonstrate their skill by breaking boards. Success depends on finding the right combination of speed, mass, and aim for the karate chop and on the length, width, thickness, and strength of the target board.

Through work on the investigations in this unit, you will develop the understanding and skill needed to solve problems that involve several variables and relationships among those variables. Key ideas will be developed through your work on three lessons.

Lessons

1 Direct and Inverse Variation

Use algebraic ideas and symbols to express direct and inverse variation relationships among variables, to write those relationships in useful equivalent forms, and to solve problems where direct and inverse variation are involved.

2 Multivariable Functions

Use functions of two variables to represent quantitative relationships that involve combinations of direct and inverse variation and sums of direct variation expressions. Use graphs to study solutions for linear equations with two variables.

3 Systems of Linear Equations

Use estimation and symbolic reasoning to solve systems of two linear equations with two variables by methods involving inspection of graphs, substitution of variables, and elimination of variables.

FUNCTIONS, EQUATIONS, AND SYSTEMS

Unit Overview

This first algebra and functions unit of Course 2 builds on the units of Course 1 that developed student understanding of functions and their representation in tables, graphs, and symbolic rules and the particular properties of linear, exponential, and quadratic functions. The first lesson provides a review of those concepts and skills. The subsequent lessons are designed to extend algebraic thinking and problem solving to functions and equations involving several independent variables and finally systems of linear equations with two variables.

The following material gives overviews of the three main lessons in *Functions, Equations, and Systems*.

Lesson 1 *Direct and Inverse Variation* The goal of this lesson is to review patterns of change that are modeled well by single-variable functions—with special attention to direct and inverse variation relations. Students are asked to collect, organize, and analyze data from experiments and then to search in their toolkit of familiar functions for mathematical models of the observed quantitative patterns.

Lesson 2 *Multivariable Functions* The goal of this lesson is to extend the notions of direct and inverse variation to functions of two independent variables. For example, if $z = k \cdot \frac{x}{y}$, we say that z is directly proportional to x and inversely proportional to y. Then a different kind of two-variable function $z = ax + by$ is examined with special focus on the set of solutions (x, y) for linear equations in the form $ax + by = c$ and their graphs.

Lesson 3 *Systems of Linear Equations* The investigations of this lesson develop the understanding and skill required to set up and solve systems of two linear equations in two variables using a graphical method, a substitution method, and an elimination method. Investigation 3 develops the ability to recognize the forms of system equations that result in 0, 1, or 2 solutions.

- Review familiar families of single variable functions (especially linear, exponential, and quadratic functions)
- Recognize direct and inverse variation functions with one or more independent variables, express those relationships in symbolic form, and manipulate those expressions into equivalent useful forms
- Recognize and represent graphically and symbolically relationships in which one variable is a linear function of two independent variables and graph solutions of equations in the form "$ax + by = c$"
- Set up and solve systems involving two linear equations with two variables by use of graphing, substitution, and elimination methods. Recognize whether systems have 0, 1, or 2 solutions by inspecting the equations

CPMP-Tools

CPMP-Tools software is a suite of Java-based mathematical software specifically designed to support student learning and problem solving in each strand of *Core-Plus Mathematics*. The software includes four families of programs: *Algebra* (spreadsheet and CAS), *Geometry* (coordinate and synthetic), *Statistics*, and *Discrete Math*. Each content area includes specific custom tools and some data sets used in investigations and homework. Additional information about the course-specific software for Course 2 is included in the front matter of this Teacher's Guide.

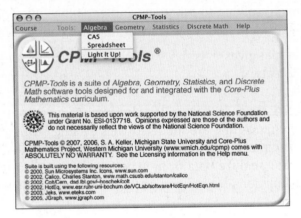

In Lesson 1 of this unit on page 10, students can use the CAS software under the Algebra menu to explore the shapes of graphs of functions of the form $y = kx^r$ and $y = \dfrac{k}{x^r}$ for various values of k and r.

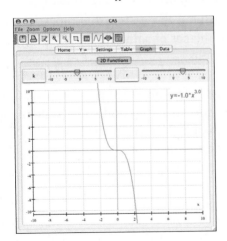

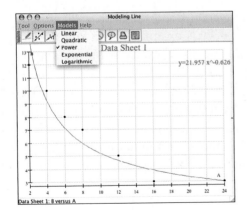

Also under the Algebra menu, you will find the "Light It Up!" custom tool to use to explore Ohm's Law in Lesson 2. Additionally, the data for On Your Own Task 12 on page 21 is built into the software. Students can access this data from the *StudentWorks* CD to quickly complete the task at home.

Review and Practice

Core-Plus Mathematics includes review tasks in the homework sets. The purpose of the review tasks is two-fold. Some tasks are **just-in-time review** of skills needed in the following lesson. These tasks will be designated by a clock icon near the solution. Some tasks provide **distributed practice** of mathematical skills to maintain procedural fluency. These tasks should be completed outside of class by students. If a few students are identified as needing additional assistance with specific skills, they should be given additional assistance outside of class.

Practicing for Standardized Tests

Opportunities for additional review and practice are provided in the Practicing for Standardized Tests masters in each Unit Resources booklet. Each Practicing for Standardized Tests master presents 10 questions that draw on all content strands. The questions are presented in the form of test items similar to how they often appear in standardized tests such as state assessment tests, the Preliminary Scholastic Aptitude Test (PSAT), or the ACT PLAN. We suggest using these practice sets following the unit assessment so students can become familiar with the formats of standardized tests and develop effective test-taking strategies for performing well on such tests.

Developing a Collaborative Classroom

Core-Plus Mathematics has been designed to support learning through interactive problem-based investigations. As you help your students get to know each other in the first days of the school year, you should develop collaborative group behavior guidelines similar to the ones below:

- Each member contributes to the group's work.
- Each member of the group is responsible for listening carefully when another group member is talking.
- Each member of the group has the responsibility and the right to ask questions.
- Each group member should help others in the group when asked.
- Each member of the group should be considerate and encouraging.
- All group members should work together until everyone understands and can explain the group's results.

One way to help students work together effectively is to choose a collaborative skill on which to focus for a particular investigation. Introduce the skill to the class by discussing what that skill might look and sound like. Once students have worked in their groups for a class period, provide a collaborative-processing prompt that leads to a full-class discussion of the particular skill. Suggestions for skills and the corresponding collaboration processing prompts are often provided in the Teacher's Guide. Holding students accountable to established group norms and giving them positive feedback regarding their group's interaction is particularly important at the early stages of developing effective groups.

Unit 1

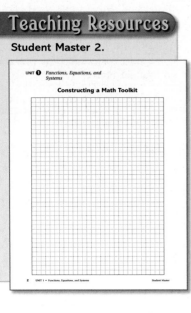

Additional resources and guidelines related to inquiry-based classrooms are in *Implementing Core-Plus Mathematics* which is included on the *TeacherWorks* CD.

Access and Equity Matters

Research by Jo Boaler (Boaler, J. 1998, 2000, 2002) and by the Quasar Project (Brown, C. A. Stein, M. K. and Favar, E. A., 1996) has identified particular teaching practices with curricula such as *Core-Plus Mathematics* that promote greater access and equity in mathematics classrooms. See the front matter of this Teacher's Guide for more information. (p. xvi)

These practices include:

• introducing activities through class discussion.

• teaching students to explain and justify.

• making real-world contexts accessible by discussing the contexts.

Core-Plus Mathematics offers many opportunities for teachers to incorporate these practices into daily routines. The Think About This Situation is one built-in opportunity to introduce investigations through discussion. You may wish to begin investigations in a similar way. Since much of the mathematical content is based in real-world contexts, it is important that all students understand the contexts and draw on their own or a classmate's background knowledge when possible. Opportunities for students to explain and justify their thinking are built into all curriculum features. Encourage the habit of mind of justifying claims.

Writing Thorough Responses

Helping students develop skills in writing complete and concise solutions is one of the goals of this curriculum. However, always writing thorough responses can unnecessarily slow student progress through the investigations. As a guideline, we suggest that during investigations, students should make notes of their thinking and discussion of ideas rather than use complete sentences. Investigation time can be thought of as draft work or getting ideas out for discussion. For investigation problems that ask students to explain reasoning or to compare, you may want to require complete-sentence responses. Student responses to the Summarize the Mathematics and Math Toolkit entries should be more complete. If these responses are written following the class summary of important mathematical ideas, students will be able to write more thorough responses. Homework tasks from the On Your Own sets should also be thoroughly written.

Lesson Objectives	On Your Own Assignments*	Suggested Pacing	Materials
Lesson 1 *Direct and Inverse Variation* • Recognize numeric and graphic patterns of change in direct and inverse variation relationships • Express direct and inverse variation relationships in symbolic forms • Recognize and represent relationships between variables that can be modeled by power functions $y = ax^r$ ($r \neq 0$) • Solve problems involving direct and inverse variation	**After Investigation 1:** A1, A2 or A3, C8 or C9, C10, R13–R15, R18, Rv21–Rv25 **After Investigation 2:** A4–A7, C11, C12, R16–R18, E19 or E20, Rv26, Rv27	9 days (including assessment)	• Balls or toy cars, ramp materials, tape measures or rulers, and stop watches for the experiment in Investigation 1 (See TG p. T3.) • Graph poster paper • *CPMP-Tools* CAS • Unit Resources
Lesson 2 *Multivariable Functions* • Write rules to define functions of two variables that combine direct and inverse variation • Solve for one variable in terms of the others in situations where the variables are related by direct and inverse variation • Write equations in the general form $ax + by = c$ to express conditions relating two variables • Solve linear equations for one variable in terms of the other • Graph linear equations in the form $ax + by = c$	**After Investigation 1:** A1, A2 or A3, A4, A5 or A6, C11, C12, R19, choose two of E23–E26, Rv29–Rv33 **After Investigation 2:** A7 or A8, A9, A10, C13, C14 or C15, C16, C17 or C18, R20–R22, E27, E28, Rv34–Rv37	6 days (including assessment)	• *CPMP-Tools* "Light It Up!" custom tool for Ohm's Law • Graph poster paper • Unit Resources
Lesson 3 *Systems of Linear Equations* • Write systems of linear equations to match given problem conditions • Solve linear systems by graphing, substitution, and elimination methods • Recognize linear systems with zero or infinitely many solutions by inspecting graphs, equation forms, and results of reasoning by substitution and elimination	**After Investigation 1:** A1–A3, C10, R16, R17, Rv27, Rv28 **After Investigation 2:** A4, A5, C12, R18, R19, choose one of E22–E26, Rv29, Rv30 **After Investigation 3:** A6–A9, C11, C13, C14 or C15, R20, R21, E25 or E26, Rv31 *Take Home Assessment Task 3 can be assigned as an alternative to A6–A9 for students who do not need additional work applying what they learned in Inv 3.*	8 days (including assessment)	• Unit Resources
Lesson 4 *Looking Back* • Review and synthesize the major objectives of the unit		3 days (including assessment)	• Unit Resources

* When choice is indicated, it is important to leave the choice to the student.

Note: It is best if Connections tasks are discussed as a whole class after they have been assigned as homework.

LESSON 1

Direct and Inverse Variation

The Winter Olympic Games include downhill, Super G, slalom, and giant slalom ski-race events. The downhill has the longest runs (over 3,000 meters) and the greatest vertical drops (over 800 meters) with the greatest distance between turns and the highest speeds—Olympic downhill racers achieve speeds of up to 85 miles per hour! The slalom, most technical of the four events, has the shortest runs and the smallest vertical drops with the least distance between turns. However, the goal in all four events is the same—to reach the finish line in the shortest time.

If you have ever raced down a hill—on foot, skis, a sled, a bike, inline skates, or a skateboard—then experience tells you that the time it takes depends on many variables.

Direct and
Inverse Variation

One of the central ideas in the algebra and functions strand of *Core-Plus Mathematics* is the notion that algebraic expressions can be used in a variety of ways to represent and reason about relationships between variables in scientific and business problems. Units in Course 1 focused on this general theme and on particular families of algebraic functions that are especially useful—linear, exponential, and quadratic.

This lesson of *Functions, Equations, and Systems* provides a bridge between students' prior experience with functions and algebraic expressions that involve a single independent variable and a single dependent variable and more complex functions and expressions involving three or more variables.

The first investigation engages students in thinking about and experimenting with a simplified race course. Students consider how *run time* for a downhill race relates to *ramp length* and *platform height*. Then they are asked to connect the quantitative relationships in this situation to patterns produced by a variety of single-variable functions with special attention to direct and inverse variation.

The second investigation extends the notions of direct and inverse variation to power functions where the dependent variable is directly or inversely proportional to some power of the independent variable.

Lesson Objectives

- Recognize numeric and graphic patterns of change in direct and inverse variation relationships
- Express direct and inverse variation relationships in symbolic forms
- Recognize and represent relationships between variables that can be modeled by power functions $y = ax^r$ $(r \neq 0)$
- Solve problems involving direct and inverse variation

Lesson Launch

Students might have a variety of ideas about the questions concerning critical factors in downhill racing. No "right answers" are required, but it might be a good idea to record some of the conjectures to return to after the experiment in Investigation 1.

Think About This Situation

Consider various sports that involve downhill racing. Think about the factors that decrease or increase the time it takes to travel from top to bottom.

a For downhill or slalom skiing, how will changes in the length of the course affect race time? How will changes in vertical drop of the course affect race time? How will changes in the distance between turns affect race time?

b What other factors will affect downhill or slalom ski-race times? How will changes in each of those variables increase or decrease race time?

c Pick another downhill race sport that interests you and think about the variables that affect race time in that sport event. What changes in those variables will increase the time to travel from top to bottom? What changes will decrease the time?

In previous courses, you used tables of values, graphs, and symbolic rules to represent functions relating independent and dependent variables. You recognized and described a variety of common patterns in those relationships. In this lesson, you will develop your understanding and skill in dealing with two special types of relationships—direct and inverse variation.

Investigation 1 On a Roll

In downhill racing on skis, sleds, bikes, or skateboards, changes in two variables may have opposite effects on time from top to bottom. This makes it difficult to predict the combined effect if two variables change at the same time. However, through experimentation, you can examine the effects of change in each variable separately and then build a model of the multivariable relation.

As you work on the questions of this investigation, look for answers to these questions:

How do course length and steepness affect run time for a downhill race?

How can the relationship between those variables be expressed in symbolic form?

Think About This Situation

Unit 1

ⓐ For downhill or slalom skiing, lengthening the racecourse will increase race times and shortening the course will decrease race time. Increasing the vertical drop will decrease race time and decreasing the vertical drop will increase race time. Increasing the distance between turns will probably decrease race time assuming that overall length of the course remains constant.

ⓑ Students might mention a variety of other factors affecting race time, such as ski quality and wax, snow conditions, smoothness or bumpiness of the race course, wind, and skier skill. Each will have a somewhat different effect on race time in the ways one would expect.

ⓒ Answers to this question will vary, but the question offers an opportunity for many different students to participate in the discussion by sharing things that interest them.

Investigation ① On a Roll

When a situation involves two or more independent variables, changes in those variables might have opposite or otherwise interacting effects on the dependent variable. The problems of this investigation are designed to get students thinking about such situations, to review what they know about patterns of change associated with single variable functions, and to focus particular attention on direct and inverse variation.

The goal of the investigation is to help students develop their skills in matching function types and symbolic rules to observed data patterns. In Lesson 2, students will use their knowledge of single-variable functions to develop expressions for combined variation patterns involving two or more independent variables.

Students are asked to think about variables that affect the time required for a variety of downhill races. They replicate Galileo's classic inclined plane experiment as a test of their conjectures. Then they compare the patterns of change relating *run time* to *ramp length* and *platform height* to familiar function families. By looking separately at the effects of the two independent variables *ramp length* and *platform height* on *run time*, students encounter examples of direct and inverse variation, leading to formal definitions of those concepts and generalizations of the patterns that occur with function rules in the forms $y = ax$ and $y = \frac{a}{x}$.

COLLABORATION SKILL
Encourage contributions by all members.

This investigation is arranged in three sections. Classes with short meeting times can break the investigation into three class sessions. The first section asks students to make conjectures about the combined effects of two variables on the roll time for objects rolling down an inclined ramp and then to test those conjectures by experimentation. The second section reviews the families of single-variable functions with which students are familiar, comparing the patterns of change to what has been observed in the inclined plane experiment. Then the third section defines and develops properties of direct and inverse variation.

Setting Up The Experiment You can build a ramp with a piece of plastic, wood, or metal. Some teachers have used 8-foot plastic gutters or drain pipe (PVC) as shown on page T3B. These materials can be purchased at almost any lumber or builder's supply store. Be sure your ramp is straight and does not sag in the middle. Small toy cars or balls are good to use. Since accurate timing is quite important for a successful experiment, use a stopwatch.

There are four data collection experiments embedded in Problems 2 and 3. Distribute each experiment to a separate group, repeating experiments as needed. It would be helpful to have at least two different sets of results for each experiment. To improve accuracy, students might use the average time of three or four separate runs.

Encourage students to be precise in their measurements and to think carefully about whether their measurements make sense. You may want to have results from each of the four experiments displayed on large paper to reference in Problem 5 and again in Lesson 2.

Design for Ramp

Materials

1   10-foot, $2\frac{1}{2}$-inch PVC pipe

1   golf ball

2   $3\frac{1}{2} \times 24 \times \frac{1}{2}$-inch plywood sides

1   $3\frac{1}{2} \times 3\frac{1}{2} \times \frac{1}{2}$-inch top

2   $3\frac{1}{2} \times 12 \times \frac{1}{2}$-inch bottom and back

1   $\frac{1}{4}$-inch round rod 6 inches long

Source: Mike Verkaik

PVC Pipe

Golf ball holes: Lay the PVC pipe flat and cut $1\frac{3}{4}$-inch holes at 36, 48, 60, 72, 84, and 96 inches from the bottom.

Peg holes: Rotate the PVC pipe 90° counterclockwise and drill $\frac{5}{16}$-inch holes in the side of the stand at 38, 50, 62, 74, 86, and 98 inches from the bottom. Then rotate it 180° and drill $\frac{5}{16}$-inch holes at the same distances so that these holes are across from each other.

Stand

Drill $\frac{5}{16}$-inch holes on the side boards at 4, 7, 10, 13, 16, 19 inches. This will allow the bottom of the ramp (PVC pipe) to be about 0.25, 0.5, 0.75, 1, and 1.5 feet off the ground. A notch may need to be cut out of the top-center of the back of the stand in order to allow the PVC pipe to be placed at the lowest height. This will depend upon your construction.

Platform Height, Ramp Length, and Ride Time Ramps are often used in skateboarding, not just for "getting air," but also for starting into terrain parks or street races. Many ramps are attached to a raised platform as pictured below.

1 The height of the platform and length of the ramp affect the time it takes to roll down the ramp.

  a. For a fixed ramp length, how do you think the time it takes to ride down the ramp will change as platform height increases?

  b. For a fixed platform height, how do you think the time it takes to ride down the ramp will change as ramp length increases?

  c. Suppose that one skateboard ramp is twice as long as another ramp. What relationship between platform heights for those ramps do you think will allow skateboarders starting at the top of each ramp at the same time to reach the bottom at the same time?

To explore the effects of platform height and ramp length on the time it takes to ride downhill, you can conduct an experiment designed by Galileo over 500 years ago. To get ideas about the effects of gravity, he timed trips of a ball rolling down ramps of various heights and lengths. You can build a ramp with a piece of V-shaped wood or metal. You will find it easier to do accurate timing if the ramps are fairly long and gently sloped.

Carry out the ramp experiments described in Problems 2 and 3 below. Divide the experimental work among the members of your class, with each team taking one fixed ramp length or platform height to study.

Ramp Length

Platform Height

The goal of Problem 1 is to get students to think about the relationships between roll time and ramp length and platform height using their intuition. This problem can be used as a whole-class launch, but provide students some individual think time before group or class discussion. Then ask students to either sketch a graph of the patterns of change that they expect or use arm movements to relay this pattern.

 a. For a fixed ramp length, the time it takes to ride down the ramp will decrease as platform height increases.

   (Physical theory predicts that ride time is inversely proportional to the square root of platform height, so you might press students for more specific guesses about the pattern of change that they would expect by a question like this: Which of the graphs at the right would you expect to match the relationship between ride time and platform height? Graph I represents an inversely proportional situation, but leave the "guesses" as such for now.)

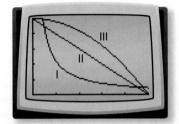

b. For a fixed platform height, the time it takes to ride down the ramp will increase as ramp length increases.

   (Physical theory predicts that this will be a linear relationship, as in Graph II. You might ask students for a conjecture about the shape of this direct variation graph by a question like this: Which of the graphs at the right would you expect to match the relationship between run time and ramp length?)

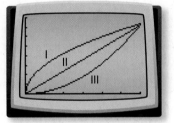

c. If one skateboard ramp is twice as long as another ramp, students might think that starting the longer ramp from a platform that is twice as high will guarantee that skateboarders starting at the top of each ramp at the same time will reach the bottom at the same time. Because the relationship between ride time and platform height is not simple inverse variation, that intuitively appealing conjecture is not true. Have students keep their idea in mind; so when they get some experimental data, they can check it against their conjecture.

(2) To see how the time T it takes a ball to roll down a ramp changes as the ramp length L increases, experiment with ramps that have lengths varying from 3 feet to 8 feet but a platform height of 0.5 feet in each case. Then rerun the experiment using a platform height of 0.25 feet in each case.

a. Record the results of each experiment in a table like this:

Ramp Length (in feet)	3	4	5	6	7	8
Roll Time (in seconds) at 0.5-ft Height						
Roll Time (in seconds) at 0.25-ft Height						

b. To study the patterns relating roll time to ramp length, make plots of the (L, T) data—one for each platform height.

c. Examine the data patterns from the two experiments. For each platform height, describe the relationship between roll time and ramp length.

(3) To see how the time T it takes a ball to roll down a ramp changes as the platform height H increases, experiment with platform heights varying from 0.25 feet to 1.5 feet but fixed ramp length of 8 feet in each case. Then change the fixed ramp length to 4 feet and see how roll time is related to platform height in that case.

a. Record the results of each experiment in a table like this:

Platform Height (in feet)	0.25	0.5	0.75	1.0	1.25	1.5
Roll Time (in seconds) for 8-ft Ramp						
Roll Time (in seconds) for 4-ft Ramp						

b. To study the patterns relating platform height and roll time, make plots of the (H, T) data—one for each ramp length.

c. Examine the data patterns from the two experiments. For a fixed ramp length, describe the relationship between roll time and platform height.

(4) Compare the results from your experiments in Problems 2 and 3 to your responses to the questions of Problem 1. Discuss any surprises and try to explain why the results make sense.

Families of Variation Patterns The data patterns and graphs that show how roll time depends on ramp length and platform height may remind you of other relationships between variables that you have seen in prior mathematical studies.

(5) Decide which of the following functions have table and graph patterns that:

- are similar to the (*ramp length, time*) relationship.

- are similar to the (*platform height, time*) relationship.

- are different from those relationships.

Be prepared to explain your decisions.

a. The sales tax on store purchases in Michigan is a function of the purchase price and can be calculated with the formula $T = 0.06p$.

2 **a.** Students' experiments might produce somewhat different data than the results below:

Ramp Length (in feet)	3	4	5	6	7	8
Roll Time (in seconds) at 0.5-ft Height	1.2	1.7	2.2	2.8	3.3	3.7
Roll Time (in seconds) at 0.25-ft Height	2.7	3.5	4.1	4.9	5.6	6.2

b.

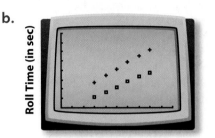

Roll Time (in sec) / Ramp Length (in ft)

c. For any fixed platform height, as ramp length increases, the roll time increases in a roughly linear pattern.

3 **a.**

Platform Height (in feet)	0.25	0.5	0.75	1.0	1.25	1.5
Roll Time (in seconds) for 8-ft Ramp	6.1	3.6	2.5	2.0	1.7	1.6
Roll Time (in seconds) for 4-ft Ramp	3.7	1.8	1.6	1.4	1.3	1.2

b.

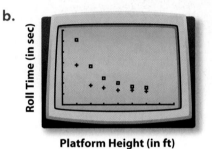

Roll Time (in sec) / Platform Height (in ft)

c. For any fixed ramp length, as platform height increases, the roll time decreases, at a decreasing rate.

4 Students are likely to have generally confirming results.

INSTRUCTIONAL NOTE The next part of this investigation is designed to help students review and reveal to you what they know about common families of functions and the tables, graphs, and symbolic rules for those functions. Since students will have plots and data tables from their experiments to study the relationships between roll time and ramp length and roll time and platform height, they can reference their function toolkit and consider possible models of those relationships by using what they know about symbolic function rules and the patterns found in tables and graphs.

Thus, the decisions about whether given functions are similar to the (*length, time*) or (*height, time*) patterns or a quite different pattern is intended to be informally justified by comparing data tables and graph shapes, not proven in any formal way by reasoning from scientific principles. Students should be able to explain their reasoning in terms of the shape of the graph and the pattern in the table that they deal with in each situation. They should be expected to use terms like *increasing* or *decreasing* and *linear* or *curved*, plus other ideas related to intercepts.

POSSIBLE ERROR
Because time is not the independent variable, some students may incorrectly put time on the horizontal axis.

Teaching Resources

Student Master 5.

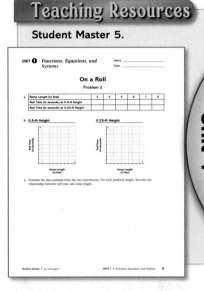

Unit 1

POSSIBLE MISCONCEPTION The data for doubling ramp length while keeping roll time constant may lead students to incorrectly assume (as the data above seem to indicate) that doubling the height for the 8-ft ramp gives the same time for the two ramps.

Teaching Resources

Student Master 6.

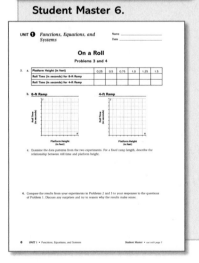

b. When a club was planning its Halloween party at the Fun House, the planners figured the cost per person using $C = \frac{225}{n}$, where n is the number of club members who would attend.

c. The number of tickets sold to a charity basketball game is a function of the price charged with rule $N = 4{,}000 - 50p$.

d. When a doctor or nurse gives an injection of medicine like penicillin, the amount of active medicine t hours later can be estimated by a function like $M = 300(0.6^t)$.

e. The circumference of a circle is related to the radius by the formula $C = 2\pi r$.

f. When a football punt leaves the kicker's foot, its height above the ground at any time in its flight is given by a function like $h = -16t^2 + 80t + 4$.

g. The average speed for the Daytona 500 race is a function of the time it takes to complete the race with rule $s = \frac{500}{t}$.

 Using your data plots from Problems 2 and 3, experiment with function graphs to find function rules that seem to be good models for the relationships between:

a. roll time T and ramp length L for each platform height you tested in Problem 2.

b. roll time T and platform height H for each ramp length you tested in Problem 3.

Basic Variation Patterns The situations in this investigation involved a variety of functions relating dependent and independent variables. Several examples involved special patterns called *direct* and *inverse variation*.

⑤ INSTRUCTIONAL NOTE When you notice the words, "Be prepared to explain your decisions or thinking," students are not expected to write their thinking. For this problem, using the student activity master will provide students a way to organize their thinking without extensive writing. By making these notes, it will be easy for students to retrieve their thinking for a class discussion if it is needed.

Rule	Similar to (L, T)	Similar to (H, T)	Different Relationship	Explanation
a. $T = 0.06D$	Yes	No	No	Linear but with different slope
b. $c = \dfrac{225}{n}$	No	Yes	No	Decreases for increasing values of n. (Some students might note that when $n = 0$, there is an infinite cost per person; in the same way, when the platform height is 0, the ball will take infinite time to roll from one end to the other!)
c. $N = 4{,}000 - 50p$	Yes	No	Yes	Linear as (L, T) but negative slope. (Students might also answer this by indicating they are different.)
d. $m = 300(0.6^t)$	No	No	Yes	Exponential decay. Has a vertical intercept value of 300 while the (H, T) relationship has no meaningful value at $H = 0$.
e. $C = 2\pi r$	Yes	No	No	Linear with vertical intercept of 0, much like the pattern relating roll time to ramp length. (Some students might be puzzled by the 2π, not realizing that this is simply a number close to 6.28.)
f. $h = -16t^2 + 80t + 4$	No	No	Yes	Quadratic pattern with a graph shaped like ∩.
g. $s = \dfrac{500}{t}$	No	Yes	No	Curve that decreases as t increases; has no vertical intercept

⑥ INSTRUCTIONAL NOTE Students might have a variety of ideas on the types of functions that would be good models for the various data patterns. As students look for a function rule in Part a, you might focus student thinking on the context by asking what the time would be for a ramp length of 0. They should recognize that the model must have a y-intercept of $(0, 0)$. After students have some time to search for rules, discuss their findings as a whole class. It is not important to dwell on this problem to get the models right at this time. The point here is to get students to connect the patterns of graphs for expressions in Problem 5 to the data plots in Problems 2 and 3 in order to identify the form of the symbolic expression that would best represent the roll-time data. (Students should not use the calculator regression feature to determine a function rule.)

a. $T = kL$, where k is some number adjusted so that the function rule matches the specific data points that the students got in their own experiments. Values of k that might turn out to be reasonable would be in the range of 0.3 to 0.8, depending on the platform height used.

b. $T = \dfrac{k}{H}$, where k is a number in the range 1.0 to 2.0, depending on the ramp length used. (On page 13, students will find that this relationship is modeled by $T = \dfrac{k}{\sqrt{H}}$.)

Direct and Inverse Variation   **T6**

Direct Variation: If the relationship of variables y and x can be expressed in the form:

$$y = kx \text{ for some constant } k,$$

then we say that **y varies directly with x** or that **y is directly proportional to x**. The number k is called the *constant of proportionality* for the relationship.

The close connection between multiplication and division of numbers implies that if y is directly proportional to x, then $\frac{y}{x} = k$. The symbolic form $\frac{y}{x} = k$ shows that the ratio of y to x is constant, for any corresponding values of y and x.

7 Explain why the perimeter P of a square is directly proportional to the length s of a side.

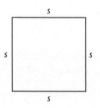

a. What equation shows this direct proportionality relationship?

b. What is the constant of proportionality?

c. How does the value of P change as the value of s increases steadily? How is this pattern of change related to the constant of proportionality?

8 Identify the direct variation relationships in Problem 5. For each:

a. Explain how the value of the dependent variable changes as the value of the independent variable steadily increases.

b. Describe the relationship of the variables involved by completing a sentence like this: "The variable _____ is directly proportional to _____, with constant of proportionality _____."

c. Express the relationship between the variables in an equivalent symbolic form that shows the constant ratio of the two variables.

Inverse Variation: If the relationship of variables y and x can be expressed in the form:

$$y = \frac{k}{x} \text{ for some constant } k,$$

then we say that **y varies inversely with x** or that **y is inversely proportional to x**. The number k is called the *constant of proportionality* for the relationship.

Once again, the close connection between multiplication and division of numbers implies that if y is inversely proportional to x, then $xy = k$. The symbolic form $xy = k$ shows that the product of y and x is constant, for any corresponding values of x and y.

7 The perimeter of a square is 4 times the length of a side.

   a. The equation is $P = 4 \cdot s$.

   b. The constant of proportionality is 4.

   c. For every increase of 1 unit in side length s, perimeter P increases by 4 units, the constant of proportionality in the equation.

8 There are two direct variation relationships in Problem 5—the Michigan sales tax ($T = 0.06p$) and the circumference of a circle ($C = 2\pi r$).

   a. For each increase of $1 in purchase price, the sales tax in Michigan increases by 6¢.

     For each increase of 1 unit in the radius, the circumference increases by 2π units.

   b. The variable _sales tax in Michigan_ is directly proportional to _purchase price_ with constant of proportionality _0.06_.

     The variable _circumference of a circle_ is directly proportional to _radius_ with constant of proportionality _2π_.

   c. Different forms that emphasize the ratios are of the form $\frac{T}{P} = 0.06$ and $\frac{C}{r} = 2\pi$.

INSTRUCTIONAL NOTE

People using quantitative reasoning in science, business, and government problem solving use the phrases _directly proportional_, _inversely proportional_, _varies directly with_, and _varies inversely with_ frequently to describe the ways that two or more variables are related to each other. The next segment of this investigation draws student attention to those two very important function types and the language used to talk about situations in which they occur.

POSSIBLE MISCONCEPTION

While $N = 4{,}000 - 5p$ is a linear relationship, it is not a direct variation relationship.

Unit 1

(9) The time t required to download a 4-megabyte music file from an Internet music seller is inversely proportional to the rate r at which data is transferred to the receiving computer.

a. How long will it take to download a 4-megabyte file if the transmission occurs at a rate of 2.5 megabytes per minute? How long if the transmission rate is 0.8 megabytes per minute?

b. How can the relationship of t and r be expressed in symbolic form?

c. How does the value of t change as the value of r increases steadily? How is this pattern of change related to the constant of proportionality?

(10) Identify the inverse variation relationships in Problem 5. For each:

a. Explain how the value of the dependent variable changes as the value of the independent variable increases steadily.

b. Express the relationship between the variables in two different but equivalent symbolic forms.

c. Describe the relationship of the variables involved by completing a sentence like this: "The variable _____ is inversely proportional to _____, with constant of proportionality _____."

(11) Examine the tables below, each of which describes a relation between x and y.

Table I

x	25	50	60	100	150
y	8	4	3.33	2	1.33

Table II

x	10	15	25	40	100
y	6	9	15	24	60

Table III

x	5	15	30	64	80
y	9.6	3.2	1.6	0.75	0.6

a. Which relations involve direct variation? What is the constant of proportionality in each case?

b. Which relations involve inverse variation? What is the constant of proportionality in each case?

9 a. 1.6 minutes, or about 96 seconds; 5 minutes, or 300 seconds

b. $t = \frac{4}{r}$ and $tr = 4$

c. As the value of r increases steadily, the value of t decreases, but it does so rapidly at first (for small r) and then more slowly as r becomes larger (see a graph of $t = \frac{4}{r}$ for $0 < r < 10$).

Since $t \cdot r = k$, when r increases, t must decrease in order for their product to remain equal to the constant of proportionality k.

INSTRUCTIONAL NOTE
See the note before Problem 7.

10 There are two inverse variation examples in Problem 5—the Halloween party cost function and the Daytona 500 average speed functions.

a. The cost per person decreases as the number attending increases, with greatest rate of decrease when n is small.

The average speed decreases as the time increases, again with the greatest rate of decrease when t is small.

b. $C = \frac{225}{n}$ and $Cn = 225$

$s = \frac{500}{t}$ and $st = 500$

c. The variable _cost per person for the party_ is inversely proportional to the _number of club members_ who attend with constant of proportionality _225_.

The variable _average speed for the race_ is inversely proportional to the _time it takes to complete the race_ with constant of proportionality _500_.

11 a. Table II involves direct variation with a constant of proportionality of 0.6.

b. Table I involves inverse variation with a constant of proportionality of 200.

Table III involves inverse variation with a constant of proportionality of 48.

INSTRUCTIONAL NOTE
You might have students individually think about Problem 11 first, before sharing their thinking in their group.

Unit 1

Summarize
the Mathematics

Functions that model direct and inverse variation relationships have tables, graphs, and rules that are related in ways that make reasoning about them easy.

a Suppose y is directly proportional to x with constant of proportionality $k > 0$.

   i. If the value of x increases by 1, how will the value of y change?

   ii. If the value of x doubles, how will the value of y change?

   iii. What will the graph of the function look like?

b A function with rule $y = mx + b$ ($b \neq 0$) is *not* a model of direct variation.

   i. How is the graph of such a linear function different from that of the related direct variation function $y = mx$? How are graphs of the two types of functions similar?

   ii. How is the table of (x, y) values for such a linear function different from that of the related direct variation function $y = mx$? How are tables of the two types of functions similar?

c Suppose y is inversely proportional to x with constant of proportionality $k > 0$.

   i. How will the value of y change as the value of x increases?

   ii. If the value of x doubles, how will the value of y change?

   iii. What will the graph of the function look like?

Be prepared to share your ideas and reasoning with the class.

✔ Check Your Understanding

For each of the following functions, indicate whether it involves direct variation, inverse variation, or neither of those special relationships. For those that do involve direct or inverse variation, identify the constant of proportionality and write a sentence like those in Problems 8 and 10 that describes the relationship.

a. The number of sheets in a stack of copier paper is related to the height of the stack in centimeters by $N = 100h$.

b. If you step on a dirty nail, you might get bacteria in the wound. An initial number of 50 bacteria could grow to $B = 50(2^t)$ bacteria at a time t hours later.

c. If a car uses g gallons of gasoline in a 200-mile test run, its fuel efficiency is calculated by the formula $E = \frac{200}{g}$.

d. The stretch of a bungee cord (in feet) is related to the jumper's weight (in pounds) by $C = 0.2w$.

e. The upward velocity v (in feet per second) of a high volleyball serve is related to time in flight t (in seconds) by $v = 64 - 32t$.

Summarize
the Mathematics

(a)
  i. The value of y increases by k for every increase of 1 in the value of x.

  ii. The value of y will double. (Students should be able to provide reasoning to justify this answer.)

  iii. The graph of the function will always be a line with positive slope containing the point (0, 0).

(b)
  i. The graph of $y = mx + b$ ($b \neq 0$) differs from that of the related direct variation function $y = mx$ only in its y-intercept (0, b). It does not pass through the point (0, 0). The graphs are parallel because they have the same slope.

  ii. The table of (x, y) values for $y = mx + b$ ($b \neq 0$) is different from that of the related direct variation function $y = mx$ in that values of y are not simply constant multiples of values of x. Also, (0, b) replaces (0, 0) in the table. The y values in the two function tables do increase at the same constant rate of m per increase of 1 in x.

(c)
  i. Values of y decrease as values of x increase, but the change in y values (for $x > 0$) is rapid at first and then levels off approaching $y = 0$. Looking at the full graph of such a relationship (including for $x < 0$), the rate of change is always greatest for x near 0.

  ii. y will be multiplied by a factor of $\frac{1}{2}$. This can be seen from the form of the equation $y = \frac{k}{x}$. (When the value of x doubles, k is divided by a number twice as large as before, or $\frac{1}{2} \cdot \frac{k}{x}$.

  iii. The graph of the function will approach the x-axis for very large positive and very small negative values of x and approach the y-axis as x values get very close to 0. Be sure students recognize that inverse variation functions have no y-intercept. This is one clue that the relationship is not represented by exponential decay. (The idea of asymptotes is developed in Course 3.)

✓ Check Your Understanding

a. The number of sheets of paper in a stack is directly proportional to the height of the stack in centimeters with constant of proportionality 100.

b. neither

c. Fuel efficiency of a car in a 200-mile test run is inversely proportional to the gallons of fuel consumed with constant of proportionality 200.

d. Stretch of the bungee cord is directly proportional to weight that is attached with constant of proportionality 0.2.

e. neither

Teaching Resources
Transparency Master 8.

UNIT ❶ *Functions, Equations, and Systems*

Summarize the Mathematics

Functions that model direct and inverse variation relationships have tables, graphs, and rules that are related in ways that make reasoning about them easy.

❶ Suppose y is directly proportional to x with constant of proportionality $k > 0$.

  i. If the value of x increases by 1, how will the value of y change?

  ii. If the value of x doubles, how will the value of y change?

  iii. What will the graph of the function look like?

❷ A function with rule $y = mx + b$ ($b \neq 0$) is not a model of direct variation.

  i. How is the graph of such a linear function different from that of the related direct variation function $y = mx$? How are graphs of the two types of functions similar?

  ii. How is the table of (x, y) values for such a linear function different from that of the related direct variation function $y = mx$? How are tables of the two types of functions similar?

❸ Suppose y is inversely proportional to x with constant of proportionality $k > 0$.

  i. How will the value of y change as the value of x increases?

  ii. If the value of x doubles, how will the value of y change?

  iii. What will the graph of the function look like?

Be prepared to share your ideas and reasoning with the class.

POSSIBLE MISCONCEPTION
Students may incorrectly think that anytime y decreases as x increases, this means inverse variation exists. Counterexamples are lines with negative slope and exponential decay relationships.

MATH TOOLKIT Pick an example of direct variation and one of inverse variation; write the relationship in the form that you used for Problems 5 and 8. Then sketch a graph that shows the pattern of change for each type of variation when $k > 0$.

PROCESSING PROMPT
Things we said to encourage one another to contribute ideas:

1. _____
2. _____
3. _____

The most common forms of direct and inverse variation can be expressed by the equations $y = kx$ and $y = \frac{k}{x}$. But there are other important examples of direct and inverse variation—expressed with rules in the form $y = kx^r$ and $y = \frac{k}{x^r}$. Because the pattern relating x and y is determined by the exponent or power r in each case, these relationships are called **power functions**.

As you work on the problems of this investigation, look for answers to these questions:

What are the patterns of variation that can be modeled well by power functions?

What practical and scientific problems can be solved by use of power functions?

Modeling Sound and Light Intensity

The intensity of sound from a voice or of light from a flashlight is related to the distance from the source to the receiving ear or surface. The more distant the source, the lower the sound or light intensity at the receiving end.

1 The following graphs show three possible patterns for functions relating sound or light intensity to distance. The graphs show distance from source to receiver as the independent variable and sound or light intensity as the dependent variable.

Graph I **Graph II** **Graph III**

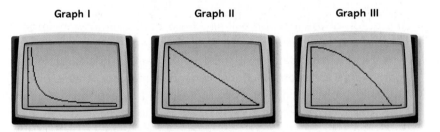

a. How would you describe the patterns of change in sound or light intensity shown by each graph?

b. Which graph do you believe is most likely to model accurately the relationship between sound or light intensity and distance from the source? Be prepared to explain your thinking.

Investigation 2   Power Models

The purpose of this investigation is to extend the notions of direct and inverse variation to include cases involving powers of the independent variable other than 1. These kinds of variation occur quite commonly and are given the name *power functions* or when used to represent patterns of change in application settings, *power models*. Power models have the general form $y = ax^r$ for some nonzero rational number r.

For example, the volume of a sphere is directly proportional to the cube of the radius $\left(V = \frac{4\pi r^3}{3}\right)$ with constant of proportionality $\frac{4\pi}{3}$. There are several important inverse square laws in physics. For example, the gravitational attraction of two bodies is inversely proportional to the square of the distance between their centers of mass.

This investigation has three main sections. The first looks at the inverse square relationship between light intensity and distance from the light source. The second section asks students to look more generally, without support of context clues, at the patterns of change associated with some of the key power-function types. The third section looks again at the inverse relationship of roll time and platform height in the inclined-plane experiment.

Although sound and light are transmitted in quite different physical forms, they both involve energy that is distributed over larger and larger areas as they spread from the source. This diffusion of energy is what explains the inverse square law of intensity as a function of distance. You can imagine a large sphere of energy expanding outward from the source. As the radius increases linearly, the surface area of the sphere grows proportional to the square of the radius. Thus, the energy per unit of surface area is inversely proportional to the area of the sphere and also inversely proportional to the square of the radius or distance from the source. Problems 1 and 2 are designed to help students discover this relationship.

Launch

To launch this investigation, it may help to bring a flashlight to class to demonstrate how the light circle of the flashlight grows as the light is moved away from a target surface. Students will also notice how the intensity of light falling on the target surface diminishes (rather rapidly) as the distance increases. Another way to suggest what analysis is going to reveal is to show a balloon at various stages of inflation and to ask "How is the thickness of the balloon material changing as the radius is increasing?". It should be reasonably imaginable that a fixed amount of balloon material must spread out thinner to cover increasing surface area. Following this discussion, allow students to think individually about Problem 1 and then present their thoughts. Students need not write a solution to Problem 1.

1
   a. Graph I shows rapid drop-off early; Graph II shows steady drop-off as distance increases; Graph III shows slow drop-off early and then a rapid drop-off as distance gets larger.

   b. Theory predicts that Graph I is the best model, but the goal at this point is to invite students to express what their intuition suggests to them. Return to this problem after work on Problem 2 Part f.

POSSIBLE MISCONCEPTION
After defining and focusing on direct and inverse variation in Investigation 1, students might believe that those are the only direct and inverse models and not expand these concepts to power functions.

COLLABORATION SKILL
Listen thoughtfully to group members in order to provide input or ask questions to make discussion deeper.

ASSIGNMENT NOTE
Be sure to assign Review Task 25 now if it has not been done.

2 You could test your ideas about the (*distance, intensity*) relationship by collecting data from an experiment. But you can also get good ideas by mathematical reasoning alone. Consider what would happen if you were to enter a dark room and shine a small flashlight directly at a flat surface like a wall. The flashlight will create a circle of light on the wall.

a. Complete entries in the following table that contains measurements of light circle diameter for one flashlight that has been held at several distances from a wall. Distance and diameter measurements are in feet. Express the area in terms of π.

Light Circle Measurements

Distance from Light Source, *x*	1	2	3	4	5	6
Diameter of Light Circle, *d*	2	4	6	8	10	12
Radius of Light Circle, *r*						
Area of Light Circle, *A*						

b. Write rules that show:

   i. diameter of light circle as a function of distance from the light source.

   ii. radius of light circle as a function of distance from the light source.

   iii. area of light circle as a function of distance from the light source.

c. Describe the relationships of the geometric variables diameter, radius, and area by completing sentences like this: "The variable _____ is _____ proportional to _____, with constant of proportionality _____."

d. Light energy is measured in a unit called *lumens*. The intensity of light is measured in lumens per unit of area. As the light circle of a flashlight or lamp increases in size, the intensity of light decreases.

To explore how that decrease in light intensity is related to distance from source to target, suppose that the flashlight that gave (*distance, diameter*) values in Part a produces 160 lumens of light energy. Use the area data from Part a to complete this table relating light intensity *I* to distance *x*.

Light Intensity Measurements

Distance from Light, *x*	1	2	3	4	5
Area of Light Circle, *A*	π	4π			
Light Intensity, *I*	$\dfrac{160}{\pi}$	$\dfrac{160}{4\pi}$			

② **a.** Answers are in bold.

Light Circle Measurements

Distance from Light Source, x	1	2	3	4	5	6
Diameter of Light Circle, d	2	4	6	8	10	12
Radius of Light Circle, r	1	2	3	4	5	6
Area of Light Circle, A	π	4π	9π	16π	25π	36π

b. **i.** $d = 2x$

    ii. $r = x$

    iii. $A = \pi x^2$

c. The variable *diameter* is directly proportional to *distance* with constant of proportionality *2*. The variable *radius* is directly proportional to *distance* with constant of proportionality *1*. The variable *area* is directly proportional to the *square of distance* with constant of proportionality π.

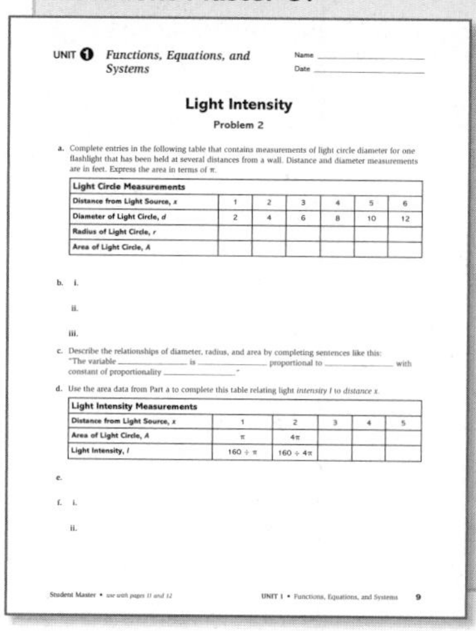

d. Answers are in bold:

Light Intensity Measurements

Distance from Light, x	1	2	3	4	5
Area of Light Circle, A	π	4π	9π	16π	25π
Light Intensity, I	$\dfrac{160}{\pi}$	$\dfrac{160}{\pi}$	$\dfrac{160}{9\pi}$	$\dfrac{160}{16\pi}$	$\dfrac{160}{25\pi}$

Students using calculators might be tempted to enter these figures as decimal approximations. However, in looking for a general relationship, it is helpful to keep the calculations as shown here.

UNIT ❶ *Functions, Equations, and Systems*

Name
Date

Light Intensity
Problem 2

Unit 1

INSTRUCTIONAL NOTE
For Problem 2, students should express area in terms of π for the entire problem.

e. Write a rule that shows light intensity I as a function of distance x from source to receiving surface.

f. Study the graph of the light intensity function in Part e.

    i. Which of the graph shapes in Problem 1 seems to best model the pattern of change in light intensity as distance from source to receiver increases?

    ii. Explain in words what the pattern of change shown by the light intensity function and its graph tells about the effective range of a flashlight or lamp.

The Power Function Family The functions describing dependence of light circle area and light intensity on distance are only two of many direct and inverse variation patterns that can be modeled by rules in the form $y = kx^r$ and $y = \dfrac{k}{x^r}$.

Use your calculator or a computer graphing tool to explore the relationship between the power r, the constant of proportionality k, and the numerical patterns relating x and y. To get a good picture of each graph, be sure to set your graphing window so you see both positive and negative values of x and y. You can use the zoom feature of your graphing tool to see more of each graph.

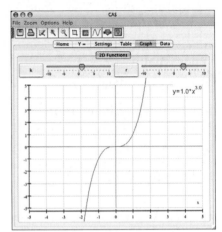

3. How is shape of the graph for a direct variation function $y = kx^r$ related to the values of r and k?

a. To see patterns that help answer this question, you might begin by studying examples in which $k = 1$ and $r = 1, 2, 3, 4, 5,$ and 6. Then explore what happens for different positive and negative values of the proportionality constant k. Describe the patterns you observe.

b. Based on the calculations involved in the different rules used in Part a, explain why the different observed patterns make sense.

4. How is the shape of the graph for an inverse variation function $y = \dfrac{k}{x^r}$ related to the values of r and k?

a. To see patterns that help answer this question, you might begin by studying examples in which $k = 1$ and $r = 1, 2, 3, 4, 5,$ and 6. Then explore what happens for different positive and negative values of the proportionality constant k. Describe the patterns that you observe.

b. Based on the calculations involved in the different rules that you used in Part a, explain why those patterns make sense.

e. $I = \dfrac{160}{\pi x^2}$

f. **i.** Graph I in Problem 1 seems most like the graph of the intensity function.

    ii. The pattern of change shows that light intensity drops off rapidly as the flashlight is drawn away from the target surface, and then further backing off produces only small absolute change in light intensity. This suggests that the effective range of a flashlight or lamp is fairly short, unless the light is focused by some sort of special lens that makes it cohere into some relatively narrow beam.

INSTRUCTIONAL NOTE Problems 3 and 4 ask students to look more generally at the patterns of change that can be expected from various possible power functions, regardless of the problem context in which those functions might prove useful as models. Students can use a graphing calculator or computer to quickly explore the basic graph-shape possibilities, then review their knowledge of exponent rules to rewrite the given function rules in equivalent power function form. For Problem 3 Part a, using a graphing window of $-3 \le x \le 3$ and $-3 \le y \le 3$ will give reasonably comparable pictures. For Part b, be sure that students are discussing why the differences for different powers occur as they do.

CPMP-Tools A few computers available as stations would allow groups to explore parameter effects for Problems 3 and 4. Alternatively, students could explore individually at home using their *StudentWorks* CD or access the updated software at www.glencoe.com/sec/math/cpmp/CPMP-Tools/. Students could compare their findings in the following class period. Note that by clicking on the parameter scale rather than using the k and r sliders, the parameter increases or decreases by 1 unit.

3 **a.** The graphs are related to the exponents as follows ($k = 1$) where the window used is $-3 \le x \le 3$ and $-3 \le y \le 3$ in each case:

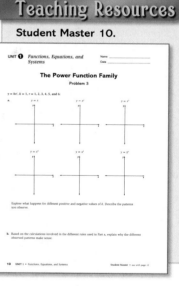

$y = x^1$ $y = x^2$ $y = x^3$

$y = x^4$ $y = x^5$ $y = x^6$

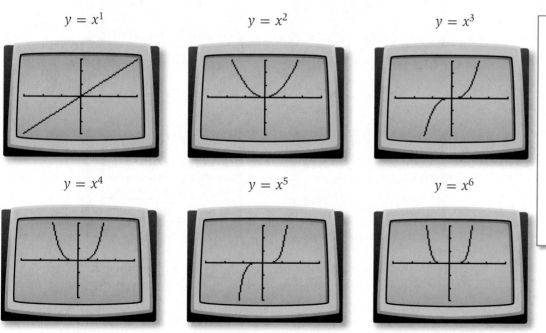

In general as k increases for positive values, the graphs retain their basic shapes, with steeper slopes. When k is negative, the graphs are mirror image reflections across the x-axis of what is shown above.

b. The fact that the graphs of even power functions are symmetric across the y-axis makes sense because for any particular number x, the product of an even number of such factors will be positive as will the product of an even number of factors of $(-x)$. The fact that the graphs of the odd power functions are symmetric about the origin makes sense because for any particular number x, the product of an odd number of factors of x will be the opposite of the product of that odd number of factors of $(-x)$. Students will probably not explain their thinking in such general terms. They might use illustrative examples like $(-5)(-5)(-5)(-5) = (5)(5)(5)(5)$, but $(-5)(-5)(-5) = -(5)(5)(5)$.

(4) **a.** The graphs are related to the exponents as follows ($k = 1$) where the window used is $-3 \le x \le 3$ and $-3 \le y \le 3$ in each case:

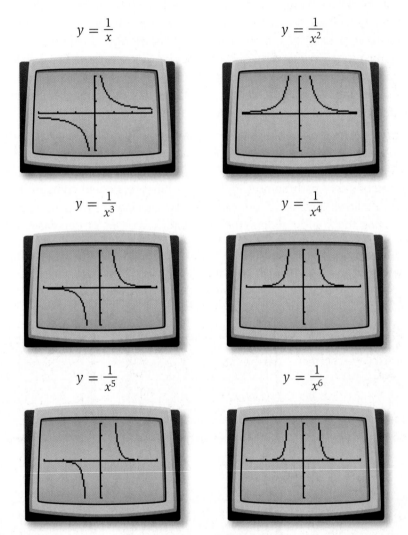

$$y = \frac{1}{x} \qquad\qquad y = \frac{1}{x^2}$$

$$y = \frac{1}{x^3} \qquad\qquad y = \frac{1}{x^4}$$

$$y = \frac{1}{x^5} \qquad\qquad y = \frac{1}{x^6}$$

The value of r affects the pattern of change in that for odd values of r, the graphs have values in both the first and third quadrants. For even r, the graphs have values in the first and second quadrants. As r increases, the rate of change near zero increases and the rate of change away from zero decreases.

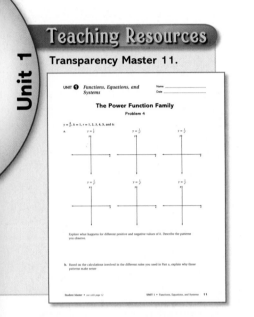

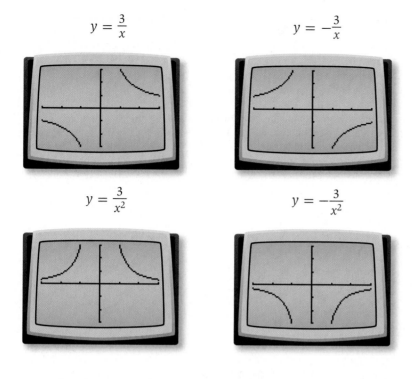

$$y = \frac{3}{x}$$

$$y = -\frac{3}{x}$$

$$y = \frac{3}{x^2}$$

$$y = -\frac{3}{x^2}$$

For a fixed r, an increase in the absolute value of k creates a slower rate of change closer to $x = 0$ but also decreases at a slower rate for values of x away from zero. For negative values of k, the graphs are mirror image reflections across the x-axis of what is described above.

b. There are several ways to make sense of these patterns. First, the fact that the graphs are all asymptotic to the y-axis is explained by the fact that dividing a constant numerator by a denominator with smaller and smaller absolute value leads to larger and larger absolute value results. The fact that the graphs are all asymptotic to the x-axis ($y = 0$) is explained by the fact that as the denominator of a fraction gets larger and larger (with numerator held constant), the absolute value of the fraction gets smaller and smaller. You might choose to introduce the word *asymptote* here or to speak of the property in more informal language.

The differences between even and odd powers can be explained in the same way as the results in Problem 3.

Modeling Roll-Time Data Patterns Scientists often get ideas for theories by studying patterns in experimental data. They usually test their theories by comparing predictions of theory to results of further experiments.

In searching for functions that are accurate models for the relationship between roll time T and platform height H, you probably found that the patterns of data from your experiments looked a lot like those of inverse variation functions. The following display shows a plot of data from experiments with an 8-foot ramp at various platform heights. A graph of $T = \frac{2}{H}$ is plotted on top of the data.

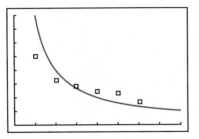

The match of function and data plot is not bad. However, scientific theories predict that (for an 8-foot ramp) roll time T and platform height H will be related by the function

$$T = \frac{2}{\sqrt{H}} \text{ which is equivalent to } T = \frac{2}{H^{0.5}} \text{ and } T = 2H^{-0.5}.$$

Scientists describe this relationship by saying, "Time is inversely proportional to the square root of platform height, with constant of proportionality 2."

5 Use the data from your own experiments of Investigation 1 and the function $T = \frac{2}{\sqrt{H}}$ to complete the following table.

Platform Height (in feet)	0.25	0.5	0.75	1.0	1.25	1.5
Experimental Roll Time (in sec) for 8-ft Ramp						
Theoretical Roll Time (in sec) for 8-ft Ramp						

a. Plot the experimental (H, T) values and the function $T = \frac{2}{\sqrt{H}}$ on a graph.

b. Why will the theoretical (predicted) and experimental (actual) results be somewhat different?

5 The theoretical predictions and sample experimental data have been entered into the following table.

Platform Height (in feet)	0.25	0.5	0.75	1.0	1.25	1.5
Experimental Roll Time (in sec) for 8-ft Ramp	6.1	3.6	2.5	2.0	1.7	1.6
Theoretical Roll Time (in sec) for 8-ft Ramp	4.00	2.83	2.31	2.00	1.79	1.63

a. A graph of the experimental data in the preceding table and the theoretical rule will look like this.

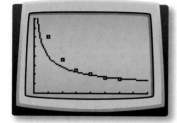 

b. When students compare their own (*platform height, roll time*) data to the model suggested by theory, they may not see a very good match because the theory ignores friction, and experimental conditions seldom match ideal models of phenomena. There should be at least a general trend in the student data that is similar to what the model predicts.

6 When you suspect that the relationship between two variables will be modeled well by a power function, you can use a calculator or computer curve-fitting tool to find a power regression rule for the function.

   a. Use the (*distance, area*) values from your table in Problem 2 Part a and a curve-fitting tool to find the power model that fits the data pattern. Explain why the rule derived in this way is similar to or different from what you developed by reasoning alone.

   b. Use the (*distance, intensity*) values from your table in Problem 2 Part d and a curve-fitting tool to find the power model that fits the data pattern. Explain why the rule derived in this way is similar to or different from what you developed by reasoning alone.

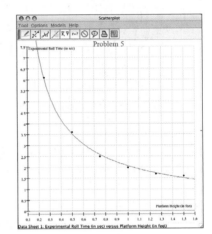

   c. Use the (*platform height, experimental roll time*) values from your table in Problem 5 and a curve-fitting tool to find the power model that fits the data pattern.

Summarize
the Mathematics

The situations in this investigation involved extensions of the basic direct and inverse variation patterns you explored in Investigation 1.

a What types of graphs occur for direct variation power functions $y = kx^r$:

   i. when r is a positive even integer and k is positive?

   ii. when r is a positive odd integer and k is positive?

b How do the answers to Part a change if k is negative?

c What types of graphs occur for inverse variation power functions $y = \dfrac{k}{x^r}$:

   i. when r is a positive even integer and k is positive?

   ii. when r is a positive odd integer and k is positive?

d How do the answers to Part c change if k is negative?

e What types of graphs occur for direct and inverse variation when r is 0.5 or −0.5?

Be prepared to share your ideas and reasoning with the class.

6 **a.** (*distance, area*) regression equation: $y = 3.14159x^2$

This method results in basically the same rule because the points were simply a result of applying the formula $A = \pi r^2$. The points used to find the regression equation were those points. So, the statistical tool was reversing the same process but rounds the coefficient on x^2.

b. (*distance, intensity*) regression equation: $y = 50.9296x^{-2}$

This regression equation also rounds π as in Part a.

c. Results of student work will vary. Using the experimental data offered in this Teacher's Guide for Problem 3 Part a of Investigation 1, one gets the power regression model $T = 2.066H^{-0.77}$ which is somewhat different from the theoretical model $T = 2H^{-0.5}$. There are a number of possible explanations for the difference in powers of the model for experimental data and theoretical predictions—the most notable being that theory does not account for friction at all.

> **DIFFERENTIATION**
> Consider assigning Extensions Task 19 to your more capable students.

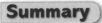

Unit 1

Summary

You might have each small group write their responses on large graph paper or individual whiteboards. Encourage students to use mathematical language as you come up with complete descriptions as a class.

Summarize the Mathematics

ⓐ i. When $k > 0$ and r is a positive even integer, the graphs are U-shaped opening upward. The graph lies in the first and second quadrants. As x increases, the y values decrease to zero and then increase. The graphs have reflection symmetry across the y-axis and a minimum value 0 at the origin.

  ii. When $k > 0$ and r is a positive odd integer, the graphs are always increasing. The graph lies in the first and third quadrants and passes through the origin. As x increases, the y values increase quickly at first then level off as x gets close to zero then increase again slowly at first and then more quickly. The graphs have half-turn symmetry about the origin.

r is positive and even, $k > 0$

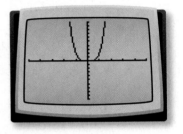

r is positive and odd, $k > 0$

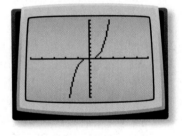

ⓑ When $k < 0$, the graphs are reflected across the x-axis. Students' descriptions of the graphs should be similar to those in Part a but for the graphs below.

r is positive and even, $k < 0$ r is positive and odd, $k < 0$

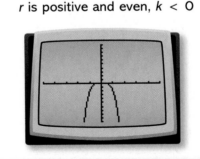
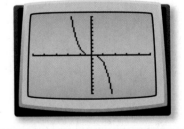

c **i.** When $k > 0$ and r is a positive even integer, the graphs lie in the first and second quadrants. In the second quadrant, as x increases, the y values increase. In the first quadrant, as x increases, the y values decrease. The graph has no y-intercept. The graphs have reflection symmetry across the y-axis.

r is positive and even, $k > 0$

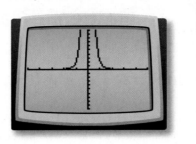

ii. When $k > 0$ and r is a positive odd integer, the graphs lie in the first and third quadrants. In the third quadrant, as x increases, the the y values decrease. In the first quadrant, as x increases, the y values decrease. The graph has no y-intercept. The graphs have half-turn symmetry about the origin.

r is positive and odd, $k > 0$

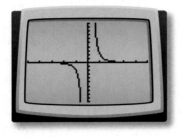

d When $k < 0$, the graphs are reflected across the x-axis. Students' descriptions of the graphs should be similar to those in Part a but for the graphs below.

r is positive and even, $k < 0$ r is positive and odd, $k < 0$

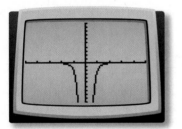 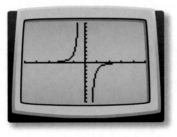

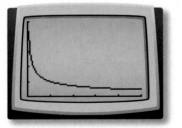 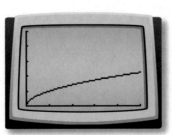

e The graphs one expects for direct and inverse variation when r is 0.5 or -0.5 are shown below:

$$y = x^{-0.5}$$ $$y = x^{0.5}$$

If $k < 0$, the graphs are reflected across the x-axis.

Summarize the Mathematics, *page 14*

Teacher: You have looked at contexts in this investigation that are a little more complex than the basic direct variation pattern $y = kx$ and the basic inverse variation pattern $y = \frac{k}{x}$. I would like you to take a minute individually to think about Part a in the Summarize the Mathematics on page 14. Make sketches, if you wish, to represent your thinking. In a couple of minutes, we will share thinking about that item.

(Students work individually for 2 minutes.)

Teacher: Missy, tell us your thoughts about the types of graphs that occur for $y = kx^r$ when r is a positive even integer and k is positive.

Missy: The graphs are all U-shaped and facing up.

Teacher: Anything else?

Missy: They also go through the origin at the lowest point.

Teacher: What do others think?

Kristen: I got the same types of graphs. But as k gets larger, the graph gets skinnier.

(Students have not used the terminology of "parabola" in their descriptions, but the teacher waits to ask for more mathematical terminology to see if it comes up as they formalize the response to Part a.)

Teacher: Okay, let's try to summarize these types of graphs for the direct variation power function using both Missy's and Kristen's ideas and also mathematical language. Who would like to give a first cut at this description?

Jon: I will. When the exponent is even and the number in front is positive, the graphs are U-shaped. These U-shapes get skinnier when k gets larger and have the minimum at the origin.

Teacher: Any clarifications or additions? *(silence—teacher waits)*

Derek: Sounds good to me.

Teacher: Jon, would you please quickly write your description on the board. You can abbreviate some of the words if you like, as long as we know what you said. *(Jon writes his description.)*

It seems that we are all agreed that Jon's description is correct. One of the ways to think about whether or not a description is helpful, as well as correct, is to reread it and see if someone who was not in our discussion could get a fairly good idea of what you mean. Try that with Jon's description. With your group, discuss whether or not this description could be clarified. *(Groups discuss Jon's description for a couple of minutes. The teacher feels that since it is early in Course 2, it is important to spend some time helping students develop good descriptions and explanations. As groups discuss, the teacher may prompt a few groups to consider the form of the rule.)*

Teacher: Okay, what are you thinking? Sam?

Sam: We decided that if someone walked into the room and looked at that description, they wouldn't really know what k and r were—that we were talking about functions like $y = kx^r$. So, we thought we would start with saying something like, "For rules like $y = kx^r$," and then continue.

Celia: We thought that, too. But Jake remembered that we can call the number k the coefficient. Could we add that, too?

Teacher: Let's get these ideas into Jon's description. Halley, would you please come up here to add these ideas. What should Halley write?

Halley: Just add, "For rules like $y = kx^r$, when the exponent is even and the number in front is positive, the graphs are U-shaped. These U-shapes get skinnier when k gets larger and have the minimum at the origin."

Mike: We could add "r" by the exponent and use "k" or "the coefficient k" instead of "the number in front." That would help clarify it.

Carlotta: Hey, I just noticed that the graphs are symmetric to the *y*-axis. Shall we add that, too?

Teacher: Good idea! Notice that Carlotta's observation compliments Missy's statement that the minimum point is at the origin. Carlotta, would you please incorporate Mike's and your thoughts into Halley's response? Let's begin by stating: "For direct variation power functions of the form $y = kx^r$, ..."

(Carlotta, with input from the class writes, "For direct variation power functions of the form $y = kx^r$, when the exponent r is even and the coefficient k is positive, the graphs are U-shaped. They are symmetric across the y-axis and have a minimum at the origin. When k (which is positive) gets larger, the graph gets skinnier.)

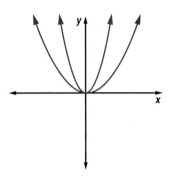

Carlotta: Look at these graphs to see what I mean. *(She points to her sketch.)*

Teacher: I really like how you added a sketch to this explanation. Many times in explaining or doing mathematics, it is very helpful to have a sketch to help understand the ideas.

The sketch Carlotta has drawn shows how the shape of an even power function changes when the positive value *k* is increased. Isaiah, would you sketch a graph showing how the shape changes when the exponent increases say from 2 to 6? *(Isaiah sketches the following graph.)*

Isaiah: Notice that I made the second graph flatter on the bottom and goes up faster away from the *y*-axis. That is what happens when the exponent increases by even integers.

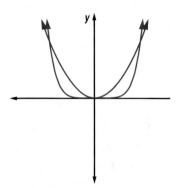

Teacher: Thanks, Isaiah. Have we included this idea in our description? *(Students indicate that it is not included.)* Please do so. Then, using your response to Part a as a model, discuss Parts b–e in your groups. I will ask different groups to write responses to different parts to share with the whole group. You will not need to write a complete response to each part since we will have a whole class discussion in a few minutes.

(Students work for a few minutes. The teacher checks that they are thinking correctly at each group. Then various groups display their solution to one of the parts in the STM. Editing occurs by students with teacher guidance as needed.)

✔ Check Your Understanding

Without using your calculator or computer graphing tool, match each function rule with its graph. In each case, write a sentence explaining the type of variation that relates x and y. For example, "y is (inversely) proportional to ... with constant of proportionality ... ."

a. $y = 0.5x^2$

b. $y = \dfrac{5}{x^2}$

c. $y = x^3$

d. $y = \dfrac{1}{x^3}$

e. $y = 3\sqrt{x}$

f. $y = (0.5^x)$

I

II

III

IV

V

VI

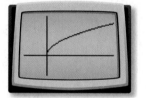

✔ Check Your Understanding

a. Graph VI; y is directly proportional to the square of x with constant of proportionality 0.5.

b. Graph III; y is inversely proportional to the square of x with constant of proportionality 5.

c. Graph I; y is directly proportional to the cube of x with constant of proportionality 1.

d. Graph II; y is inversely proportional to the cube of x with constant of proportionality 1.

e. Graph V; y is directly proportional to the square root of x with constant of proportionality 3.

f. Graph IV; y is not proportional to x.

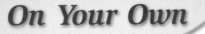

On Your Own

Applications

These tasks provide opportunities for you to use and strengthen your understanding of the ideas you have learned in the lesson.

1 For each of the following relations, indicate whether it is an example of direct variation, inverse variation, or neither.

For those relations that are examples of direct or inverse variation, identify the constant of proportionality and write a sentence describing the relationship in the language of direct and inverse variation or proportionality.

a. The rule $E = 7.50h$ gives wages earned at a job as a function of number of hours worked.

b. When members of an agriculture cooperative pool their money to buy a $40,000 hay baler, the cost per member depends on the number of members, and is calculated using $c = \dfrac{40,000}{n}$.

c. Daily profit at the Wheel Away roller rink is related to the number of paying customers by the rule $P = 8n - 350$.

d. Because, on average, Latisha makes 60% of the free throws she shoots in a basketball game, the number of points she scores on free throws depends on the number of shots she gets.

e. If a runner can average 5 miles per hour for quite a long run, the distance covered is a function of the total running time.

f. If a marathon runner covers 26 miles, the average running speed for that race is a function of the time the runner takes to complete it.

g. In any square, the side length s and the diagonal length d are related by $\dfrac{d}{s} = \sqrt{2}$.

h. In any rectangle with area 40 square inches, the length L and width W are related by $LW = 40$.

2 In many European countries, shoppers pay a *value added tax* (VAT) on most purchases. The VAT rate can be as high as 25%.

a. Suppose that the VAT rate in a country is 25%. Express the direct relationship between the value added tax T and item price P in two equivalent forms.

Unit 1

Applications

1 **a.** *Wages earned* is directly proportional to the *number of hours worked* with constant of proportionality *7.50*, or wages vary directly with hours worked.

b. *Cost per member* is inversely proportional to the *number of members* with constant of proportionality *40,000*, or cost per member varies inversely with number of members.

c. *Daily profit* is a linear function of the *number of customers*, but it *is not* an example of direct variation.

d. *Number of points scored on free throws* is directly proportional to the *number of shots* with constant of proportionality *0.6*. (Because there is probably an element of randomness in her shooting, this is not quite the same as a precise direct variation.)

e. *Distance d covered* is directly proportional to the *running time t* with constant of proportionality *5*, or distance varies directly with time: $d = 5t$.

f. *Average speed s* is inversely proportional to or varies inversely with *time t* with constant of proportionality *26*: $s = \frac{26}{t}$.

g. The *length of diagonal d of a square* is directly proportional to or varies directly with the *length of a side s* with constant of proportionality $\sqrt{2}$: $d = \sqrt{2}s$.

h. The *length L of a rectangle* with area of 40 square inches varies inversely with or is inversely proportional to the *width W* with constant of proportionality *40*: $L = \frac{40}{w}$. (Alternatively, students might choose width varies inversely with length.)

2 **a.** $T = 0.25P$ or $\frac{T}{P} = 0.25$

b. Use either of the direct variation forms that you developed in Part a to write and solve equations to answer these questions about VAT amounts:

   i. What is the value added tax on an item priced at 40 Euros?

   ii. What is the price of an item on which the VAT is 15 Euros?

   iii. What is the total purchase price (including VAT) of an item selling for 95 Euros?

c. Which direct variation form was most helpful for answering the questions in Part b? Why?

(3) The time required for a race car to complete a 400-mile race is inversely proportional to the average speed that the car maintains.

a. Express the relationship between race time and average speed in two equivalent forms.

b. Use either of the inverse variation forms you developed in Part a to write and solve equations to answer these questions about race speed and time.

   i. What average speed is required to complete the race in 2.5 hours?

   ii. How long will it take to complete the race if the average speed is 140 miles per hour?

c. Which inverse variation form was most helpful for answering the questions in Part b? Why?

(4) Simple pendulums are interesting and important physical devices. You may have studied pendulum motion in science experiments by attaching a weight to a string and looking for patterns relating the weight, the length of the string, and the motion of the weight as it swings from side to side.

It turns out that the frequency of a pendulum (in swings per time unit) depends only on the length of the pendulum arm (not the weight of the bob or the initial starting point of the swings). The function $F = \frac{30}{\sqrt{L}}$ is a good model for the relationship between pendulum arm length L and frequency of swing F when length is measured in meters and frequency in swings per minute.

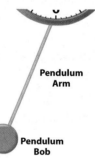

Pendulum Arm

Pendulum Bob

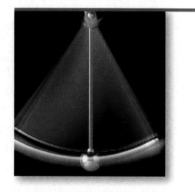

a. Write the rule for pendulum frequency in the form of a power function.

LESSON 1 • Direct and Inverse Variation   **17**

b. i. $T = 10$ Euros

ii. $P = 60$ Euros

iii. Total purchase price is $95 + 0.25(95) = 118.75$ Euros.

c. Most students will likely pick the form $T = 0.25P$ because for parts i and iii, they were asked to find the tax. Even for part ii, knowing the value of T, the form $T = 0.25P$ is useable for finding P. Generally, it is easier to solve for a variable when it is not on the denominator of an expression.

③ a. $T = \dfrac{400}{s}$ and $Ts = 400$

b. i. $2.5s = 400$ when $s = 160$ miles per hour.

ii. $T = \dfrac{400}{140}$ when $T \approx 2.86$ hours.

c. The form $Ts = 400$ was easiest for part i, solving for s, because s is a factor and not in the denominator. The form $T = \dfrac{400}{s}$ is easiest in part ii because s is known.

④ a. $F = 30L^{-0.5}$

b. Sketch a graph of the frequency function and explain what its shape tells about the way that pendulum frequency changes as the pendulum arm length increases.

c. Estimate the frequency of pendulums with arm length 1 meter and 0.5 meters.

d. Estimate the pendulum length required for a frequency of 1 swing per *second*.

5 For each of the following functions, indicate whether it is an example of direct variation, inverse variation, or neither.

For those functions that are examples of direct or inverse variation, identify the constant of proportionality and write a sentence describing the relationship in the language of direct and inverse variation or proportionality.

a. The surface area of a cube with edge length e is given by $A = 6e^2$.

b. When a basketball player attempts a shot from mid-court, the height of the ball h is a function of time in flight t. Those variables might be related by a rule like $h = -16t^2 + 32t + 7$.

c. The volume V of a sphere is related to the radius r of the sphere by $V = \frac{4}{3}\pi r^3$.

d. The diameter d of a large tree is related to the circumference C of that tree by $d = \frac{C}{\pi}$.

e. The radius r of a circle is related to the area A of that circle by $r = \frac{\sqrt{A}}{\sqrt{\pi}}$.

f. The balance B of a savings account after n years with initial investment of $500 earning 6% annual interest is given by $B = 500(1.06^n)$.

6 Suppose that a spotlight is used for lighting objects at many different distances and that the area A of the light circle produced is related to the distance x to the lighted object by $A = 0.1x^2$.

a. If the spotlight produces 250 lumens of light energy, what function gives the intensity of the light I (in lumens per square foot) as a function of the distance x in feet from the spotlight to its target?

b. Write and solve equations that match these questions about the light intensity from the spotlight.

   i. What is the intensity of light on an object that is 20 feet from the spotlight source?

   ii. How far from the spotlight is an object that receives 100 lumens of light energy per square foot?

b. The frequency function (for $0 < L \leq 5$ meters and $0 < F \leq 50$ swings per minute) will look like this:

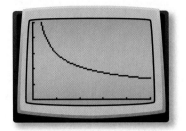

The shape of the graph tells you that the swings per minute drops quickly at first as the length of the arm increases. Then the swings per minute continues to decrease but at a slowing rate.

c. A pendulum with arm length 1 meter should swing back and forth about 30 times per minute; if the arm is 0.5 meters long, its frequency should be about 42 swings per minute.

d. A pendulum that is 0.25 meters long will swing with frequency 60 per minute or 1 per second.

NOTE Task 4 Part d requires students to change units from swings per minute to swings per second.

5 **a.** *Surface area of a cube* is directly proportional to (or varies directly with) the *square of each edge length* with constant of proportionality *6*.

b. *Height of the ball* is a quadratic function of *time in flight* but *not* direct or inverse variation.

c. *Volume of a sphere* is directly proportional to (or varies directly with) the *cube of the radius* with constant of proportionality $\frac{4}{3}\pi$.

d. *Diameter of a circular tree* is directly proportional to (or varies directly with) the *circumference* with constant of proportionality $\frac{1}{\pi}$.

e. The *radius of a circle* is directly proportional to the *square root* of the area of the circle with constant of proportionality $\frac{1}{\sqrt{\pi}}$.

f. The *balance of a savings account* is an exponential function. It is *not* an example of direct variation.

6 **a.** $I = \dfrac{250}{0.1x^2}$

b. **i.** $I = \dfrac{250}{0.1(20)^2} = 6.25$ lumens/ft^2

　　ii. $100 = \dfrac{250}{0.1x^2}$; $0.1x^2 = 2.5$; $x^2 = 25$; $x = 5$ feet

7 Without using a graphing tool, match each of the following functions with its graph in the collection that follows. The scales on the *x*-axis and *y*-axis are 1 on all graphs.

Function List: $y = 1.5x$ $y = 0.5x^2$ $y = -0.5x^2$

                $y = 2x^3$ $y = \sqrt{x}$ $y = \dfrac{1}{x}$

                $y = -\dfrac{1}{x}$ $y = \dfrac{1}{x^2}$ $y = \dfrac{1}{\sqrt{x}}$

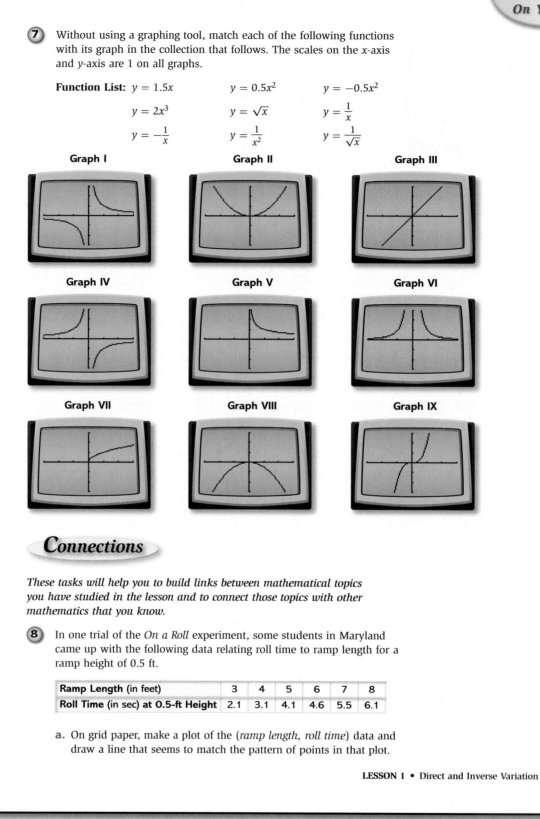

Graph I   Graph II   Graph III

Graph IV   Graph V   Graph VI

Graph VII   Graph VIII   Graph IX

Connections

These tasks will help you to build links between mathematical topics you have studied in the lesson and to connect those topics with other mathematics that you know.

8 In one trial of the *On a Roll* experiment, some students in Maryland came up with the following data relating roll time to ramp length for a ramp height of 0.5 ft.

Ramp Length (in feet)	3	4	5	6	7	8
Roll Time (in sec) at 0.5-ft Height	2.1	3.1	4.1	4.6	5.5	6.1

a. On grid paper, make a plot of the (*ramp length, roll time*) data and draw a line that seems to match the pattern of points in that plot.

LESSON 1 • Direct and Inverse Variation   **19**

7 Graph I: $y = \dfrac{1}{x}$ Graph II: $y = 0.5x^2$ Graph III: $y = 1.5x$

Graph IV: $y = -\dfrac{1}{x}$ Graph V: $y = \dfrac{1}{\sqrt{x}}$ Graph VI: $y = \dfrac{1}{x^2}$

Graph VII: $y = \sqrt{x}$ Graph VIII: $y = -0.5x^2$ Graph IX: $y = 2x^3$

Connections

8   a. **Plot for Ramp Height 0.5 Feet**

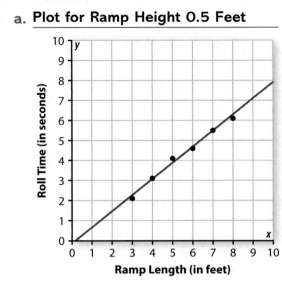

Unit 1

b. Find the equation of the line that you drew to model the data pattern and explain what the numbers in that equation tell about the relationship between ramp length and roll time.

c. Use a calculator or computer linear regression tool to find the equation of a "best-fit" linear model for the (*ramp length, roll time*) pattern.

d. Compare the actual data to values of length and time predicted by the best-fit regression line and locate the largest error of prediction for the best-fit equation.

9 In one class that did the *On a Roll* experiment, students decided to test each combination of ramp length and platform height 3 times. Which of the following strategies would you recommend for a study aimed at finding an algebraic model for the relationship between roll time and the 2 independent variables, and why?

a. Use the mean of each set of 3 test-result roll times as the representative data.

b. Use the median of each set of 3 test-result roll times as the representative data.

c. Make a scatterplot using all data points.

d. Use results from the test roll that seemed to be done best.

e. Use some other strategy to find models of the relationships involved. Explain.

10 In testing the effect of platform height on roll time for the *On a Roll* experiment, it makes sense to use a single ramp length in all rolls. Suppose that an 8-foot ramp length was the choice.

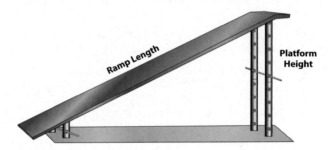

a. If the platform is 1 foot high, how can you calculate the distance from the base of the platform to the end of the ramp? What is the slope of the ramp in that case?

b. Complete a copy of a table like that shown below.

Platform Height (in feet)	Distance from Base to End of Ramp (in feet)	Slope of Ramp
1		
2		
0		
8		

b. The approximating line shown in the preceding diagram has rule $y = 0.8x - 0.1$. The coefficient of x tells that for every increase of one foot in ramp length, the roll time should increase about 0.8 seconds. The -0.1 constant term suggests that a ramp of length 0 will require -0.1 seconds to roll. This obviously makes little sense physically. However, since the constant term is really quite small, the model is not far off what is theoretically reasonable.

c. The rule in Part b is the linear regression equation (with numbers rounded to nearest tenth). To three decimals, it is $y = 0.791x - 0.103$.

d. The following table shows the time values predicted by the regression equation and the original data values.

Ramp Length (in feet)	3	4	5	6	7	8
Roll Time (in sec) at 0.5-ft Height	2.1	3.1	4.1	4.6	5.5	6.1
Model Roll Time Predictions (in sec)	2.3	3.1	3.9	4.7	5.5	6.3

The largest error of prediction is 0.2 seconds (which occurs 3 times).

9 **a–e.** Students will have a variety of ideas about strategies to find an algebraic model. Using the mean essentially gives each data point equal weight in establishing the representative figure for each platform height and ramp length combination. Using the median would avoid the possible distorting effects of one poorly done roll that produced outlier data. Making a scatterplot using all data points does just that, uses all the data; however, it may include some outlier data that may have resulted from poor experimental technique. Using data from the test roll that "seemed to be done best" relies on a kind of subjective judgment that might not be scientifically valid.

10 **a–b.**

Platform Height (in feet)	Distance from Base to End of Ramp (in feet)	Slope of Ramp
1	$\sqrt{63} \approx 7.937$	$\frac{1}{\sqrt{63}} \approx 0.126$
2	$\sqrt{60} \approx 7.75$	$\frac{2}{\sqrt{60}} \approx 0.258$
0	8	0
8	0	Undefined

11 Describe the symmetries of the graphs of the basic types of power functions.

   a. Functions of the form $y = x^2$, $y = x^3$, $y = x^4$, $y = x^5$

   b. Functions of the form $y = \frac{1}{x}$, $y = \frac{1}{x^2}$, $y = \frac{1}{x^3}$, $y = \frac{1}{x^4}$

   c. Based on your work in Parts a and b, make a conjecture about the symmetries of the graphs of functions of the form $y = x^n$, where n is an *even* integer.

   d. Make a conjecture about the symmetries of the graphs of functions of the form $y = x^n$, where n is an *odd* integer.

12 From television sets and radios to X-rays, microwave, and wireless telephone signals, we are surrounded by the energy of *electro-magnetic fields* (EMF). As sources of EMF have become more common in our everyday lives, scientists have become concerned about possible health hazards caused by exposure to EMF.

   Data in the following table show patterns of EMF measurements (in a unit called *milligauss*) at various distances from the front and back of a television set and from a VCR.

EMF Measurements

Distance (in cm)	2	4	6	8	12	16	24	32	48
TV Front	12	10	8	7	5	3	3	—	—
TV Back	—	184	—	126	82	49	20	8	2
VCR	23	13	6	4	2	1	—	—	—

   a. Look at the patterns relating EMF to distance for each electronic device and decide on the type of function (direct variation, exponential, power, or inverse variation) that you think would best model the data pattern in each case.

   b. Make a scatterplot of the data relating EMF from the front of a television set to distance from the set. Then use your calculator or computer curve-fitting tool to find two types of best-fit function models for the data pattern—a linear function and one other promising type. Decide which of the two seems to be the best model and explain your reasoning.

   c. Make a scatterplot of the data relating EMF from the VCR to distance from the VCR. Then use your calculator or computer curve-fitting tool to find two types of best-fit function models for the data pattern—linear and one other promising type. Decide which of the two seems to be the best model and explain your reasoning.

11 **a.** For $y = x^2$ and $y = x^4$, the graphs have reflection symmetry across the *y*-axis.

For $y = x^3$ and $y = x^5$, the graphs have half-turn symmetry about the origin.

b. For $y = \frac{1}{x}$ and $y = \frac{1}{x^3}$, the graphs have half-turn symmetry about the origin. The graph of $y = \frac{1}{x}$ also has reflection symmetry across the lines $y = x$ and $y = -x$. (These line reflections will be revisited in Unit 3 where students develop coordinate rules for transformations.)

For $y = \frac{1}{x^2}$ and $y = \frac{1}{x^4}$, the graphs have reflection symmetry across the *y*-axis.

c. When *n* is an even integer, the graph of $y = x^n$ is symmetric across the *y*-axis.

d. When *n* is an odd integer, the graph of $y = x^n$ has half-turn symmetry about the origin.

INSTRUCTIONAL NOTE
You may wish to alert students to the nonuniform changes in distance on the EMF table.

12 **a.** Students might look at the table values or plot points to decide on the type of function. Because of the nonconstant downward pattern to the data, students should select inverse variation or exponential (decay) as the best model for each case.

b. The relationship between distance and EMF measurement for the TV Front produces the data pattern below. Students should select the power or exponential model rather than the linear model as the best fit.

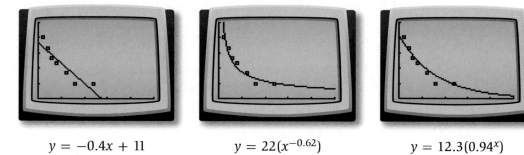

$$y = -0.4x + 11 \qquad y = 22(x^{-0.62}) \qquad y = 12.3(0.94^x)$$

c. For the VCR, the following diagrams show data plots and several possible modeling functions.

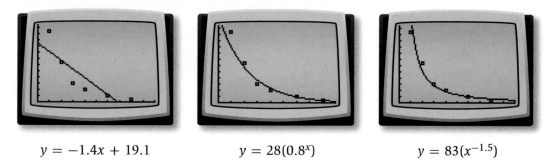

$$y = -1.4x + 19.1 \qquad y = 28(0.8^x) \qquad y = 83(x^{-1.5})$$

Students should select the power or exponential model rather than the linear model as the best fit.

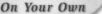

Reflections

These tasks provide opportunities for you to re-examine your thinking about ideas in the lesson.

13 When examining a table of (x, y) data, what clues would suggest that the relation between x and y is an inverse variation? A direct variation?

14 When Wanda and Troy were asked to explain how they recognized graphs of direct variation functions, they said, "The graph has to go through the origin $(0, 0)$." Give explanations or counterexamples to justify your answers to these questions.

a. Does every direct variation graph contain $(0, 0)$?

b. Is every function with a graph containing $(0, 0)$ an example of direct variation?

15 For each of the following rules, indicate whether it is an increasing linear function, decreasing linear function, exponential growth function, exponential decay function, quadratic function, or none of those types. Try to answer first without using a graphing tool and then check your ideas and resolve differences between your first ideas and what the calculator suggests.

a. $y = 65 - 2.5x$ b. $y = 7 - 2x^2$

c. $y = \frac{x}{3} + 42$ d. $y = 5(3^x)$

e. $y = 2^x + x^2$ f. $y = 5(0.3^x)$

g. $y = 0.5(1.5^x)$ h. $y = 4.5$

16 Of the various types of functions that you've worked with in this lesson:

a. Which seem to occur most often in solving interesting or important problems?

b. Which are usually easy to match with problem conditions?

c. Which lead to equations that can be solved easily by reasoning and symbol manipulation alone?

d. Which lead to equations that are most easily solved by use of calculator or computer tools?

17 Which approach to finding models for relationships between variables do you prefer? Why?

- Collecting some data and looking for a pattern in that data
- Thinking about how variables in the situation are related to each other and figuring out a function rule by logical reasoning alone
- Some combination of data analysis and logical deduction

Reflections

13 Clues for inverse variation: As x values increase, y values decrease. The decrease in y values is large at first and then gets smaller.

Clues for direct variation: As x values increase, y values either increase or decrease at a constant rate.

INSTRUCTIONAL NOTE
The answers to R13 and R14 are based only on knowledge from Investigation 1. These tasks should be assigned after Investigation 1.

14 **a.** Yes, every direct variation graph does pass through (0, 0) because every $y = kx$ gives a y value of 0 when $x = 0$.

   b. No, there are functions with graphs passing through (0, 0) that are not direct variation functions. Students' counterexamples might be sketches of graphs of functions passing through the origin such as $y = x^2 + x$ or $y = 2^x - 1$.

15 **a.** decreasing linear function

   b. quadratic function

   c. increasing linear function

   d. exponential growth function

   e. none of the special types of functions

   f. exponential decay function

   g. exponential growth function

   h. linear function, but it is neither increasing nor decreasing

16 **a–d.** Since this task asks for student opinions, answers will vary. Thus, you may want to simply talk about this with the whole class in a think-pair-share activity.

17 Once again, student opinions on these approaches will vary. The point we want to highlight is that both looking for data patterns and reasoning from scientific principles are useful strategies for finding modeling function rules. Being able to explain the reason for choice of a particular model from scientific or other principles is ultimately most desirable because it implies understanding of *why* things work.

Unit 1

(18) Directions on flash cameras suggest that the focus object of a flash picture should not be very far from the camera. How could your discoveries about the relationship between distance and light intensity explain that advice?

Extensions

These tasks provide opportunities for you to explore further or more deeply the mathematics you are learning.

(19) In one trial of the *On a Roll* experiment, some students in Iowa came up with the following data relating roll time to platform height, using an 8-foot ramp.

Platform Height (in feet)	0.25	0.5	0.75	1.0	1.25	1.5
Roll Time (in sec) at 0.5-ft Height	7.5	3.6	2.9	2.5	2.3	1.7

   a. Use calculator or computer plotting and curve-fitting tools to find best-fitting linear, exponential, quadratic, and power regression models for the (*platform height, roll time*) data pattern.

   b. Compare graphs of the various best-fit modeling functions to a plot of the actual test data and see which function type seems the best fit.

   c. What difference between the graphs of an inverse variation model and an exponential decay model (near a platform height of 0) suggests that the inverse variation function is more likely to be appropriate in this context?

(20) Suppose that the intensity I of light energy (in lumens per square foot) shining on an object x feet from a spotlight is given by $I = \dfrac{2{,}500}{x^2}$.
Compare the light intensity on objects at 10, 20, 40, and 80 feet from the spotlight to complete this conjecture: "If the distance from light source to light target doubles, then the light intensity is reduced by a factor of ____." Explain why the pattern that you observed makes sense in terms of the function rule.

Review

These tasks provide opportunities for you to review previously learned mathematics and to refine your skills in using that mathematics.

(21) Answer each of the following arithmetic questions. Then support each claim with a check using a related arithmetic operation.

   Example: Does $15 - 12 = 3$?
               Yes, because $15 = 3 + 12$.

   a. Does $7.4 \times 5 = 37$?
   b. Does $24 \div 6 = 4$?
   c. Does $-13 = -39 \div 3$?
   d. Does $12 - 15 = -3$?
   e. Does $7.5 + 4.6 = 11.1$?
   f. Does $225 = 9 \times 25$?

18 Light intensity is inversely related to distance from source to target. Thus, as distance from a flash camera increases, the effect of the flash lighting diminishes rapidly.

Extensions

19 **a.** Linear: $y = -3.8x + 6.75$ Exponential: $y = 7.4(0.36^x)$

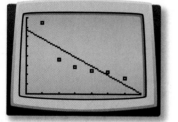   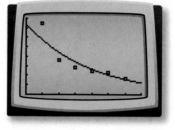

Quadratic: $y = 5.3x^2 - 13x + 9.8$ Power: $y = 2.4(x^{-0.76})$

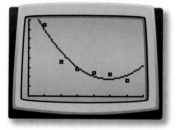   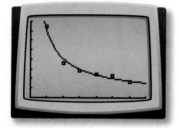

b. The power function clearly seems to be the best fit.

c. The power model (with negative exponent suggesting inverse variation) has the additional attractive theoretical feature that as x approaches 0, the value of y grows without bound. In the context of the experiment, what this says is that for a ramp with platform height 0 and thus slope of 0, the ball will take an infinite time to roll "across" the ramp. The exponential functions will always approach their y-intercept values as x approaches 0.

> **INSTRUCTIONAL NOTE**
> The analysis in Part c illustrates the common interplay of data-based and theoretical reasoning that is most productive in mathematical modeling.

20

x	10	20	40	80
I	25	6.25	1.5625	0.390625

The pattern shows that when distance doubles, intensity is divided by four (or multiplied by a factor of $\frac{1}{4}$).

The following algebraic reasoning shows why this happens:

$$\frac{2,500}{(2x)^2} = \frac{2,500}{4x^2} = \frac{1}{4}I, \text{ where } I = \frac{2,500}{x^2}.$$

Review

21 One possible response is provided for each part.

a. Yes, because $7.4 = 37 \div 5$.   **b.** Yes, because $24 = 6 \times 4$.

c. Yes, because $-13(3) = -39$.   **d.** Yes, because $12 = -3 + 15$.

e. No, because $7.5 \neq 11.1 - 4.6$.   **f.** Yes, because $225 \div 25 = 9$.

Unit 1

22 Find values of x that make the following statements true.

a. $3^x \times 3^4 = 3^{11}$

b. $5^7 \times 5^3 = 5^x$

c. $5^0 = x$

d. $\sqrt{5} = 5^x$

e. $\dfrac{5}{7^3} = 5(7^x)$

f. $\sqrt[3]{x}\,\sqrt[3]{7} = 2\sqrt[3]{7}$

23 Solve each of the following equations for x.

a. $3x - 8 = 29$

b. $3(x - 8) = 29$

c. $3(x - 8) + 17 = 29$

d. $7x + 12 = 3x - 8$

24 Find equations for the lines that contain these pairs of points.

a. $(0, 0)$ and $(2, 6)$

b. $(0, 0)$ and $(5, 8)$

c. $(1, 2)$ and $(7, 11)$

25 Use what you know about exponents and radicals to write each of the following function rules in equivalent form, $y = kx^r$.

a. $y = \dfrac{4}{x}$

b. $y = -7\sqrt{x}$

c. $y = \dfrac{4}{\sqrt{x}}$

d. $y = \dfrac{5}{x^3}$

e. $y = \dfrac{3}{4x^2}$

f. $y = (3x)^2$

26 In the diagram below, points A, C, and E are all on the same line. What is the value of x?

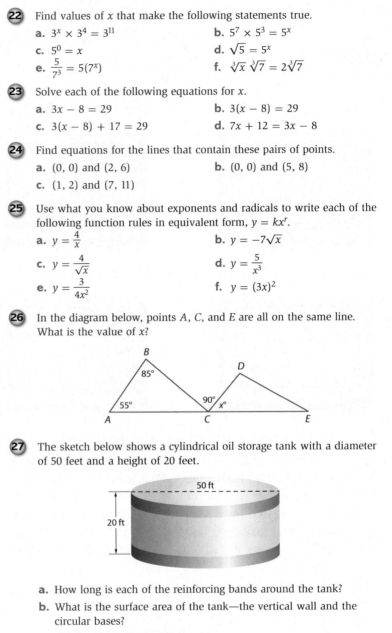

27 The sketch below shows a cylindrical oil storage tank with a diameter of 50 feet and a height of 20 feet.

a. How long is each of the reinforcing bands around the tank?

b. What is the surface area of the tank—the vertical wall and the circular bases?

c. What is the volume of the tank?

d. One cubic foot is equivalent to about 7.5 gallons. What is the capacity of the oil tank in gallons?

22 a. $x = 7$ b. $x = 10$

c. $x = 1$ d. $x = 0.5$

e. $x = -3$

23 a. $x = \frac{37}{3}$ b. $x = \frac{53}{3}$

c. $x = 12$ d. $x = -5$

24 a. $y = 3x$ b. $y = 1.6x$

c. $y = 1.5x + 0.5$

Just in Time

25 a. $y = 4x^{-1}$ b. $y = -7x^{0.5}$

c. $y = 4x^{-0.5}$ d. $y = 5x^{-3}$

e. $y = \frac{3}{4}x^{-2}$ f. $y = 9x^2$

26 $x = 50$

27 a. 157.1 ft

b. 7,068.6 ft^2

c. 39,269.9 ft^3

d. 294,524.3 gallons

Unit 1

ASSIGNMENT NOTE It is recommended that this task be assigned just prior to or at the start of Investigation 2.

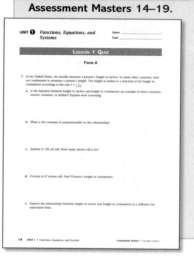

Teaching Resources

Assessment Masters 14–19.

LESSON 2

Multivariable Functions

Relations among several variables are often used to express scientific principles. For example, in the electrical circuits that provide power for flashlights, appliances, and tools, the key variables—*voltage*, *current*, and *resistance*—are related by a principle called Ohm's Law.

In a flashlight, the battery supplies electrical pressure (measured in *volts*) that creates a flow of electrons called current (measured in *amperes*) through the wire and bulb circuit. The wire and the bulb offer resistance (measured in *ohms*) to the flow of electrons.

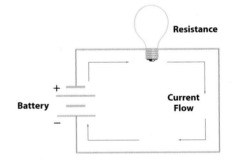

One way to think about the relationship among current, voltage, and resistance in an electrical circuit is to imagine the flow of water generated by pumps like those in circulating fountains or fish tanks. The pump (like a battery) pushes a current of water (like electrons) through a hose (like a wire), and squeezing the hose creates resistance to that flow.

Multivariable Functions

The goal of this lesson is to extend the notions of direct and inverse variation to functions of two independent variables. For example, if $z = \frac{x}{y}$, we say that z is directly proportional to x and inversely proportional to y. Then a different kind of two-variable function $z = f(x, y)$ or $z = ax + by$ is examined. The focus is on the set of solutions (x, y) for linear equations in the form $ax + by = c$ and their graphs.

Throughout the lesson, students will be asked to express given relationships in equivalent alternative forms. For instance, a relationship in the form $z = \frac{x}{y}$ can be expressed equivalently as $zy = x$, and a relationship in the form $z = x + y$ can be expressed equivalently as $z - y = x$. The manipulations take advantage of the close connections between multiplication and division and between addition and subtraction, respectively. While students should know those relationships from prior work in arithmetic, they will probably need reminders or hints if they get stuck on problems that require that reasoning.

You may be accustomed to an approach to those equivalence transformations based on "doing the same thing to both sides of an equation" like this:

$$\text{If } z = \frac{x}{y},$$
$$\text{then } zy = \frac{x}{y} \cdot y.$$
$$zy = x \cdot \frac{1}{y} \cdot y$$
$$zy = x \cdot \frac{y}{y}$$
$$zy = x \cdot 1$$
$$zy = x$$

$$\text{If } z = x + y,$$
$$\text{then } z - y = (x + y) - y.$$
$$z - y = x + (y - y)$$
$$z - y = x + 0$$
$$z - y = x$$

This more formal approach to algebraic manipulation will be addressed in subsequent units. At this point, we believe it is intuitively more convincing and algebraically adequate to focus on the connection between pairs of inverse arithmetic operations. In any event, it is probably useful to let students try to reason out the relationships among variables with guidance from the context rather than to tell them in advance just how to do things in the conventional ways.

Lesson Objectives

- Write rules to define functions of two variables that combine direct and inverse variation
- Solve for one variable in terms of the others in situations where the variables are related by direct and inverse variation
- Write equations in the general form $ax + by = c$ to express conditions relating two variables
- Solve linear equations for one variable in terms of the other
- Graph linear equations in the form of $ax + by = c$

Think About This Situation

Suppose that you were to run some experiments by changing the batteries and bulbs in a working flashlight circuit. Think about what would happen to the current flow and thus the light bulb.

a How would you expect the current to change if the original battery was replaced by one of higher voltage? What if the new battery had lower voltage?

b How would you expect the current to change if the original bulb was replaced by one of higher resistance? What if the new bulb had lower resistance?

c How would you expect the current to change if the original battery was replaced by one of higher voltage and the bulb by one of lower resistance? What if the voltage decreased and the resistance increased?

d How would you expect the current to change if both the voltage and resistance were increased? What if both the voltage and the resistance were decreased?

In this lesson, you will develop your skill in reasoning about multivariable relationships and functions.

Investigation 1 — Combining Direct and Inverse Variation

The flashlights we use for various lighting tasks come with many different combinations of batteries and bulbs. The relationship between current I, voltage V, and resistance R is important. If the current is too great, the bulb may break; if the current is too low, the bulb may barely light. As you work on the problems of this investigation, look for an answer to these questions:

What symbolic rules represent the relationship of current, voltage, and resistance in a simple electrical circuit?

How can relationships among several variables be written in useful equivalent forms?

1 Based on your reasoning about how changes in voltage and resistance affect current in a flashlight circuit, which of the following formulas might possibly express the numerical relationship among those variables? Be prepared to explain your reasoning.

$$I = V - R \qquad I = V + R \qquad I = V \cdot R \qquad I = \frac{V}{R} \qquad I = \frac{R}{V}$$

Use the flashlight and electrical circuit art in the text to ask students how they think these circuits work. Because the water-flow analogy may be more accessible to some students, it may be a good idea to redraw the bulb/battery/current diagram with the analogous water components written beside the electronic components.

Think About This Situation

a Student responses will vary depending on their experiences with electronic devices. With some prompting, though, all students should be able to reason that an increase or decrease in voltage would yield to a corresponding increase or decrease in the current.

b Students should be able to reason that an increase or decrease in resistance would yield to a corresponding decrease or increase in the current.

c In this first case, the current would increase. In the second, the current would decrease.

d There is no way to tell how, or if, the current will change if both voltage and resistance are increased or both are decreased. Students may not be aware of this at this point in the lesson, but they will address the issue later.

Teaching Resources

Transparency Master 20.

UNIT **❶** *Functions, Equations, and Systems*

Think About This Situation

Suppose that you were to run some experiments by changing the batteries and bulbs in a working flashlight circuit. Think about what would happen to the current flow and thus the light bulb.

a How would you expect the current to change if the original battery was replaced by one of higher voltage? What if the new battery had lower voltage?

b How would you expect the current to change if the original bulb was replaced by one of higher resistance? What if the new bulb had lower resistance?

c How would you expect the current to change if the original battery was replaced by one of higher voltage and the bulb by one of lower resistance? What if the voltage decreased and the resistance increased?

d How would you expect the current to change if both the voltage and resistance were increased? What if both the voltage and the resistance were decreased?

20 UNIT 1 • *Functions, Equations, and Systems*   *Transparency Master • use with page 26*

Think About This Situation, *page 26*

Teacher: Have any of you studied electrical circuits in your previous math or science classes? *(There is no indication of previous exposure to this concept.)* Does anyone have experience with water pumps like those in fish tanks where the pump helps circulate water through a hose?

Dustin: I have a fish tank with a pump.

Caleb: Me, too. The pump is electric and helps circulate the water so that air bubbles are put into the water, so the fish can breathe.

Teacher: Circulating fountains or flashlights can help us think about the scientific principal called Ohm's Law that relates voltage, current, and resistance. The pump (like a battery) pushes a current of water (like electrons) through a hose (like a wire). What might create resistance to the flow of water through the hose in a fish tank?

Diana: Sometimes slime builds up in the hose so the water can't flow as well.

Caleb: Sometimes the hose gets crimped or a pebble gets lodged in the hose and plugs it up.

Dustin: Some hoses have valves to adjust the flow of water into the tank.

Teacher: Look up here at these models of an electrical circuit. Which features of this display of a circuit would represent the voltage, resistance, and current? *(The class studies the graphic and its relationship to the three variables, current, voltage, and resistance.)*

Teacher: Okay, let's think about what happens to the current and thus the light bulb if the battery was replaced by one of higher or lower voltage.

Michael: Well, if the battery was stronger, the current would be stronger and the light would be brighter. A weaker battery would have less current and the light bulb would be dimmer.

Teacher: Other thoughts? *(No replies.)* How would you expect the current to change if the resistance was increased or decreased?

Sheri: The current would slow down if the resistance increased. I like thinking about my fish tank pump. If you clean out the hose and get rid of the slime, the current increases. Or if you had a pebble in the hose, the flow might even stop.

Teacher: How does cleaning out the hose represent a change in the resistance, Sheri?

Sheri: If you clean it out, there is less resistance and more water can flow through the hose.

Teacher: Okay, let's be sure that we understand these ideas in the context of the light circuit here. What would we expect to happen to the light bulb if we increased the voltage represented by the battery? *(Students respond with "brighter bulb.")* What if we increased the resistance? *(Students say "the bulb would dim.")* Now what would happen if the voltage was increased and the resistance decreased?

Marie: That would really increase the brightness of the bulb!

Teacher: What change would you expect to the current if the battery was replaced by one of lower voltage and the resistance was increased?

Josh: That would make the current decrease and the light bulb would be dimmer.

Ben: Yeah, both of those changes make the bulb dimmer.

Teacher: Okay, but what if we increase both the voltage and resistance, then how will the current change?

Paul: I'm not sure. If you increase the voltage a lot and the resistance a little, the effect might still be an increase in the current.

Tara: Maybe they just cancel each other out and nothing happens. It seems like it would depend on the amounts, like Paul said.

Teacher: Would the case of decreasing both the voltage and the resistance be similar to increasing both?

Isaiah: Yeah, similar in that we can't really say what would happen … .

Teacher: Okay. Open your book to page 26 and think about Problem 1 by yourself for a minute. Did you all decide on a formula? Then discuss the reasons you have for selecting a particular formula with your group members. You may have more than one reasonable formula option at this point. You will be collecting some data using a computer custom tool "Light it Up!" when you do Problem 2. Then you will use this data to confirm or select between formula options in Problem 1.

Combining Direct and Inverse Variation

In this investigation, students are asked to think about the relationship of *current* to *voltage* and *resistance* in simple circuits as an example of a multivariable function that combines direct and inverse variation. Then they revisit the inclined plane experiment data and work on a model of the combined effect of ramp length and platform height on roll time. Finally, they are asked to generalize these function ideas to consider general patterns in relationships of the form $z = xy$ and $z = \frac{x}{y}$.

It may be necessary to provide a strategy for students to organize their data in the "Light it Up!" experiment. While at first it is encouraged that the students "play around" with the custom tool, in order to end up with the proper relationship, it is important that at least one student per computer is recording the corresponding current, voltage, and resistance values.

Some students may find it best to hold either the voltage or the resistance (in Ω) constant and record the results of "sliding" the value of the other variable. This is a tactic similar to that used in the ramp experiment in Lesson 1.

The "Light It Up!" custom tool is on the *StudentWorks* CD and also at www.glencoe.com/sec/math/cpmp/CPMP-Tools/. You may wish to collect data as a class and allow students to adjust the values for resistance and voltage for Part a of Problem 2. Alternatively, if you only have time to launch the lesson in class, students could individually do Problems 1 and 2 at home and confer with their group on answers at the beginning of the next class period.

1 **INSTRUCTIONAL NOTE** This question is presented before the following investigation to promote reasoning about the algebraic form of the models presented and the situation at hand. The students will then confirm their conjectures through the "Light it Up!" experiment.

Students should be able to narrow their choices to either the first or fourth formula. They may then reason that the fourth formula makes the most sense for certain situations (e.g., current can never be negative, no matter how great the resistance—this would rule out the first formula).

Unit 1

2. Engineers designing electrical circuits have tools to measure voltage, current, and resistance of designs they want to test. You could use those instruments to run some experiments and collect data on combinations of volts, amps, and ohms in flashlight circuits that function properly. Computer software like the "Light it Up!" custom tool can be used to simulate experiments with batteries and bulbs in search of the relationship among I, V, and R.

   a. Use the simulation to find at least 5 combinations of values for these variables that will produce working battery and bulb circuits.

   b. Write a formula showing how I depends on V and R in all cases. Compare your formula with those of your classmates. Resolve any differences.

   c. Use the language of direct and inverse variation to explain in words how current varies as voltage and resistance change.

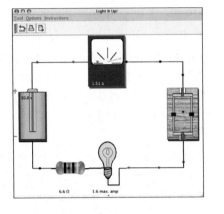

3. Design of a working battery and bulb circuit requires finding values for 3 related variables. In some cases, you might know values of V and R and need to calculate the corresponding value of I. In other cases, you might know values of I and R or values of I and V.

   a. What is the resistance in a circuit that includes a 9-volt battery and has current flow of 2 amps? What if the circuit includes a 12-volt battery and has current flow of 5 amps? What formula expresses R as a function of V and I?

   b. What size battery (in volts) is required to produce a current flow of 2.5 amps when the resistance of the circuit is 4 ohms? What if the circuit must have a current flow of 4 amps and the resistance is 7 ohms? What formula expresses V as a function of R and I?

   c. How do Ohm's Law $I = \frac{V}{R}$ and the natural connection between multiplication and division provide algebraic justification for the formula in Part b that expresses V in terms of I and R?

4. The questions of Problems 2 and 3 asked you to write Ohm's Law in three different ways. You can use the formula $I = \frac{V}{R}$ to reason about how and why changes in R and V will cause changes in I. For example,

   If V stays the same and R is increased, then I *will decrease* because *when the denominator of a positive fraction increases and the numerator stays the same, the value of the fraction will decrease.*

2 **INSTRUCTIONAL NOTE** If the "Light it Up!" custom tool is not accessible in your class, you might have to provide some sample V, R, I data and ask the students to explore the data in search of a pattern relating those variables. At the right is a small set that you might choose to use.

V	R	I
1	0.5	2
1.5	0.5	3
5	0.5	10
5	2	2.5
1.5	2	0.75
1	2	0.5
9	2	4.5
9	0.5	18
9	5	1.8
12	3	4

a. Possible combinations will vary but should fit the $I = \dfrac{V}{R}$ relationship.

b. The formula $I = \dfrac{V}{R}$ shows the proper relationship for all cases. Students should compare answers with classmates and resolve any differences.

c. Current is directly proportional to voltage and inversely proportional to resistance.

3 **a.** $R = 4.5$ ohms when $V = 9$ volts and $I = 2$ amps.
$R = 2.4$ ohms when $V = 12$ volts and $I = 5$ amps.
The formula $R = \dfrac{V}{I}$ expresses R as a function of V and I.

b. $V = 10$ volts when $R = 4$ ohms and $I = 2.5$ amps.
$V = 28$ volts when $R = 7$ ohms and $I = 4$ amps.
The formula $V = R \cdot I$ expresses V as a function of R and I.

c. The formula giving V as a function of R and I follows from that which expresses I as a function of R and V by applying the general principle that $a = \dfrac{b}{c}$ and $ac = b$ make equivalent statements about the relationship of the numbers a, b, and c. That is, the derivation utilizes the fundamental connection between multiplication and division.

Use the formula and similar reasoning to complete each of the following sentences about how the three variables are related.

a. If R stays the same and V is increased, then I _____ because _____.

b. If R and V are each doubled, then I _____ because _____.

c. If R is cut in half and V is doubled, then I _____ because _____.

⑤ Revisiting Roll Time, Ramp Length, and Platform Height Scientists can use theories about the effects of gravity on falling objects to deduce the relationship of roll time T, ramp length L, and platform height H, for an experiment like the one you did in Lesson 1. Ignoring possible effects of friction, theory predicts that these variables will be related by the function $T = \dfrac{L}{4\sqrt{H}}$.

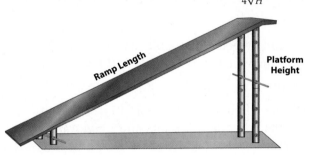

a. Use the language of direct and inverse variation to describe the theoretical relationship of T to L and H. What is the constant of proportionality?

b. Use the function $T = \dfrac{L}{4\sqrt{H}}$ to complete the following tables of predicted roll time values for various combinations of ramp length and platform height. Then plot the sample (L, T) and (H, T) values on separate graphs.

Ramp Length (in feet)	4	5	6	7	8
Roll Time (in sec) at 0.25-ft Height					

Platform Height (in feet)	0.25	0.5	0.75	1.0	1.25
Roll Time (in sec) for 8-ft Ramp					

c. Compare patterns in the tables and plots in Part b to your experimental results from Lesson 1. Explain any differences.

4 **a.** If R is held constant and V is increased, then I increases. When the numerator of a positive fraction increases and the denominator stays the same, the value of the fraction increases.

b. If R and V are each doubled, then I will remain the same as before doubling because $\frac{2V}{2R} = \frac{V}{R}$.

c. If R is cut in half and V is doubled, then I will be 4 times greater because $\frac{2V}{\frac{1}{2}R} = \frac{4V}{R}$.

5 **a.** T is directly proportional to L and inversely proportional to $\sqrt{H}$. The constant of proportionality is $\frac{1}{4}$.

INSTRUCTIONAL NOTE
In Problem 5 Part a, students may not use parentheses around the expression in the denominator and so will have incorrect roll-time values in their tables.

b.

Ramp Length (in feet)	4	5	6	7	8
Roll Time (in sec) at 0.25-ft Height	2	2.5	3	3.5	4

Platform Height (in feet)	0.25	0.5	0.75	1.0	1.25
Roll Time (in sec) for 8-ft Ramp	4	2.828	2.309	2	1.789

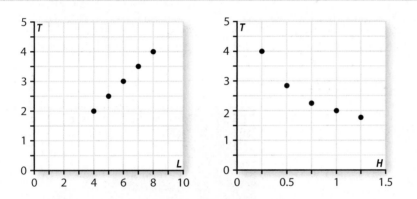

c. Comparisons and explanations will vary depending on the results of the Lesson 1 experiments. (Students may wonder why the (L, T) graph for the 0.25-ft platform is linear. Inspection of the function $T = \dfrac{L}{4\sqrt{0.25}}$ shows that the function is equivalent to $T = \frac{1}{2}L$.)

Teaching Resources

Student Master 22.

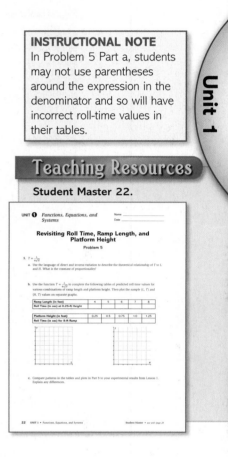

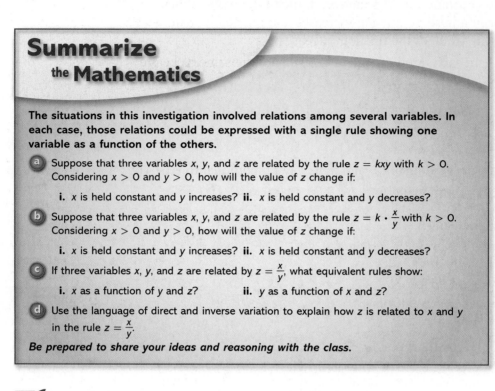

Summarize
the Mathematics

The situations in this investigation involved relations among several variables. In each case, those relations could be expressed with a single rule showing one variable as a function of the others.

a Suppose that three variables x, y, and z are related by the rule $z = kxy$ with $k > 0$. Considering $x > 0$ and $y > 0$, how will the value of z change if:

  i. x is held constant and y increases? **ii.** x is held constant and y decreases?

b Suppose that three variables x, y, and z are related by the rule $z = k \cdot \frac{x}{y}$ with $k > 0$. Considering $x > 0$ and $y > 0$, how will the value of z change if:

  i. x is held constant and y increases? **ii.** x is held constant and y decreases?

c If three variables x, y, and z are related by $z = \frac{x}{y}$, what equivalent rules show:

  i. x as a function of y and z?   **ii.** y as a function of x and z?

d Use the language of direct and inverse variation to explain how z is related to x and y in the rule $z = \frac{x}{y}$.

Be prepared to share your ideas and reasoning with the class.

✔ Check Your Understanding

The volume V of an elastic container for air—like a tire or a balloon—is related to the temperature T and to the pressure P of the air inside the container. The formula $V = k \cdot \frac{T}{P}$ is one way of expressing that relationship. The number $k > 0$ is a constant depending on the units of measurement for volume, temperature, and pressure.

a. How will volume of a balloon change if:

  i. pressure remains constant, but temperature increases?

  ii. pressure remains constant, but temperature decreases?

  iii. temperature remains constant, but pressure increases?

  iv. temperature remains constant, but pressure decreases?

b. How can the relationship among P, T, and V be expressed to show:

  i. P as a function of T, V, and k?

  ii. T as a function of V, P, and k?

Summarize the Mathematics

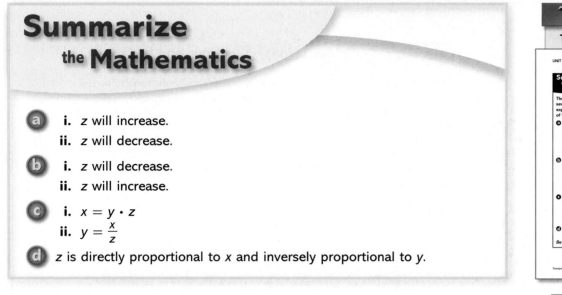

a   **i.** z will increase.
     ii. z will decrease.

b   **i.** z will decrease.
     ii. z will increase.

c   **i.** $x = y \cdot z$
     ii. $y = \dfrac{x}{z}$

d z is directly proportional to x and inversely proportional to y.

✔ Check Your Understanding

a.   **i.** The volume will increase.
     ii. The volume will decrease.
     iii. The volume will decrease.
     iv. The volume will increase.

b.   **i.** $P = k \cdot \dfrac{T}{V}$
     ii. $T = \dfrac{V \cdot P}{k}$

Teaching Resources

Transparency Master 23.

MATH TOOLKIT Some students may wish to rewrite $z = \dfrac{x}{y}$ in the form expressing y as a function of x and z.

PROCESSING PROMPT We responded to ideas respectfully by … .

INSTRUCTIONAL NOTE Students may struggle with Parts bi and bii. Remind them that k is the constant and to include it in the rule.

Unit 1

Problems that occur in business situations often require expressing income as a linear function of one variable like time worked or number of sales. For example, if an employee earns \$7.25 per hour, then income I earned for working h hours is given by $I = 7.25h$. If a movie theater charges \$8.50 for admission, then the income R from selling n admission tickets is given by $R = 8.50n$.

Questions about those situations can be expressed as equations or inequalities. For example, the question "How many hours does the employee need to work to earn \$290?" is represented by the equation $290 = 7.25h$. The question "How many admission tickets does the movie theater need to sell to collect at least \$1,000?" is represented by the inequality $8.50n \geq 1,000$.

In many business situations, income is a function of several variables. The income function is built by combining two or more simple linear functions. As you work on the problems of this investigation, look for answers to these questions:

How can you use linear functions of two independent variables to represent problem situations?

How can you graph and find solutions for linear equations in two variables?

1 Many middle- and high-school students work on a service-for-hire basis until they reach the minimum age required to apply for a "real" job. Bret mows lawns and washes cars in his neighborhood to earn spending money. He charges \$20 per lawn and \$10 per car wash.

a. How much money would Bret earn for mowing 15 lawns? For washing 20 cars? What would be Bret's total income for 15 lawns and 20 car washes?

b. Bret's total income I is a function of the numbers of lawns mowed L and cars washed C. Write a rule that expresses I as a function of L and C.

c. Suppose that Bret has a goal to earn \$1,200 and has scheduled 50 lawn-mowing jobs for the summer. How many cars must Bret wash to reach the income goal? What if Bret only schedules 40 lawn-mowing jobs?

Linear Functions and Equations

This investigation develops student understanding of equations in the general form $ax + by = c$ and their graphs. Connections to linear functions of one variable are made as well.

COLLABORATION SKILL
Help groups check thinking or solutions.

1   **a.** For 15 lawns, $300; for 20 cars, $200; total income would be $500.

   b. $I = 20L + 10C$

   c. If 50 lawns are mowed, 20 cars must be washed.
      If only 40 lawns are mowed, he must also wash 40 cars.

Unit 1

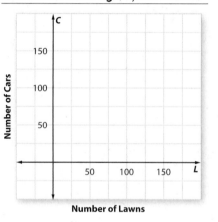

(2) Suppose that Bret sets an income goal of $2,000.

a. Write an equation that represents the question "How many lawn mowings and how many car washes will it take to achieve Bret's income goal?"

b. If Bret only mows lawns, how many would it take to reach the income goal?

c. How many cars would Bret have to wash to meet the income goal by car washing only?

d. Find 2 more combinations of number of lawn mowings and number of car washes that would achieve Bret's income goal. Be prepared to explain why these (L, C) combinations are *solutions* of the equation from Part a.

(3) Plot the (L, C) pairs that you found to be solutions of $20L + 10C = 2,000$ on a coordinate grid like that pictured below. Identify coordinates of two other points that seem to fit the pattern of the plotted points. Check to see if those pairs of numbers are also solutions of the equation.

Combinations Giving $2,000 Income

(4) The graph of (L, C) pairs that will achieve the $2,000 income goal suggests that C is a linear function of L.

a. Rewrite the equation $20L + 10C = 2,000$ to express C as a linear function of L.

b. Write a rule expressing L as a function of C. Is L a linear function of C? Explain why or why not.

2 **a.** $2{,}000 = 20L + 10C$, for non-negative integer values of L and C.

b. 100 lawns; (100, 0)

c. 200 cars; (0, 200)

d. Two possible combinations are 50 lawns with 100 cars and 5 lawns with 190 cars. These numbers are solutions because when multiplied by the prices and added, Bret would make $2,000.

3 First quadrant lattice points are: (0, 200), (5, 190), (25, 150), (50, 100), (75, 50), and (100, 0). Any non-negative integer ordered pairs that fit $20L + 10C = 2{,}000$ are solutions for the practical domain and range.

Combinations Giving $2,000 Income

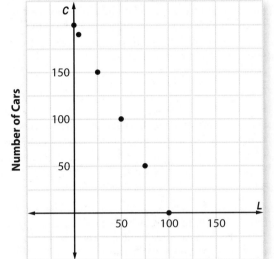

Number of Lawns

4 **a.** $C = 200 - 2L$

b. $L = 100 - 0.5C$; L is a linear function of C because the equation is in the form $y = a \pm bx$ where $a = 100$ and bx is $0.5C$.

INSTRUCTIONAL NOTE
In Problem 2 Parts b and c, students are finding the solutions that correspond to x- and y-intercepts of the graph of the equation. This strategy for graphing may need to be made more explicit for some students.

Teaching Resources

Student Master 24.

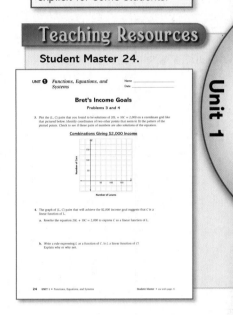

Unit 1

5 Many entertainment events do not charge one fixed price for admission. Discounted tickets are usually offered for matinee showings, children, and seniors. The income I, in dollars, for the Kingstown Playhouse is given by $I = 12r + 8d$, where r is the number of regular admission tickets and d is the number of discounted admission tickets.

a. How much does the playhouse charge for each regular admission ticket? How much for each discounted admission ticket?

b. How does I change as r increases? As d increases?

6 *A Mother's Dream* is currently showing at the Kingstown Playhouse. The production costs of the play total $24,000, and ticket prices are the same as in Problem 5.

a. Write an equation using variables r and d that represents the question "How many regular and discounted admissions are needed in order for the producers of the play to break even?"

b. Find 5 solutions to your equation from Part a. Record the solutions in a table like the one below.

r					
d					

c. Draw a graph showing all solutions to the equation from Part a for which values of both r and d make sense in this situation.

d. Write a rule that shows how to calculate the number of regular admission tickets r as a function of the number of discounted admissions d, if the play is to break even.

7 The Freedom High School booster club sponsors a fund-raising carnival each fall. In the basketball shooting game, participants pay $2 for a chance to make three shots in a row and win a basketball as a prize. A local sporting goods store sells the basketballs to the booster club for a special price of $5 each. The club can return any remaining balls when the carnival is over.

a. Write a rule that shows how fund-raiser profit P depends on the number of customers c and the number of winners w.

b. How does profit change as the number of customers increases? As the number of wins increases?

c. If the basketball shooting game has 25 customers and 8 winners, it will earn a profit of $10.

   i. Find 4 other pairs of number of customers and number of winners that will result in profit for the game that is greater than 0.

   ii. Write an algebraic condition that describes all pairs (c, w) that will guarantee a positive profit for the game.

   iii. Draw a graph that shows all (c, w) pairs that guarantee positive profit.

d. Suppose that the free-throw booth attracts 40 customers. How many customers were winners if the game generated profit of $50 for the booster club?

5 **a.** $12 is charged for regular admission and $8 for a discounted ticket.

b. As r increases by 1, I increases by 12. As d increases by 1, I increases by 8.

6 **a.** $24{,}000 = 12r + 8d$, for non-negative integer values of r and d.

b. Some possible solutions follow:

r	0	100	1,000	1,600	1,800	2,000
d	3,000	2,850	1,500	600	300	0

c.

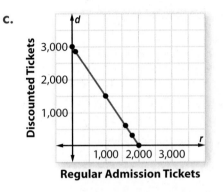

Regular Admission Tickets

Solutions are non-negative integer pairs on the line segment shown on the graph at the left.

DIFFERENTIATION This is an opportunity to address restricted domains.

d. $r = \dfrac{24{,}000 - 8d}{12}$ or $r = 2{,}000 - \dfrac{2}{3}d$

7 **a.** $P = 2c - 5w$

b. As number of customers increases, profit increases.
As number of wins increases, profit decreases.

POSSIBLE MISCONCEPTION
Students may *try* to factor into this problem the probability of making 3 baskets.

c. **i–ii.** Any combinations such that $2c - 5w > 0$, or $2c > 5w$, where c and w are non-negative integers.

iii. Solutions are points with integer coordinates in the shaded region below (not on) the line $w = \dfrac{2}{5}c$.

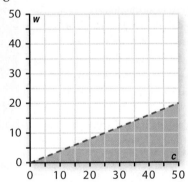

d. $P = 2c - 5w$
$50 = 2(40) - 5w$
$5w = 30$
$w = 6$

Unit 1

Summarize the Mathematics

For variables related by functions such as $I = 20x + 10y$, we say that I is a *linear function* of x and y. Equations of the form $2{,}000 = 20x + 10y$ are called *linear equations* in x and y. Linear equations in two variables can be rewritten to express one of the variables as a linear function of the other.

a Why does it make sense to call equations of the form $2{,}000 = 20x + 10y$ *linear equations*?

b Based on what you have learned previously about linear functions, why does it make sense to say that I is a linear function of x and y when these variables are related by a rule like $I = 20x + 10y$?

c Is $(4, 10)$ a solution of $5x + 10y = 120$? How could you check using the equation? Using a graph?

d What strategies can be used to find solutions for equations such as $2{,}000 = 20x + 10y$?

e How can you rewrite equations like $2{,}000 = 20x + 10y$ to express x as a function of y? To express y as a function of x?

f What is the slope of the graph of solutions for the equation $2{,}000 = 20x + 10y$?

Be prepared to share your ideas and reasoning with the class.

✔Check Your Understanding

When the event planners at the Cellar decided to sponsor a fall costume party, they set two ticket prices: $10 for advance tickets and $15 for tickets at the door.

a. What total ticket income will the party generate for the following combinations of ticket sales?

   i. 60 advance tickets and 85 tickets at the door

   ii. 98 advance tickets and 32 tickets at the door

b. Write a rule for income as a function of the numbers of tickets sold in advance and at the door.

c. Suppose that the event planners have a goal of $1,500 in ticket income and have sold 75 tickets in advance. How many tickets must be sold at the door to reach the income goal?

d. If the income goal is set at $2,000, what equation represents the question of how many tickets must be sold in advance and at the door to reach the income goal? Make a table and draw a graph showing non-negative solutions for this equation.

e. Rewrite the equation from Part d to express the number of tickets that need to be sold at the door as a function of the number of tickets sold in advance.

Summarize
the Mathematics

a All (x, y) solutions of $2,000 = 20x + 10y$ lie on the same line.

b Students should recognize that each part of I, the $20x$ and $10y$, are linear terms. They might think of I as adding two linear functions $A = 20x$ and $B = 10y$. Thus, I is a linear function of x and y.

c Yes, it is a solution. Using the equation, you would first substitute the values for x and y in the appropriate places in the equation and check the correctness of the equality: $5(4) + 10(10) = 120$.

To use a graph, you could solve for y to get y as a function of x. This linear function could then be graphed and then one could check to make sure the point $(4, 10)$ lies on the graph of the function.

d Strategies include:

(1) Choose a value for one variable and compute the corresponding value of the other variable.

(2) Graph the line by plotting x- and y-intercepts and look for solutions visually.

e With x as a function of y, $x = \dfrac{2,000 - 10y}{20}$ or $x = 100 - 0.5y$.

With y as a function of x, $y = \dfrac{2,000 - 20x}{10}$ or $y = 200 - 2x$.

f The slope of the graph of solutions for $2,000 = 20x + 10y$ is -2.

MATH TOOLKIT Show how to rewrite the equation $400 = 3x + 7y$ to express y as a function of x.

PROCESSING PROMPT
We checked our thinking by ... .

✓ Check Your Understanding

a. **i.** $1,875

  ii. $1,460

b. $I = 10A + 15D$, where A represents the number of advance-sale tickets and D represents the number of tickets sold at the door.

c. Fifty tickets must be sold at the door.

d. $2,000 = 10A + 15D$

A	D
20	120
50	100
200	0

Solutions are non-negative integer pairs on the segment on the graph at the right.

e. $D = \dfrac{2,000 - 10A}{15}$

On Your Own

Applications

(1) For each of the following functions, write a sentence describing the relationship among the variables in the language of direct and inverse variation.

a. Earned wages E at a job are a function of hours worked h and hourly pay rate r, given by the rule $E = rh$.

b. When members of a sailing club pool their money to buy a boat, the cost per member c depends on the number of members n and the cost of the boat B according to $c = \frac{B}{n}$.

c. When a flashlight shines on a flat surface at night, the brightness B of the light on that surface is a function of the distance d from the flashlight to the surface and the lumen strength L of the flashlight beam; the rule that relates them is $B = \frac{L}{d^2}$.

d. If a runner can average m miles per hour for quite a long run, the distance covered d is a function of the total running time t and average speed m.

(2) When a car, van, or small truck is involved in a traffic accident, the likelihood that a passenger will be fatally injured depends on many conditions. Two key variables are speed and mass of the vehicle in which the passenger is riding.

a. What general relationship would you expect between the rate of fatalities in auto accidents and the speed and mass of the vehicle in which a passenger is riding?

b. What data on highway accidents would help you develop a function relating the rate of passenger fatalities, vehicle speed, and vehicle mass?

c. If A represents the fatality rate in auto accidents, s represents vehicle speed, and m represents vehicle mass, which of the following functions would you expect to best express the relation among those variables? Explain your choice.

Function I $A = 200(s + m)$	**Function II** $A = 200(s - m)$
Function III $A = 200\frac{s}{m}$	**Function IV** $A = 200sm$

Applications

1. **INSTRUCTIONAL NOTE** The concept of expressing a relationship in the language of direct and inverse variation is a crucial concept for students to master, especially when more than one variable influences another. Students may have difficulties formulating sentences like "Current is directly proportional to voltage and inversely proportional to resistance."

   a. Earned wages E varies directly with hours worked h and pay rate r.

   b. Cost per member c varies directly with cost of boat B and inversely with number of members n.

   c. Brightness B varies directly with lumen strength L and inversely with the distance from the flashlight squared d^2.

   d. Since $d = mt$, distance d varies directly with both speed m and time t.

2. a. As speed increases, one would probably expect the rate of fatalities to also increase. The greater the mass of the passenger's vehicle, one might expect a lesser rate of fatalities. (Some students may express this relationship as $F = \frac{s}{m}$.)

   b. Data such as the model of cars involved, the speed upon impact, the total number of such accidents, and the number of fatal accidents would be helpful in developing a function.

   c. Function III: $A = 200\frac{s}{m}$

   The fatality rate is likely directly proportional to speed and inversely proportional to the mass of the vehicle.

③ An important consideration in construction is the weight a steel or wooden beam can hold without breaking. Some beam materials are stronger than others. But for any particular material, two important variables that influence the breaking weight are the length and thickness of the beam.

a. Which beam do you think would support the greatest weight? The least weight?

b. The beams differ in length and thickness. How would you expect those two variables to affect the breaking weight of a beam?

c. Breaking weight W depends on beam length L and thickness T. What sort of rule might be used to express W as a function of L and T?

d. The table that follows shows data collected by a class that used strands of raw spaghetti spanning gaps of various lengths to investigate the breaking weight of "spaghetti bridges":

Breaking Weight in grams

		Number of Strands			
		1	2	3	4
	2	92.5	145.1	188.1	261.6
	3	47.8	109.9	128.4	185.8
Gap Length (in inches)	4	38.6	69.9	98.5	124.7
	5	29.6	43.7	79.1	95.9
	6	23.8	28.3	66.5	78.4

Do the patterns of change shown in the data table support or change your thinking about the sort of rule that might be used to express W as a function of L and T?

e. Based on the data in the table above, the class developed the rule $W = 137\frac{T}{L}$ to express W as a function of T and L.

   i. Rewrite the rule to express T as a function of L and W.

   ii. Rewrite the rule to express L as a function of W and T.

④ If a variable z is directly proportional to x and inversely proportional to y, the relationship of those variables can be expressed in the form $z = \frac{kx}{y}$, where k is the constant of proportionality. Write similar rules to represent the relationships described in these situations.

a. The volume V of a cylindrical container is directly proportional to its height h and the square of its radius r.

b. The force F required to lift some object with a lever is directly proportional to the mass m of the object and inversely proportional to the length L of the lever.

(3) a. most—3rd beam
   least—2nd beam

b. One might expect possible *weight* supported to be directly proportional to *thickness* and inversely proportional to *length*.

c. $W = k\frac{T}{L}$ (Students might not include k at this point.)

d. This question provides an opportunity for students to confirm or correct their thinking.

e. i. $T = \frac{LW}{137}$

   ii. $L = 137\frac{T}{W}$

(4) a. $V = k(hr^2)$ or precisely $v = \pi h r^2$

b. $F = \frac{km}{L}$

c. The attraction F between two objects in space varies directly with the product of their masses m_1 and m_2 and inversely with the square of the distance d between them.

5 A group of 13 machine shop workers in Ohio regularly pooled their money to buy lottery tickets. On July 29, 1998, they won a lump sum payment of $161.5 million.

a. How much did each of the 13 winners receive, assuming they shared the winnings equally?

b. How would the amount received by each winner change if more workers had participated in the lottery pool? If fewer workers had participated?

c. How would the amount received by each winner change if the lottery jackpot had been larger? What if the lottery jackpot had been smaller?

d. Write a rule that gives the share of the winnings S for each person as a function of the lottery jackpot L and the number of people N in the pool.

e. Rewrite the rule in Part d to express N as a function of L and S.

6 The population density of any country or region is usually measured by calculating the number of people per unit of area. For example, in 1790, the United States had a population density of 4.5 people per square mile; in 2000, that figure had risen to 79.6 people per square mile. In that time period, both the number of people and the land area of the country grew.

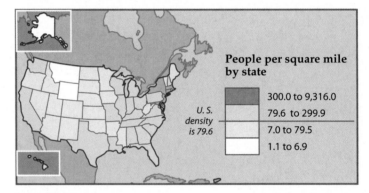

Source: U.S. Census Bureau

a. What are some land areas that were added to the United States after 1790?

b. What function rule shows how to calculate population density D for a region from the area A and population P of that region?

c. $F = \dfrac{km_1m_2}{d^2}$

5 **a.** Each winner received $12,423,076.92.

b. If more workers had participated, each winner would receive less. If fewer workers participated, each would receive more.

c. If the jackpot was larger, each winner would receive more. If the jackpot was smaller, each winner would receive less.

d. $S = \dfrac{L}{N}$

e. $N = \dfrac{L}{S}$

6 **a.** Common answers might include: the Louisiana Purchase, the Southwest, Alaska, and Hawaii.

b. $D = \dfrac{P}{A}$

c. How do increases in the population of a region affect the population density? How about decreases in the population?

d. What change in population density of a region will result if both population and land area increase? What if both decrease?

e. How would you complete the following sentence to describe the dependence of population density on both total population and land area?

"The population density of a country is (directly/inversely) related to the total population and (directly/inversely) related to the area of the country."

7 A local radio station sponsors a T-shirt toss and floppy hat drop during home pro basketball games. The T-shirts cost the radio station $8 each, and the hats cost $12 each.

a. The promotional cost C for the radio station depends on the numbers of shirts s and hats h given away at the game. Write a rule expressing C as a function of s and h.

b. How will the radio station's cost change as the number of shirts given away increases? How will cost change as the number of hats given away increases?

c. Suppose the radio station has budgeted $2,400 per game for giveaways. Write an equation that represents the question "How many shirts and hats can the radio station give away for $2,400?"

d. List 4 solutions to your equation from Part c. Draw a graph that shows all of the possible solutions.

e. Rewrite your equation from Part c to express s as a function of h. Explain what the slope and s-intercept of this linear function tell you about the situation.

8 Aidan is planning to build a small goldfish pond in his back yard. He plans to keep fantail goldfish, which can grow to be 4 inches, and common goldfish, which can grow to be 8 inches.

a. The *fish load* of a pond is measured in total inches of fish lengths.

i. Suppose Aidan wants to keep 5 fantail goldfish and 8 common goldfish. When the fish reach full size, what will the fish load of the pond be?

ii. Write an algebraic rule that shows how pond fish load L depends on the number f of full-size fantail goldfish and the number c of full-size common goldfish in the pond.

iii. How will the fish load of the pond change as the number of full-size fantail goldfish increases? How will it change as the number of full-size common goldfish increases?

c. If the population increases, the density will increase (for the same size area).
If the population decreases, the density will decrease (for the same size area).

d. It depends on the size of the increase or decrease in each variable.

e. The population density of a country is directly related to the total population and inversely related to the area of the country.

7 **a.** $C = 8s + 12h$

b. Costs will increase $8 per shirt and $12 per hat.

c. $2,400 = 8s + 12h$

d. While choice will vary, possible solutions are as follows:
   300 shirts and 0 hats
   150 shirts and 100 hats
   75 shirts and 150 hats
   0 shirts and 200 hats

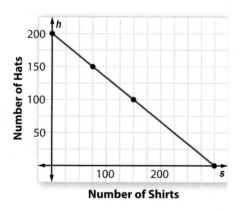

Number of Shirts

Solutions are non-negative integer pairs on the graph.

e. $s = \dfrac{2,400 - 12h}{8}$, or $s = 300 - 1.5h$

In this case, the slope indicates that for every hat that is given away, 1.5 fewer shirts can be given away (this might make more sense to think in terms of giving away 3 fewer shirts for every 2 hats given away). The s-intercept lets one know that if 0 hats are given away, then 300 shirts can be given away.

8 **a.** **i.** The fish load will be 84. The fish load will increase by 4 for each additional fantail and increase by 8 for each additional common goldfish.

   ii. $L = 4f + 8c$

   iii. The fish load will increase in both cases.

Unit 1

b. Aidan is considering a pond kit that is rated for 140 inches of goldfish. How many full-size fantail and common goldfish can be supported in this pond? Be sure to include the following in your response:

- an equation that represents the question;

- a table showing several combinations of numbers of full-size fantail and common goldfish that meet the pond rating limit;

- a graph of all possible solutions.

c. As the number of common goldfish in a pond increases, how will the number of fantail goldfish that can be supported in the pond change?

9 Find three specific solutions of the linear equation $3x - 2y = 12$. Then graph the full solution set of this equation.

10 Rewrite each of the following linear equations to express y as a function of x. Determine the slope and y-intercept for the graph of the solution set of each equation.

a. $2x + y = 6$ **b.** $8x - 5y = 20$ **c.** $-4x - 3y = 15$

Connections

11 Ms. Williams gives her students a 10-point quiz every week.

a. Suppose a student has an average quiz score of 8 after 5 quizzes.

   i. How many total quiz points has the student earned?

   ii. If the student scores 2 points on the sixth quiz, what is the student's average quiz score?

b. Suppose the student still has an average quiz score of 8 after 15 quizzes.

   i. How many total quiz points has the student earned?

   ii. If the student scores 2 points on the sixteenth quiz, what is the student's average quiz score?

c. How does a single quiz score's impact on the average score change as the number of quizzes increases?

12 The three key variables in racing are distance, speed, and time.

a. If a runner covers 400 meters in 50 seconds, what is the runner's average speed? What if it takes the runner 60 seconds to cover the same distance? What formula expresses average speed s as a function of distance d and time t?

b. If a NASCAR racer covers 240 miles at an average speed of 150 miles per hour, how long will the race take? What if the average speed is 180 miles per hour? What formula expresses race time t as a function of distance d and average speed s?

b. 140 = 4f + 8c

A few whole number possibilities are (35, 0), (27, 4), and (3, 16).

Solutions are integer pairs on the part of the line in the first quadrant.

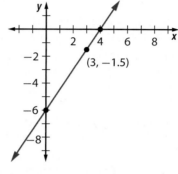

c. The number of fantail goldfish that can be supported decreases by 2 for each additional common goldfish.

9 Students might use technology or make a quick plot of their three points and sketch the line containing them. Three possible solutions are (4, 0), (3, −1.5), and (0, −6).

10 **a.** y = 6 − 2x; slope of −2, y-intercept of (0, 6)

b. y = −4 + $\frac{8}{5}$x; slope of $\frac{8}{5}$, y-intercept of (0, −4)

c. y = −5 − $\frac{4}{3}$x; slope of −$\frac{4}{3}$, y-intercept of (0, −5)

Connections

11 **a.** **i.** 40 points

ii. $\frac{42}{6}$ = 7

b. **i.** 120 points

ii. $\frac{122}{16}$ = 7.625

c. A single quiz score impacts the average score less and less as the number of scores increases.

12 **a.** 8 meters/second; approximately 6.67 meters/second

The formula s = $\frac{d}{t}$ represents speed as a function of distance and time.

b. 1.6 hours (96 minutes); approximately 1.33 hours (80 minutes)

The formula t = $\frac{d}{s}$ represents time as a function of distance and speed.

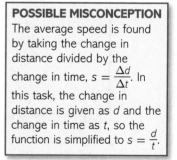

POSSIBLE MISCONCEPTION
The average speed is found by taking the change in distance divided by the change in time, s = $\frac{\Delta d}{\Delta t}$. In this task, the change in distance is given as d and the change in time as t, so the function is simplified to s = $\frac{d}{t}$.

c. If a participant in a triathlon swims at an average speed of 1.2 meters per second for 40 minutes, how much distance will be covered? What if the average speed drops to 0.9 meters per second and the time increases to 50 minutes? What formula expresses distance d as a function of average speed s and time t?

13 For each of the following geometric formulas, solve for the stated variable and answer the related questions.

a. Solve $C = \pi d$ for d.

    i. If a circular swimming pool is 200 feet around, what is the diameter of the pool?

    ii. A circular garden is enclosed with 50 feet of fencing. What is the diameter of the garden?

b. Solve $A = \ell w$ for w.

    i. If the length of a rectangular sandbox is set at 16 feet, what width is required to obtain an area of 200 square feet?

    ii. If the length of the sandbox was to increase but the area was to remain 200 square feet, how would the width have to change?

c. Solve $P = 2\ell + 2w$ for w.

    i. If you have 52 feet of lumber to construct the sides of a rectangular sandbox, and the length is set at 16 feet, how wide can the sandbox be?

    ii. If the length of the sandbox was to increase but the perimeter was to remain 52 feet, how would the width have to change?

d. Solve $V = \ell w h$ for h.

    i. In designing a box to have volume 1,000 cm³, length 20 cm, and width 10 cm, what is the height?

    ii. If the volume of the box was to increase but the length and width were to remain unchanged, how would the height have to change?

14 In Course 1, you may have discovered *Euler's formula* $V + F = E + 2$, which relates the number of vertices V, the number of faces F, and the number of edges E of simple polyhedra.

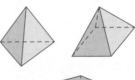

a. Write an equivalent form of Euler's formula that expresses E as a function of V and F. Check your answer using the polyhedra shown at the right.

b. Write an equivalent form of Euler's formula that expresses F as a function of V and E. Check your answer.

c. 2,880 meters; 2,700 meters

   The formula $d = st$ represents distance as a function of speed and time. (Note: A common error for the first two parts of this problem is to multiply 1.2 m/s by 40 minutes. However, an extra factor of 60 seconds/minute must be applied in order to arrive at the correct answers.)

13 a. $d = \frac{C}{\pi}$

   i. $d = \frac{200}{\pi} \approx 63.7$ feet

   ii. $d = \frac{50}{\pi} \approx 15.9$ feet

   b. $w = \frac{A}{\ell}$

   i. $w = \frac{200}{16} = 12.5$ feet

   ii. The width of the rectangle will decrease as the length increases and the area is fixed. The relationship is an inverse variation.

   c. $w = \frac{P - 2\ell}{2}$

   i. $w = \frac{52 - 2 \cdot 16}{2} = 10$ feet

   ii. The width of the rectangle will decrease as the length increases and the perimeter is fixed. The relationship is linear.

   d. $h = \frac{v}{\ell w}$

   i. Height is 5 cm.

   ii. The height will increase as the volume increases, for fixed length and width. The relationship is a direct variation.

14 a. $E = V + F - 2$

   For the triangular pyramid, $V + F - 2 = 4 + 4 - 2 = 6 = E$.
   For the square pyramid, $V + F - 2 = 5 + 5 - 2 = 8 = E$.
   For the rectangular box, $V + F - 2 = 8 + 6 - 2 = 12 = E$.

   b. $F = E - V + 2$

   Students may check by substituting values for F, E, and V in an equation or reason symbolically.

15 Consider the rules $z = 2x + 3y$ and $z = 5x - 4y$ expressing z as linear functions of x and y.

a. For each function, complete a table like that below showing the value of z for different values of x and y:

z = 2x + 3y

			x		
		0	1	2	3
	0				
	1				
y	2				
	3				

b. For $z = 2x + 3y$ and any fixed value of y, how does z change for each unit increase in x? For any fixed value of x, how does z change as y increases?

c. For $z = 5x - 4y$ and any fixed value of y, how does z change for each unit increase in x? For any fixed value of x, how does z change as y increases?

d. How do the patterns of change in Parts b and c relate to what you have learned previously about patterns of change in linear functions?

e. If $z = ax + by$, how will z change as x increases? As y increases?

16 Look back at your work in Applications Task 10. Each equation is a specific case of the general form of a linear equation $ax + by = c$, where a, b, and c are constants.

a. What is the slope of the graph of $ax + by = c$? Are there any conditions on a, b, or c?

b. What is the y-intercept of $ax + by = c$? Are there any conditions on a, b, or c?

Be prepared to provide algebraic reasoning that justifies your answers to these questions.

17 When radio or television transmitters are placed on tall towers, it is common to support those towers with wires anchored at various points on the tower and the ground.

There are three variables involved in placement of those support wires.

h = height of the point where the wire is anchored on the tower

b = distance of the ground anchor from the base of the tower

w = length of the support wire itself

15 **a.** $z = 2x + 3y$

		x			
		0	**1**	**2**	**3**
	0	0	2	4	6
	1	3	5	7	9
y	**2**	6	8	10	12
	3	9	11	13	15

$z = 5x - 4y$

		x			
		0	**1**	**2**	**3**
	0	0	5	10	15
	1	−4	1	6	11
y	**2**	−8	−3	2	7
	3	−12	−7	−2	3

b. $z = 2x + 3y$:

For any fixed value of y, z increases by 2 for every increase of 1 in x.
For any fixed value of x, z increases by 3 for every increase of 1 in y.

c. $z = 5x - 4y$:

For any fixed value of y, z increases by 5 for every increase of 1 in x.
For any fixed value of x, z decreases by 4 for every increase of 1 in y.

d. When either the x or y values are held constant, the patterns found in the columns and rows are linear patterns.

e. For each increase of 1 in x, z changes by a; for each increase of 1 in y, z changes by b.

16 **a.** As in Applications Task 10, rewrite $ax + by = c$ in the "$y = \ldots$" form.

$$ax + by = c$$
$$by = -ax + c$$
$$y = -\frac{a}{b}x + \frac{c}{b}$$

Slope $= -\frac{a}{b}$, $b \neq 0$. If $b = 0$, then the slope is undefined.

b. The y-intercept is $\left(0, \frac{c}{b}\right)$, $b \neq 0$. If $b = 0$, then there is no y-intercept.

Teaching Resources

Student Master 26.

UNIT **1** *Functions, Equations, and Systems*   Name ____
                                                 Date ____

Linear Functions of x and y
Connections Task 15

Suppose that there is an anchor in the ground at a point 40 feet from the base of the tower.

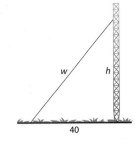

a. If $h = 60$ feet, what is w? What if $h = 90$ feet?

b. What function shows how the length w of the support wire from that anchor point depends on the height h of the point where it is to be connected to the tower?

c. Make a table that shows how the length of the support wire w changes as the anchor point on the tower moves up from 0 to 30 to 60 to 90 to 120 feet above the ground. Plot these (h, w) pairs on a graph and use your calculator for help in sketching a graph of the function in Part b for $0 \leq h \leq 150$.

d. How are the function, the table of values, and the graph for the situation similar to or different from those that you have worked with in earlier investigations?

18 Now suppose that there is a support wire, like that in Connections Task 17, that is 130 feet long.

a. What function shows how to calculate b if the 130-foot wire is to be attached to the tower at a point h feet up from the ground?

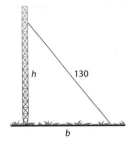

b. Make a table showing how the distance b from the ground anchor to the base of the tower changes as the height of the anchor point on the tower h moves up from 0 to 30 to 60 to 90 to 120 feet. Plot these (h, b) pairs on a graph and use your calculator or computer software for help in sketching a graph of the function in Part a for $0 \leq h \leq 130$.

17 **a.** $w = \sqrt{60^2 + 40^2} \approx 72$ feet

$w = \sqrt{90^2 + 40^2} \approx 98$ feet

b. $w = \sqrt{h^2 + 40^2} = \sqrt{h^2 + 1,600}$

c.

h	0	30	60	90	120
w	40	50	72.11	98.49	126.49

d. The graph suggests an increasing function like linear functions with positive slope, some quadratics, and exponential growth. However, the pattern of increase is not identical to any of those familiar cases. In fact, what happens is that as h gets large, values of the expression $\sqrt{h^2 + 1,600}$ seem to increase in a nearly linear pattern. This is because for large values of h, $\sqrt{h^2 + 1,600} \approx \sqrt{h^2} = h$.

18 **a.** $b = \sqrt{130^2 - h^2} = \sqrt{16,900 - h^2}$

b.

h	0	30	60	90	120
b	130	126	115	94	50

Unit 1

Reflections

19 Three different kinds of functions you have studied can be used to model situations in which increase in the independent variable leads to decrease in the dependent variable—linear functions with negative slope, exponential decay functions, and inverse variation functions (for positive constant of proportionality). What clues do you use to decide which of those functions might be useful in modeling a particular data pattern?

20 Studying patterns of change in a function with two independent variables, like Ohm's Law, is a bit more complicated than work with single-variable functions. How do you go about understanding the pattern of change in a function like $c = \frac{B}{n}$? How about a function like $z = 5x + 7y$?

21 Mathematicians generally use the words *function*, *expression*, and *equation* with different meanings in mind.

   a. Which terms would you use to label each of the following algebraic items?

      i. $7x^2 - 5x$

      ii. $y = 7x^2 - 5x$

      iii. $7x^2 - 5x = 0$

   b. What do you think mathematicians have in mind as a rule for deciding when to use *function*, when to use *expression*, and when to use *equation*?

22 To quickly sketch the graph of the solution set of a linear equation like $6x - 4y = 12$, Vera described the following method.

> I find the coordinates of the *x*-intercept by mentally substituting O for *y* and then solve for *x*. To find the coordinates of the *y*-intercept, I substitute O for *x* and then solve for *y*. Then I draw the line through the two intercept points.

Try Vera's method for the equation $6x - 4y = 12$ and explain why it works.

Extensions

23 The time T it takes a ball to roll down a ramp of length L that is supported at one end by a platform of height H is described by the formula

$$T = k \cdot \frac{L}{\sqrt{H}},$$

where k is some positive constant.

Reflections

19 Students should consider the data pattern as revealed in a table and a plot.

A linear function should be evident to the students from the plot of a straight line and in the table by a constant decrease in dependent variable values for the same change in independent variable values.

To distinguish between exponential decay and inverse variation as the best model, students may consider the behavior of the data near the origin. If a *y*-intercept exists, then the function is modeled best by exponential decay.

20 By this point, one strategy that students should be accustomed to is holding one (or more) of the independent variables constant and noticing how the remaining independent variable affects the dependent variable.

21 a. **i.** expression

   ii. function

   iii. equation

   b. Ideas are likely to vary greatly, but the following are some potential ideas:

   The term *function* is used when we are interested in how values of one variable depend on values of other(s). The rule for a function generally shows how to calculate values of a dependent variable from values of one or more independent variables.

   The term *expression* is used when we see a collection of symbols that show how to combine values of one or more variables through arithmetic operations to produce a numerical output, but there is no equation indicating the name of the output variable.

   The term *equation* is generally used when the implied task is to find values of the variables that make expressions on each side of an = sign equal in value.

22 For $6x - 4y = 12$, the intercepts are $(0, -3)$ and $(2, 0)$. The graph is shown at the right. This method works because the *x*-intercept has a *y* value of 0 and the *y*-intercept has an *x* value of 0. Since you only need 2 points to determine a line, you have the graph with only those 2 points.

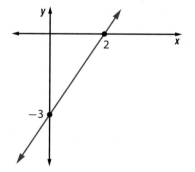

a. Solve $T = k \cdot \dfrac{L}{\sqrt{H}}$ for k.

b. Refer back to the data you collected for the first ramp experiment in Lesson 1 (page 4). Calculate k from T, L, and H for each data point.

c. Describe the shape, center, and spread of the values you obtained for k.

d. Determine an estimate for the value of k and substitute this value for k in the original formula. How could you determine how well this function models the data from the ramp experiment?

24 When Leon learned Ohm's Law, he wrote a simple spreadsheet program to help with calculations in various homework tasks.

a. One part of the spreadsheet calculates current, when voltage and resistance are known. What formula would be used in cell **B3** if the spreadsheet user enters numerical values of voltage and resistance in cells **B1** and **B2**, respectively?

Ohm's Law.xls

	A	B
1	voltage =	
2	resistance =	
3	current =	
4		

b. How could you modify the spreadsheet of Part a so that it calculates voltage when numerical values of current and resistance are entered?

c. How could you modify the spreadsheet of Part a so that it calculates resistance when numerical values of current and voltage are entered?

d. The following table starts to show values of current for every combination of voltage and resistance from 1 to 10 in steps of 1. Create a spreadsheet that produces entries in all of the cells by entering only 2 numbers and 3 formulas and then applying several fill down or fill right commands.

Ohm's Law.xls

	A	B	C	D	E	F	G	H	I	J	K
1		1	2	3	4	5	6	7	8	9	10
2	1	1	0.5	0.33	0.25	0.2	0.17	...			
3	2	2	1	0.67	0.5	0.4	...				
4	3	3	1.5	1	0.75	...					
5	4	4	2	1.33							
6	5	5	2.5								
7	6	6									
8	7	...									
9	8										
10	9										
11	10										

Extensions

23 **a.** $k = \dfrac{T\sqrt{H}}{L}$, or $k = T \cdot \dfrac{\sqrt{H}}{L}$

b. Using the data from Problem 2 on page 5, k is calculated.

H	L	T	$k = \dfrac{T\sqrt{H}}{L}$
0.5	3	1.2	0.283
0.5	4	1.7	0.301
0.5	5	2.2	0.311
0.5	6	2.8	0.330
0.5	7	3.3	0.333
0.5	8	3.7	0.327
0.25	3	2.7	0.45
0.25	4	3.5	0.44
0.25	5	4.1	0.41
0.25	6	4.9	0.41
0.25	7	5.6	0.4
0.25	8	6.2	0.388

c. The data for k in the table above has $\bar{x} \approx 0.365$ and $\sigma \approx 0.05$. A box plot display gives the impression that this distribution is symmetric. This difference in pattern of the results suggests that change in ramp height also causes change in uncontrollable experimental conditions (like friction) that affect results in significant ways.

d. Using an estimate for k of 0.365, the time estimates will be high for the 0.5-ft ramp and low for the 0.25-ft ramp.

24 **a.** The formula "=B1/B2" would be used.

b. In cell **B1**, the formula "=B2*B3" would be used.

c. In cell **B2**, the formula "=B1/B3" would be used.

d. In cells **B1** and **A2**, enter "1." Row **1** would be created by entering "=B1+1" in **C1** and using the fill right command. Column **A** would be created by entering "=A2+1" in **A3** and using the fill down command. Each of the remaining columns could be created by entering "=$A2/B$1" into cell **B2** and using the fill right command and then the fill down command.

25 The resistance in an electrical wire depends on the length and the thickness of the wire as measured by its cross-sectional diameter.

Diameter, d

Length, L

a. Suppose you are experimenting with battery and bulb circuits of different designs. How would you expect the resistance of the circuit to change as the length of the wire used in the design is increased? As the diameter of the wire used is increased?

b. Suppose that the formula $R = 5 \cdot \frac{L}{d^2}$ was proposed for the relationship among resistance R, length L, and diameter d of the wire in an electrical circuit. How does this formula fit with your expectations from Part a?

c. Rewrite the formula from Part b to express L as a function of R and d. You can check your reasoning with the computer algebra system command **solve(R=5*L/d^2,L)**.

d. Rewrite the formula from Part b to express d as a function of R and L. You can check your reasoning with the computer algebra system command **solve(R=5*L/d^2,d)**.

26 One formula for estimating heat flow through a solid material such as glass, wood, or aluminum involves 5 variables: $R = kA\frac{\Delta T}{t}$. The symbols and what they represent are as follows:

R = Rate of heat flow, in BTUs (British thermal units) per hour
k = Thermal conductivity for the specific material
A = Area of the material, in square feet
ΔT = Difference in temperature between outside and inside, in degrees Fahrenheit
t = Thickness of the material, in inches

a. Suppose sheets of glass, wood, and aluminum of the same area and thickness are exposed to the same difference in temperature. How would you expect the rate of heat flow to be different for these sheets of material?

25 **a.** As the length increases, the resistance will also increase. As the diameter increases, the resistance will decrease.

b. Student answers will vary depending on their answer to Part a, but here is an argument that is plausible from a scientific perspective: The resistance of the wire will decrease as the cross-sectional area increases. The cross-sectional area is calculated by πr^2 or $\pi\left(\frac{d}{2}\right)^2$. Thus, one could expect that the resistance is inversely proportional to the square of the diameter.

c. $L = \frac{Rd^2}{5}$

d. $d = \sqrt{\frac{5L}{R}}$

26 **a.** Aluminum would have the greatest rate of heat flow followed by glass and then by wood. (Students will check their responses in Part c.)

b. Consider a window opening that has an area of 6 square feet. Use the following information about the thermal conductivity of different materials to determine the heat flow rate through the window opening on a day when the outside temperature is 5°F and the inside temperature is 68°F.

   i. The thermal conductivity of glass is 5.8. What is the heat flow rate for a glass window that is 0.5 inches thick?

   ii. Suppose that instead of glass, the same opening is covered with wood having thermal conductivity of 0.78. What is the heat flow for the same temperature conditions if the wood is 0.5 inches thick?

   iii. The thermal conductivity of aluminum is 1,400. What is the heat flow under the same conditions if the opening is covered with aluminum 0.5 inches thick?

   iv. For this window opening, what thickness of glass would be required to achieve the same heat flow rate as the wood in part ii?

c. Review your response to Part a. Were you correct? If not, modify your response.

d. The symbol k stands for the thermal conductivity of the material. Would you conclude that materials with low k values are good conductors of heat or good insulators? What would you conclude about materials with high k values? Provide evidence to support your answers.

e. What changes in the variables A, ΔT, and t would cause the rate of heat flow to increase or decrease? Why does this make sense based on your thinking about the variables involved?

(27) Many questions about linear functions can be represented by linear inequalities.

a. Refer back to Problems 1 and 2 of Investigation 2 (pages 30–31). The equation $20L + 10C = 2,000$ represents the question of how many lawn mowing jobs and how many car washes it will take to achieve Bret's income goal of $2,000. In reality, Bret is probably interested in making *at least* $2,000, not *exactly* $2,000.

   i. Write an inequality to represent the question "How many lawn services and how many car washes will it take to achieve Bret's income goal of *at least* $2,000?"

   ii. How might you represent all possible solutions to the inequality on a graph?

b. Refer back to Applications Task 7 (page 37). Write an inequality that represents the question "How many shirts and hats can the radio station give away for *no more than* $2,400?" Graph all possible solutions of this inequality.

c. Graph the solution sets of the following inequalities.

   i. $6x + 3y \geq 12$

   ii. $2x + 5y \leq 30$

b. **i.** $R = (5.8)(6)\left(\frac{63}{0.5}\right) = 4{,}384.8$ BTU/hour

ii. $R = (0.78)(6)\left(\frac{63}{0.5}\right) = 589.68$ BTU/hour

iii. $R = (1{,}400)(6)\left(\frac{63}{0.5}\right) = 1{,}058{,}400$ BTU/hour

iv. Solve $589.68 = (5.8)(6)\left(\frac{63}{t}\right)$. $t \approx 3.72$ inches thick.

c. Responses will depend on Part a responses.

d. The lower the k value, the better the insulator. High k values would indicate good conductors. The results from Part b could be used as evidence, though some students might wish to research other materials and their conductivity.

e. If A and ΔT increase, the rate of flow would also increase. If A and ΔT decrease, the rate of flow would also decrease. If t were to decrease, the rate of flow would increase. If t were to increase, the rate of flow would decrease.

These results make sense because a larger window or greater difference between inside and outside temperature should lead to greater heat flow through the window. Also, greater thickness of the window covering should reduce heat flow.

27 **a.** **i.** $20L + 10C \geq 2{,}000$

ii. Shade the appropriate region.

b. $8s + 12h \leq 2{,}400$

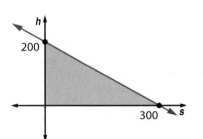

c. **i.** $6x + 3y \geq 12$ **ii.** $2x + 5y \leq 30$

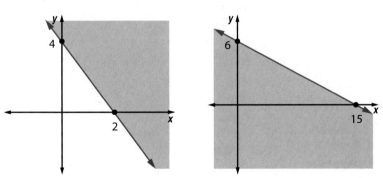

28 When several electrical appliances are drawing power from the same supply circuit in your home, the current drawn by the total circuit is the sum of the currents drawn by the separate appliances. The voltage remains constant at the standard 120 volts for household use in the United States.

If two appliances with resistances R_1 and R_2 are operating at the same time, the current flow I will be given by the following formula:

$$I = \frac{120}{R_1} + \frac{120}{R_2}$$

a. If a microwave with resistance 25 ohms and a refrigerator with resistance 15 ohms are operating at the same time on a kitchen circuit, what current is used?

b. Suppose a television and a hairdryer are both operating from the same bedroom circuit, drawing a total current of 6.5 amps. If the resistance of the hairdryer is 20 ohms, what is the resistance of the television set?

c. Use a computer algebra system to rewrite the given equation so that it expresses R_1 as a function of I and R_2. Then use that form to explain how R_1 changes as I and R_2 change in various ways (both increasing, both decreasing, one increasing and the other decreasing).

Review

29 Without using a calculator, evaluate the following expressions for the given values of the variables.

a. $3x - 2y$ when $x = 5$ and $y = -1$

b. $\frac{ab}{c}$ when $a = -6$, $b = -2$, and $c = -4$

c. $10 - pq$ when $p = 3$ and $q = -5$

28 **a.** 12.8 amps are used. $\frac{120}{25} + \frac{120}{15} = 12.8$

b. The resistance is 240 ohms.

$$6.5 = \frac{120}{20} + \frac{120}{R_2}$$

$$\frac{1}{2} = \frac{120}{R_2}$$

$$R_2 = 240$$

c. $R_1 = \dfrac{120R_2}{IR_2 - 120}$

As I and R_2 increase, R_1 would decrease. If I and R_2 both decrease, R_1 would increase. If I and R_2 move in different directions, one would not be able to tell if R_1 would increase or decrease without knowing more information.

Students might observe that to answer the questions about effect of change in I and R_2 it turns out to be much easier to use the original form of the relationship than the equivalent form derived to show R_1 as a function of I and R_2.

Review

Just in Time

29 **a.** 17

b. −3

c. 25

30 Make a copy of isosceles △*ABC*.

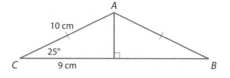

a. Fill in the lengths of as many sides as you can and the measures of as many angles as you can.

b. Find the area of △*ABC*.

31 Recall that the *reciprocal* of any nonzero number a is the number $\frac{1}{a}$.

a. Complete the following table showing relationships among a number, its reciprocal, and their product.

Number	2	$\frac{1}{4}$	$\frac{3}{5}$	−6	n
Reciprocal	$\frac{1}{2}$				
Product	1				

b. Recall that subtraction can be rewritten as addition: $a - b$ can be rewritten as $a + (-b)$. Division can also be rewritten as multiplication. How can you rewrite $\frac{a}{b}$ as a product?

c. Use your results from Parts a and b to justify each step in simplifying the product below.

$$5 \cdot \frac{3}{5} = 5 \cdot 3 \cdot \frac{1}{5}$$
$$= 5 \cdot \frac{1}{5} \cdot 3$$
$$= 1 \cdot 3$$
$$= 3$$

d. Use similar reasoning to simplify the following products.

  i. $2 \cdot \frac{7}{2}$

  ii. $3 \cdot \frac{2}{3}$

  iii. $b \cdot \frac{a}{b}$

32 Solve each of the following equations for x.

a. $17 = 5 - 3x$

b. $\frac{2x}{3} + 5 = 21$

c. $-12(x - 9) = -6(8 - 3x)$

33 Find equations for the lines that contain these pairs of points.

a. $(0, -4)$ and $(5, 3)$

b. $(-2, 4)$ and $(2, 0)$

30 **a.**

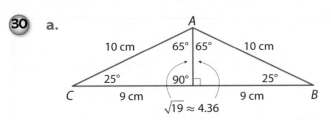

b. $9(\sqrt{19}) \approx 39.2$ cm^2

⏱ **Just in Time**

31 **a.**

Number	2	$\frac{1}{4}$	$\frac{3}{5}$	-6	n
Reciprocal	$\frac{1}{2}$	4	$\frac{5}{3}$	$-\frac{1}{6}$	$\frac{1}{n}$
Product	1	1	1	1	1

b. Either $a \cdot \frac{1}{b}$ or $\frac{1}{b} \cdot a$

c. $5 \cdot \frac{3}{5} = 5 \cdot 3 \cdot \frac{1}{5}$ Rewriting a fraction as the product of its numerator and the reciprocal of its denominator

       $= 5 \cdot \frac{1}{5} \cdot 3$ The Commutative Property for Multiplication

       $= 1 \cdot 3$ The product of a number and its reciprocal is 1.

       $= 3$ The product of any number and 1 is the number itself.

d. **i.** 7

    ii. 2

    iii. a

⏱ **Just in Time**

32 **a.** $x = -4$

    b. $x = 24$

    c. $x = 5.2$

33 **a.** $y = 1.4x - 4$

    b. $y = -x + 2$

34 The box plot below shows the price in dollars of 20 models of cordless phones.

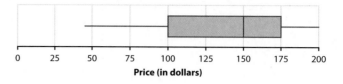

Price (in dollars)

a. What is the approximate median of the data?

b. What are the approximate lower and upper quartiles of the data?

c. Write a brief description of the distribution.

35 Solve each of these equations for x.

a. $x^2 + 4 = 13$

b. $3x^2 + 4 = 31$

c. $3x^2 + 12x = 0$

36 Write each of the following radicals in equivalent form with a smaller integer under the radical sign.

a. $\sqrt{20}$

b. $\sqrt{48}$

c. $\sqrt{72}$

d. $\sqrt{18a^2}$, $a > 0$

37 Consider the three equations:

$$3x + 2y = 6 \qquad 9x + 6y = 18 \qquad -6x - 4y = -12$$

a. Show that the ordered pairs $(0, 3)$, $(2, 0)$, $(-2, 6)$, and $(4, -3)$ are solutions to all three equations, but the ordered pair $(-3, 4)$ is not a solution to any of the equations.

b. If another student claimed that any ordered pair (a, b) satisfying one of the three equations is certain to satisfy the other two, would you agree? Why or why not?

c. What result would you expect if you graphed solutions for all three equations? Why?

34   **a.** $150

      b. $Q_1 = \$100$; $Q_3 = \$175$

      c. The distribution is skewed to the left. This means that half of the phone prices (10) are clustered at the high price range between $150 and $200. The bottom half of the prices are very spread out. These 10 phones range from a cost of around $45 to $150.

35   **a.** $x = \pm 3$

      b. $x = \pm 3$

      c. $x = 0, -4$

36   **a.** $2\sqrt{5}$

      b. $4\sqrt{3}$

      c. $6\sqrt{2}$ or $3\sqrt{8}$ or $2\sqrt{18}$

      d. $3a\sqrt{2}$

Just in Time

37   **a.** $3(0) + 2(3) = 6$; $9(0) + 6(3) = 18$; $-6(0) - 4(3) = -12$
          $3(2) + 2(0) = 6$; $9(2) + 6(0) = 18$; $-6(2) - 4(0) = -12$
          $3(-2) + 2(6) = 6$; $9(-2) + 6(6) = 18$; $-6(-2) - 4(6) = -12$
          $3(4) + 2(-3) = 6$; $9(4) + 6(-3) = 18$; $-6(4) - 4(-3) = -12$
          $3(-3) + 2(4) \neq 6$; $9(-3) + 6(4) \neq 18$; $-6(-3) - 4(4) \neq -12$

      b. One should agree. Arguments may vary—one possibility is that all three can be written in the form of the first ($3x + 2y = 6$).

      c. One should expect all three equations to be represented by the same line. Based on Parts a and b, all seem to have the exact same solutions.

Teaching Resources

Assessment Masters 27–32.

UNIT ❶ *Functions, Equations, and Systems*

Name _____
Date _____

LESSON 2 QUIZ

Form A

1. The volume of sand in a prism can be found using the formula $V = Bh$ where B is the area of the base of the prism and h is the height of the prism.

   a. The area of the base of a prism is 80 cm². Suppose you pour 500 cm³ of sand into the prism. How high up the side of the prism will the sand go?

   b. For a constant volume, how does the height change as the area of the base increases?

   c. How will the volume of the prism change if the height remains constant but the area of the base decreases?

   d. Write a formula that expresses h as a function of V and B.

2. Tamika pays $0.08 a minute for any daytime (7 a.m.–7 p.m. on weekdays) long-distance calls she makes and $0.04 a minute for night and weekend long-distance calls she makes.

   a. Tamika's long-distance bill B depends on the number of daytime minutes d and the number of night/weekend minutes w she uses. Write a rule expressing B as a function of d and w.

Assessment Master • use after Lesson 2   UNIT 1 • Functions, Equations, and Systems   **27**

Unit 1

Systems of Linear Equations

In Lesson 2, you gained experience in writing linear equations with two variables to express a variety of problem conditions. Sometimes, problems involve two linear equations that have to be solved simultaneously. The task is to find one pair (x, y) of values that satisfies both linear equations.

Students in the Hamilton High School science club faced this kind of problem when they tried to raise $240 to buy a special eyepiece for the high-powered telescope at their school. The school PTA offered to pay club members for an after-school work project that would clean up a nearby park and recreation center building.

Because the outdoor work was harder and dirtier, the deal with the PTA would pay $16 for each outdoor worker and $10 for each indoor worker. The club had 18 members eager to work on the project. But, most members would prefer the easier indoor work.

Systems of Linear Equations

The goal of this lesson is to develop the understanding and skill required to set up and solve systems of two linear equations in two variables. While the goals of the lesson are similar to those one might find in a chapter on systems of equations in a first-year algebra text, the skills and thinking involved in such goals are developed in a different manner. This is particularly evident in Investigation 2 when students reason through the necessary steps in the elimination method.

Lesson Objectives

- Write systems of linear equations to match given problem conditions
- Solve linear systems by graphing, substitution, and elimination methods
- Recognize linear systems with zero or infinitely many solutions by inspecting graphs, equation forms, and results of reasoning by substitution and elimination

Lesson Launch

It is neither likely nor critical that students will suggest much more than graphing, tables, or guess-and-check as strategies in Part d of the Think About This Situation. The TATS discussion should not introduce new methods unless they are brought up by the students.

Think About This Situation

In Lesson 2, you learned that conditions in the science club's situation could be represented by linear equations like these:

$$16x + 10y = 240 \quad \text{and} \quad x + y = 18$$

a What do the variables x and y represent in these equations?

b What problem condition is represented by each equation?

c What are some combinations of numbers of outdoor and indoor workers that will allow the club to earn just enough money to buy the telescope eyepiece? Will any of those combinations also put each willing club member to work?

d What different strategies could you use to find a pair of values for x and y that satisfy both linear equations simultaneously?

Work on the problems of this lesson will develop your skill in writing, interpreting, and solving systems of linear equations.

Investigation 1 — Solving With Graphs and Substitution

There are several different methods for solving systems of linear equations. As you work on the problems of this investigation, look for answers to this question:

How can graphs and algebraic substitution be used to solve systems of linear equations?

As you discussed in the Think About This Situation, a system of linear equations expressing the conditions in the science club's situation is:

$$\begin{cases} 16x + 10y = 240 \\ x + y = 18 \end{cases}$$

The first equation shows that the amount of money they can earn is a linear function of the variables x and y, where x and y represent the number of outdoor and indoor workers, respectively. The second equation shows that the number of club members who will work is also a linear function of those variables.

Think About This Situation

a The *x* represents the number of outdoor workers and *y* the number of indoor workers.

b The equation $16x + 10y = 240$ represents the total amount of money the science club is trying to raise. The equation $x + y = 18$ represents the total number of club members that will work.

c Answers may vary. It is *not* important that the students find an ordered pair that is a solution for both equations at this point.

d Students may suggest looking at graphs and tables to find an ordered pair that satisfies both equations.

Unit 1

Investigation 1 — Solving with Graphs and Substitution

As the title suggests, students develop graphic strategies for finding solutions to linear systems by locating intersection points of graphs and the substitution strategy for reducing a linear system with two variables to a single equation with one variable.

Graphs are provided in Problem 1 so that students are more quickly presented (and somewhat reminded of) the idea of graphing as a solution method. They will have opportunities to create their own graphs in future problems.

COLLABORATION SKILL
Ask questions when I am not sure I understand what we are doing.

1 In Lesson 2, you learned that equations in the form $ax + by = c$ are called linear equations because graphs of their solutions are straight lines. The diagram below shows graphs (in the first quadrant) of solutions to the equations $16x + 10y = 240$ and $x + y = 18$.

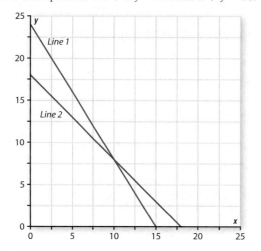

a. Match the graphs to the linear equations they represent. Explain how you know that your answers are correct.

b. Use the graphs to estimate a solution (x, y) for the system of equations—values for x and y that satisfy both equations. Explain what the solution tells about the science club's fund-raising situation.

c. Since graphs give only estimates for solutions of equations, it is important to check the estimates. Show how your graph-based estimate can be checked to see if it is an exact solution to the system.

2 When the date for the work project was set, it turned out that only 13 science club members could participate. The club president talked again with the PTA president and got a new pay deal—$20 per outdoor worker and $15 per indoor worker.

a. Write a system of linear equations in which one equation expresses the new conditions about payment and the other shows the new number of workers.

b. Estimate the solution for this system of equations by using graphs of the two equations. Then check your estimate.

There are many cases when it is easy to solve systems of equations without taking the trouble to produce graphs and estimate the required x and y values. One such symbolic solution strategy, the **substitution method**, combines two equations with two variables into a single equation with only one variable by *substituting* from one equation into the other.

1

a. One quick method for checking linear graph accuracy is to find the x- and y-intercepts.

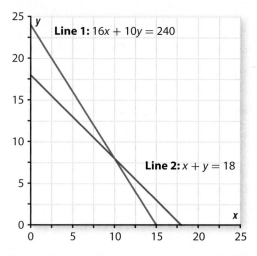

Line 1: $16x + 10y = 240$

Line 2: $x + y = 18$

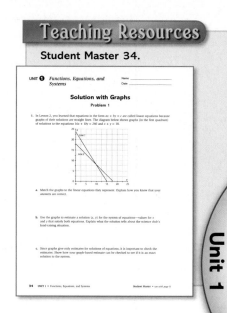
b. Estimates should be close to the actual solution of (10, 8). The solution indicates that 10 outdoor workers and 8 indoor workers should be used in order to meet both conditions.

c. One could substitute the estimate's values into both of the equations to check its accuracy.

2

a. $\begin{cases} 20x + 15y = 240 \\ x + y = 13 \end{cases}$

b. Estimates should be close to the actual solution of (9, 4).

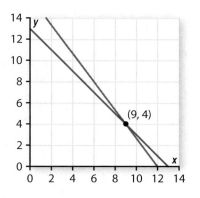

(9, 4)

3 Recall the science club's goal of purchasing a $240 telescope eyepiece and the prospect of having 18 workers. Using the substitution method, you could start toward a solution of the system of equations representing this situation by reasoning like this.

Step 1: We have to find values of x and y that satisfy both $16x + 10y = 240$ and $x + y = 18$.

Step 2: If $x + y = 18$, then $y = 18 - x$.

Step 3: That means that $16x + 10(18 - x) = 240$.

This reasoning has led to an equation in Step 3 that contains only one variable, x.

a. Explain each step in the reasoning.

b. Continue the reasoning above to complete a solution of the system.

Step 4: Solve the equation in Step 3 for x. What does this value of x tell you?

Step 5: Use the value of x to find a value for y that satisfies the original equation.

c. How could you check your solution from Part b?

d. Explain what your solution for the system of equations tells about the numbers of club members doing outdoor and indoor work necessary to reach their earning goal of $240.

4 Look back at the reasoning used in Problem 3 to solve the system $16x + 10y = 240$ and $x + y = 18$.

a. In Step 2, the equation $x + y = 18$ can also be written as $x = 18 - y$. How can this fact be used to write an alternative to Step 3 that gives a single linear equation involving y alone?

b. Check that this alternative strategy leads to the same solution for the original system.

5 Use reasoning similar to that in Problem 3 or 4 to solve the system of equations that you developed in Problem 2 to model the new conditions—only 13 workers and different pay for each kind of work.

6 Use a graphing method to estimate solutions for three of the following systems of equations. Then use the substitution method to solve the three remaining systems. Check your solutions for all six systems by showing that the values of x and y you find make both equations true statements.

a. $\begin{cases} y = 5x \\ 6x - 2y = -4 \end{cases}$ **b.** $\begin{cases} 5x - y = -15 \\ x + y = -3 \end{cases}$

c. $\begin{cases} 4x - y = 5 \\ x = 8 - 2y \end{cases}$ **d.** $\begin{cases} -7x + y = 32 \\ 2x + 3y = 27 \end{cases}$

e. $\begin{cases} 2x + y = 5 \\ 4x - 3y = -10 \end{cases}$ **f.** $\begin{cases} 4x + 2y = 7 \\ x - 5y = 10 \end{cases}$

(3) **a.** **Step 1:** True, because the values of numbers of workers x and y need to work in both equations.

Step 2: True, by the Subtraction Property of Equality. (Subtracting the same value from both sides of an equation makes an equivalent equation.)

Step 3: True, y is replaced with $18 - x$ because it is equal to y.

b. **Step 4:** $16x + 10(18 - x) = 240$
$$16x + 180 - 10x = 240$$
$$6x = 60$$
$$x = 10$$

This means that the x-coordinate of the point of intersection is 10.

Step 5: Find y when $x = 10$.
$$(10) + y = 18$$
$$y = 8$$

So, the solution is $(10, 8)$.

c. You can check your answers by substituting the values of x and y back into the original equations: $10 + 8 = 18$ and $16(10) + 10(8) = 240$

d. The solution tells that 10 outdoor workers and 8 indoor workers should be used in order to meet both conditions.

(4) **a.** If $x = 18 - y$ had been used, the equation involving y alone would be $16(18 - y) + 10y = 240$.

b. Simplifying $16(18 - y) + 10y = 240$ gives $y = 8$. So, $10 = x$ and we have the same solution.

(5) $20x + 15(13 - x) = 240$ $(9) + y = 13$
$20x + 195 - 15x = 240$ $y = 4$
$5x = 45$
$x = 9$

(6) **INSTRUCTIONAL NOTE** Students can estimate solutions by sketching graphs or using technology-produced graphs. Then they should use the substitution method to obtain the solutions below.

a. $(1, 5)$

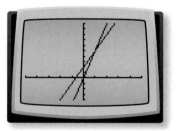

b. $(-3, 0)$

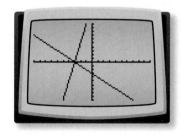

c. $(2, 3)$

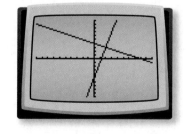

d. $(-3, 11)$

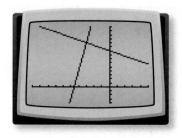

e. $(0.5, 4)$

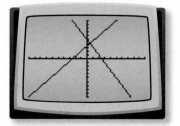

f. $(2.5, -1.5)$

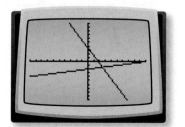

Summarize the Mathematics

Many problem situations can be modeled by systems of linear equations. It is important to know how to solve such systems.

a What does it mean to *solve* a system of linear equations?

b How can you use graphs to estimate the solution for a system of linear equations?

c Explain how to use the substitution method to solve a system of linear equations.

d In what cases would graphing probably be more convenient than substitution? When would substitution be more convenient than graphing?

e Once you have solved a system of equations, how can you check your solution?

Be prepared to share your ideas with others in the class.

✓ Check Your Understanding

As you complete the following tasks, think about the advantages and disadvantages of solving systems of linear equations by graphing and by substitution.

a. Solve the following system of equations in two ways: by graphing the equations and by using substitution.

$$\begin{cases} 2x - y = 2 \\ x + 2y = 18.5 \end{cases}$$

b. The Kesling Middle School booster club is planning a community event to raise money for the school's art department. Based on previous fund-raising events, they estimate that the event will be a sellout—filling all 300 seats in the school auditorium. Plans are to charge adults $8 and children $3 admission. The club wants to earn $2,000 from admission charges.

  i. Write an equation that expresses the relationship among adult attendance, child attendance, and the goal for income from admission charges. Explain what the variables represent.

  ii. Write an equation that expresses the relationship among number of adults, number of children, and total attendance. Explain what the variables represent.

  iii. Describe at least two different ways you could find the numbers of adults and children at the event if the club is to meet their income goal of $2,000 and their attendance estimate of 300 people.

  iv. Solve the system of linear equations and check your solution.

To help formalize the students' ideas, you may want to have the students put their answers on large paper or whiteboards and display all their answers. Then pull from these ideas to formulate complete answers. As a follow-up to the discussion in Part c, ask students, "How do you decide whether to solve for $y =$ _____ or $x =$ _____ when applying the substitution method?".

Summarize the Mathematics

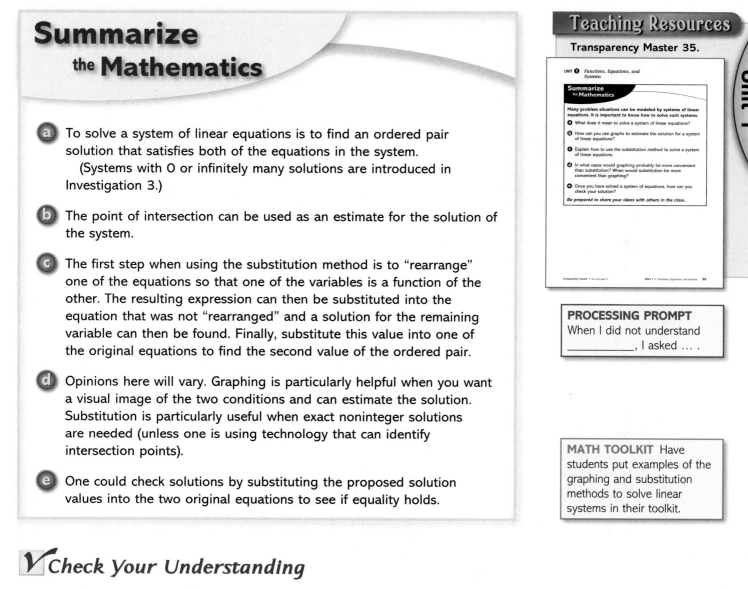

a To solve a system of linear equations is to find an ordered pair solution that satisfies both of the equations in the system.
(Systems with 0 or infinitely many solutions are introduced in Investigation 3.)

b The point of intersection can be used as an estimate for the solution of the system.

c The first step when using the substitution method is to "rearrange" one of the equations so that one of the variables is a function of the other. The resulting expression can then be substituted into the equation that was not "rearranged" and a solution for the remaining variable can then be found. Finally, substitute this value into one of the original equations to find the second value of the ordered pair.

d Opinions here will vary. Graphing is particularly helpful when you want a visual image of the two conditions and can estimate the solution. Substitution is particularly useful when exact noninteger solutions are needed (unless one is using technology that can identify intersection points).

e One could check solutions by substituting the proposed solution values into the two original equations to see if equality holds.

Teaching Resources

Transparency Master 35.

> **UNIT ❶** *Functions, Equations, and Systems*
>
> **Summarize the Mathematics**
>
> Many problem situations can be modeled by systems of linear equations. It is important to know how to solve such systems.
>
> **ⓐ** What does it mean to solve a system of linear equations?
>
> **ⓑ** How can you use graphs to estimate the solution for a system of linear equations?
>
> **ⓒ** Explain how to use the substitution method to solve a system of linear equations.
>
> **ⓓ** In what cases would graphing probably be more convenient than substitution? When would substitution be more convenient than graphing?
>
> **ⓔ** Once you have solved a system of equations, how can you check your solution?
>
> *Be prepared to share your ideas with others in the class.*

PROCESSING PROMPT
When I did not understand _____, I asked … .

MATH TOOLKIT Have students put examples of the graphing and substitution methods to solve linear systems in their toolkit.

✔ Check Your Understanding

a. (4.5, 7)

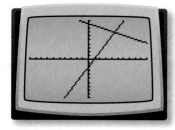

$$2(18.5 - 2y) - y = 2 \qquad x + 2(7) = 18.5$$
$$37 - 4y - y = 2 \qquad\qquad x = 4.5$$
$$-5y = -35$$
$$y = 7$$

NOTE The solutions to Part b are on page T54.

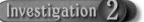

Solving by Elimination

Graphing and substitution strategies for solving systems of linear equations are convenient in some situations but not in others. The graphing method requires careful plotting of points, and it may give only estimates of solutions. The substitution method is most attractive when it is easy to solve for one variable in terms of the other. As you work on the problems of this investigation, look for an answer to this question:

How can the elimination of a variable be used to solve a system of linear equations?

Three friends—Conrad, Jenna, and Andrea—went to the Wild Adventures Theme Park during summer vacation. At lunch, Conrad offered to get 2 slices of pizza for Andrea, and Jenna offered to get a drink for Andrea, while Andrea looked for a table where they could sit together.

Prices were not posted at the small pizza stand, but Conrad was charged $10.50 for 4 slices of pizza and 1 large drink, and Jenna was charged $7.50 for 2 slices of pizza and 2 large drinks. Andrea wanted to pay her friends for the food they got her; but at first, all they could figure out was a system of linear equations that expressed the conditions:

$$\begin{cases} 4p + d = 10.50 \\ 2p + 2d = 7.50 \end{cases}$$

1. Analyze and complete the following reasoning used by the friends to solve the system.

   a. What do the variables p and d represent in the given system, and why do the given equations accurately represent the problem conditions?

   b. Conrad claimed that 8 slices of pizza and 2 drinks would cost $21. Is he right? How do you know?

   c. Andrea claimed that 6 slices of pizza and 3 drinks would cost $18. Is she right? How do you know?

   d. Jenna did not find either of these results very useful. She figured that 1 slice of pizza and 1 drink would cost $3.75, so she could solve the problem by solving the system:

   $$\begin{cases} 4p + d = 10.50 \\ p + d = 3.75 \end{cases}$$

   Is she right? How do you know?

   e. By examining the system of equations in Part d, Andrea figured out that 3 slices of pizza would have to cost $6.75, and she wrote the equation $3p = 6.75$. Is she right? How do you know?

   f. Based on this reasoning, what do you think they calculated for the cost of 1 slice of pizza? How about the cost of 1 large drink? How could you check these answers?

b. **i.** $8x + 3y = 2,000$; x is the number of adult attendees, y is the number of children attendees.

    ii. $x + y = 300$; x is the number of adult attendees, y is the number of children attendees, and 300 is the total attendees.

    iii. Three methods suggested might be graphing, substitution, or tables.

    iv. (220, 80)

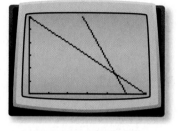

$$8(300 - y) + 3y = 2,000 \qquad\qquad x + 80 = 300$$
$$2,400 - 8y + 3y = 2,000 \qquad\qquad\quad x = 220$$
$$-5y = -400$$
$$y = 80$$

Investigation 2 — Solving by Elimination

This investigation presents the traditional method of solving a system by elimination with practical and student-centered reasoning provided for the steps. As indicated by the name, the primary goal of this method is to use linear combinations of the two equations in a system to produce a single equation with one variable (i.e., *eliminate* the other variable). Some students may see the solution to the resulting single equation as their solution to the system; it is important to remind students that this is only part of the solution (i.e., the other variable has not been *truly* eliminated).

COLLABORATION SKILL
Share thinking and listen to the thinking of others.

1 **a.** p represents the cost of 1 slice of pizza and d the cost of 1 drink. The equations accurately represent the situation because the coefficients on the ps are the correct number of slices of pizza, the coefficients on the ds are the correct number of drinks, and the prices in the equations are correct for the sums.

    b. Yes, he doubled an order of 4 slices and 1 drink.

    c. Yes, she combined the 2 original orders.

    d. Yes, she is right; she cut the 2-slice and 2-drink order in half.

    e. Yes, she subtracted 1 slice and 1 drink from the "top" order and the cost of 1 slice and 1 drink from the cost of the "top" order.

    f. One slice of pizza would cost $2.25, while 1 drink would cost $1.50. This solution can be checked by substituting the value 2.25 for p and 1.5 for d in the original equations as follows:
$4(2.25) + 1.50 = 10.50$ and $2(2.25) + 2(1.50) = 7.50$.

INSTRUCTIONAL NOTE
Avoid making the elimination method explicit at this time. Problem 1 develops the method in context and Problem 2 takes students through step-by-step. Problem 1 Part d is the important part and some students may need more scaffolding to recognize what Jenna did.

Whether they knew it or not, Conrad, Jenna, and Andrea solved the system of linear equations using a strategy called the **elimination method**. That method is based on two key properties of equations:

- If both sides of an equation are multiplied or divided by the same (nonzero) number, then the solutions of the new equation are identical to those of the original.

  For example, the solutions of $2p + 2d = 7.50$ are identical to those of $p + d = 3.75$.

- If you find the sum or difference of two equations in a system, the result often gives useful new information about the unknown values of the variables.

  For example, if $p + d = 3.75$ is subtracted from $4p + d = 10.50$, the result is $3p = 6.75$. From this, we can conclude that $p = 2.25$ and then that $d = 1.50$.

The challenge in using these ideas is finding the multiples, sums, and differences of given equations that lead to a single equation revealing part of the solution.

2 Consider the system of equations: $\begin{cases} 3x - y = 6 \\ x + 2y = 5.5 \end{cases}$

    a. For each of the steps below, explain what actions have been taken since the previous step. Justify the actions using previous mathematical knowledge and the two properties stated above.

        Start: $\begin{cases} 3x - y = 6 \\ x + 2y = 5.5 \end{cases}$

        Step 1: $\begin{cases} 6x - 2y = 12 \\ x + 2y = 5.5 \end{cases}$

        Step 2: $7x = 17.5$

        Step 3: $x = 2.5$

        Step 4: $2.5 + 2y = 5.5$

        Step 5: $2y = 3$

        Step 6: $y = 1.5$

        Check: $\begin{cases} 3(2.5) - 1.5 = 6 \\ 2.5 + 2(1.5) = 5.5 \end{cases}$

    b. Look back closely at the start of the solution in Part a.

        i. Why was 2 chosen as the constant to multiply both sides of the first equation in the original system to obtain the system in Step 1?

        ii. How could you start the solution process by leaving the first equation as $3x - y = 6$ and multiplying both sides of the *second* equation by a number that makes it easy to eliminate the x variable?

        Show the solution steps that would follow from choosing that multiplier.

2 **a. Start:** $\begin{cases} 3x - y = 6 \\ x + 2y = 5.5 \end{cases}$

Step 1: $\begin{cases} 6x - 2y = 12 \\ x + 2y = 5.5 \end{cases}$ Top equation multiplied by 2

Step 2: $7x = 17.5$ "Sum" of the two equations

Step 3: $x = 2.5$ Both sides of the equation divided by 7

Step 4: $2.5 + 2y = 5.5$ x value substituted in the original bottom equation

Step 5: $2y = 3$ 2.5 subtracted from both sides

Step 6: $y = 1.5$ Both sides divided by 2

Check: $\begin{cases} 3(2.5) - 1.5 = 6 \\ 2.5 + 2(1.5) = 5.5 \end{cases}$ x and y values substituted into original equations

b. **i.** Two was chosen as the constant multiplier so the y terms would be "eliminated" in Step 2.

ii. If you were to multiply both sides of the second equation by 3 and then subtract the result from the first equation, you would get a single equation $-7y = -10.5$, leading to $y = 1.5$ and eventually to $x = 2.5$, just as in the first solution procedure. You could also multiply the second equation by -3 and then add that result to the first equation with essentially the same result.

NOTE The method in Part a suggested uses addition of equations since fewer arithmetic errors are likely with addition than with subtraction of equations.

INSTRUCTIONAL NOTE
You may wish to have students write the reasons for their steps for another problem as they develop and then practice the elimination method in this lesson.

③ The steps in solving the system $\begin{cases} 3x - y = 6 \\ x + 2y = 5.5 \end{cases}$ in Part a of Problem 2

produced a total of eight different equations listed below—each telling something about the values of x and y that satisfy the original equations.

$3x - y = 6$	$x + 2y = 5.5$	$6x - 2y = 12$	$7x = 17.5$
	$x = 2.5$	$2.5 + 2y = 5.5$	$2y = 3$	$y = 1.5$

The diagram below shows graphs of solutions for these eight equations. The scale on each axis is 1.

a. Match each equation with the line that represent its solutions.

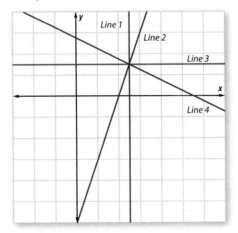

b. Why does it take only four lines on the diagram to represent solutions for all eight equations?

c. What can you conclude from the fact that graphs of all eight equations pass through a single point?

d. Estimate coordinates of the point through which all four lines pass and check to see if those coordinates provide a solution to the original system of equations.

④ Solve these systems of equations using the elimination method. Check each solution.

a. $\begin{cases} 3x + y = 13 \\ x - 5y = 15 \end{cases}$ **b.** $\begin{cases} 6x - y = 14 \\ 2x + y = 12 \end{cases}$

c. $\begin{cases} 2x + y = -9 \\ 4x + 3y = 1 \end{cases}$ **d.** $\begin{cases} 3x - 4y = 22 \\ 2x + 5y = 7 \end{cases}$

3 **a.** $3x - y = 6$ Line 2
$x + 2y = 5.5$ Line 4
$6x - 2y = 12$ Line 2
$7x = 17.5$ Line 1
$x = 2.5$ Line 1
$2.5 + 2y = 5.5$ Line 3
$2y = 3$ Line 3
$y = 1.5$ Line 3

b. Line 1 represents $7x = 17.5$ and $x = 2.5$ because they are equivalent equations.

Line 2 represents $3x - y = 6$ and $6x - 2y = 12$ because the second equation is twice the first. This holds all solution pairs of the first equation to be the same as solution pairs of the second.

Line 3 represents the last three equivalent equations.

So, seven of the eight equations are represented by only three lines.

By finding equivalent algebraic representations for the same line in the coordinate plane, variables can be manipulated in such a way that the vertical and horizontal lines are a result. The equations never truly change as long as the equations can be visually represented by the same line in the coordinate plane.

c. This point is a solution for all eight equations.

d. Estimates should be close to the actual solution of $(2.5, 1.5)$.

KEY IDEA The key in Problem 4 is that variables and algebraic expressions are manipulated to produce equations which all pass through the same point, our solution.

4 **a.** $(5, -2)$
b. $(3.25, 5.5)$
c. $(-14, 19)$
d. $(6, -1)$

Unit 1

DIFFERENTIATION For your more capable students, you might assign two parts of Problem 4 and Extensions Task 25.

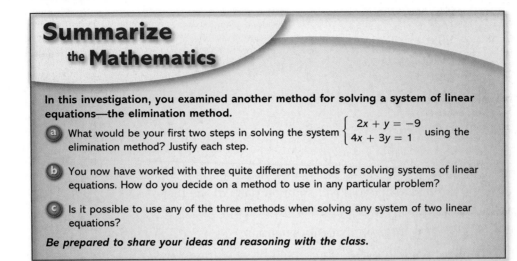

Summarize the Mathematics

In this investigation, you examined another method for solving a system of linear equations—the elimination method.

a What would be your first two steps in solving the system $\begin{cases} 2x + y = -9 \\ 4x + 3y = 1 \end{cases}$ using the elimination method? Justify each step.

b You now have worked with three quite different methods for solving systems of linear equations. How do you decide on a method to use in any particular problem?

c Is it possible to use any of the three methods when solving any system of two linear equations?

Be prepared to share your ideas and reasoning with the class.

✓Check Your Understanding

As you complete these tasks, think about the advantages and disadvantages of using the elimination method for solving a system of linear equations.

a. Use the elimination method to solve each of these systems of linear equations. Check your solutions.

   i. $\begin{cases} 2x + y = 6 \\ 3x + 5y = 16 \end{cases}$

   ii. $\begin{cases} 6x - y = 18 \\ 2x + y = 2 \end{cases}$

   iii. $\begin{cases} 2x + 3y = 5 \\ -3x + 2y = -14 \end{cases}$

b. Given a choice between graphing, substitution, and elimination, which would you choose to solve each of the systems in Part a? Explain the reasoning for your choices.

Investigation 3 — Systems with Zero and Infinitely Many Solutions

Systems of linear equations do not always have solutions consisting of a single ordered pair (x, y). As you work through this investigation, look for answers to this question:

> *What are the properties of linear systems that do not have exactly one ordered pair solution?*

Summarize
the Mathematics

(a) Students may choose a variety of first steps, but thinking should be along these lines:

Multiplying the first equation by −2 would be a good first step as it would allow one to "eliminate" the x terms in the next step when the equations are added.

(b) Student responses will vary, depending on strengths and weaknesses, but they should be developing their own strategies for when to use which method.

(c) Yes, it is possible, but certainly some are much more convenient in certain situations. When at least one equation is in the "y = ..." form, it seems reasonable to choose substitution.

PROCESSING PROMPT Today, I shared my thinking about _____
                                                          (mathematical idea)
and listened to the thinking of _____ about _____ .
                                (group member's name)   *(mathematical idea)*

MATH TOOLKIT Solve the system in Part a of the STM, then check using the elimination method. Write yourself notes about why you chose the particular multiplier in your solution.

✔Check Your Understanding

a. Student choices of multipliers for the elimination method will vary. Solutions are provided below.

   i. (2, 2)

   ii. (2.5, −3)

   iii. (4, −1)

b. Preferences will vary.

Investigation 3 Systems with Zero and Infinitely Many Solutions

In this investigation, students interpret graphic and symbolic calculation results that reveal cases when a given system of linear equations will have zero or infinitely many solutions. It is important to the development of the skills and concepts addressed in this lesson that connections are regularly made to what is being done symbolically and what is happening graphically with the systems presented.

COLLABORATION SKILL
Reach consensus or agree to disagree.

1 Think about the graphing method for estimating solutions to a system of two linear equations.

  a. Suppose (5, 8) is the solution to a system of linear equations. How could you see this by looking at the graphs of the equations?

  b. Sketch graphs of a system of linear equations that has *no* solution.

  c. Is it possible for a system of linear equations to have *infinitely many* solutions? What would the graphs look like in this case?

2 For some people, like athletes and astronauts, selection of a good diet is a carefully planned scientific process. In the case of astronauts, proper nutrition is provided in limited forms. For example, drinks might come in disposable boxes and solid food in energy bars.

  Suppose that, in planning daily diets for a space shuttle team, nutritionists work toward these goals.

  - Drinks each provide 30 grams of carbohydrate, energy bars each provide 40 grams of carbohydrate, and the optimal diet should contain 600 grams of carbohydrate per day.

  - Drinks each provide 15 grams of protein, energy bars each provide 20 grams of protein, and the optimal diet should contain 200 grams of protein.

  The problem is to find a number of drinks and a number of energy bars that will provide just the right nutrition for each astronaut. If we use x to represent the number of drinks and y for the number of energy bars, the goals in diet planning can be expressed as a system of linear equations:

$$\begin{cases} 30x + 40y = 600 \\ 15x + 20y = 200 \end{cases}$$

  a. What does the first equation represent? The second?

  Solving that system by the elimination method might follow steps like these.

  Step 1: $\begin{cases} 30x + 40y = 600 \\ 30x + 40y = 400 \end{cases}$

  Step 2: $0 = 200$

1 **a.** The graphs of the two lines should intersect at (5, 8).

   b. Students should sketch parallel lines.

   c. This question may prompt students to say either "yes" or "no." (Some students may think that when a system of two equations represents one line, it is not a system. This will be clarified in Problem 3.)

2 **a.** The first equation represents the grams of carbohydrate from drinks, energy bars, and the total amount for each day.

   The second equation represents the grams of protein from drinks, energy bars, and the total amount for each day.

Unit 1

b. What properties of equations justify Steps 1 and 2 in this solution method?

c. What does the equation in Step 2 say about the possibility of finding (x, y) values that satisfy the original system?

d. The diagram at the right shows graphs of solutions to the two original linear equations. How does it help explain the difficulty in finding a solution for the system?

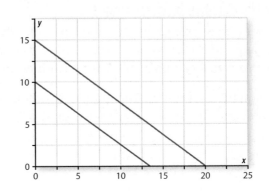

3. Suppose that the condition on protein in Problem 2 was revised to require 300 grams per day.

a. Write the new system of equations expressing the conditions relating number of drink boxes and number of food bars to the required grams of carbohydrate and protein in the diet.

b. Use the elimination method to solve this new system. What happens? What does this tell you?

c. Sketch a graph for each equation in the system in Part a. What do the graphs tell you about solutions for this system?

4. Solve each of the following systems of linear equations in two ways:

- first by estimation using graphs of the two equations,

- then by either substitution or elimination.

In each case, be prepared to explain what the result tells about solutions for the system and how that result is demonstrated in the graph and in the algebraic solution process.

a. $\begin{cases} x - y = 4 \\ 2x - 2y = 8 \end{cases}$ **b.** $\begin{cases} 3x - 6y = -46.5 \\ -x + 2y = 15.5 \end{cases}$

c. $\begin{cases} y = -5x + 12 \\ y = -5x - 7 \end{cases}$ **d.** $\begin{cases} x - 2y = 0 \\ 3x - 5y = 2.5 \end{cases}$

5. For which of the systems in Problem 4 could you determine the number of solutions just by examining the equations? How could you tell?

6. In the problems of this lesson, you've studied systems of linear equations that have unique solutions—a single pair of values for the variables that satisfy both equations—and others that have infinitely many solutions or no solutions at all. Find values of a, b, and c that will guarantee the system $\begin{cases} 3x - 2y = 4 \\ ax + by = c \end{cases}$ has:

a. exactly one solution (x, y).

b. infinitely many solutions.

c. no solutions.

b. Step 1: Both sides of the bottom equation were multiplied by 2.

Step 2: The equations in the new system were subtracted.

c. There are no possible solutions since $0 \neq 200$.

d. Since the two lines are parallel, they do not intersect, and therefore, there is no solution to the system.

3 **a.** $\begin{cases} 30x + 40y = 600 \\ 15x + 20y = 300 \end{cases}$

b. $\begin{cases} 30x + 40y = 600 \\ 30x + 40y = 600 \end{cases}$

$\overline{\hspace{1.5cm} 0 = 0 \hspace{1.5cm}}$

Any solution for the carbohydrate equation will also be a solution for the protein equation and vice versa.

c. Student sketches should show one line, $30x + 40y = 600$. The two equations are represented by the same line, so there will be infinitely many solutions to the system. (In the context, there are infinitely many solutions also if one assumes that grams can be measured to any degree of accuracy. Do not make this differentiation for students at this time unless they raise the issue.)

4 **a.**

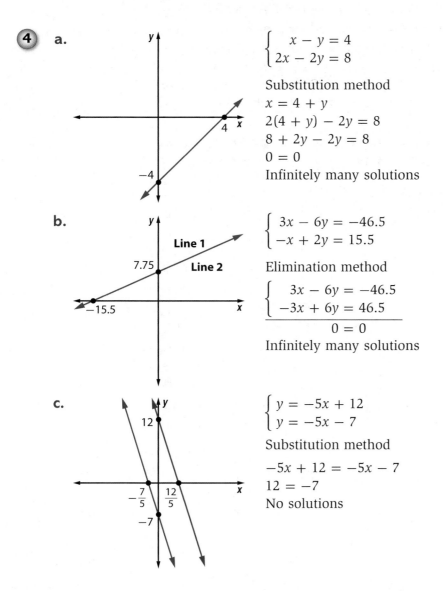

$\begin{cases} x - y = 4 \\ 2x - 2y = 8 \end{cases}$

Substitution method

$x = 4 + y$

$2(4 + y) - 2y = 8$

$8 + 2y - 2y = 8$

$0 = 0$

Infinitely many solutions

b.

$\begin{cases} 3x - 6y = -46.5 \\ -x + 2y = 15.5 \end{cases}$

Elimination method

$\begin{cases} 3x - 6y = -46.5 \\ -3x + 6y = 46.5 \end{cases}$

$\overline{\hspace{1.5cm} 0 = 0 \hspace{1.5cm}}$

Infinitely many solutions

c.

$\begin{cases} y = -5x + 12 \\ y = -5x - 7 \end{cases}$

Substitution method

$-5x + 12 = -5x - 7$

$12 = -7$

No solutions

d.

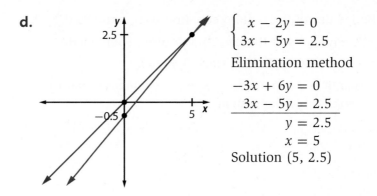

$$\begin{cases} x - 2y = 0 \\ 3x - 5y = 2.5 \end{cases}$$

Elimination method

$$-3x + 6y = 0$$
$$\underline{3x - 5y = 2.5}$$
$$y = 2.5$$
$$x = 5$$

Solution (5, 2.5)

5 **a.** Infinitely many solutions; both sides of the bottom equation are exactly twice those in the top equation.

b. Infinitely many solutions; both sides of the bottom equation could be multiplied by −3 to obtain the top equation.

c. No solutions; it is clear that these linear equations have the same slope but with different y-intercepts they will never intersect.

d. One solution; (5, 2.5), there is no constant multiplier k that would make $(x - 2y)k = 3x - 5y$.

6 Student answers will have specific values for a, b, and c.

a. There is exactly one solution if a and b are not the same as, or both the same multiple of, 3 and −2, respectively.

b. There are infinitely many solutions if $ax + by = c$ is a multiple of $3x - 2y = 4$.

c. There are no solutions if $ax + by$ is a multiple of $3x - 2y$ and c is not the same multiple of 4.

Teacher Notes

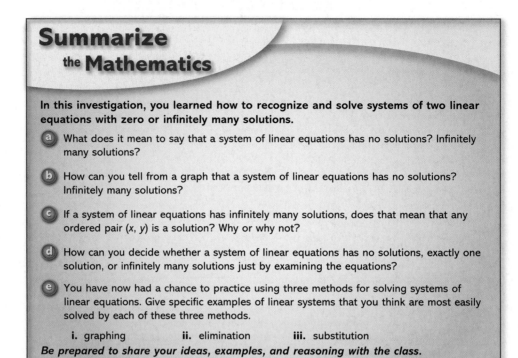

Summarize the Mathematics

In this investigation, you learned how to recognize and solve systems of two linear equations with zero or infinitely many solutions.

a What does it mean to say that a system of linear equations has no solutions? Infinitely many solutions?

b How can you tell from a graph that a system of linear equations has no solutions? Infinitely many solutions?

c If a system of linear equations has infinitely many solutions, does that mean that any ordered pair (x, y) is a solution? Why or why not?

d How can you decide whether a system of linear equations has no solutions, exactly one solution, or infinitely many solutions just by examining the equations?

e You have now had a chance to practice using three methods for solving systems of linear equations. Give specific examples of linear systems that you think are most easily solved by each of these three methods.

    i. graphing   **ii.** elimination   **iii.** substitution

Be prepared to share your ideas, examples, and reasoning with the class.

✔ Check Your Understanding

Use what you have learned about systems of equations to answer these questions.

a. Find values of a and b so that the system $\begin{cases} 3x + 2y = 5 \\ ax + 4y = b \end{cases}$ has infinitely many solutions. Explain how the graphs of the equations will be related.

b. Find values of a and b so that the system $\begin{cases} 3x + 6y = 12 \\ x + ay = b \end{cases}$ has no solutions. Explain how the graphs of the equations will be related.

c. Find values of a and b so that the system $\begin{cases} 3x + 2y = 5 \\ ax + 4y = b \end{cases}$ has exactly one solution. Explain how the graphs of the equations will be related.

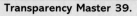
Summarize the Mathematics

a When a system has no solutions, it means that there is no ordered pair that satisfies both equations in the system. When a system has an infinite number of solutions, it means that every solution for one of the equations is also a solution for the other equation.

b If two lines are parallel, then the system representing those lines will not have a solution. If the graphs of two equations turn out to be the same line, then *all* points on this line are solutions to both equations. Since a line contains an infinite number of points, the system will have an infinite number of solutions.

c Not *any* ordered pair; the ordered pair must fit one equation. Since the two equations are the same, it will fit the other also. There are many ordered pairs that do not fit the equation just as there are many points not on the graph of the line.

d Students' methods may vary but should include discussion of the relationship between the coefficients and constants of the two system equations as indicated in the solution to Problem 5.

   If the equations are easily written in slope-intercept form, check the slopes of the two linear equations. If the slopes are different, the system must have exactly one solution. If the slopes are the same, the system has either zero or infinitely many solutions: there are no solutions if the lines have different y-intercepts and infinitely many solutions if the y-intercepts are the same.

e **i–iii.** Strategies and examples will vary.

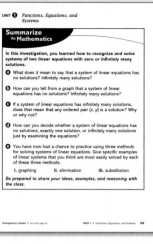

POSSIBLE MISCONCEPTION Students may think that "If there are infinitely many solutions, then *every* ordered pair must be a solution." The comparison of both symbolic and graphic solutions, as well as the checking of solutions, should help address this misconception. This is addressed in Part c.

MATH TOOLKIT Write a complete solution including examples to Part d of the STM.

PROCESSING PROMPT In this lesson, we reached consensus on Problem

_____ . The specific characteristics of our collaboration that helped

build consensus are ... .

✓Check Your Understanding

Students' systems will vary. One example is provided.

a. $a = 6$ and $b = 10$

   The graphs of the two equations will lie exactly on top of each other.

b. $a = 2$ and $b \neq 4$

   The graphs of the two equations will be parallel lines.

c. Any value of $a \neq 6$ will give a system with a unique solution.

   The graphs of the two equations will intersect at a single point.

DIFFERENTIATION For students who do not need additional work applying what they have learned in Investigation 3, consider replacing the assignment tasks A6–A9 with Take Home Assessment Task 3.

Applications

(1) To participate in a school trip, Kim had to earn $85 in one week. Kim could earn $8 per hour babysitting and $15 per hour for yard work, but Kim's parents limit work time to 8 hours per week.

a. Write two equations, one that represents the condition on total number of hours to be worked and the other which relates the number of hours worked at each job toward the fund-raising goal.

b. Solve the system of equations you wrote in Part a to find out how many hours Kim will have to work at each job to exactly meet the income goal and the time constraint.

(2) Solve the following systems of equations, using graphing as the method for one of them.

a. $\begin{cases} y = 3x - 5 \\ 8x - 4y = 30 \end{cases}$ **b.** $\begin{cases} y = 5x \\ 6x - 2y = 12 \end{cases}$ **c.** $\begin{cases} y = 5x + 15 \\ y = -x - 3 \end{cases}$

(3) The relationship between *supply* and *demand* is important in the business world. A supply function indicates the relationship between price of a product and the amount of that product that will be available from suppliers. A demand function indicates the relationship between price of a product and the amount of the product that will be purchased by consumers.

An electronics store devised the following functions to study supply and demand for its best-selling DVD players.

Demand: $y = -0.5x + 90$, where y stands for the estimated number sold, and x stands for the price of the DVD player.

Supply: $y = 1.5x - 30$, where y stands for the number available, and x represents the price of the DVD player.

a. Why do you suspect the demand function has a negative slope but the supply function's slope is positive?

b. *Equilibrium* is reached when supply is equal to demand. At what price should the store sell the DVD player in order to reach equilibrium between supply and demand?

Applications

① **a.** Total hours: $x + y = 8$
Earnings: $8x + 15y = 85$

b. $x = 8 - y$
$8(8 - y) + 15y = 85$
$64 - 8y + 15y = 85$
$7y = 21$
$y = 3$

She will have to babysit for 5 hours and do yard work for 3 hours to meet her goals *exactly*.

② One solution should be done graphically and the others using substitution.

a. $(-2.5, -12.5)$

b. $(-3, -15)$

c. $(-3, 0)$

③ **a.** As the price of a product goes up, it is logical to think that fewer people will want to buy it; so, the demand decreases. This translates into a negative slope for the line representing demand. Similarly, as the price goes up, manufacturers will be encouraged to produce more of the DVD players, increasing supply to retail stores. This translates into a positive slope for the line representing supply.

b. Equilibrium will be reached at a price of $60. This is found by solving the system of equations and using the *x*-coordinate since it represents the price of the DVD player.

Unit 1

4 Carly is training for an upcoming fitness competition and is trying to find a breakfast combination that meets her nutritional requirements of 950 calories and 25 grams of protein. One serving of her cereal of choice has 200 calories and 2 grams of protein. Her favorite brand of peanut butter contains 180 calories and 8 grams of protein per serving.

   a. Write an equation that relates the number of servings of cereal and the number of servings of peanut butter to the total number of calories she needs for breakfast.

   b. Write another equation that relates the number of servings of cereal and the number of servings of peanut butter to the total amount of protein she needs for breakfast.

   c. What numbers of servings for each type of food would meet both of her nutrition goals?

5 Laura and Andy are trying to earn money to buy airplane tickets to visit their favorite aunt, Annie. Laura's ticket is going to cost her $280 while Andy found a ticket for $230 on the Internet. To earn their money, they have both decided to mow lawns and babysit. Laura charges $7 per hour for babysitting while Andy charges $5 per hour. To mow a lawn, Laura charges $14 per lawn while Andy charges $16 per lawn.

   a. Write an equation relating income from Laura's work to her ticket cost. Use B to represent number of hours babysitting and L to represent number of lawns mowed. Use the same variables to write another equation relating income from Andy's work to his ticket cost.

   b. Is it possible that Laura and Andy could each reach their ticket price goal by mowing the same number of lawns and babysitting the same number of hours? If so, find those numbers; if not, explain how you know.

6 Solve the following systems of equations and check your solutions. Show that you know how to use different solution strategies by using each of the three methods once—graphing, substitution, and elimination. Be prepared to explain your choice of solution method in each case.

   a. $\begin{cases} -2x - y = 3 \\ x + 2y = 4 \end{cases}$ **b.** $\begin{cases} x = 5 - 2y \\ 3x - y = 15 \end{cases}$ **c.** $\begin{cases} -2x + y = 3 \\ -4x + 2y = 2 \end{cases}$

7 For each system below, without graphing, determine if the lines represented by the equations are the same, are different and intersect at a point, or are different and parallel. Explain your reasoning in each case. If there is exactly one solution, find and check it.

   a. $\begin{cases} y = -4x + 5 \\ y = -4x - 2 \end{cases}$ **b.** $\begin{cases} y = 6x - 2 \\ y = 3x - 2 \end{cases}$ **c.** $\begin{cases} y = 1.5x + 9 \\ y = \frac{3}{2}x + 9 \end{cases}$

4 a. $200x + 180y = 950$

b. $2x + 8y = 25$

c. 2.5 servings of each would meet both of the goals.

5 a. Laura: $7B + 14L = 280$
Andy: $5B + 16L = 230$
B is the number of hours of babysitting and L is the number of lawns mowed.

b. There is a possibility that the same number of lawns mowed and hours of babysitting could meet their goals. By graphing the equations or checking tables, it is easy to identify the common solution of 30 hours of babysitting and 5 lawn jobs. (Some students may choose to use the elimination or substitution methods for this task.)

6 a. $\left(-3\frac{1}{3}, 3\frac{2}{3}\right)$

b. $(5, 0)$

c. No solutions

7 a. Different and parallel; they have the same slope but different y-intercepts.

b. Different and intersect at a point; they have different slopes; therefore, they must intersect. Solution: $(0, -2)$

c. Same line; they have the same slope *and* the same y-intercept.

Unit 1

8 Without graphing the equations, determine if the lines represented in each system below are the same, are different and intersect at a point, or are different and parallel. Explain your reasoning in each case. If there is exactly one solution, find and check it.

a. $\begin{cases} x + 2y = 8 \\ 2x + y = 4 \end{cases}$

b. $\begin{cases} x - 3y = 6 \\ 3x - 9y = 18 \end{cases}$

c. $\begin{cases} 3x - 2y = 1 \\ 6x - 4y = 10 \end{cases}$

d. $\begin{cases} x + 7 = 10 \\ 2x - 5y = 16 \end{cases}$

9 Find values of a, b, and c that will guarantee that the system

$\begin{cases} x + 2y = 3 \\ ax + by = c \end{cases}$ has:

a. exactly one solution.

b. infinitely many solutions.

c. no solutions.

Connections

10 Imagine yourself as the manager of a local movie theater. Clearly, you are interested in both filling your movie theater and reaching a certain level of revenue.

a. Let x stand for the number of full-price tickets and y for the number of discounted tickets. Then write an equation that relates x and y to the theater capacity of 800 moviegoers.

b. To meet your goal of $6,000 ticket revenue, you have set ticket prices at $9 for full-price tickets and $4 for discounted tickets. Write another equation that relates the number of full-price tickets x and the number of discounted tickets y to the revenue goal of $6,000.

c. How many tickets of each type would you have to sell to fill the theater and meet your financial goal?

11 Suppose a system of two linear equations has the indicated number of solutions. In each case, what can you say about the slopes and y-intercepts of their graphs?

a. infinitely many solutions

b. no solutions

c. exactly one solution

8 **a.** Different and intersect at a point; no constant multiplier could "eliminate both variables." Solution: $(0, 4)$

    b. Same line; both sides of the top equation could be multiplied by 3 to obtain the bottom equation.

    c. Different and parallel; the coefficients of x and y in the bottom equation are twice those in the top equation, but the constants are not the same multiple of each other.

    d. Different and intersect at a point; the first equation is the vertical line $x = 3$ and the second equation is oblique. Solution: $(3, -2)$.

9 **a.** One possible combination is $a = 4$, $b = 2$, $c = 5$.

    b. One possible combination is $a = 2$, $b = 4$, $c = 6$.

    c. One possible combination is $a = 2$, $b = 4$, $c = 5$.

Connections

10 **a.** $x + y = 800$

    b. $9x + 4y = 6{,}000$

    c. 560 full-price tickets and 240 discounted tickets would meet both criteria.

11 **a.** The slopes and y-intercepts will be the same.

    b. The slopes will be the same, but the y-intercepts will be different.

    c. The slopes will be different; the y-intercept may be different.

12 The work below shows a solution of the system of equations
$\begin{cases} 6x - 3y = 12 \\ x + y = 5 \end{cases}$ by the method of elimination. The diagram shows
graphs of lines representing solutions of the various separate linear equations that occur in steps of the solution. The scales on both axes are 1.

Start: $\begin{cases} 6x - 3y = 12 \\ x + y = 5 \end{cases}$

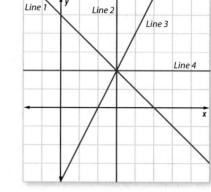

Step 1: $\begin{cases} 6x - 3y = 12 \\ 3x + 3y = 15 \end{cases}$

Step 2: $9x = 27$

Step 3: $x = 3$

Step 4: $6(3) - 3y = 12$

Step 5: $y = 2$

Step 6: Solution is $(3, 2)$.

a. Match each equation with the line representing its solutions.

$$6x - 3y = 12 \qquad x + y = 5 \qquad 3x + 3y = 15$$

$$9x = 27 \qquad x = 3 \qquad y = 2$$

b. Explain why the four different lines have exactly one point in common.

13 Solve the following linear equations. Explain how the results are similar to or different from the possibilities for solutions of systems with two linear equations and two variables.

a. $3(5 + 2x) = 6x - 10$

b. $3(5 + 2x) = 6x + 15$

c. $2(5 + 2x) = 6x - 10$

14 Solve the following quadratic equations. Explain how the results are similar to or different from the possibilities for solutions of systems with two linear equations and two variables.

a. $2x^2 + 1 = 9$ **b.** $2x^2 + 1 = 1$ **c.** $2x^2 + 10 = 6$

15 The quadratic formula says that any equation of the form $ax^2 + bx + c = 0$ has solutions given by

$$x = \frac{-b}{2a} + \frac{\sqrt{b^2 - 4ac}}{2a} \quad \text{and} \quad x = \frac{-b}{2a} - \frac{\sqrt{b^2 - 4ac}}{2a}.$$

Solve the quadratic equations below. Explain how the results are similar to or different from the possibilities for solutions of systems with two linear equations and two variables.

a. $x^2 + 5x + 6 = 0$

b. $x^2 + 10x + 25 = 0$

c. $x^2 + 5x + 7 = 0$

12 **a.** $6x - 3y = 12$ Line 3
     $x + y = 5$ Line 1
     $3x + 3y = 15$ Line 1
     $9x = 27$ Line 2
     $x = 3$ Line 2
     $y = 2$ Line 4

b. All four different lines have the same point in common because that point is the common solution to the original pair of equations and every equation that occurs in the solution process is either a multiple of one of the original equations or a sum or difference of two equations that are multiples of the original equations. If (x, y) satisfies $ax + by = c$ and $dx + ey = f$, then that same pair satisfies $(ax + by) + (dx + ey) = c + f$.

13 **a.** no solution

b. Equivalent statements; so, there are infinitely many solutions (all real numbers).

c. $x = 10$

Just as with systems of linear equations, there can be 0, 1, or infinitely many solutions. The difference is that if a linear equation like those in Parts a–c has a solution, it is simply a value for x that makes the equation true rather than an ordered (x, y) pair as in the case of a system of linear equations.

14 **a.** $x = \pm 2$

b. $x = 0$

c. no solution

Solutions of quadratic equations are not ordered pairs since there is only one variable, x. It is also possible to have infinitely many solutions with an equation like $x^2 + 5x = x(x + 5)$.

15 **a.** $x = -2, -3$

b. $x = -5$

c. no solution

Solutions of quadratic equations are not ordered pairs since there is only one variable, x. The case of 0, 1, or 2 solutions is determined by whether the discriminant $b^2 - 4ac$ is negative, zero, or positive, respectively. As explained in Connections Task 14, there may be infinitely many solutions.

Reflections

16 Changes in the cost of the telescope eyepiece and the number of club members willing to work required solving the system $16x + 10y = 245$ and $x + y = 20$, where x and y represent the number of workers on outdoor and indoor work, respectively.

Robin produced this graph to use in estimating the solution. She estimated that $x = 7.5$ and $y = 12.5$ was the solution.

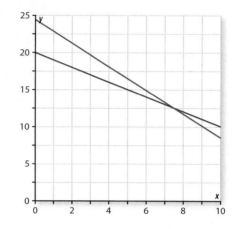

a. Is that an accurate estimate?

b. Does the solution make sense in the problem situation? Why or why not?

17 Faced with the following system of equations, two students, Lincoln and Claire, both decided to use the substitution method to find the solution(s).

$$\begin{cases} 5x - y = -15 \\ x + y = -3 \end{cases}$$

Lincoln's method:

$x = -3 - y$

So, $5(-3 - y) - y = -15$.
$-15 - y - y = -15$
$-15 - 2y = -15$
$-2y = 0$
$y = 0$

So, $x + (0) = -3$.
$x = -3$

The solution is $(-3, 0)$.

Claire's method:

$y = -3 - x$

So, $5x - (-3 - x) = -15$.
$5x + 3 - x = -15$
$4x + 3 = -15$
$4x = -18$
$x = -4.5$

So, $(-4.5) + y = -3$.
$y = 1.5$

The solution is $(-4.5, 1.5)$.

There are errors in the work of both Lincoln and Claire, but one of them was "lucky" and got the correct solution.

a. What are the errors in each case?

b. Which student got the correct solution? How do you know?

Reflections

16 **a.** Based on the graph and the substitution of the estimate into the system's equations, it is accurate.

b. It is a bit strange to consider "7.5" workers, but this is done in the workplace quite often (half-time workers, 0.7 of a full-time job, etc.).

17 **a.** Lincoln got the right answer despite his procedural error. This can be demonstrated by substituting his values for x and y into the original equations and verifying that they produce equalities in both. Claire did not "distribute the negative" in the third line of her work.

b. Lincoln got "lucky" because the y solution remained 0 even with the mistake.

18 After examining the methods used by Lincoln and Claire in Task 17, Danil decided to try using the elimination method to make sure that he got the correct solution. In which steps, if any, did Danil make an error in reasoning?

Danil's method:

Start: $\begin{cases} 5x - y = -15 \\ x + y = -3 \end{cases}$

Step 1: $6x = -18$

Step 2: $x = -3$

Step 3: $5(-3) - y = -15$

Step 4: $-15 - y = -15$

Step 5: $y = -30$

Step 6: Solution is $(-3, -30)$.

19 What kinds of errors have you made in using substitution or elimination methods to solve systems of linear equations. What do you think you can do to reduce those errors?

20 Consider the following system of linear equations.

$$\begin{cases} 2x - 3y = -80 \\ 6x - y = 160 \end{cases}$$

a. How can you tell by examining the two equations that the system has one solution?

b. Which method would you use to solve the system? Why?

21 What are the strengths and weaknesses of each method for solving systems of linear equations? Which method do you prefer to use?

Extensions

22 Even after learning three methods for solving systems of linear equations, Jamie likes to use a guess-and-test method first. To help with the testing part of that strategy, Jamie wrote a simple spreadsheet program that could be modified for any given system. Here is what the formulas in Jamie's spreadsheet looked like as he worked on one system.

Systems of Linear Equations.xls

◇	A	B	C	
1	x =			
2	y =			
3	Condition 1:	=2*B1−3*B2	6	
4	Condition 2:	=B1+2*B2	10	
5				

18 His Step 5 is incorrect. It should indicate $y = 0$.

19 Responses will vary but likely be related to errors in arithmetic or algebra calculations or choices of constant multiplier for the elimination method.

20 **a.** The coefficients of x and y in the second equation are not common multiples of the corresponding coefficients in the first equation.

   b. Substitution might be chosen since the bottom equation could quickly be written as $y = 6x - 160$. Elimination is an option since only one equation needs to be multiplied by a factor to allow the combination to result in an equation with one variable.

21 Students should discuss the limits of the graphical method when solutions are not integers. They may also discuss the presented forms of the equations (e.g., $y = mx + b$) as advantages for one method or another.

a. What system of linear equations does it seem Jamie was trying to solve?

b. What numbers will appear in cells **B3** and **B4** if Jamie enters **5** in **B1** and **−3** in **B2**?

c. How will Jamie know when the spreadsheet shows a solution?

23 In the Think About This Situation problem (page 50) that involved raising money for the science club to buy a new eyepiece for the Hamilton High School telescope, it is not very realistic to aim at earning exactly $240. More than that amount would certainly be acceptable.

a. How do you think you could find all combinations of indoor and outdoor work by 18 workers that would give at least $240 of income from the PTA?

b. What would the graph of this situation look like, in comparison with the graph of the two linear equations?

24 Given the linear equations $ax + by = c$ and $dx + ey = f$ and nonzero numbers m and n, the equation $m(ax + by) + n(dx + ey) = mc + nf$ is called a **linear combination** of the two equations.

a. If (h, k) is a solution of the system $ax + by = c$ and $dx + ey = f$, is (h, k) also a solution to the linear combination of the two equations? Explain your reasoning.

b. How must a, d, m, and n be related in order to eliminate the x term from the linear combination?

c. How must b, e, m, and n be related in order to eliminate the y term from the linear combination?

25 Modify the substitution or elimination methods for solving systems of linear equations with two equations and two variables to solve these systems involving *three* equations and *three* variables.

a. $\begin{cases} 2x - y + z = 15 \\ x + y - 3z = -6 \\ z = 3 \end{cases}$ **b.** $\begin{cases} x + y + z = 6 \\ 2x + y - z = 7 \\ x - y + z = 2 \end{cases}$

26 During Investigation 1, you had the opportunity to find out ways that the Hamilton High School science club could meet two requirements, total number of workers and total money earned, in saving money to buy a new telescope eyepiece. Both of their requirements (sometimes called *constraints*) involved equality. In other words, they had to use *exactly* 18 workers, and they had to earn *exactly* $240.

a. Suppose that the club could provide *at most* 18 workers. Write an inequality that expresses this constraint.

b. The club needs to earn *at least* $240 for the new eyepiece. Write an inequality that expresses this constraint.

c. Find some ordered pairs that meet the new constraints.

d. Solve the new system of inequalities by finding the region on a graph where coordinates of points meet both inequality constraints.

Extensions

22 **a.** $\begin{cases} 2x - 3y = 6 \\ x + 2y = 10 \end{cases}$

b. 19 will appear in **B3** and −1 in **B4**.

c. When **B3** reads "6" and **B4** reads "10", Jamie will have a correct solution.

23 **a.** You would find the points that fit $x + y = 18$ and $16x + 10y \geq 240$.

b. The graph of the solution would not be the point of intersection. Instead, it would be the part of the line $x + y = 18$ where (x, y) values fit $16x + 10y \geq 240$. Graphically, this solution is the red segment of $x + y = 18$ above $16x + 10y \geq 240$.

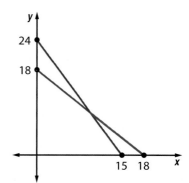

24 **a.** Yes. If a point satisfies the two separate equations, it also satisfies their sum. That is, if (h, k) satisfies the original system, then $ah + bk = c$ and $dh + ek = f$. So, $m(ah + bk) + n(dh + ek) = m(c) + n(f) = mc + nf$. Thus, (h, k) also satisfies the linear combination.

b. $ma = -nd$

c. $mb = -ne$

25 **a.** $\begin{cases} 2x - y + 3 = 15 \\ x + y - 9 = -6 \end{cases}$

$\begin{cases} 2x - y = 12 \\ x + y = 3 \end{cases}$

$\overline{}$

$3x = 15$

$x = 5$

$(5, -2, 3); x = 5, y = -2, z = 3$

b. $\begin{cases} x + y + z = 6 \\ -x + y - z = -2 \end{cases}$

$\overline{}$

$2y = 4$

$y = 2$

$\begin{cases} x + z = 4 \\ 2x - z = 5 \end{cases}$

$\overline{}$

$3x = 9$

$x = 3$

$x + y + z = 6$

So, $z = 1$.

$(3, 2, 1); x = 3, y = 2, z = 1$

26 **a.** $x + y \leq 18$

b. $16x + 10y \geq 240$

c. Answers will vary.

d. The shaded region and its edges represent the solution.

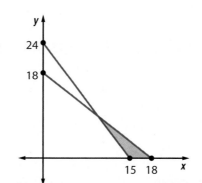

SCOPE AND SEQUENCE
A matrix method for solving systems will be introduced in Unit 2, *Matrix Methods*.

Review

27 Recall that in the formula $I = Prt$, I represents the amount of simple interest earned, P represents the initial amount invested (sometimes called the principal), r represents the interest rate, and t represents the number of years of investment. Use the formula to complete the following tasks.

a. Write three new formulas, expressing each of the variables (P, r, and t) as a function of the other three.

In Parts b–e, select and use the formula that makes required calculations easiest.

b. How much simple interest is gained on $1,500 invested for 12 years at a rate of 6%?

c. What interest rate is needed to earn $80 in simple interest on an initial investment of $600 over 3 years?

d. How much would you need to invest to earn $125 in simple interest in 5 years at a 4% interest rate?

e. How long would it take to earn $100 interest on an investment of $500 earning simple interest at a rate of 12% per year?

28 In the diagram at the right, $\overline{CD} \cong \overline{CB}$ and $\angle ACD \cong \angle ACB$.

a. Explain why $\triangle ACD \cong \triangle ACB$.

b. Is $\overline{AD} \cong \overline{AB}$? Why?

29 Without using a calculator, sketch graphs you would expect from the following functions.

a. $y = \dfrac{3}{x}$

b. $y = 3.5x - 3.5$

c. $y = 3.5^x$

d. $y = 3.5x^2 + 3.5$

30 Which of the following vertex-edge graphs contain an Euler circuit? Explain your answer.

Graph I   **Graph II**   **Graph III**

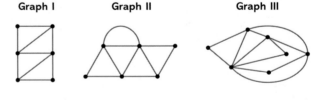

31 For each of the following equations, solve for x and check your solution(s).

a. $x^2 = 0.16$

b. $x^2 - 10 = 111$

c. $x^2 - 4x = 21$

d. $3x^2 + 11.5x = 2$

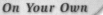

Review

27 **a.** $P = \frac{I}{rt}$, $r = \frac{I}{Pt}$, and $t = \frac{I}{Pr}$

    b. $1,080 simple interest is gained.

    c. An interest rate of 4.44% is needed.

    d. $625 would need to be invested.

    e. It would take 1 year and 8 months.

28 **a.** $\overline{AC}$ is a side of both triangles, so $\overline{AC} \cong \overline{AC}$. $\angle ACD \cong \angle ACB$, and $\overline{CD} \cong \overline{CB}$; so, $\triangle ACD \cong \triangle ACB$ by the SAS Triangle Congruence Property.

    b. $\overline{AD} \cong \overline{AB}$ because they are corresponding parts of congruent triangles.

29 **a.** $y = \frac{3}{x}$ **b.** $y = 3.5x - 3.5$

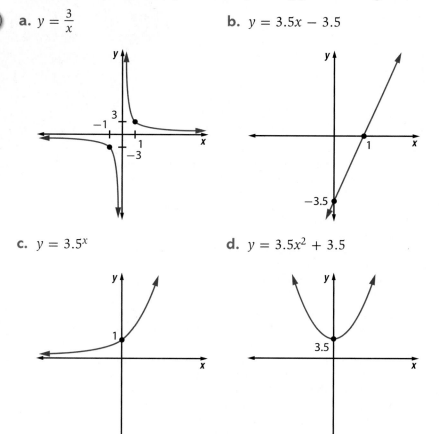

    c. $y = 3.5^x$ **d.** $y = 3.5x^2 + 3.5$

30 Graph III has an Euler circuit because it is the only graph with all even vertices.

31 **a.** $x = \pm 0.4$ **b.** $x = \pm 11$

    c. $x = -3, 7$ **d.** $x = -4, \frac{1}{6}$

Looking Back

The lessons in this unit involved many different situations in which two or more variables were related to each other. Comparing the functions and equations that were used to express relationships and conditions in those settings, you discovered a few common patterns occurring again and again.

As a result of your work on problems in the lessons, you should be better able to recognize situations in which variables are related by direct and inverse variation and by systems of linear equations. You should also be better able to use symbolic expressions and equations to describe and reason about those kinds of relationships.

The tasks in this final lesson will help you review and organize your thinking about functions, equations, and systems.

1 **Sound Wave Properties** The sounds that you hear—from musical instruments and human voices to whispering wind and crackling lightning—are all carried by vibrating waves of air. The pitch of a sound is determined by the frequency of vibration. A higher frequency gives a higher pitch. Sound frequency depends on properties of the sound source.

For example, when the drummer in a band hits one of the cymbals, the frequency F of its sound is related to the density d of the material and the square of the cymbal's radius r.

The pattern of that relationship is expressed well by the formula $F = 0.25\dfrac{d}{r^2}$.

   a. What changes in the variables d and r would lead to higher-pitched sound? What changes would lead to lower-pitched sound?

   b. How are the patterns of change you described in Part a supported by your experience playing or listening to cymbals, drums, or other similar musical instruments?

   c. What formula expresses the relationship among frequency, density, and radius in equivalent form showing d as a function of F and r?

   d. What formula expresses the relationship among frequency, density, and radius in equivalent form showing r as a function of F and d?

Looking Back

This lesson includes tasks intended to provide review and practice of key ideas developed throughout the unit and summary questions designed to stimulate student articulation of the key principles and techniques.

1 **a.** Either an increase in d or a decrease in r would lead to a higher-pitched sound. Alternatively, a decrease in d or an increase in r would lead to a lower-pitched sound.

b. Answers may vary but should follow the ideas from Part a.

c. $d = \dfrac{Fr^2}{0.25}$, or $d = 4Fr^2$

d. $r = \sqrt{\dfrac{0.25d}{F}}$, or $r = \dfrac{1}{2}\sqrt{\dfrac{d}{F}}$

> **INSTRUCTIONAL NOTE**
> Encourage students to refer to their toolkits if they are struggling.

2) Karate Physics Karate is an impressive form of the martial arts. Highly-trained men, women, boys, and girls break bricks and boards with chops from their hands, feet, or even heads. Some of you may have even attempted a karate chop and discovered that, without proper training and technique, it can hurt.

Karate chops break bricks and boards by applying carefully-aimed bursts of energy. Different targets require different amounts of energy. Think about the four target boards pictured here:

1   2   3   4

a. Which board do you think would require the greatest energy to break?

b. The target boards differ in length and thickness. How would you expect those variables to affect the required breaking energy?

c. Breaking energy E depends on board length L and thickness T. Which of the following do you think expresses the relationship between those variables?

$$E = T \cdot L \qquad E = T + L \qquad E = T - L \qquad E = \frac{T}{L}$$

3) Production-Line Economics Since Henry Ford introduced assembly line ideas for production of the Model T Ford car in 1908, manufacturing companies of all kinds have found ways to use machines and human workers in schemes for mass production of many different products.

Suppose that the Kalamazoo bottling company has two machines for filling spring water bottles—one that fills 3,000 per hour and another that fills 4,000 per hour. The factory has orders for 64,000 bottles per day, so the plant manager wants to set a production schedule that just fills the demand. The plant operates two 8-hour shifts per day, but neither machine can run longer than 14 hours per day, allowing time for start-up, cleanup, and repairs.

a. Find four combinations of operating hours for the two machines that will just meet the production quota within the two working shifts.

b. Sketch a graph showing all possibilities for x hours of operation for machine 1 and y hours of operation for machine 2 that meet the daily production quota of 64,000 bottles.

c. If machine 1 is operated for only 8 hours, how long must machine 2 operate?

d. If machine 2 is operated for only 12 hours, how long must machine 1 operate?

INSTRUCTIONAL NOTE To help students think about the equation in Part c, you may want to ask the following questions:

> *How does the energy required to break the board*
> *change as the thickness of the board increases?*
>
> *How does the energy required to break the board*
> *change as the length of the board increases?*

a. Answers may vary, but the board in Figure 3 seems to be the most reasonable answer.

b. The shorter and thicker the board, the more energy it would require to break it. Conversely, the longer and thinner the board, the less energy it would require to break it.

c. The $E = \dfrac{T}{L}$ formula would express the relationship best. Students should reason that they need a formula that shows two relationships: as thickness increases, the energy required to break the board increases; and as length increases, the energy required decreases.

③ **a.** Possible pairs are $(2.\overline{6}, 14)$, $(3, 13.75)$, $(4, 13)$, $(6, 11.5)$, $(8, 10)$, $(12, 7)$, and $(14, 5.5)$.

b. Since both machines have a maximum operation time of 14 hours per day, the graph of all possible solutions over the domain is a segment with endpoints $(2.\overline{6}, 14)$ and $(14, 5.5)$.

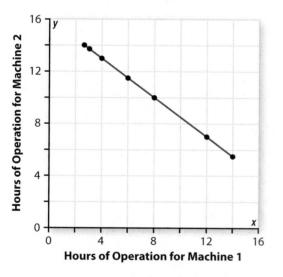

c. Machine 2 must be operated for 10 hours.

d. Machine 1 must be operated for $5\frac{1}{3}$ hours.

e. Use a system of linear equations to find a combination of operating hours for machines 1 and 2 that meet the production quota and use a total of 18 hours of operator labor.

(4) Counting Coins Collecting coins is a popular hobby. Some people try to locate rare coins; others simply try to collect lots of coins as a saving strategy.

Grocery chains have now placed coin-counting machines in their stores. The machines provide customers with an easy way to turn their loose change into cash. The machines are programmed to make a profit for their owners by giving the customer credit for only about 90% of the value they deposit.

Kris had been saving quarters and dimes for the past few months and had decided that it was time to cash in her savings. After gathering all of her coins, she took them down to her favorite grocery store to place them in the coin-counting machine.

The receipt stated that she had placed a total of $54.35 worth of dimes and quarters into the machine. She knew that she had collected 275 coins, but she did not know how many of each coin she had deposited.

a. See if you can figure out the missing information.

  i. Write a system of linear equations in which one equation expresses the condition about the number of coins that Kris deposited and the other relates the numbers of dimes and quarters to the total value of the money deposited.

  ii. Find the solution of the system of equations you wrote in part i using any of the methods you have learned in this unit. How many of each coin did she deposit?

  iii. Solve the system you wrote in part i using a different method than the one you chose in part ii.

b. Kris decided it would be much more efficient to save only quarters. She and her friend Tim, another quarter collector, decided to combine their quarters and deposit them into the same coin-counting machine Kris had used before. They combined their quarters before they each counted their individual contribution but later found there were a total of 65 coins.

  i. How much total money did they deposit?

  ii. Write a system of linear equations in which one equation expresses the condition about Tim's and Kris's total quarters and the other relates each of their contribution to the amount of money deposited.

  iii. Find and check the solution of the system of equations you wrote in part ii using any of the methods you have learned in this unit. How many quarters did each of the students deposit?

  iv. How would knowing that Kris contributed 4 times as many coins as Tim help you find how much each contributed?

e. $\begin{cases} x + y = 18 \\ 3{,}000x + 4{,}000y = 64{,}000 \end{cases}$

x stands for the number of hours machine 1 is operated, and y stands for the number of hours machine 2 is operated. Solution: $(8, 10)$

4 **a.** **i.** $\begin{cases} d + q = 275 \\ 0.1d + 0.25q = 54.35 \end{cases}$

d stands for the number of dimes collected and q represents the number of quarters collected.

ii. She deposited 96 dimes and 179 quarters.

iii. Solution methods in parts ii and iii should be different.

b. **i.** They deposited $65 \times 0.25 = \$16.25$.

ii. $\begin{cases} T + K = 65 \\ 0.25T + 0.25K = 16.25 \end{cases}$

T represents the number of quarters contributed by Tim, and K represents the number of quarters contributed by Kris.

iii. Theoretically, there is an infinite number of combinations that would work. In a practical sense, only non-negative integer pairs that sum to 65 quarters would result in a total of $16.25.

iv. Knowing that extra piece of information would allow you to write an equation such as $4T = K$. Using this relationship, $4T$ could be substituted for K in either of the equations from part ii. This would result in an equation where you could solve for T (which turns out to be 13 quarters).

Summarize
the Mathematics

In this unit, you investigated a variety of situations in which two or more variables were related to each other by functions or equations. In some cases, the relationship could be expressed by a single function or equation; in other cases, the key questions required work with a system of two equations.

a Consider relations expressed in forms like $z = \dfrac{kx}{y}$, where x, y, and $k > 0$.

  i. How does z change as x increases or decreases?

  ii. How does z change as y increases or decreases?

  iii. What equivalent forms express x as a function of z and y? y as a function of x and z?

  iv. How, if at all, will your answers change if $k < 0$?

b Consider equations expressed in the form $ax + by = c$.

  i. How many pairs of (x, y) values can be found to satisfy such equations?

  ii. What pattern can be expected in graphs of the solution pairs?

c Consider systems of linear equations like $\begin{cases} ax + by = c \\ dx + ey = f \end{cases}$.

  i. What are the possible numbers of solutions for such systems? How are those possibilities illustrated in graphs of the solutions for the separate equations?

  ii. How can you tell the number of solutions by examining the symbolic forms of the equations?

  iii. What methods can be used to find the solution(s)?

  iv. What are the key steps in application of each method?

  v. How do you decide which method to use in a particular case?

Be prepared to share your responses and reasoning with the class.

✔Check Your Understanding

Write, in outline form, a summary of the important mathematical concepts and methods developed in this unit. Organize your summary so that it can be used as a quick reference in future units and courses.

The final STM for each unit provides an opportunity to review and synthesize the content presented in the unit. You may wish to have students discuss but not write solutions to the STM items. Following the class discussion, students could complete the unit summary located in the unit resources to summarize the unit. For any particular unit STM, there might be one or two parts that you wish to have students add to their unit summary so that their notes are complete. See the discourse scenario provided on pages T72B-C.

PROMOTING MATHEMATICAL DISCOURSE

Teaching Resources

Transparency Master 46–47.

Summarize
the Mathematics

a

i. As x increases, z increases; as x decreases, z decreases.

ii. As y increases, z decreases; as y decreases, z increases.

iii. $x = \dfrac{yz}{k}$, $y = \dfrac{kx}{z}$

iv. The relationships will reverse. In other words, as x increases, z decreases; as x decreases, z increases. Also, as y increases, z increases; as y decreases, z decreases.

b

i. There are infinitely many solutions that can satisfy such equations. (You might follow this question by asking "How many pairs of (x, y) values do not satisfy such equations?".)

ii. A linear pattern should be expected in graphs of the solution pairs.

c

i. It is possible for there to be 0, 1, or infinitely many solutions in such systems as seen in the graphs below.

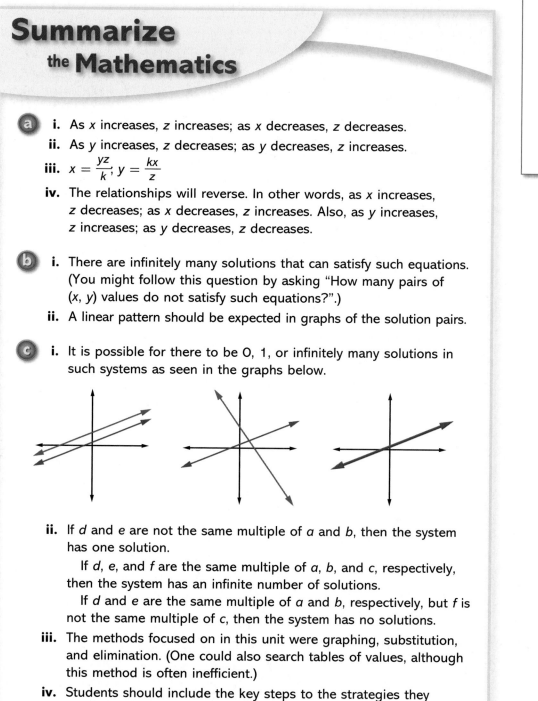

ii. If d and e are not the same multiple of a and b, then the system has one solution.

   If d, e, and f are the same multiple of a, b, and c, respectively, then the system has an infinite number of solutions.

   If d and e are the same multiple of a and b, respectively, but f is not the same multiple of c, then the system has no solutions.

iii. The methods focused on in this unit were graphing, substitution, and elimination. (One could also search tables of values, although this method is often inefficient.)

iv. Students should include the key steps to the strategies they mention in part iii.

v. Students should have their own strategies in place at this point.

Student Masters 48–50.

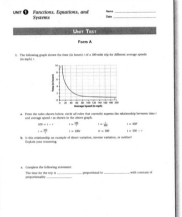

Assessment Masters 51–65.

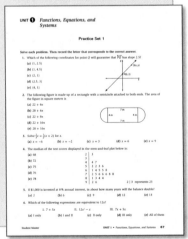

Student Masters 67–68.

✓ Check Your Understanding

You may wish to have students use the Teaching Master, *Functions, Equations, and Systems* Unit Summary, to help them organize the information. Above all, this should be something that is useful to the individual student.

Practicing for Standardized Tests

Each Practicing for Standardized Tests master presents 10 questions in the multiple-choice format of test items similar to how they often appear in standardized tests. Answers are provided below.

Answers to Practice Set 1

1. (b)	**2.** (b)	**3.** (d)	**4.** (b)	**5.** (c)
6. (d)	**7.** (c)	**8.** (b)	**9.** (a)	**10.** (d)

Summarize the Mathematics, *page 72*

Teacher: James, please read the two sentences in the introduction of the STM for the class. *(James reads.)* Would someone be willing to give us an example, either from this Looking Back lesson or other lessons, in which a single function or equation expressed the situation? *(The teacher is using this strategy to help students develop the habit of mind of connecting reading to their learning experiences. This strategy is particularly helpful for struggling students. Students should be repeatedly encouraged to ask themselves these types of questions. Make this learning strategy explicit for students where appropriate.)*

Tamu: The sound wave problem we just did had only one equation.

Sheldon: The karate problem had only one equation, too.

Teacher: How about problems that required two equations?

Isabel: The problem we just did with the two machines had two equations. And so did the coin problem.

Teacher: What clues from problem situations might indicate that you should have one or two equations?

Marcus: It seems like we have two equations when there are two separate things going on. Like in the coin problem. We had a total number of dimes and quarters and a total dollar amount. These variables needed to be represented in two different equations.

Lucy: Yeah, and sometimes we had a lot of variables, but they were all tied together as with the heat-flow problem we did in Lesson 1.

Teacher: What do you mean "tied together?"

Lucy: Um. I guess I mean that the different variables were needed to get the heat flow. Like the easier example of the sound waves. Both the density and the radius of the cymbal were needed to compute the frequency.

Teacher: Okay. For this STM discussion, we will consider one part at a time. Please discuss Part a with your group members. Make some brief notes or graphs of your thinking if it will help in reporting your responses in a couple of minutes. Be prepared, as always, to explain your thinking. *(Students are given a few minutes for Part a.)*

Teacher: Let's take a random student name from our pack of named Popsicle sticks, to report out your group's thinking on Part a. Alar, please draw a name. *("Stacy" is drawn.)* Stacy, please read Part a and the first question, and provide your thinking. Then ask if there are other thoughts from the class. When the discussion is over, refer part ii to someone else in your group.

Stacy: We said that as x increases, z will increase also. This is because x is on the numerator of the fraction. Thus, x and z are in a direct relationship. So, if x decreases, z will decrease, too. How does this sound to the rest of you?

Kristen: That is a very good answer. I like how you connected the numerator and the direct relationship. That helps me understand it. We have to remember though that k is positive for this to be true. *(The teacher is not sure that Stacy or Kristen, as well as other students, understand why the numerator variable is connected to direct variation. He decides to wait to see how students discuss inverse variation before pressing for understanding.)*

Stacy: Okay, Bernie, it is your turn to do part ii.

Bernie: We said that as y increases, z will decrease. This is because y is on the denominator of the fraction. Thus, y and z have an inverse relationship. So, if y decreases, z will increase. James, you do part iii.

Teacher: Before we go to James' explanation for part iii, did you notice that Bernie built on the language that was introduced by Stacy to describe the relationship between variables in an inverse relationship? We have now expressed that the direct relationship exists when the variable on the right side of the equation *(points to equation)* is in the numerator and an inverse relationship exists when the variable on the right side is in the denominator. Let's be sure that we understand why this is true. Knowing how to do mathematics is important, but so is understanding it. Will someone offer a general explanation or an example that shows understanding?

Talib: I think about z as the answer to the arithmetic problem k times x divided by y; you can see that multiplying k by a larger number and keeping y the same makes the calculation of $\frac{kx}{y}$ larger. For example, use $\frac{4x}{2}$. The answer to the calculation when x is 2 is $\frac{8}{4} = 2$. When you use 100 for x, the answer is 200. So, you see that z gets larger as x gets larger.
The opposite happens to the answer when the denominator y gets larger. If the denominator goes from 4 to 400, you will be dividing by a much larger number so the answer (z) gets smaller.

Teacher: *(Addressing the class)* Did this explanation seem reasonable to you? If so, what in particular did you like about the explanation?

Jolline: I liked how Talib used an example with numbers. Especially when he used the jump from a 4 to a 400 in the denominator. A big jump really helps you think about what happens to the calculation. I also liked how he thought about z as the answer.

Teacher: Seems like we're ready to have James continue now.

James: Can I show the answer to this on the board? It is hard to explain in words. *(The teacher indicates that this is always acceptable protocol in their classroom. James shows how to express x as a function of z, and y and y as a function of x and z. Then he asks for feedback from the class and passes the final part to Jen.)*

Jen: We said that the equivalent forms for part iii are exactly the same whether or not *k* is positive or negative. But the question of how *z* changes as *x* or *y* changes is exactly opposite.

Teacher: Can you show us an example of what you mean?

Jen: *(Goes to the board.)* For example, think about $z = -\frac{4x}{2}$. Remember that both *x* and *y* are positive numbers. So, as *x* increases from say 1 to 2, *z* goes from -2 to -4. It gets smaller.

Teacher: On to Part b. Let's consider individually and then as a class. *(The teacher gives a minute for students individually and then calls for responses.)*

Nadia: We said that there is an infinite number of solutions to the equation. It represents a line on a graph.

Teacher: Does everyone agree with this response? *(Students nod agreement.)* Now what about some of the problem situations we explored in this unit. Was it always the case that an equation of this form had an infinite number of solutions?

Alar: No, sometimes when we had a problem such as the hats and shirts though, solutions had to be integer pairs. This made for fewer numbers of solutions—but sometimes still quite a few solutions, not just one.

Teacher: Now discuss the questions in Part c. Again, make brief notes about your ideas so we can discuss them as a class in a couple of minutes. *(Students discuss. The teacher notices that students understand part i and have graphs sketched to explain their thinking. Thus, he decides to move to part ii for the class summary. He indicates this to students and randomly selects another student to respond to part ii.)*

Tim: We said that you needed to look at the coefficients of the two separate equations. Check the ratios of $\frac{a}{b}$ and $\frac{d}{e}$. If they are the same, then the linear equations are lines with the same slope and may even be the same line. So, they have either no solutions or an infinite number of solutions. You can tell if the equations are really the same if one equation is a multiple of the other one. Then their graphs are the same and there are an infinite number of solutions. We said that if the ratios $\frac{a}{b}$ and $\frac{d}{e}$ are not the same, then the lines are not parallel—they intersect—and there is one solution.

Teacher: Okay, let's take parts iii, iv, and v together. Clariss, please name one method for solving the system of equations.

Clariss: Well, one method is the substitution method. For that method, you write one of the equations as $x =$ or $y =$ and then substitute or replace the *x* or *y* with that expression. This makes an equation with only one variable to solve. After solving for that value,

you can find the other part of the pair of values that make up the intersection point by putting that value in one of the two equations and solving again for one variable.

Teacher: And how do you decide to use that method?

Clariss: Oh, I use it when I see one of the two equations written as $y =$ or $x =$.

James: I also might use it if it is very easy to solve an equation like $5x - y = 10$ for $y =$.

Teacher: Okay, *(randomly drawing a name)* Grace, please pick another method for solving a system of linear equations; provide the key steps in applying the method and when you might use that method.

Grace: I like the graphing method, particularly when I know that the problem is about, say, hats and shirts, and the answers will be whole numbers. These are easy to see on the graph. You see the solution by graphing the two lines and find the point where they meet.

Teacher: Remember class, if you have follow-up questions when classmates respond, you should raise your hand to be acknowledged by the speaker. Any questions at this time? *(No student responses.)* Then, I have a question for Grace. What method do you use for graphing the lines?

Grace: It depends. If I am using a graphing calculator, I solve for *y* so I can put the equations in the $y =$ menu. If I am graphing by hand, I usually find the *x*- and *y*-intercepts.

Tamu: How do you find the *x*- and *y*-intercepts?

Grace: I do this by entering $x = 0$ in the equation and finding *y*, and then $y = 0$ and finding *x*. This works because the *x*-intercept has $y = 0$ and the *y*-intercept has $x = 0$.

Teacher: Did you notice that Tamu asked Grace a follow-up question and that Grace voluntarily explained her thinking about why her method of finding the *x*- and *y*-intercepts works? These behaviors, asking each other follow-up questions and always explaining thinking, are ones we agreed to work at. Good job! Okay, have we discussed all the methods for finding solutions to systems of linear equations?

Nate: No, we did not talk about the elimination method. I will show an example on the board and talk about how and when I use it.

(Nate proceeds to do an example and explains that he uses it when he sees negative signs in one of the equations because he makes mistakes when using the substitution method when there are negative signs. He also indicates that he uses this method when it does not seem easy to use the substitution method. Other students provide their reasons for choosing this method.)

Teacher: Great discussion. Now I would like you to take the ideas from this discussion and complete the unit summary that I am passing out. This unit summary will provide you a quick reference to add to your Math Toolkit notes for the mathematics in this unit. We will also reference the summary as we continue the course.

Teacher Notes

UNIT 2

MATRIX METHODS

Often, you need to organize information before you can use it to solve related problems. A *matrix* is a rectangular array consisting of rows and columns that can help you organize, display, and analyze information, and solve many types of problems. For example, *matrices* can be used to track consumer demand, create computer graphics, rank tournaments, classify ancient pottery, study friendship and trust, and solve systems of linear equations.

In this unit of *Core-Plus Mathematics*, you will study matrices and their properties and use matrices to solve problems in a wide variety of settings, both real-world and purely mathematical. The necessary concepts and skills are developed in three lessons.

Lessons

1 Constructing, Interpreting, and Operating on Matrices

Construct matrices to represent and analyze information, interpret given matrices, and operate on matrices using row sums, matrix addition, and multiplication of a matrix by a number.

2 Multiplying Matrices

Use matrix multiplication, including powers of matrices, to solve a variety of problems.

3 Matrices and Systems of Linear Equations

Compare properties of matrices and matrix operations to corresponding properties of real numbers and their operations. Use matrices and their properties to solve systems of linear equations.

MATRIX METHODS

Unit Overview

In this unit of *Core-Plus Mathematics*, students learn about matrices and matrix methods. The unit introduces and develops matrices as powerful tools that are used in many applications and throughout mathematics. In particular, students see the interconnectedness of mathematics as they use matrices to solve problems in algebra, geometry, statistics, and discrete mathematics. This unit also offers an opportunity for students to practice arithmetic skills and number-sense abilities as they work with matrices in a variety of settings.

In the first lesson, students learn what a matrix is; they construct matrices to organize information; they analyze and interpret given matrices; and they operate on matrices using row sums, matrix addition, and scalar multiplication. Lesson 2 focuses on the important topic of matrix multiplication. Students learn the method of matrix multiplication as it arises naturally when trying to solve applied problems. Thus, matrix multiplication is seen as sensible rather than mysterious and arcane. In Lesson 3, students study some of the properties of matrices and compare them to properties of real numbers. This provides an accessible and important introduction to algebraic structure, as they see that some properties are the same for real numbers and matrices and some are not. Finally, they learn in Lesson 3 how to use matrices and their properties to solve systems of linear equations and then compare various methods of solving these systems.

Unit Objectives

- See the interconnectedness of mathematics through use of matrices to solve problems in algebra, geometry, statistics, and discrete mathematics
- Use matrices to organize, display, and analyze data from a variety of contexts, such as archeology, sociology, ecology, sports, and business
- Understand, carry out, and interpret matrix operations—row and column sums, matrix addition and subtraction, scalar multiplication (multiply a matrix by a number), and matrix multiplication
- Understand and apply properties of matrices and matrix operations, compare properties of matrices to those of real numbers, and thereby gain a gentle introduction to algebraic structure
- Use matrices to solve systems of two linear equations
- Compare and analyze different methods for solving systems of two linear equations by considering limitations, advantages, and disadvantages of methods learned in this and prior units

CPMP-Tools

CPMP-Tools is a suite of Java-based mathematical software specifically designed to support student learning and problem solving in each strand of *Core-Plus Mathematics*. The software includes four families of programs: *Algebra* (spreadsheet and CAS), *Geometry* (coordinate and synthetic), *Statistics*, and *Discrete Math*. Each content-area tool includes specific custom tools and electronic copies of many data sets used in investigations and homework. Additional information about the course-specific software for Course 2 is included in the front matter of this Course 2 *Teacher's Guide*.

The following features of *CPMP-Tools* are particularly useful for this unit:

- Discrete Math → Willow Forest Ecosystem
- Discrete Math → Vertex-Edge Graph → Sample Graphs → Unit 2 Matrix Methods
- Discrete Math → Vertex-Edge Graph → Options (see matrix options)
- Algebra → CAS → Matrices

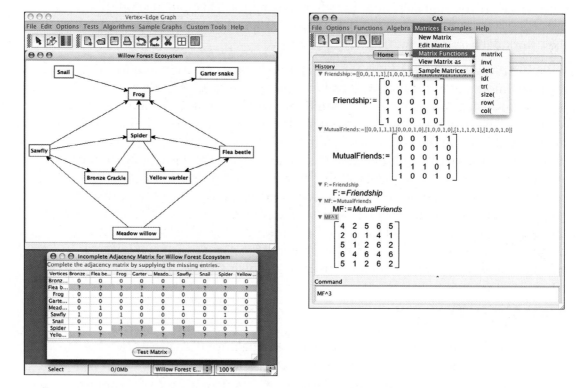

A note related to the "Willow Forest Ecosystem" custom tool appears on page T113.

Lesson Objectives	On Your Own Assignments*	Suggested Pacing	Materials
Lesson 1 Constructing, Interpreting, and Operating On Matrices • Construct matrices to organize, display, and analyze information • Interpret given matrices • Understand, carry out, and interpret matrix operations—row and column sums, matrix addition and subtraction, and scalar multiplication	**After Investigation 1:** A2, C7, C11, R12, R14, E18, Rv22–Rv25 **After Investigation 2:** A1, C8–C10, R13 or R15, E19, Rv26–Rv28 **After Investigation 3:** A3, A4 or A5, A6, R16, R17, E20, E21, Rv29–Rv31	5 days (including assessment)	• Unit Resources
Lesson 2 Multiplying Matrices • Understand, carry out, and interpret matrix multiplication • Use matrix multiplication, including powers of matrices, to solve problems in a variety of settings • Represent a vertex-edge graph as a matrix and use powers of that matrix to analyze the situation modeled by the vertex-edge graph	**After Investigation 1:** A1, A2, Rv23–Rv27 **After Investigation 2:** A3, A4, C8, C9, R12, R13, E17, Rv28–Rv31 **After Investigation 3:** A5 or A6, A7, C10, C11, choose one of R14–R16, E18 or E19, choose one of E20–E22, Rv32	10 days (including assessment)	• *CPMP-Tools* custom tool "Willow Forest Ecosystem" • Unit Resources
Lesson 3 Matrices and Systems of Linear Equations • Examine properties of operations with matrices • Compare properties of matrices with those of real numbers • Use matrices and their properties to solve systems of linear equations • Review, analyze, and compare various methods for solving systems of linear equations	**After Investigation 1:** A1, A2, C7, C8, R12, Rv20–Rv23 **After Investigation 2:** A3, A4, C9, R13 or R14, E16 or E17, Rv24–Rv26 **After Investigation 3:** A5, A6, C10 or C11, R15, E18, E19, Rv27–Rv30	8 days (including assessment)	• Unit Resources
Lesson 4 Looking Back • Review and synthesize the major objectives of the unit		3 days (including assessment)	• Unit Resources

* When choice is indicated, it is important to leave the choice to the student.

Note: It is best if Connections tasks are discussed as a whole class after they have been assigned as homework.

Unit 2

Constructing, Interpreting, and Operating On Matrices

In prior *Core-Plus Mathematics* units, you studied several useful mathematical objects, including linear, exponential, and quadratic functions, polygons and polyhedra, data and probability distributions, and vertex-edge graphs. In this unit, you will investigate another important mathematical object, a *matrix*. Matrices and matrix methods provide powerful tools for solving a wide variety of problems. Matrices also provide useful ways for representing ideas in geometry, algebra, statistics, and discrete mathematics. For example, matrices can be used to represent geometric transformations and vertex-edge graphs, to solve systems of linear equations, and to organize and analyze data.

Matrices even relate to the shoes you wear. Many people wear athletic shoes these days, whether on the job, in school, or on the playing field. Marketing and sales of athletic shoes is big business. There are huge megastores in many cities, such as the one in Chicago pictured here. In 2004, Americans bought 361,929,000 pairs of athletic shoes. (Source: ShoeStats 2005, American Apparel & Footware Association)

Constructing, Interpreting, and Operating on Matrices

This lesson introduces matrices as a tool for displaying, organizing, and analyzing information. Students construct, interpret, and informally operate on matrices. The first investigation emphasizes constructing matrices. The problems in Investigation 2 show that a matrix can be used to organize data in many different contexts. Students interpret the matrices and they operate informally on matrices in a variety of ways before they investigate the standard matrix operations. One useful "nonstandard" operation that students will use throughout the unit is summing rows or columns. In the third investigation, students develop the standard matrix operations of matrix addition, matrix subtraction, and scalar multiplication (multiplication of a matrix by a number). In Lessons 2 and 3, they learn about matrix multiplication and how to use matrices to solve systems of linear equations.

Lesson Objectives

- Construct matrices to organize, display, and analyze information
- Interpret given matrices
- Understand, carry out, and interpret matrix operations—row and column sums, matrix addition and subtraction, and scalar multiplication

Lesson Launch

This full-class discussion should be kept brief. The goal is to have students thinking about a situation of some interest to them and to motivate the need for some mathematics to understand the situation.

Think About This Situation

Managing an athletic shoe store is a complicated job. Sales need to be tracked, inventory must be controlled carefully, and changes in the market must be anticipated. In particular, the store manager needs to know which shoes will sell. Think about the shoe store where you bought your last pair of athletic shoes.

a What information might the manager of the store want to know about the kinds of shoes the customers prefer? Make a list.

b It is not enough just to have information. The manager needs to organize and manage the information in order to make good decisions. What are some ways the manager might organize the information?

In this lesson, you will learn how to construct matrices to help organize and analyze data; how to interpret matrices in diverse settings; and how to combine and operate on matrices in several ways, including using row sums, matrix addition, and multiplication of a matrix by a number.

 **Investigation 1** There's No Business Like Shoe Business

There are many different brands of athletic shoes, and each brand of shoe has many different styles and sizes. Shoe-store managers need to know which shoes their customers prefer so they can have the right shoes in stock. As you explore shoe data in this investigation, look for answers to this question:

How can you construct and use a rectangular array of numbers (a matrix) to organize, display, and analyze information?

1 Work together with the whole class to find out about the brands of athletic shoes preferred by students in your class.

a. Make a list of all the different brands of athletic shoes preferred by students in your class.

b. How many males prefer each brand? How many females prefer each brand?

Teaching Resources

Transparency Master 1.

UNIT 2 *Matrix Methods*

Think About
This **Situation**

Managing an athletic shoe store is a complicated job. Sales
need to be tracked, inventory must be controlled carefully,
and changes in the market must be anticipated. In particular,
the store manager needs to know which shoes will sell. Think
about the shoe store where you bought your last pair of
athletic shoes.

ⓐ What information might the manager of the store want to
know about the kinds of shoes the customers prefer? Make
a list.

ⓑ It is not enough just to have information. The manager needs
to organize and manage the information in order to make
good decisions. What are some ways the manager might
organize the information?

Transparency Master • *see unit page 75*   UNIT 2 • Matrix Methods   1

Think About This Situation

ⓐ Students might think about shoe brands, sizes, colors, styles, men's and women's shoes, prices, etc.

ⓑ Some quick brainstorming here will help students see the possibility of and the need for organizing the information in a useful way. They might think about tables, lists, bar graphs, line graphs, box plots, and charts like in *USA Today*, etc.

Investigation 1 — There's No Business Like Shoe Business

In this investigation, students learn what a matrix is and how to construct matrices, and they begin to analyze and interpret matrices. Tables provide a natural entry into the study of matrices. However, tables and matrices are not the same. A matrix is a rectangular array of numbers. We often append labels and titles to matrices to make them more informative and to help students make sense of them; but technically, the matrix is just the array of numbers. Do not get bogged down on this point, but be aware and mention to students as appropriate. For more detail, see Reflections Task 17.

INSTRUCTIONAL NOTE
Students will use the list generated in Part a of the TATS in Problem 3, so you may want to write the list on the board for future reference.

Launch

Work together as a whole class to collect data on their shoe preferences as suggested in Problem 1. Leave it disorganized at this stage, since one of the purposes of using matrices is to organize data. You may wish to have students leave their books closed so they do not see the matrix in Problem 2 at this point. Write the information on the board or have a student do it, since you will need to refer to the class data later. Encourage the class to generate a rich list, but try to keep it manageable—that is, not too much data, not too little. For future problems, it will be best if you include at least 3 different shoe brands in the class data here.

In Problem 2, students learn some basic terminology—matrix, row, column, and size. Students will probably find this to be a natural and obvious way to organize the data. That is the point; matrices are natural and easy.

COLLABORATION SKILL
An initiator offers ideas or thought-provoking questions to get the group discussion started. During this investigation, we will be sure each group member has an opportunity to initiate discussion.

1 **a–b.** Collect class data on shoe preferences.

2 One way to organize and display these data is to use a kind of table. You can do this by listing the brands down one side, writing "Men" and "Women" across the top, and then entering the appropriate numbers.

a. Complete a table like the one below for your class data. Add or remove rows as needed. A rectangular array of numbers like this is called a **matrix**.

Athletic-Shoe Brands

	Men	Women
Converse	____	____
Nike	____	____
Reebok	____	____

b. The matrix above has 3 **rows** and 2 **columns**. How many rows were needed in the matrix you constructed to display your class data? How many columns?

c. Could you organize your class data using a matrix with 2 rows? If so, how many columns would it have?

d. The **size of a matrix** is written as $m \times n$, where m is the number of *rows* and n is the number of *columns*. Thus, the sample matrix in Part a is a 3×2 matrix (which is read as "3 by 2"). What is the size of the matrix you constructed to display your class data?

3 Knowing the brands of shoes that customers prefer certainly will help a store manager decide which shoes to stock. Other information that will be useful to a store manager can also be organized in *matrices* (plural of matrix).

a. What other information might the manager of the store want to know about the kinds of shoes the customers prefer? Look back at the list you generated for the Think About This Situation and add to it if necessary.

b. Construct a matrix that could be used to organize some of the information from your list in Part a. (You probably won't be able to organize all of the information on your list in one matrix.) Don't worry about actually collecting the information; just set up the matrix, label the rows and columns, and give the matrix a title according to the information that it will show.

c. Compare your matrix with those made by others.

i. Do all of the matrices make sense? If not, explain why not.

ii. Are the row and column labels and titles appropriate? If not, how would you modify them?

iii. How many different variables can be represented in one matrix? Explain your thinking.

2 **a.** Responses will vary based on class data. Some classes may choose different brand names for the athletic shoes.

b. Responses will vary based on class data.

c. You could use "Men" and Women" as rows instead of columns. That is, the rows and columns of the sample matrix could be switched.

d. The size depends on the class matrix.

TERMINOLOGY The **size** of a matrix is sometimes described by referring to the numbers of rows and columns as the **dimensions** of the matrix. Or, less commonly, the size of a matrix may be called the **dimension** of the matrix.

3 **INSTRUCTIONAL NOTE** In this problem, students think more carefully about what is a matrix and how to construct a matrix. Students should understand how a matrix is constructed using rows and columns. They should get in the habit of labeling the rows and columns and giving the matrix a title. This will often make it easier for students to interpret matrices and will help them make sense of how to operate with and on them. Furthermore, they should understand that because a matrix consists of entries for each row and column, a matrix can be used to represent data (in the entries) related to two categories of information (represented by the rows and columns). All of these ideas will be developed throughout the unit and are only initially raised here.

a. Other information might include size, style, color, or price.

b. Matrices will vary depending on what information students choose to organize. For example, they might consider a matrix titled "Athletic Shoe Styles" in which they organize information about which styles are purchased by men and women; or a "Brand-by-Price Sales" matrix in which the columns are different brands, the rows are price ranges, and the entries are the number of sales for each brand in each price range.

c. i–iii. Students should make sure that their matrices are sensible and have appropriate labels. Concerning how many variables can be represented in one matrix, students may say two, since there are two fundamental components of a matrix: rows and columns. Or, more accurately, they may say three variables can be represented since the *entries* of a matrix represent information about the *row* and *column* variables.

INSTRUCTIONAL NOTE Labeling rows and columns and giving a title to a matrix will often help students interpret the matrix and make sense of how to operate with and on matrices.

INSTRUCTIONAL NOTE It is important to monitor students' responses to Part c. This could be done by pointedly checking each group's work on Part c or by conducting a brief whole-class discussion of this problem.

Unit 2

(4) Suppose you are a manager of a local FleetFeet shoe store. Data on monthly sales of Converse, Nike, and Reebok shoes are shown in the matrix below. Each entry represents the number of pairs of shoes sold.

Monthly Sales

	J	F	M	A	M	J	J	A	S	O	N	D
Converse	40	35	50	55	70	60	40	70	40	35	30	80
Nike	55	55	75	70	70	65	60	75	60	55	50	75
Reebok	50	30	60	80	70	50	10	75	40	35	40	70

a. Describe any patterns you see in the data.

b. Describe any general trends over time that you observe. Which months have the highest sales? What could be a reason for the high sales?

c. Are there any outliers in the data? If so, explain why you think they could have occurred.

d. How many pairs of Nikes were sold over the year?

e. How many pairs of all three brands together were sold in February?

Summarize the Mathematics

In this investigation, you explored how matrices can be used to organize and display data.

a The Shoe Outlet sells women's shoes, sizes 5 to 11, and men's shoes, sizes 6 to 13. The manager would like to have an organized display of the number of pairs sold this year for each shoe size. Describe a matrix that could be used to organize these data. What is the size of your matrix?

b What are some advantages of using matrices to organize and display data? What are some disadvantages?

c Explain how the same information can be displayed in a matrix in different ways.

Be prepared to share your explanations and thinking with the entire class.

✓ Check Your Understanding

Suppose that the FleetFeet shoe store chain has stores in Chicago, Atlanta, and San Diego; the top-selling brands are Nike and Reebok; and in 2007, the average sales figures per month were as follows: 250 pairs of Nike and 195 pairs of Reebok in Chicago, 175 pairs of Nike and 175 pairs of Reebok in Atlanta, and 185 pairs of Nike and 275 pairs of Reebok in San Diego.

4　a. Possible patterns: Nike seems to have consistent sales over the year. Nike outsold both other brands in almost every month. Also, see Part b.

　b. Trends over time: Sales are down at the beginning of the year, up during spring, down in the middle of summer, up at the beginning of school in the fall, down later in the fall, up at Christmas. The highest sales months for each brand are: Converse–December, Nike–March, April, and December, Reebok–April. Possible reasons for the high sales are Christmas, the start of school, and the beginning of spring. Students may also note that these months coincide somewhat with new sports seasons.

　c. The "10" in July for Reebok is much lower than might be expected. Either sales are low due to some event (maybe a production or distribution problem) or data were entered incorrectly. Students need to be aware of both possibilities. To check for an outlier, students can simply note that 10 is clearly much different than the other values. Using the formula for outliers: Q3 + 1.5(IQR) or Q1 − 1.5(IQR), 10 is not an outlier.

　d. 765 pairs (Sum the row.)

　e. 120 pairs were sold in February. (Sum the column.)

INSTRUCTIONAL NOTE
The goal here is for students to begin analyzing and operating on matrices. Note that Parts d and e lead into considering summing rows and summing columns, more of which will be done in the next investigation.

Summary

Different students or groups could report on different parts while you facilitate clarifications and agreements.

Summarize
the Mathematics

Teaching Resources

Transparency Master 2.

UNIT 2　*Matrix Methods*

Summarize
the Mathematics

In this investigation, you explored how matrices can be used to organize and display data.

ⓐ The Shoe Outlet sells women's shoes, sizes 5 to 11, and men's shoes, sizes 6 to 13. The manager would like to have an organized display of the number of pairs sold this year for each shoe size. Describe a matrix that could be used to organize these data. What is the size of your matrix?

ⓑ What are some advantages of using matrices to organize and display data? What are some disadvantages?

ⓒ Explain how the same information can be displayed in a matrix in different ways.

Be prepared to share your explanations and thinking with the entire class.

ⓐ Responses may vary. Students may choose to display sizes from 5 to 13, which is nine different sizes (assuming no half sizes), along the rows or columns. If a particular size includes both men's and women's shoes, then a single number showing sales of this size is possible, but it would be more informative to show men's sales separate from women's sales. This would require a 2 × 9 or 9 × 2 matrix with the two variables being size and gender. If half sizes are included, the matrix would be 2 × 17 or 17 × 2. Some students may not want to combine male and female sizes in the same matrix. If so, they should support their decision with some rationale.

ⓑ Some advantages are that matrices are straightforward, a natural modification of tables, useful for information about two variables, and easily stored in a computer. Some disadvantages are that they are only useful for information about two variables, not as visual as graphs, and quick summary data are not available visually.

ⓒ The same information can be represented in a matrix in different ways. For example, (1) you might switch (transpose) rows and columns, (2) you might list the possibilities for a variable in a different order along the rows or columns, or (3) you might choose different variables for the rows or columns.

PROCESSING PROMPT
During this investigation, I initiated our discussion on Problem _____ by … .

a. Organize these data using one matrix. Label the rows and columns and give the matrix a title.

b. What is the size of the matrix?

c. How many pairs of Reebok shoes are sold in all three cities combined?

d. In which city were the most shoes sold?

Investigation 2 Analyzing Matrices

Matrices can be used to organize all sorts of data, not just sales data. In this investigation, you will analyze some situations in archeology, sociology, and sports. As you explore these different situations, look for answers to this question:

How can you interpret and operate on a matrix to help understand and analyze data?

Archeology Archeologists study ancient civilizations and their cultures. One way they study these cultures is by exploring sites where the people once lived and analyzing objects that they made. Archeologists use matrices to classify and then compare the objects they find at various archeological sites. For example, suppose that pieces of pottery are found at five different sites. The pottery pieces have certain characteristics: they are either glazed or not glazed, ornamented or not, colored or natural, thin or thick.

✓ Check Your Understanding

a. One possible matrix:

Athletic-Shoe Brands

	Nike	Reebok
Chicago	250	195
Atlanta	175	175
San Diego	185	275

b. The size of the matrix given in Part a is 3 × 2. Students may switch rows and columns and get a 2 × 3 matrix.

c. 645 pairs of Reebok

d. San Diego

Investigation 2 — Analyzing Matrices

In this investigation, students will see how matrices can be used in a variety of contexts. They will interpret given matrices, and they will learn to operate on matrices in formal and informal ways, including finding row and column sums.

There are three main contexts in this investigation: archeology, sociology, and sports. The details of the specific examples are not of primary importance; rather, it is the use of matrices in different ways and in different contexts that is important. These are engaging and perhaps novel applications of matrices.

DIFFERENTIATION For some students or classes, you may decide to skip the archeology problems (1–4) or sports problems (Check Your Understanding). Perhaps some students need more or less practice using and interpreting matrices. You need to do the sociology problems (5–7) in order to do later problems.

1 Information about the characteristics of the pottery pieces at all five sites is organized in the matrix below. A "1" means the pottery piece has the characteristic and a "0" means it does not have the characteristic.

Pottery Characteristics

	Glaze	Orn	Color	Thin
Site A	0	1	0	0
Site B	1	0	0	0
Site C	1	0	1	0
Site D	1	1	1	1
Site E	0	1	1	1

a. What does it mean for pottery to be "glazed"? "Ornamented"?

b. What does the "1" in the third row and the first column mean?

c. Is the pottery at site E thick or thin?

d. Which site has pottery pieces that are glazed and thick but are not ornamented or colored?

e. How many of the sites have glazed pottery? Explain how you used the rows or columns of the matrix to answer the question.

2 You can use the matrix in Problem 1 to determine how much the pottery pieces differ between sites. For example, the pieces found at sites A and B differ on exactly two characteristics—glaze and ornamentation. So, you can say that the **degree of difference** between the pottery pieces at sites A and B is 2.

a. Explain why the degree of difference between pottery pieces at sites A and C is 3.

b. Find the degree of difference between the pottery pieces at sites D and E.

3 You can construct a new matrix that summarizes the degree of difference information.

Degree of Difference

	A	B	C	D	E
A	_	2	3	_	_
B	2	_	_	_	_
C	3	_	_	_	_
D	_	_	_	_	_
E	_	_	_	_	_

a. What number would best describe the difference between site A and site A?

b. What number should be placed in the third row, fourth column? What does this number tell you about the pottery at these two sites?

c. Complete a copy of the degree of difference matrix shown above.

d. Describe one or two patterns you see in the degree of difference matrix.

1 **a.** This question is to ensure that students understand the meaning of the words "glazed" and "ornamented." "Glazed" means glossy finish as opposed to dull finish. "Ornamented" means that it has designs on it as opposed to being plain.

b. At site C, the pottery was glazed.

c. Site E had thin pottery.

d. Site B. Examine the rows to find a 1 under the column labeled "glaze" and 0s in the columns under "orn," "color," and "thin."

e. Three sites had glazed pottery. You can sum the first column to obtain the total number of sites with glazed pottery.

2 **a.** By comparing the rows for A and C, you can see that the entries only agree in the "thin" column. Thus, they disagree in 3 columns, so it is reasonable to say that the degree of difference is 3.

b. The degree of difference between D and E is 1.

3 **a.** 0, because there is no difference

b. The entry should be "2." This number indicates that the pottery at sites C and D differs on exactly 2 characteristics, ornamentation and thickness.

c. **Degree of Difference**

$$
\begin{array}{c c c c c c}
 & A & B & C & D & E \\
A & 0 & 2 & 3 & 3 & 2 \\
B & 2 & 0 & 1 & 3 & 4 \\
C & 3 & 1 & 0 & 2 & 3 \\
D & 3 & 3 & 2 & 0 & 1 \\
E & 2 & 4 & 3 & 1 & 0
\end{array}
$$

d. Patterns include: the same labels are used for rows and columns, there is the same number of rows as columns, the nth row is the same as the nth column, the matrix is symmetric across the diagonal of zeroes. (Students will consider this symmetry in Connections Task 8. It need not be mentioned at this point.)

Teaching Resources

Student Master 3.

UNIT 2 *Metrix Methods*

Name
Date

Degree of Difference Matrix for Pottery Characteristics
Problem 3

Unit 2

④ Archeologists want to learn about the civilizations that existed at the sites. For instance, they would like to know whether different sites represent different civilizations and whether one civilization was more advanced than another. A lot of evidence is needed to make such decisions. However, you can make some conjectures based just on the pottery data in the matrices from Problems 1 and 3.

   a. Find two sites that you think might be from the same civilization. Explain how the pottery evidence supports your choice.

   b. Find two sites that you think might be from different civilizations. Give an argument defending your choice.

   c. Give an argument supporting the claim that the civilization at site D was more advanced than the others. What assumptions are you making about what it means for a civilization to be "advanced"?

Sociology Sociologists study human social behavior. They may use matrices in their analysis of social relations.

⑤ Suppose a sociologist is studying friendship and trust among five classmates at a certain high school. The classmates are asked to indicate with whom they would like to go to a movie and to whom they would loan $10. Their responses are summarized in the following two matrices. Each matrix is read from row to column. "1" means "yes" and "0" means "no". For example, the "1" in the first row and fourth column of the movie matrix means that student A would like to go to a movie with student D.

Movie Matrix

Would Like to Go to a Movie

	with				
	A	B	C	D	E
A	0	1	1	1	1
B	0	0	1	1	1
C	1	0	0	1	0
D	0	1	1	0	1
E	1	0	0	1	0

Loan Matrix

Would Loan Money

	to				
	A	B	C	D	E
A	0	0	0	1	1
B	1	0	0	1	0
C	0	0	0	1	0
D	1	1	0	0	1
E	0	1	1	0	0

   a. Would student A like to go to a movie with student B? Would student B like to go to a movie with student A?

   b. With whom would student D like to go to a movie?

   c. What does the "0" in the fourth row, third column of the loan matrix mean?

   d. To whom would student A loan $10?

   e. A **square matrix** has the same number of rows and columns. The **main diagonal** of a square matrix is the diagonal line of entries running from the top-left corner to the bottom-right corner.

      i. Why do you think there are zeroes for each entry in the main diagonals of the movie matrix and the loan matrix?

      ii. Could you use different entries, or no entries, in the diagonals? Explain.

4 **a.** Possible response: Two sites might be from the same civilization if they have a small degree of difference. The pottery at sites D and E differ only in the "glaze" category, and the pottery at sites B and C differ only in the "color" category, so maybe the two sites are from the same civilization. However, this is certainly not definitive evidence for such a conclusion. (Students should see the need to support their claims as thoroughly as possible as well as be aware of the limitations of their analysis.)

b. Possible response: The pottery at sites B and E differ in each category, so maybe these sites represent two different civilizations.

c. Possible response: The pottery at site D is glazed, ornamented, colored, and thin, all of which seem to be "advanced" characteristics. Students might think of "advanced" in terms of technologically advanced, in which case they might generate the possible argument stated above. On the other hand, it is certainly possible that a civilization is advanced and yet does not produce pottery that is glazed, ornamented, or colored.

5 **a.** Yes, student A would like to go to a movie with B, but B would not like to go to a movie with A.

b. Student D would like to go to a movie with students B, C, and E.

c. The "0" means that D would not loan money to C.

d. Student A would loan money to D and E.

e. **i.** It seems plausible that a zero would represent the idea that a student would not like to go to a movie with or loan money to himself or herself.

ii. It is also reasonable to simply put blanks in the diagonal entries. Or, especially in the movie matrix, it is plausible that some entries in the main diagonal could be 1s. Different interpretations are possible. However, in this analysis, the behavior of a person with himself or herself is not important, and we have used 0s in the diagonal to facilitate future work with these matrices.

6 Now consider additional information conveyed by the matrices on page 80.

 a. Explain why the movie matrix could be used to describe *friendship*, while the loan matrix could describe *trust*.

 b. Write two interesting statements about friendship and trust among these five students, based on the information in the matrices.

7 Discuss with your classmates how you can use the rows or columns of the movie and loan matrices to answer the following questions.

 a. How many students does student C consider as friends?

 b. How many students consider student C as a friend?

 c. Who seems to be the most trustworthy student?

 d. Who seems to be the most popular student?

Summarize the Mathematics

In the previous investigations, you analyzed matrices to get useful information about the situations being studied.

a Give three examples from your analysis of shoe sales, pottery, or friendship and trust that show how you performed computations on or compared the entries of the given matrix to get useful information. For each example, describe the situation, the computation or comparison, and the information obtained.

b One common and useful matrix operation is to sum all of the numbers in a row or in a column. The resulting number is called a *row sum* or *column sum*. Describe one example in which you computed a row sum. Give another example where you found a column sum.

Be prepared to share your examples and thinking with the class.

✓ Check Your Understanding

In 2006, the University of Maryland won the NCAA women's basketball championship. They defeated Duke 78-75 in overtime, completing a 34-4 season.

 Crystal Langhorne was Maryland's high scorer for the season with 654 points. Teammate Shay Doron was the next highest scorer with 511 points, followed by Marissa Coleman with 510 points, and Laura Harper with 413 points.

6 **a.** You go to movies with friends and loan money to people you trust to pay you back.

   b. Possible specific statements: (1) Student A considers everyone to be a friend, but only two people name A as a friend. (2) Student C does not trust many and is not trusted by many.

   Possible general statements: (1) Just because student X considers student Y to be a friend, it does not follow that Y considers X to be a friend. (2) It is possible to consider someone to be a friend and yet not trust the person enough to loan him or her $10.

INSTRUCTIONAL NOTE
The goal in Part b is to have students read, think about, and interpret matrices.

7 **a.** Student C names 2 friends. Sum the third row of the movie matrix to find how many classmates student C considers a friend.

   b. Three students name C as a friend. Sum the third or "C" column of the movie matrix to find how many students consider C as a friend.

   c. Student D seems the most trustworthy because the sum of the "D" column in the loan matrix is 3, more than any other column sum.

   d. Student D seems the most popular because the sum of the "D" column in the movie matrix is 4, more than any other column sum.

INSTRUCTIONAL NOTE
Students will likely only record numbers for Problem 7. In Part b of the STM, students might reference these questions as examples of a row sum or a column sum.

Summarize
the Mathematics

Teaching Resources
Transparency Master 4.

UNIT **2** *Matrix Methods*

Summarize
the **Mathematics**

In the previous investigations, you analyzed matrices to get useful information about the situations being studied.

a Give three examples from your analysis of shoe sales, pottery, or friendship and trust that show how you performed computations on or compared the entries of the given matrix to get useful information. For each example, describe the situation, the computation or comparison, and the information obtained.

b One common and useful matrix operation is to sum all of the numbers in a row or in a column. The resulting number is called a *row sum* or *column sum*. Describe one example in which you computed a row sum. Give another example where you found a column sum.

Be prepared to share your examples and thinking with the class.

a Examples include the following:
   • In the pottery matrix, the sum of a column tells how many sites had glazed pottery.
   • In the pottery matrix, the degree of difference was found by comparing rows.
   • In the shoe-sales matrix, the sum of the Nike row gives the number of Nikes sold that year.
   • In the shoe-sales matrix, the mean of a row is the mean number of pairs of shoes sold per month for a particular brand.
   • In the shoe-sales matrix, summing a column results in the number of shoes sold in that month for all three brands.
   • In the movie matrix, the sum of a column tells how many people would like to go to a movie with a particular person. You then could compare these to find the most popular student.

b It is likely that some row and column sum examples will have been described in Part a. If so, that is fine. If not, students should describe such examples now.

The matrix below shows some of the nonshooting performance statistics for the top four Maryland scorers for the entire 2005–06 season.

Nonshooting Performance Statistics

	Assists	Steals	Rebounds	Blocked Shots	Turnovers	Fouls
Langhorne	77	27	325	14	98	70
Doron	149	67	143	11	118	80
Coleman	115	48	299	52	115	83
Harper	26	31	258	70	80	108

Source: umterps.cstv.com/sports/w-baskbl/stats/2005-2006/teamcume.html

a. A "turnover" is when an action (other than a foul, steal, or scoring a basket) gives the other team control of the ball. How many turnovers did Coleman have?

b. How many rebounds were made by all of these players combined during the season?

c. Which of the performance factors do you think are positive, that is, they contribute to winning a game? Which performance factors do you think are negative?

d. Describe how you could give a "nonshooting performance score" to each player. The score should include both positive and negative factors. Compute this score for each player. Which player do you think contributed most to the team over the season in the area of nonshooting performance? Explain your choice.

e. Below are two possible methods to compute the "nonshooting performance scores." For each method, did you use that method when you computed the scores in Part d? If not, use the method now. Compare the method and the score you get to your work in Part d.

   i. Modify the matrix above so that the entries reflect positive and negative performance factors. Then use row sums to find the "nonshooting performance scores."

   ii. Construct two matrices–one for the positive factors and one for the negative factors. Then combine these two matrices to find the "nonshooting performance scores."

f. There were 38 games in the season. Langhorne and Doron played all 38 games. Coleman played in 37 games, and Harper played in 36 games. Adjust the numbers in the given matrix to give estimates if all 4 players had played in all 38 games. Then compute a "nonshooting performance score" for each player. Compare to what you found in Part e.

 **Investigation 3** **Combining Matrices**

You have seen that a matrix can be used to store and organize data. You also have seen that you can operate on the numbers in the rows or columns of a matrix to get additional information and draw conclusions about the data. In this investigation, you will consider situations in which it is also

✓ Check Your Understanding

a. Coleman had 115 turnovers. (A turnover is when the player throws the ball either to the other team or out of bounds, or there is a violation that stops play and transfers possession of the ball to the other team. An example is traveling, or walking with the ball.)

b. A rebound is when a player gets the ball after a missed shot. These four players combined for 1,025 rebounds during the season. This is the sum of the "Rebound" column.

c. Assists, steals, rebounds, and blocked shots are the performance factors that contribute toward winning the game. Turnovers and fouls are the negative performance statistics. (Some students may argue that fouls are not always negative. In fact, there are times when fouling is the best thing to do. If students feel strongly about this, you might suggest that they just eliminate the "foul" column from the matrix.)

d. Responses may vary. See Part f for two possible approaches—row sums and matrix addition. Students will likely use one of these approaches. You could modify the given matrix by making the entries for turnovers and fouls negative numbers. Then compute the row sums for this modified matrix. Using these numbers, Coleman would be said to have contributed the most to the team over the season, taking into account both positive and negative factors. The row sums are: Langhorne–275, Doron–172, Coleman–316, Harper–197.

e.   **i.** See Part d.

   ii. The positive factor matrix contains assists, steals, rebounds, and blocked shots with the same entries as in the original matrix. The negative factor matrix contains turnovers and fouls. If the entries in the negative factor matrix stay positive, then subtract the two matrices. Alternatively, make the entries in the negative factor matrix negative numbers and then add the two matrices.

f. The numbers in the original matrix could be adjusted by figuring out each player's per-game statistics by dividing the totals given by the number of games played and then multiplying by 38 to get a 38-game estimate. Doing so yields the following matrix:

	Assists	Steals	Rebounds	Blocked Shots	Turn-overs	Fouls
Langhorne	77	27	325	14	98	70
Doron	149	67	143	11	118	80
Coleman	118	49	307	53	118	85
Harper	27	33	272	74	84	114

Using this matrix and the method on Part ei gives the following nonshooting performance scores: Langhorne–275, Doron–172, Coleman–324, Harper–208. These are slightly different numbers, but the same relative ranking of Coleman-Langhorne-Harper-Doron. (Students may note that this is quite different from the ranking based on points scored, which without accounting for games played is: Langhorne-Doron-Coleman-Harper; and with adjustment for games played is: Langhorne-Coleman-Doron-Harper.)

useful to combine two matrices. As you work through the problems, keep track of answers to the following question:

What are some other useful methods for operating on a matrix or combining two matrices?

1 The movie and loan matrices from the previous investigation are shown below. You can analyze these matrices together to see how friendship and trust are related in this group of five students.

Movie Matrix

Would Like to Go to a Movie

with

$$\begin{array}{c} & \begin{array}{ccccc} A & B & C & D & E \end{array} \\ \begin{array}{c} A \\ B \\ C \\ D \\ E \end{array} & \left[\begin{array}{ccccc} 0 & 1 & 1 & 1 & 1 \\ 0 & 0 & 1 & 1 & 1 \\ 1 & 0 & 0 & 1 & 0 \\ 0 & 1 & 1 & 0 & 1 \\ 1 & 0 & 0 & 1 & 0 \end{array}\right] \end{array}$$

Loan Matrix

Would Loan Money

to

$$\begin{array}{c} & \begin{array}{ccccc} A & B & C & D & E \end{array} \\ \begin{array}{c} A \\ B \\ C \\ D \\ E \end{array} & \left[\begin{array}{ccccc} 0 & 0 & 0 & 1 & 1 \\ 1 & 0 & 0 & 1 & 0 \\ 0 & 0 & 0 & 1 & 0 \\ 1 & 1 & 0 & 0 & 1 \\ 0 & 1 & 1 & 0 & 0 \end{array}\right] \end{array}$$

    a. Who does student A consider a friend and yet does not trust enough to loan $10?

    b. Do you think it is reasonable that a student could have a friend who he or she does not trust enough to loan $10?

    c. Who does student B trust and yet does not consider that person to be friends?

    d. Who does student D trust and also consider to be a friend?

2 A friend you trust is a *trustworthy friend*.

    a. Combine the movie and loan matrices to construct a new matrix that shows who each of the five students considers to be a trustworthy friend.

    b. Write down a systematic procedure explaining how to construct the trustworthy-friend matrix.

    c. Compare your procedure with that of others.

    d. Write two interesting observations about the information in this new matrix.

In the next situation, you will explore other methods of combining matrices and learn some of the ways in which matrix operations are used in business and in industry.

Motor vehicles are produced in many regions around the world. Production levels significantly affect the economies of many countries, and thus they are tracked carefully.

Unit 2

Combining Matrices

In this investigation, students will continue to analyze and operate on matrices in sensible ways. In particular, they will learn how to add and subtract matrices and multiply a matrix by a number (scalar multiplication).

COLLABORATION SKILL
Ask questions to be sure that other group members and I understand the mathematics.

In Problem 2, students should see that there are several sensible ways to combine the two matrices (see Part b). (This is important so that students realize that mathematics makes sense and is not just a collection of obscure procedures for them to memorize.) It is likely that some students will multiply the two matrices entry-by-entry, which is a reasonable strategy for this problem. In Lesson 2, they will learn that a more common and powerful method of multiplying matrices is the standard "row-by-column" method.

1   **a.** Students B and C are people whom student A considers friends but does not trust enough to loan $10.

     b. Students probably will agree that a person could be a friend yet not be a person to whom you would want to loan $10. Students might answer, "No, if they are a friend, they will pay you back." However, students need to at least consider the possibility of a friend that is not trusted in order to proceed.

     c. Student B trusts student A yet does not consider A to be a friend.

     d. Student D trusts students B and E and considers them to be friends.

2   **a.** Two possible trustworthy-friend matrices are below. They correspond to the procedures described in Part b.

INSTRUCTIONAL NOTE
As you monitor the students, remind them that it is useful to properly label the rows and columns and give good titles for their matrices.

$$
\begin{array}{c c}
& \begin{matrix} A & B & C & D & E \end{matrix} \\
\begin{matrix} A \\ B \\ C \\ D \\ E \end{matrix} &
\begin{bmatrix}
0 & 0 & 0 & 1 & 1 \\
0 & 0 & 0 & 1 & 0 \\
0 & 0 & 0 & 1 & 0 \\
0 & 1 & 0 & 0 & 1 \\
0 & 0 & 0 & 0 & 0
\end{bmatrix}
\end{array}
\qquad
\begin{array}{c c}
& \begin{matrix} A & B & C & D & E \end{matrix} \\
\begin{matrix} A \\ B \\ C \\ D \\ E \end{matrix} &
\begin{bmatrix}
0 & 1 & 1 & 2 & 2 \\
1 & 0 & 1 & 2 & 1 \\
1 & 0 & 0 & 2 & 0 \\
1 & 2 & 1 & 0 & 2 \\
1 & 1 & 1 & 1 & 0
\end{bmatrix}
\end{array}
$$

   b. Possible responses:

     To determine an entry in the "trustworthy friend" matrix, look at the corresponding entries in the movie matrix and the loan matrix. If they are both 1s, then put a 1 in that position in the "trustworthy friend" matrix; otherwise, put a 0 in that position.

     Multiplying the two matrices entry-by-entry gives the same resulting matrix as described just above.

     Sum the entries in the same positions. If there is a 2 in a position, then the "column" person is a trustworthy friend of the "row" person.

   c. Students should compare procedures.

   d. Possible responses:

     Nobody considers student A to be a trustworthy friend.

     Everybody except student E has at least one trustworthy friend in this group of students.

     Student D is considered a trustworthy friend by everybody except student E.

INSTRUCTIONAL NOTE
The comparison in Part c could be accomplished as a class discussion. Hopefully, student procedures will lead to a good discussion of combining matrices in sensible ways.

The two matrices below show the production of passenger vehicles (PV), light commercial vehicles (LCV), and heavy trucks (HT) in three regions for the years 2004 and 2005. The numbers shown are in thousands.

2004 Vehicle Production

	PV	LCV	HT
North America	6,359	9,406	470
South America	1,992	419	122
European Union	14,664	1,637	522
Japan	8,720	1,009	770

2005 Vehicle Production

	PV	LCV	HT
North America	6,667	9,087	549
South America	2,290	522	138
European Union	14,178	1,680	550
Japan	9,016	1,047	724

Source: www.oica.net

3 Analyze the two matrices above.

  a. How many vehicles are represented by the entry in the first row and first column of the matrix for 2004?

  b. According to these data, how many heavy trucks were produced in South America in 2005?

  c. Explain the meaning of the entry in the third row and second column of the 2004 matrix.

  d. Describe any patterns you see in these data.

4 Additional information can be derived by combining the two matrices.

  a. According to these data, by how much did passenger vehicle production increase in South America from 2004 to 2005?

  b. Construct a new matrix with the same row and column labels that shows how much vehicle production changed from 2004 to 2005 for each region and each type of vehicle.

  i. How did you obtain entries in the new matrix from the two given matrices?

  ii. Explain any trends or unusual entries in the new matrix.

5 Construct a matrix with the same row and column labels as the given matrices that shows the total number of motor vehicles produced over the two-year period 2004 through 2005. How did you obtain the new matrix?

6 Suppose that the auto industry projected a 10% increase in vehicle production from 2005 to 2006 over all regions and all types of vehicles. Construct a matrix that shows the projected 2006 production figures for each region and each type of vehicle. How did you obtain the new matrix?

3 **a.** 6,359,000 passenger vehicles

b. 138,000 heavy trucks

c. The European Union produced 1,637,000 light commercial vehicles in 2004.

d. Some patterns: Production of light commercial vehicles increased from 2004 to 2005 in all regions except North America. Passenger vehicle production decreased from 2004 to 2005 in the European Union. South America is the only region in which production levels increased from 2004 to 2005 in all 3 categories of vehicles.

4 **a.** 298,000 passenger vehicles

b. **i.** Subtract the 2004 matrix, entry-by-corresponding-entry, from the 2005 matrix.

Production Change from 2004 to 2005

	PV	LCV	HT
North America	308	−319	79
South America	298	103	16
European Union	−486	43	28
Japan	296	38	−46

ii. Possible trends: See the patterns described in Part d of Problem 3. Note how the patterns described there are readily and more easily seen in the matrix here (although students may have described patterns in Problem 3 that are not so obvious in the matrix here, especially if those patterns were not based on looking at differences between 2004 and 2005).

5 Add corresponding entries to get the new matrix. See the matrix below.

Production in 2004 and 2005 Combined

	PV	LCV	HT
North America	13,026	18,493	1,019
South America	4,282	941	260
European Union	28,842	3,317	1,072
Japan	17,736	2,056	1,494

6 Multiply each entry in the 2005 matrix by 1.10 to determine a 10% increase over 2005 production. See the matrix below. You may choose to round to the nearest integer. For example, the Japan LCV entry below is 1,151.7 which is 1,151,700 vehicles. Stated in thousands, this would round to 1,152.

Projected 2006 Production

	PV	LCV	HT
North America	7,333.7	9,995.7	603.9
South America	2,519.0	574.2	151.8
European Union	15,595.8	1,848.0	605.0
Japan	9,917.6	1,151.7	796.4

INSTRUCTIONAL NOTE
In Problems 4, 5, and 6, students learn how to subtract matrices, add matrices, and carry out scalar multiplication, respectively.

COMMON MISCONCEPTION Students may multiply the 2005 production entries by 0.10 instead of 1.10. They should recognize that their answers do not make sense and correct themselves. You may wish to ask some groups what the value of the multiplier would be for a 20% decrease.

DIFFERENTIATION For some students or classes, you may wish to discuss rounding methods, depending on time and need. Rounding to the closest integer value seems appropriate for this situation since the original numbers are given in thousands.

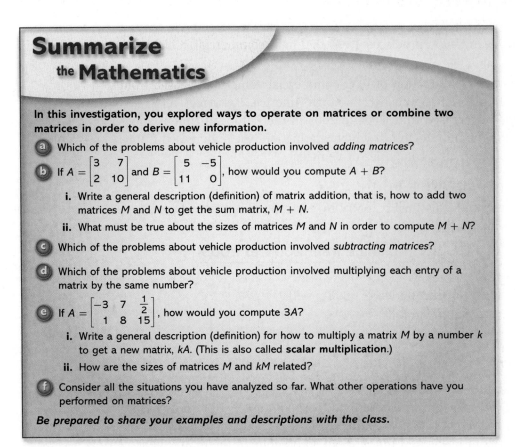

Summarize the Mathematics

In this investigation, you explored ways to operate on matrices or combine two matrices in order to derive new information.

a Which of the problems about vehicle production involved *adding matrices*?

b If $A = \begin{bmatrix} 3 & 7 \\ 2 & 10 \end{bmatrix}$ and $B = \begin{bmatrix} 5 & -5 \\ 11 & 0 \end{bmatrix}$, how would you compute $A + B$?

   i. Write a general description (definition) of matrix addition, that is, how to add two matrices M and N to get the sum matrix, $M + N$.

   ii. What must be true about the sizes of matrices M and N in order to compute $M + N$?

c Which of the problems about vehicle production involved *subtracting matrices*?

d Which of the problems about vehicle production involved multiplying each entry of a matrix by the same number?

e If $A = \begin{bmatrix} -3 & 7 & \frac{1}{2} \\ 1 & 8 & 15 \end{bmatrix}$, how would you compute $3A$?

   i. Write a general description (definition) for how to multiply a matrix M by a number k to get a new matrix, kA. (This is also called **scalar multiplication**.)

   ii. How are the sizes of matrices M and kM related?

f Consider all the situations you have analyzed so far. What other operations have you performed on matrices?

Be prepared to share your examples and descriptions with the class.

✓ Check Your Understanding

Below are two matrices showing the 2004 and 2005 regular season passing statistics for three top NFL quarterbacks. "Att" is an abbreviation for passes attempted; "Cmp" refers to passes completed; "TD" refers to passes thrown for a touchdown; and "Int" refers to passes that were intercepted.

2004 Passing Statistics

	Att	Cmp	TD	Int
Manning	497	336	49	10
Roethlisberger	295	196	17	11
Hasselbeck	474	279	22	15

2005 Passing Statistics

	Att	Cmp	TD	Int
Manning	453	305	28	10
Roethlisberger	268	168	17	9
Hasselbeck	449	294	24	9

Source: www.nfl.com/stats/2004/regular;
www.nfl.com/stats/2005/regular

LESSON 1 • Constructing, Interpreting, and Operating On Matrices   **85**

As you facilitate the Summarize the Mathematics, keep in mind that it is important that students first make sense of matrices and matrix operations in terms of analyzing problems and contexts. However, it also is important that students generalize and transfer their understanding about adding, subtracting, and multiplying by a number to situations that do not have a supporting context.

It is also important to point out to students that there are many useful and legitimate matrix operations, including all those used so far in this unit. A few of these operations have been singled out for their particular usefulness and have been given standard names, for example, matrix addition, matrix subtraction, and scalar multiplication. (Note that the phrase "scalar multiplication" is quite universal, so we use it here. However, the phrase "scalar product" should not be used here since "scalar product" often refers instead to dot product.) Another important matrix operation, matrix multiplication, is investigated in the next lesson.

PROMOTING MATHEMATICAL DISCOURSE

Summarize
the Mathematics

a Finding the total number of vehicles produced for 2004 and 2005 for each category and region (Problem 5) involved combining matrices by adding corresponding entries.

b $A + B = \begin{bmatrix} 8 & 2 \\ 13 & 10 \end{bmatrix}$

  i. You add two matrices by adding their corresponding entries, the entries in the same row and column number.

  ii. M and N must have the same size in order to compute $M + N$.

c Determining the change in vehicle production from 2004 to 2005 (Problem 4) involved combining matrices by subtracting corresponding entries.

d Projecting the production of vehicles in 2006 (Problem 6) due to a 10% increase involved multiplying each entry of a matrix by a number.

e $3A = \begin{bmatrix} -9 & 21 & \frac{3}{2} \\ 3 & 24 & 45 \end{bmatrix}$

  i. You multiply matrix M by a number k by multiplying each entry of M by k.

  ii. M and kM are the same size.

f Other operations listed may include row sums, column sums, multiplying entry-by-entry (trustworthy friend matrix), and row comparisons.

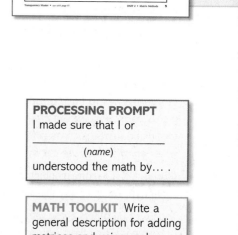

Unit 2

PROCESSING PROMPT
I made sure that I or
_____
(name)
understood the math by... .

MATH TOOLKIT Write a general description for adding matrices and using scalar multiplication. When is each of these two operations useful?

Summarize the Mathematics, *page 85*

Teacher: *(Students have spent time talking about, but not writing answers to, the Summarize the Mathematics questions in small groups.)* In this investigation, you explored ways to operate on matrices or combine two matrices in order to derive new information. Think back to the vehicle production problems.

Teacher: Group 4, which problems about vehicle productions involved adding matrices?

Andre: Problem 5.

Teacher: Please be a little more informative with your answer. In this class, we are expecting more complete answers. So, Andre, what was the context and question that required addition of matrices?

Andre: We had to find the total number of vehicles produced over the two-year period from 2004 to 2005.

Teacher: Okay, in Part b, you looked at specific matrices. Chenoa, what did your group settle on for a description or definition for adding two matrices?

Chenoa: We said that when you add two matrices, you just add up the numbers in the same position of the matrix. So, in A and B, we added 3 and 5—and the others.

Teacher: Chenoa, if you had to describe to someone who had not done this investigation what you mean by "the same position," what would you say? *(The teacher is pushing for more mathematical language.)*

Chenoa: Well, the numbers in the same row and column should be added—the same entries.

Teacher: Last year when we studied congruent triangles, we needed to link parts of two triangles to show they were congruent. We used a particular word to help us with that. Thinking about that language, how could we describe the same entries in matrices? *(The teacher wishes to build a robust understanding of the use of the word "corresponding" in mathematics because of its usefulness for linking items, such as with corresponding angles formed when parallel lines are cut by a transversal.)*

Olivia: CPCTC—corresponding parts of congruent triangles are congruent. We could say that we need to add corresponding entries.

Teacher: Do others agree with Olivia? *(Students indicate agreement.)* Okay then, who would like to reword our description of adding matrices using the language of "corresponding entries" and also using the matrices M and N to help clarify the general definition. As long as we are doing this, let's also incorporate information on the sizes of matrices that can be added. *(A couple of minutes is given for group conversation.)*

Jacob: How's this? In order to add two matrices M and N, they need to be the same size (have the same number of rows and the same number of columns). Then you add each pair of corresponding entries from M and N and put the result in the same row/column location of the new matrix, called $M + N$.

Len: That sounds good.

Teacher: Okay, take a minute to make a math toolkit entry that describes adding matrices M and N. If you want to provide an example, do that.

Teacher: Now, let's look at subtraction. Which of the vehicle production problems involved subtracting matrices?

Abigail: We subtracted matrices when we wanted to know the change in vehicle production from one year to the next.

Teacher: Abigail, would we have to change our general description for subtraction?

Abigail: No, not really. We would say subtraction rather than addition though.

Teacher: What about multiplication? Which of the problems about vehicle production involved multiplying each entry of a matrix by the same number?

Delu: We said the problem where you had to increase production by 10%. When we did that problem, we just multiplied each matrix entry by 1.10 to make the production 110% of what it was the year before.

Teacher: So, Delu, if you were going to explain to other students how to multiply a matrix by a number, which is also called scalar multiplication, what would you tell them?

Delu: I would tell them to multiply each entry in the matrix by the number they were multiplying by. So, for example, in Part e where we had to compute $3A$, we just multiplied each entry by 3.

Teacher: What did you say about the sizes of the matrices M and kM? Group 5?

Gamal: They are the same.

Teacher: Why is that?

Gamal: You just multiply by 3.

Teacher: *(The teacher thinks about asking "Multiply what by 3?" but decides to see if students clarify that when they work on the general description.)* Okay, this type of multiplication is called scalar multiplication. Let's write a general description, as we did for addition of matrices, for how to multiply matrix M by a

Unit 2

number k to get a new matrix, kM. Include information on the sizes of the matrices, too.

Stacy: To multiply a matrix M by a number k, you multiply each entry in M by the number k and put the result in a new matrix, kM. M and kM are the same size.

Teacher: Other clarifications?

Pete: Should we add that the answers go in the corresponding locations again?

Teacher: Decide in your groups whether to include that language and write a general description for scalar multiplication for your toolkits. *(Time is given.)*

Teacher: All right then—what about the final question in the Summarize the Mathematics? What other operations have you performed on matrices? Let's go around the groups. Group 2, give me one other operation you talked about in your group.

Arlen (from Group 2): We talked about row and column sums from the ranking problems.

Brigit (from Group 6): We said that, too. We also said that we did row comparisons when we looked at the degree of difference in the pottery matrix.

Esteban (from Group 3): We talked about comparisons, too. We were thinking of the basketball statistics when we compared assists and steals and other player stats.

Teacher: Group 4, would you like to add anything else?

Amina: Well, we talked about how adding matrices can give new information. Like when we added the movie and the loan matrices together, we found new information about who would be considered trustworthy friends.

Teacher: Good job. Let's take a look at what the Check Your Understanding will ask you to think about tonight for homework.

Let A represent the 2005 matrix and B represent the 2004 matrix.

a. Compute $A + B$. What does $A + B$ tell you about the passing performance of the three quarterbacks?

b. Compute $A - B$. What does $A - B$ tell you about the passing performance of the three quarterbacks?

c. Compute $B - A$.

 i. How do the numbers in $B - A$ differ from the numbers in $A - B$?

 ii. What does a negative number in the "Cmp" column of $A - B$ tell you about the trend in completions from 2004 to 2005?

 iii. What does a negative number in the "Cmp" column of $B - A$ tell you about the trend in completions from 2004 to 2005?

d. Compute $\frac{1}{2}A$. What could $\frac{1}{2}A$ mean for this situation?

e. The matrices you have been operating on in this task are related to a specific context. For practice, perform the indicated operations on the following matrices which have no context.

 i. $\begin{bmatrix} 2 & -1 & 5 \\ 6 & 3 & 4 \end{bmatrix} + \begin{bmatrix} 5 & -7 & 6 \\ 4 & -2 & -4 \end{bmatrix}$

 ii. $3\begin{bmatrix} 4 & \frac{2}{3} \\ -2 & 0 \end{bmatrix}$

 iii. $5\begin{bmatrix} 1 & 2 & 3 \\ 0 & 4 & 5 \\ 2 & 1 & -8 \end{bmatrix} + \begin{bmatrix} 2 & -1 & 2 \\ 3 & 3 & 3 \\ 4 & 1 & 4 \end{bmatrix}$

 iv. $\begin{bmatrix} 23 & 15 \\ -5 & 42 \\ 0 & 33 \end{bmatrix} - \begin{bmatrix} 18 & 20 \\ 8 & -3 \\ 0 & 10 \end{bmatrix}$

✔ Check Your Understanding

a. The result of $A + B$ tells you about the combined two-year passing performance of the three quarterbacks.

Two-year Passing Performance

	Att	Cmp	TD	Int
Manning	950	641	77	20
$A + B =$ Roethlisberger	563	364	34	20
Hasselbeck	923	573	46	24

b. $A - B$ shows the change in passing performance from 2004 to 2005.

Change from 2004 to 2005

	Att	Cmp	TD	Int
Manning	−44	−31	−21	0
$A - B =$ Roethlisberger	−27	−28	0	−2
Hasselbeck	−25	15	2	−6

c.

	Att	Cmp	TD	Int
Manning	44	31	21	0
$B - A =$ Roethlisberger	27	28	0	2
Hasselbeck	25	−15	−2	6

    i. The numbers in $B - A$ are the opposites of the numbers in $A - B$.

    ii. A negative number in the "Cmp" column of $A - B$ tells you that the number of completions decreased from 2004 to 2005.

    iii. A negative number in the "Cmp" column of $B - A$ tells you that the number of completions increased from 2004 to 2005.

d.

	Att	Cmp	TD	Int
Manning	226.5	152.5	14	5
$\frac{1}{2}A =$ Roethlisberger	134	84	8.5	4.5
Hasselbeck	224.5	147	12	4.5

Students should respond critically. For example, they may say that $\frac{1}{2}A$ corresponds to data for $\frac{1}{2}$ of the 2005 season. However, they should also note that this may not really be a legitimate interpretation for these data because it is unlikely that exactly half the data in all categories would be in each half of the season.

e.
  i. $\begin{bmatrix} 7 & -8 & 11 \\ 10 & 1 & 0 \end{bmatrix}$
            ii. $\begin{bmatrix} 12 & 2 \\ -6 & 0 \end{bmatrix}$

  iii. $\begin{bmatrix} 7 & 9 & 17 \\ 3 & 23 & 28 \\ 14 & 6 & -36 \end{bmatrix}$
    iv. $\begin{bmatrix} 5 & -5 \\ -13 & 45 \\ 0 & 23 \end{bmatrix}$

Applications

1 The movie matrix from Investigation 2 is reproduced below. Recall that the movie matrix can be thought of as describing friendship, and it is read from row to column. Thus, for example, student A considers student B as a friend since there is a "1" in the first row and second column.

Movie Matrix

with

	A	B	C	D	E
A	0	1	1	1	1
B	0	0	1	1	1
C	1	0	0	1	0
D	0	1	1	0	1
E	1	0	0	1	0

Would Like to Go to a Movie

a. *Mutual friends* are two people who consider each other as friends.

   i. Are students A and D mutual friends?

   ii. Find at least two pairs of mutual friends.

   iii. How do mutual friends appear in the matrix?

b. Construct a new matrix that shows mutual friends. To do this, list all five people across the top and also down the side. Write a "1" or a "0" for each entry, depending on whether or not the two people corresponding to that entry are mutual friends.

c. Who has the most mutual friends?

d. Compare the first row of the mutual-friends matrix to the first column. Compare each of the other rows to its corresponding column. What relationship do you see? Explain why the mutual-friends matrix has this relationship between its rows and columns. (See Connections Task 8 for more information about matrices with this property.)

2 Spreadsheets are one of the most widely-used software applications. A spreadsheet displays organized information in the same way a matrix does. One common use of spreadsheets is to itemize loans. For example, suppose that you are going to buy your first car. The one you decide to buy needs some work, but you can get it for $500. You borrow the $500 at 9% annual interest and agree to pay it back in 12 monthly payments. The following spreadsheet summarizes all the information about this loan.

LESSON 1 • Constructing, Interpreting, and Operating On Matrices **87**

On Your Own

Applications

(1) **a.** **i.** No, students A and D are not mutual friends because D does not consider A a friend.

   ii. The following are the pairs of mutual friends: A-C, A-E, B-D, C-D, and D-E.

   iii. Each person has to have a "1" for the other person. For example, A will say C is a friend and C will say A is a friend.

b. Mutual Friends

$$
\begin{array}{c c}
 & \begin{array}{c c c c c} A & B & C & D & E \end{array} \\
\begin{array}{c} A \\ B \\ C \\ D \\ E \end{array} &
\left[\begin{array}{c c c c c}
0 & 0 & 1 & 0 & 1 \\
0 & 0 & 0 & 1 & 0 \\
1 & 0 & 0 & 1 & 0 \\
0 & 1 & 1 & 0 & 1 \\
1 & 0 & 0 & 1 & 0
\end{array} \right]
\end{array}
$$

c. Student D has the most mutual friends.

d. The entries are the same for each row and corresponding column. The 1s are symmetric about the main diagonal of 0s. Mutual friends each have a 1 for the other person.

(2) Spreadsheets are a common and powerful technology tool. You may decide to ask students to create the spreadsheet shown using software such as Excel, then answer the questions.

> **TECHNOLOGY NOTE** There are many Internet sites for producing amortization schedules. (Do a search.) Students may notice that different sites produce slightly different schedules, likely because of rounding procedures.

Car Loan.xls　　　　　　　　　　　　⊟ ⊡ ☒

◇	A	B	C	D	E
1	Loan Amt. =	$500	Interest Rate/Mo.	9%/12 =	0.0075
2					
3	Month (end)	Payment	To Interest	To Principal	Balance
4	1	$43.73	$3.75	$39.98	$460.02
5	2	$43.73	$3.45	$40.28	$419.74
6	3	$43.73	$3.15	$40.58	$379.16
7	4	$43.73	$2.84	$40.89	$338.27
8	5	$43.73	$2.54	$41.19	$297.08
9	6	$43.73	$2.23	$41.50	$255.58
10	7	$43.73	$1.92	$41.81	$213.76
11	8	$43.73	$1.60	$42.13	$171.64
12	9	$43.73	$1.29	$42.44	$129.19
13	10	$43.73	$0.97	$42.76	$86.43
14	11	$43.73	$0.65	$43.08	$43.35
15	12	$43.68	$0.33	$43.35	$0.00
16	Totals	$524.71	$24.71	$500.00	
17					

a. How much principal will you still owe after the sixth payment?

b. How much interest will you pay in the fourth month?

c. In any given row, how do the entries in the "To Interest" and "To Principal" columns compare to the entry in the "Payment" column? Why are the entries related in this way?

d. Why do the entries in the "To Principal" column get bigger throughout the loan period?

e. How can you use nearby entries to compute the entries in the Month 10 row?

f. How much money will you save if you pay for the car in cash instead of borrowing the $500 and paying off the loan over a year?

3 Music is an enjoyable part of many people's lives. The format in which you get music has changed over the years and continues to change. The following matrices show shipments of music albums in the United States in different formats during the transition period between the 1990s and 2000s. The formats shown are: CD–compact disc; CASS–cassette; VNL–vinyl; DL–download. The 0* in the DL column means that it was not possible to download music at that time, or data were not yet being gathered for this format, or the number is so small that it rounds to 0. The numbers shown are millions of units.

a. $255.58

b. $2.84

c. The sum of "To Interest" and "To Principal" is the amount under "Payment." The payment is split between paying off interest and paying off the principal. None of it goes to pay anything else.

d. The interest is computed on a smaller remaining balance each month, so the interest that is added to the principal is less each month, resulting in more of the payment going toward the principal.

e. Cell **B13** is the same as **B12**.
 Cell **C13** is =E12*0.09/12.
 Cell **D13** is =B13-C13.
 Cell **E13** is =E12-D13.

f. The interest $24.71 would be saved.

③ **INSTRUCTIONAL NOTE** You might ask your students to find the latest data about album shipments and use those data in addition to or instead of the data presented here. A good resource Web site is the site for the Recording Industry Association of America: www.riaa.com.

Album Shipments Late 1990s

(in millions)

	CD	CASS	VNL	DL
1994	662.1	345.4	1.9	0*
1995	722.9	272.6	2.2	0*
1996	778.9	225.3	2.9	0*
1997	753.1	172.6	2.7	0*
1998	847.0	158.5	3.4	0*
1999	938.9	123.6	2.9	0*

Album Shipments Early 2000s

(in millions)

	CD	CASS	VNL	DL
2000	942.5	76.0	2.2	0*
2001	881.9	45.0	2.3	0*
2002	803.3	31.1	1.7	0*
2003	746.0	17.2	1.5	0*
2004	767.0	5.2	1.36	4.6
2005	705.4	2.5	1.02	13.6

Source: Recording Industry Association of America; www.riaa.com/news/marketingdata/facts.asp

a. Describe any patterns you see in these data.

b. Analyze these matrices. Use the rows or columns of the matrices to help answer the following questions.

  i. How many millions of albums were shipped in all 4 formats in 2005?

  ii. How many CDs were shipped in the early 2000s?

  iii. How many more cassettes were shipped in the late 1990s than in the early 2000s?

c. Do these two matrices have appropriate sizes so they could be added? Would it make sense to add these matrices? Explain.

d. Construct a 2 × 4 matrix that shows the total number of album shipments in each of the 4 formats for the late 1990s and the early 2000s. Use the matrix to help answer the following questions.

  i. Which format shows the greatest number of increased shipments from the late 1990s to the early 2000s? Which format shows the most dramatic increase in shipments from the late 1990s to the early 2000s?

  ii. Consider the total albums shipped in all 4 formats. Which period, the late 1990s or the early 2000s, had more albums shipped? How many more?

  iii. Describe the general trends shown in this matrix. Do you think these trends will continue? Explain.

4 An automotive manufacturer produces several styles of sport wheels. One of the styles is available in two finishes (chrome-plated and silver-painted) and three wheel sizes (15-inch, 16-inch, and 17-inch).

In October, a retailer in the Midwest purchased sixteen 15-inch chrome wheels, twenty-four 16-inch chrome wheels, eight 17-inch chrome wheels, eight 15-inch silver wheels, twelve 16-inch silver wheels, and four 17-inch silver wheels. In November, the retailer ordered twelve 15-inch chrome wheels, thirty-two 16-inch chrome wheels, sixteen 17-inch chrome wheels, twelve 15-inch silver wheels, and twenty 16-inch silver wheels.

a. Construct two matrices that show the wheel orders—one for October and one for November. Label the matrices and the rows and columns.

a. Some patterns: Although there are only two years of data for the download format, this format seems to be growing very strongly. Cassettes are decreasing to apparent extinction. Vinyl is small but seems to be surviving at a low level. CDs seem to still be popular but declining.

b. **i.** The sum of the 2005 row is 722.52. Thus, 722.52 millions of albums were shipped in all 4 formats in 2005.

   ii. The sum of the CD column in the Early 2000s matrix is 4,846.1. Thus, 4,846,100,000 CDs were shipped in the early 2000s (2000–2005).

   iii. Subtract the Early 2000s CASS column sum from the Late 1990s CASS column sum. 1,121,000,000 more cassettes were shipped in the late 1990s than in the early 2000s.

c. These matrices do have the same size, so they could be added. However, the resulting data would not make much sense.

d. **Album Shipments in Different Formats (in millions)**

$$
\begin{array}{c}
\\
\text{Late 1990s} \\
\text{Early 2000s}
\end{array}
\begin{array}{cccc}
\quad\text{CD} & \text{CASS} & \text{VNL} & \text{DL} \\
\left[\begin{array}{cccc}
4{,}702.9 & 1{,}289 & 16 & 0 \\
4{,}846.1 & 177 & 10.08 & 18.2
\end{array}\right]
\end{array}
$$

   i. The CD format shows the greatest increase in numbers. The DL format shows the most dramatic increase.

   ii. By computing row sums and then subtracting, we can see that there were 956,520,000 more album shipments in the late 1990s than in the early 2000s.

   iii. The trends that students describe here may be similar to the trends described in Part bi. Some of those trends are more easily seen in the matrix above: CD shipments did not change much from the late 1990s to the early 2000s; cassette shipments decreased sharply; vinyl shipments are small but not declining as sharply as cassettes; downloads are growing dramatically.

4 This problem begins by asking students to construct a matrix based on information contained in paragraph form. This illustrates again how matrices work well to organize data and are much easier to understand than information in paragraph form.

a.

October

$$
O = \begin{array}{c}
\\
\text{Chrome} \\
\text{Silver}
\end{array}
\begin{array}{ccc}
\text{15-in.} & \text{16-in.} & \text{17-in.} \\
\left[\begin{array}{ccc}
16 & 24 & 8 \\
8 & 12 & 4
\end{array}\right]
\end{array}
$$

November

$$
N = \begin{array}{c}
\\
\text{Chrome} \\
\text{Silver}
\end{array}
\begin{array}{ccc}
\text{15-in.} & \text{16-in.} & \text{17-in.} \\
\left[\begin{array}{ccc}
12 & 32 & 16 \\
12 & 20 & 0
\end{array}\right]
\end{array}
$$

Unit 2

b. How many of each type of wheel were ordered by the retailer during these two months combined? Represent this information in a matrix. Label the matrix and the rows and columns.

c. Suppose that over the entire fourth quarter (October, November, and December) the retailer has agreed to order the number of wheels shown in the following matrix.

Fourth-Quarter Order

	15-in.	16-in.	17-in.
Chrome	40	52	36
Silver	28	32	16

    i. Construct a matrix that shows how many of each type of wheel must be ordered in December to meet this agreement.

    ii. Explain any unusual entries in the matrix.

d. In October of the next year, the retailer orders twice the number of each type of wheel ordered the previous October. November's order is three times the number of each type of wheel ordered the previous November. Construct a matrix that shows the number of each type of wheel ordered in the two months combined.

5 The first matrix below presents combined monthly sales for three types of men's and women's jeans at JustJeans stores in three cities. The second matrix below gives the monthly sales for women's jeans.

Combined Sales

	Levi	Lee	Wrangler
Chicago	250	195	105
Atlanta	175	175	90
San Diego	185	210	275

Women's Jeans Sales

	Levi	Lee	Wrangler
Chicago	100	90	70
Atlanta	80	85	50
San Diego	105	50	150

a. Construct a matrix that shows the monthly sales for men's jeans for each brand and each city. Which matrix operation did you use to construct this matrix?

b. The total ordered during these two months combined is the sum of the two matrices in Part a.

October–November Order

	15-in.	16-in.	17-in.
Chrome	28	56	24
Silver	20	32	4

c. i. December

	15-in.	16-in.	17-in.
Chrome	12	−4	12
Silver	8	0	12

ii. The retailer has already met and exceeded the quota for ordering chrome 16-inch wheels. Thus, there is a negative value in the matrix. In reality, the retailer would not be required to order any more chrome 16-inch wheels.

d. Calculate $(2 \times O) + (3 \times N)$.

	15-in.	16-in.	17-in.
Chrome	68	144	64
Silver	52	84	8

5 **a.** This matrix is obtained by subtracting the women's jeans sales matrix from the combined sales matrix.

Men's Jeans Sales

	Levi	Lee	Wrangler
Chicago	150	105	35
Atlanta	95	90	40
San Diego	80	160	125

Unit 2

b. Organizing the data in different ways can highlight different information. Copy and complete the following matrices to show sales of men's and women's jeans in each city, for each of the three brands. Label the rows.

Chicago				Atlanta				San Diego	
M	W			M	W			M	W

$$\begin{bmatrix} & \\ & \end{bmatrix} \qquad \begin{bmatrix} & \\ & \end{bmatrix} \qquad \begin{bmatrix} & \\ & \end{bmatrix}$$

c. Refer to the matrices in Part b. Construct one matrix that shows the total sales of men's and women's jeans for each of the three brands, that is, sales in all three cities combined. Label the rows of the matrix with the brands and the columns with "M" and "W". Which matrix operation did you use to construct this matrix?

d. For the first quarter, the managers of the Chicago, Atlanta, and San Diego stores have placed jeans orders with the main warehouse as indicated in the matrices below. Let C represent the matrix for the store in Chicago, A for the store in Atlanta, and S for the store in San Diego.

Chicago

	M	W
Levi	300	330
Lee	345	300
Wrangler	120	240

Atlanta

M	W
300	255
300	270
135	165

San Diego

M	W
252	315
513	162
405	450

For the second quarter, the managers' orders for each brand are tripled in Chicago, stay the same in Atlanta, and are $\frac{2}{3}$ as big in San Diego.

i. Think about how to calculate the total-orders matrix T of men's and women's jeans in all three cities combined, for each of the three brands for the second quarter. Write a rule for calculating T in terms of C, A, and S.

ii. Compute the second row, second column entry of T. What does this entry tell you about jeans orders placed with the warehouse?

6 Consider the following matrices.

$$A = \begin{bmatrix} 2 & -4 & 6 \\ 0 & 1.5 & 3 \\ 7 & -3.5 & 8 \\ 1 & -1 & 6 \end{bmatrix} \qquad B = \begin{bmatrix} 2 & 3 & -6 \\ 0 & 1 & 6.5 \\ 11 & -3 & 6 \end{bmatrix}$$

$$C = \begin{bmatrix} 1 & 0 \\ 0 & 1 \\ 1 & 1 \end{bmatrix} \qquad D = \begin{bmatrix} -1 & 1.25 & 0 \\ 8 & -12 & 5 \\ 0 & 0 & 18 \end{bmatrix}$$

a. Compute $B + D$.

b. Compute $6C$.

LESSON 1 • Constructing, Interpreting, and Operating On Matrices **91**

b.

Chicago

	M	W
Levi	150	100
Lee	105	90
Wrangler	35	70

Atlanta

	M	W
Levi	95	80
Lee	90	85
Wrangler	40	50

San Diego

	M	W
Levi	80	105
Lee	160	50
Wrangler	125	150

c. You get the following matrix by adding the three matrices above.

Combined Sales

	M	W
Levi	325	285
Lee	355	225
Wrangler	200	270

d. i. $3C + A + \frac{2}{3}S = T$

ii. $3(300) + 270 + \frac{2}{3}(162) = 1{,}278$

This tells us that for these stores, a total of 1,278 pairs of women's Lee jeans were ordered during the second quarter.

6

a. $B + D = \begin{bmatrix} 1 & 4.25 & -6 \\ 8 & -11 & 11.5 \\ 11 & -3 & 24 \end{bmatrix}$

b. $6C = \begin{bmatrix} 6 & 0 \\ 0 & 6 \\ 6 & 6 \end{bmatrix}$

c. Compute $-A$.

d. Compute $B + B$.

e. Compute $2B - 3D$.

f. Compute $D - B$.

g. Construct a new matrix E that could be added to A. Then compute $A + E$.

Connections

(7) In Problem 4 of Investigation 1, you examined some monthly shoe sales data, reproduced below. Each entry represents the number of pairs of shoes sold.

Monthly Sales

	J	F	M	A	M	J	J	A	S	O	N	D
Converse	40	35	50	55	70	60	40	70	40	35	30	80
Nike	55	55	75	70	70	65	60	75	60	55	50	75
Reebok	50	30	60	80	70	50	10	75	40	35	40	70

a. What is the mean number of pairs of Reeboks sold per month?

b. Which brand has more variability in its monthly sales? Explain how you determined variability.

c. Identify at least two types of data plots that could be used to represent the monthly sales data.

d. Create a plot that you think would be most informative.

(8) Symmetry is an important concept in mathematics. In prior units of *Core-Plus Mathematics,* you examined geometric shapes and graphs of functions in terms of their symmetries. Symmetry also applies to matrices, but only to square matrices. A square matrix is said to be **symmetric** if it has reflection (or mirror) symmetry about its main diagonal. (Recall that the main diagonal of a square matrix is the diagonal line of entries running from the top-left to the bottom-right corner.) So, a square matrix is symmetric if the numbers in the mirror-image positions, reflected in the main diagonal, are the same. For example, consider the three matrices below. Matrices A and B are symmetric, but matrix C is not symmetric.

$$A = \begin{bmatrix} 0 & 1 & 0 & 1 \\ 1 & 0 & 1 & 1 \\ 0 & 1 & 0 & 0 \\ 1 & 1 & 0 & 0 \end{bmatrix} \quad B = \begin{bmatrix} 25 & 3 & 4 & 5 \\ 3 & 36 & 6 & 7 \\ 4 & 6 & 9 & 8 \\ 5 & 7 & 8 & 10 \end{bmatrix} \quad C = \begin{bmatrix} 0 & 0 & 1 & 1 \\ 1 & 0 & 1 & 0 \\ 0 & 1 & 0 & 0 \\ 1 & 1 & 1 & 0 \end{bmatrix}$$

a. Identify two square matrices from this lesson.

c. $-A = \begin{bmatrix} -2 & 4 & -6 \\ 0 & -1.5 & -3 \\ -7 & 3.5 & -8 \\ -1 & 1 & -6 \end{bmatrix}$

d. $B + B = \begin{bmatrix} 4 & 6 & -12 \\ 0 & 2 & 13 \\ 22 & -6 & 12 \end{bmatrix}$

e. $2B - 3D = \begin{bmatrix} 7 & 2.25 & -12 \\ -24 & 38 & -2 \\ 22 & -6 & -42 \end{bmatrix}$

f. $D - B = \begin{bmatrix} -3 & -1.75 & 6 \\ 8 & -13 & -1.5 \\ -11 & 3 & 12 \end{bmatrix}$

g. Answers will vary depending on student choice for matrix E. Note however, that E must be a 4×3 matrix.

Connections

7 a. 50.8333 pairs (Find the mean of the row.)

b. For these data, Reebok has the most variability. Students should determine the variability of each row and then compare the three variabilities. Possible measures: the range of values, the standard deviation, the interquartile range. Or, students might explain based on an informal analysis and description of a data plot, like box plots, line plots, bar graphs, or stemplots.

c. Possible types of data plots: stemplots, plots over time, bar graphs, or box plots.

d. Responses may vary. Several graphs could be useful, for example, plots over time or box plots with all three brands on the same graph, pairwise back-to-back stemplots, or combined bar graphs.

8 a. In Investigation 2, the square matrices include the movie matrix, the loan matrix, and the degree-of-difference matrix.

b. Which of the following matrices are symmetric? For those that are not symmetric, explain why not.

   i. The pottery matrix (page 79)

   ii. The degree-of-difference matrix (page 79)

   iii. The movie matrix (page 80)

   iv. The loan matrix (page 80)

   v. The nonshooting-performance-statistics matrix (page 82)

   vi. The mutual-friends matrix (Applications Task 1 Part b, page 87)

c. For those matrices in Part b that are symmetric, what is it about the situations represented by the matrix that causes the matrix to be symmetric?

d. Create your own symmetric matrix with four rows and four columns.

   i. Compare the first row to the first column. Compare the second row to the second column. Do the same for the remaining two rows and columns.

   ii. Make a conjecture about the corresponding rows and columns of a symmetric matrix.

e. Test your conjecture from Part d on the symmetric matrices you identified in Part b.

(9) You may recall from Course 1 that a vertex-edge graph is a collection of vertices with edges joining some of those vertices. A *directed graph* or **digraph** is a vertex-edge graph in which the edges have a direction, shown by arrows. An **adjacency matrix** for a digraph is a matrix where each entry tells how many direct connections (directed edges) there are from the vertex corresponding to the row to the vertex corresponding to the column. A digraph with four vertices and its adjacency matrix are shown below.

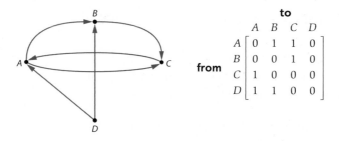

Notice that the *B-C* entry is "1" because there is a directed edge from *B* to *C* in the digraph. The *C-B* entry is "0" since there is no directed edge from *C* to *B*.

b. i–vi. The mutual-friend matrix and the degree-of-difference matrix are symmetric.

The pottery matrix and the nonshooting-performance matrix are not symmetric because they are not even square.

The movie matrix and the loan matrix are square but they are not symmetric because the numbers in the mirror-image positions, reflected in the main diagonal, are not the same.

c. For those matrices that are symmetric:

(1) The row and column labels are identical. The elements are being compared with other elements within the same group.

(2) The two elements are related in both directions. There is reciprocity, that is, if A is to B, then B is to A.

d. i. One example:

$$\begin{bmatrix} 2 & -3 & 1 & 9 \\ -3 & 0 & 8 & 7 \\ 1 & 8 & 3 & -5 \\ 9 & 7 & -5 & 4 \end{bmatrix}$$

The elements in the row are the same as the elements in the corresponding column.

ii. In a symmetric matrix, the elements in a row are the same as the elements in the corresponding column.

e. The conjecture holds for the mutual-friend and degree-of-difference matrices.

Unit 2

The movie (friendship) matrix from Investigation 2 can be thought of as an adjacency matrix for some digraph.

Movie Matrix

$$
\begin{array}{c}
\\
\\
\text{Would Like to}\\
\text{Go to a Movie}
\end{array}
\begin{array}{c}
\\
\\
A\\B\\C\\D\\E
\end{array}
\begin{array}{c}
\text{with}\\
\begin{array}{ccccc}
A & B & C & D & E
\end{array}\\
\left[
\begin{array}{ccccc}
0 & 1 & 1 & 1 & 1\\
0 & 0 & 1 & 1 & 1\\
1 & 0 & 0 & 1 & 0\\
0 & 1 & 1 & 0 & 1\\
1 & 0 & 0 & 1 & 0
\end{array}
\right]
\end{array}
$$

a. What should the vertices and directed edges of the digraph represent?

b. Draw a digraph for the movie matrix.

c. Mutual friends were defined in Applications Task 1 as two people who consider each other as friends. How can you use the digraph for the friendship matrix to find pairs of mutual friends?

d. Does each of the five students have at least one mutual friend?

e. Write down one interesting statement about friendship among these five people that is illustrated by the friendship digraph.

10 You may have seen distance charts like the one below on maps or in brochures or atlases.

Miles / Kilometers	Barstow	Bishop	Eureka	Fresno	Los Angeles	Needles	Palm Springs	Redding	Sacramento	San Diego	San Francisco
Barstow		215	685	245	115	145	125	575	415	175	420
Bishop	350		560	225	265	360	300	432	270	355	295
Eureka	1,100	900		450	645	825	750	147	290	765	275
Fresno	390	360	725		220	385	325	330	170	340	190
Los Angeles	185	430	1,040	350		260	110	540	385	125	385
Needles	230	575	1,330	620	415		210	715	455	320	560
Palm Springs	200	485	1,210	520	175	335		650	490	140	485
Redding	925	695	235	535	880	1,150	1,045		165	665	215
Sacramento	665	440	645	275	620	895	760	260		505	85
San Diego	285	570	1,235	545	200	515	225	1,075	815		505
San Francisco	675	475	440	300	615	900	785	350	135	815	

Source: visitorinfo.bookcalifornia.com/mileage.html

a. Use this chart to find the following distances in both miles and kilometers.

   i. distance between Needles and Palm Springs

   ii. distance between Needles and Los Angeles

9 **a.** The vertices represent the people and the directed edges represent the relationship between people. A directed edge from *A* to *B* indicates that student A would like to go to a movie with student B.

b. **Friends Digraph**

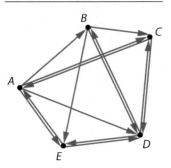

c. Look for 2 edges between the same 2 vertices. Then check to be sure that an arrow is pointing to each vertex.

d. yes

e. Possible responses:

Student D has 3 mutual friends.

Student A counts everyone as friends, but only two people count student A as a friend.

10 **a.** **i.** The distance between Needles and Palm Springs is 210 miles, or 335 km.

ii. The distance between Needles and Los Angeles is 260 miles, or 415 km.

Unit 2

b. Explain why the given chart is not symmetric.

c. Suppose you only want to know distances in kilometers. Does the bottom half of this chart (below the main diagonal) provide enough information to find the distance between any two cities shown? Explain.

d. Think about constructing an 11 × 11 matrix in which each entry shows the distance in kilometers between the respective cities. Explain why this matrix must be symmetric about the main diagonal.

11 In Applications Task 2, you investigated a computer-generated spreadsheet summarizing payments on a $500 loan borrowed at 9% annual interest. Payments were made every month for one year. All the information about this loan was summarized in the spreadsheet below. Consider how the spreadsheet entries were computed.

Car Loan.xls ▢ ▣ ☒

	A	B	C	D	E
1	Loan Amt. =	$500	Interest Rate/Mo.	9%/12 =	0.0075
2					
3	Month (end)	Payment	To Interest	To Principal	Balance
4	1	$43.73	$3.75	$39.98	$460.02
5	2	$43.73	$3.45	$40.28	$419.74
6	3	$43.73	$3.15	$40.58	$379.16
7	4	$43.73	$2.84	$40.89	$338.27
8	5	$43.73	$2.54	$41.19	$297.08
9	6	$43.73	$2.23	$41.50	$255.58
10	7	$43.73	$1.92	$41.81	$213.76
11	8	$43.73	$1.60	$42.13	$171.64
12	9	$43.73	$1.29	$42.44	$129.19
13	10	$43.73	$0.97	$42.76	$86.43
14	11	$43.73	$0.65	$43.08	$43.35
15	12	$43.68	$0.33	$43.35	$0.00
16	Totals	$524.71	$24.71	$500.00	
17					

a. Let *P* represent the entries in the "Payment" column, *TI* represent the entries in the "To Interest" column, and *TP* represent the entries in the "To Principal" column. Write an equation that shows the relationship among *P*, *TI*, and *TP*.

b. If *NOW* is the current balance and *NEXT* is the balance next month, which of the rules below show how to compute the balance next month if you know the balance this month? If a rule does not represent the *NEXT* balance, explain why it doesn't work.

i. $NEXT = NOW - (43.73 - 0.0075NOW)$

ii. $NEXT = NOW + \frac{0.09}{12}NOW - 43.73$

iii. $NEXT = 1.0075NOW - 43.73$

b. The given chart is not symmetric since the bottom half gives distances in kilometers, and the top half gives distances in miles.

c. Yes, the bottom half (below the main diagonal) provides enough information. For example, for distances from Eureka, you can read horizontally across from Eureka in the bottom half and get distances to Barstow and Bishop in kilometers; and for distances to the remaining cities, you can read down in the Eureka column.

d. An 11 × 11 kilometer matrix must be symmetric since the distance in kilometers from any city A to city B is the same as the distance in kilometers from city B to city A.

11 Spreadsheets are a common and powerful technology tool. You may decide to ask students to create the spreadsheet shown using software such as Excel or *CPMP-Tools*, and then do Parts a and b.

a. $P - TI = TP$ or an equivalent form.

b. **i–iii.** All three of these rules work. They each represent how the next month's balance is computed by applying the interest to the present balance and then subtracting the monthly payment. You can carry out algebraic operations to show that all three equations are equivalent.

Reflections

12 Mariah claims that only two variables can be represented in a matrix. Scott claims that three variables are represented in a matrix. For each of these claims, give a supporting argument.

13 A *matrix* is defined in this lesson as "a rectangular array of numbers" (see page 76). Many of the arrays that you have worked with in this lesson have additional features, such as labels on the rows and columns or entries that are numbers with units. An array with additional features is technically not a matrix, instead we would call it a *table*. The difference between a matrix and a table is not vitally important in this unit, so we have worked with the underlying array of numbers and not worried about this technical detail. In more advanced courses in mathematics, like Linear Algebra, it will be important to be very precise about matrices. For now, describe and give examples of some of the ways a table can be different from a matrix. In your description and examples, be sure to include differences related to at least these three characteristics: entries, labels, and operations.

14 In Connections Task 11, you found that the pattern of change in the monthly balance of a 12-month $500 loan at 9% annual interest could be described by three rules:

Rule I: $NEXT = NOW - (43.73 - 0.0075NOW)$

Rule II: $NEXT = NOW + \frac{0.09}{12}NOW - 43.73$

Rule III: $NEXT = 1.0075NOW - 43.73$

  a. Use algebraic reasoning to show that Rule I and Rule II are equivalent expressions.

  b. Use algebraic reasoning to show that Rule I and Rule III are equivalent expressions.

  c. Based on your work in Parts a and b, what can you conclude about Rule II and Rule III? Why?

15 In Connections Task 9, you modeled friendship with a matrix and a digraph. What do you think are the advantages of each representation?

16 For any matrix A, can you always compute $A + A$? Why or why not?

17 Tables of information are similar to matrices and are often used in newspapers and at Internet sites for reporting data. Find an example of a table in a newspaper or at an Internet site. Then complete the following tasks.

  a. Briefly describe the information displayed in the table.

  b. Describe some other way that the information could have been displayed. Why do you think the newspaper writer or Web site designer decided to display the information using a table?

Reflections

12 Mariah may be thinking the following: Matrices are two-dimensional and so can only represent two variables—one across and one down. Scott may be thinking that the entries in the matrix are the third variable.

13 Tables and matrices might be distinguished in terms of entries, labels, notation, and operations. Entries—The entries of a table may or may not be numbers, while a matrix is defined to be a rectangular array of numbers. (Note that in general, a matrix can contain mathematical objects other than numbers, but we will not consider such matrices in this course.) Labels—A table often includes labeled rows and columns and a title, while the technical definition of a matrix is that it is simply a rectangular array of numbers without any labels or titles. However, labels and titles are sometimes appended to matrices to make them more informative or to help students make sense of them. Notation—A matrix has special notation, often square brackets, while a table may not use such notation. Operations—A matrix is a mathematical object upon which you can operate. For example, you might add or multiply matrices or find the inverse of a matrix. This is not the case with tables. (Note that the technical distinction between tables and matrices is important in further study of advanced mathematics, such as linear algebra, but it is not something to get bogged down with in this unit.)

14 **a.** $NOW - (43.73 - 0.0075NOW) = NOW - 43.73 + \frac{0.09}{12} NOW$
$$= NOW + \frac{0.09}{12} NOW - 43.73$$

b. $NOW - (43.73 - 0.0075NOW) = NOW - 43.73 + 0.0075NOW$
$$= 1.0075NOW - 43.73$$

c. The two expressions to be compared here are II and III. In Part a, we showed that Rule I and Rule II are equivalent. In Part b, we showed that Rule I and Rule III are equivalent. Since Rule II and Rule III are both equivalent to Rule I, they must also be equivalent to each other. Thus, Rule II and Rule III are equivalent expressions.

15 Possible responses may include:

Matrix Representation
- You can quickly sum a row or column.
- It can be entered into a computer or calculator.
- You can easily see symmetry or nonsymmetry.
- It works well with large data sets.

Digraph Representation
- You can quickly see how many people chose a particular person and how many that person chose.
- Mutual friends are easily identified.

16 You can always add $A + A$. The matrices are the same size, so there will be a corresponding entry for each cell location to add.

17 **a.** Responses will vary, depending on the students' choices of tables.
  b. Responses will vary, depending on the students' choices of tables.

c. How is the table similar to a matrix? How is it different? (See Reflections Task 13 for more about the difference between a table and a matrix.)

d. Think of the table as a matrix. Describe an operation on the rows, columns, or entries of the matrix that will yield additional information about the situation being represented. Perform the operation and report the information gained.

Extensions

18 One characteristic of spreadsheets that makes them so useful is that you can define the entries in the spreadsheet so that when you change one entry, related entries automatically change accordingly. Using spreadsheet software, create a spreadsheet that generates loan information like that in Applications Task 2. Build the spreadsheet so you can enter any loan amount, payment amount, and interest rate. Experiment with some different loan scenarios, as follows.

a. Change the annual interest rate to 19% (which could correspond to a credit card interest rate). Will a $43.73 monthly payment be sufficient to pay off a $500 loan in one year? If not, try different loan payments in the spreadsheet to find one that works.

b. Change the borrowed amount to $1,000. Assuming a 9% annual interest rate, will an $85 monthly payment be sufficient to pay off the loan in one year? If not, try different loan payments in the spreadsheet to find one that works.

c. Change the length of the loan to 24 months, but keep the loan amount at $500 and the rate at 9%. What is the smallest monthly payment that would pay off the loan in 24 months?

19 One of the purposes of the penal system is to rehabilitate people in prison. Unfortunately, many people released from prison are reconvicted and return to prison within a few years after their release. Professionals working to solve this problem use data like those summarized in the following matrix. The entries of the matrix show the status of prisoners and released prisoners *next* year given their status *this* year. For example, look at the fourth row, fifth column. The "93%" entry means that 93% of those released from prison who are in their third year of freedom this year will remain free and be in their fourth year of freedom next year.

c. Students may describe differences between the table they have found and a matrix in terms of labels, notation, entries, operations, or other factors. (See the solution to Reflections Task 13 for a detailed comparison of tables and matrices.)

d. Responses will vary, depending on the students' choices of tables.

Extensions

18 The following spreadsheet builds upon the spreadsheet in Applications Task 2. A user can enter a loan amount in **B1**, monthly payment amount in **B2**, and interest rate in **D1** to generate the amortization schedule for those values.

Car Loan.xls						_ ☐ ✕
◇	A	B	C	D	E	∧
1	Loan Amt. =		Interest Rate (%) =			
2	Payment Amt. =		Interest Rate/Mo =	=D1/12		
3						
4	Month (end)	Payment	To Interest	To Principal	Balance	≡
5	0				=B1	
6	=A5+1	=$B$2	=E5*$D$2	=B6−C6	=E5−D6	
7	=A6+1	=$B$2	=E6*$D$2	=B7−C7	=E6−D7	
8	=A7+1	=$B$2	=E7*$D$2	=B8−C8	=E7−D8	∨
‹	‖‖‖				›	

a. To change payments, modify **B2**. No, $43.73 is not a big enough monthly payment. The balance would be $30.77 after one year. The payment would need to be slightly more than $46.

b. No, $85 is not a big enough monthly payment. There will be a balance of $30.66 at the end of the year if $85 payments were made. However, a payment of $90 would be more than enough. The minimum payment needed would be $87.46.

c. The payment would be $22.85.

19 **DIFFERENTIATION** This situation may challenge some of your students. At the same time, it will likely engage them in a thoughtful sense-making task. It is important for students to be able to make sense of real data.

Since this is an important yet potentially socially-sensitive issue, it may be worthwhile to point out that it is an issue about the system, not about individual people.

Unit 2

Freedom Status

		Next Year					
		in prison	1st yr. of freedom	2nd yr. of freedom	3rd yr. of freedom	4th yr. of freedom	> 4 yrs. of freedom
This Year	in prison	76%	24%	0%	0%	0%	0%
	1st year of freedom	19%	0%	81%	0%	0%	0%
	2nd year of freedom	12%	0%	0%	88%	0%	0%
	3rd year of freedom	7%	0%	0%	0%	93%	0%
	4th year of freedom	3%	0%	0%	0%	0%	97%
	> 4 years of freedom	0%	0%	0%	0%	0%	100%

Source: Indiana State Reformatory Data from *Cost Benefit Evaluation of Welfare Demonstration Projects*. Bethesda, MD: Resources Management Corporation, 1968.

a. Most of the 0% entries refer to impossible events. For example, look at the third row, second column. Why is it impossible for a person released from prison who is in his or her second year of freedom this year to be in his or her first year of freedom next year?

b. What percentage of people released from prison who are in their second year of freedom this year will remain free and enter a third year of freedom next year?

c. Explain what the "7%" entry in the fourth row, first column means.

d. What is the sum of each row of the matrix? Why does this make sense?

e. Based on your analysis of the matrix, describe at least one trend related to released prisoners returning to prison. What might explain the trend?

 Did you ever stop to think about your genes? (Not the jeans you wear, but the genes that determine your physical characteristics.) Geneticists are always trying to find ways to analyze genes more precisely. A commonly used method of analyzing genetic structure is to study *mutations*, or alterations, of a gene. One famous experiment examined the virus called *phage T4*. The genetic  structure of the virus was studied by looking at mutations of the gene which result when one segment of the gene is missing. As part of this experiment, it was possible to gather data showing how the segments of the gene overlap each other. The results were expressed in the form of a matrix called the *overlap matrix*. One part of that matrix showing the overlaps for nineteen segments, is shown on page 99. The segments are labeled by the codes displayed across the top and down the side. A "1" means that there is an overlap between the two segments associated with the row and column.

a. For people in their second year of freedom, there are only two choices for the next year: (1) third year of freedom or (2) back in jail.

b. 88%

c. 7% of those released from prison who are in their third year of freedom this year will be back in prison next year.

d. The rows sum to 100% because the entries in a given row account for all possibilities.

e. The trend shown indicates that the longer it is since a person has been released, the more likely it is he or she will continue to stay free. This trend could be due to the person being more completely re-assimilated into society as time goes on.

Unit 2

Gene Segments

	184	215	221	250	347	455	459	506	749	761	782	852	882	A103	B139	C4	C33	C51	H23
184	0	1	0	1	0	1	0	0	0	0	1	0	0	0	0	0	1	1	1
215	1	0	0	0	0	0	0	0	0	0	0	0	0	0	0	0	0	0	1
221	0	0	0	0	1	0	1	1	1	1	1	1	1	1	1	1	1	0	1
250	1	0	0	0	0	0	0	0	0	0	0	0	0	0	0	0	1	1	1
347	0	0	1	0	0	0	0	0	0	0	1	0	0	0	0	0	0	0	1
455	1	0	0	0	0	0	0	0	0	0	0	0	0	0	0	0	0	0	1
459	0	0	1	0	0	0	0	0	1	1	1	1	0	0	0	1	0	0	1
506	0	0	1	0	0	0	0	0	0	0	1	0	0	0	0	0	0	0	1
749	0	0	1	0	0	0	1	0	0	1	1	1	0	0	0	1	0	0	1
761	0	0	1	0	0	0	1	0	1	0	1	1	0	0	0	1	0	0	1
782	1	0	1	0	1	0	1	1	1	1	0	1	1	1	1	1	1	0	1
852	0	0	1	0	0	0	1	0	1	1	1	0	0	0	0	1	0	0	1
882	0	0	1	0	0	0	0	0	0	0	1	0	0	0	0	1	0	0	1
A103	0	0	1	0	0	0	0	0	0	0	1	0	0	0	1	0	0	0	1
B139	0	0	1	0	0	0	0	0	0	0	1	0	0	1	0	0	0	0	1
C4	0	0	1	0	0	0	1	0	1	1	1	1	1	0	0	0	0	0	1
C33	1	0	1	1	0	0	0	0	0	0	1	0	0	0	0	0	0	0	1
C51	1	0	0	1	0	0	0	0	0	0	0	0	0	0	0	0	0	0	1
H23	1	1	1	1	1	1	1	1	1	1	1	1	1	1	1	1	1	1	0

Source: On the topology of the genetic fine structure, *Proc Nat Sci Acad USA* 45 (1959).

a. Does segment 882 overlap segment 221? What does the entry in the sixth row and tenth column mean? How many segments overlap segment 749?

b. In Connections Task 8, a symmetric matrix was defined as a matrix that is symmetric about the main diagonal. Is the overlap matrix a symmetric matrix? If not, explain why not. If so, what is it about the situation being modeled that causes the matrix to be symmetric?

c. Which segments have the smallest number of overlaps?

d. Which segment do you think is the longest? Why?

21. Consider the freedom-status matrix from Extensions Task 19.

a. Often in mathematical modeling, some assumptions are made so that the situation is easier to model. In this case, it is assumed that if someone has remained out of prison for more than four years, then that person will continue to stay out of prison.

i. Which entry or entries of the matrix correspond to this assumption?

ii. Why do you think this assumption was made? Does it seem reasonable?

b. Is a person who has been out of prison for two years more or less likely to return to prison than someone who has been out for four years? Explain.

LESSON 1 • Constructing, Interpreting, and Operating On Matrices **99**

20 **a.** Yes, segments 882 and 221 overlap. The 0 in the sixth row, tenth column means that segment 455 does not overlap with segment 761. There are seven segments that overlap with segment 749.

b. Yes, this is a symmetric matrix. If segment A overlaps segment B, then segment B must overlap segment A.

c. Segments 215 and 455 have the fewest overlaps; each overlaps two other segments.

d. Segment H23 is probably the longest because it has the most overlaps.

21 **a.** **i.** Both the 100% entry in the sixth row and sixth column and the 0% entry in the sixth row and first column correspond to the assumption that if a person has remained out of prison for more than four years, then he or she will continue to stay out of prison.

ii. Given the trend shown, you would expect that after many years of freedom, the percentage of people going back to jail would become very small, and virtually all would continue to stay free after that time. Certainly this is not the case after just four years, but the four-year assumption probably was made to keep the dimension of the matrix from getting too large.

b. A released prisoner who is in the second year of freedom is more likely to go back to jail than a released prisoner who is in the fourth year of freedom. This is shown in the table by the third and fifth entries in the first column. That is, 12% of released prisoners who are in their second year of freedom this year will be back in prison next year, compared to only 3% for those in their fourth year of freedom this year.

Unit 2

c. What percentage of all those released from prison remain free for more than one year after release? For more than two years after release? For more than three years?

d. What percentage of people released from prison get reconvicted and sent back to prison within three years of their release? Compare your answer to your results in Part c.

e. If a prison has 500 inmates, how many can be expected to be released in a given year? Of these, how many can be expected to remain out of prison for more than four years?

f. Construct a digraph (see Connections Task 9) that represents the matrix from Extensions Task 19.

Review

22 Evaluate each of the following expressions without using your calculator.

a. $-4(5) + 2(-6)$

b. $-10 + 15 - 20 \cdot 2$

c. $12 \cdot 4 + 2(-3)$

d. $(-7)(-4) - 4(-2)$

e. $2(-4)^2$

23 For each of the following tables of (x, y) values, determine if the pattern of change is linear, exponential, or neither. For those that are linear or exponential, write a function rule that would match the table and a *NOW-NEXT* rule that describes the pattern of change.

a.

x	2	3	4	5	6
y	4	16	64	256	1,024

b.

x	2	3	4	5	6
y	6	10	14	18	22

c.

x	2	3	4	5	6
y	12	27	48	75	108

d.

x	2	3	4	5	6
y	75	60	45	30	15

c. 81%

88% of 81% = 71.3%

93% of 88% of 81% = 66.3%

d. (*percentage that get sent back to prison within three years*) =
100% − (*percentage that remain free for more than three years*) =
100% − 66.3% = 33.7%

Another way to compute this is

19% + (12% of 81%) + (7% of 88% of 81%).

e. Twenty-four percent of the prisoners will be released. Thus, 120 people
will get out of prison. Approximately 77 of these people
(500 × 0.24 × 0.81 × 0.88 × 0.93 × 0.97 = 77) will stay out of prison
for more than four years.

f.

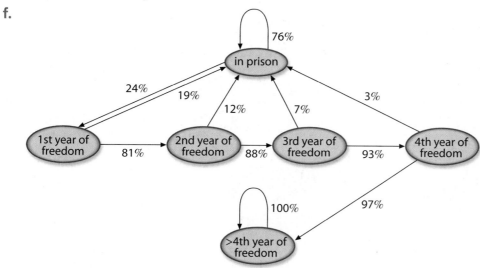

Review

22 a. −32   b. −35   c. 42

d. 36   e. 32

23 a. exponential; $y = 0.25(4^x)$; *NEXT* = 4*NOW*

b. linear; $y = 4x − 2$; *NEXT* = *NOW* + 4

c. neither

d. linear; $y = −15x + 105$; *NEXT* = *NOW* − 15

24 The matrix below is an adjacency matrix for a vertex-edge graph.

$$\begin{array}{c} & \begin{array}{ccccc} A & B & C & D & E \end{array} \\ \begin{array}{c} A \\ B \\ C \\ D \\ E \end{array} & \left[\begin{array}{ccccc} 0 & 2 & 0 & 0 & 0 \\ 2 & 0 & 1 & 1 & 1 \\ 0 & 1 & 0 & 1 & 0 \\ 0 & 1 & 1 & 0 & 2 \\ 0 & 1 & 0 & 2 & 0 \end{array} \right] \end{array}$$

a. Create a graph that matches this adjacency matrix.

b. Does your graph have an Euler circuit? Explain your reasoning.

25 Solve each of the following equations. Check your solutions.

a. $7x^2 = 252$

b. $3^x = 243$

c. $\frac{3}{4}x = 60$

d. $7x^2 + 20 = 252$

e. $2(3^x) = 486$

f. $\frac{3 + x}{4} = 60$

26 Trace each figure onto your paper. Then draw all lines of symmetry and identify all rotational symmetries of the figure.

a.

b.

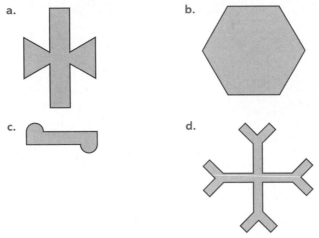

c.

d.

27 If possible, draw a triangle that meets each set of constraints. Then determine if any other triangle meeting the constraints will be congruent to the one you drew.

a. The angles have measure 30°, 70°, and 80°.

b. The sides have length 5 cm, 3 cm, and 6 cm.

c. Two sides have length 2.5 inches, and the angle between those sides has measure 140°.

d. The sides have length 5 cm, 7 cm, and 14 cm.

e. Two sides have lengths 3.5 cm and 6 cm, and one angle is 90°.

LESSON 1 • Constructing, Interpreting, and Operating On Matrices **101**

Just in Time

24 **a.**

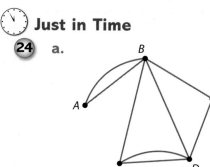

b. No, not all vertices have even degree.

NOTE If your students did not study Unit 4, *Vertex-Edge Graphs*, in Course 1, you will need to introduce them to Euler circuits and graphs and their adjacency matrices. See Course 1.

25 Students should check their solutions.

a. $x = \pm 6$

b. $x = 5$

c. $x = 80$

d. $x = \pm\sqrt{\frac{232}{7}} \approx \pm 5.76$

e. $x = 5$

f. $x = 237$

26 **a.**

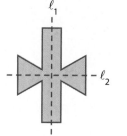

The figure has two reflection symmetries and 180° rotational symmetry.

b.

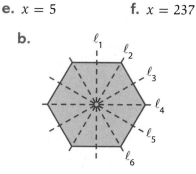

The figure has six reflection symmetries and 60°, 120°, 180°, 240°, and 300° rotational symmetries.

c.

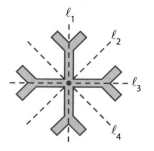

The figure has no reflection symmetries and has 180° rotational symmetry.

d.

The figure has four reflection symmetries and 90°, 180°, and 270° rotational symmetries.

27 Student sketches will vary.

a. Any scale factor dilation/reduction of the triangle will meet the constraint and not be congruent to the triangle drawn.

b. All other triangles with the same constraints will be congruent to the triangle drawn.

c. All other triangles with the same constraints will be congruent to the triangle drawn.

d. No possible triangle exists, since $5 + 7 < 14$.

e. Different possible triangles exist with the given constraints since the 90° angle could be between the two sides or not between them.

Unit 2

28 Jeremy is creating a spinner for a game he made up. He wants the spinner to meet the following conditions.

- The spinner has red, blue, green, and yellow sections on it.
- The probability of spinning red is 0.25.
- The probability of spinning blue is twice the probability of spinning red.
- The probability of spinning green is $\frac{1}{8}$.

a. Draw a spinner that meets these conditions.

b. What is the probability of spinning yellow?

29 Examine the net of a solid shown at the right.

a. What is the name of such a solid?

b. Sketch the solid and find its volume.

c. What is the surface area of the solid?

d. Sketch two other possible nets for this solid.

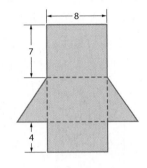

30 Write each of the following expressions in a simpler equivalent form.

a. $(5x^2y)(2x^3y^5)$

b. $\frac{6x^3y^6}{2x^5y^2}$

c. $(3x^3)^4$

d. $4x^2(2x^5)^2$

31 Complete each statement so that the pair of expressions are equivalent.

a. $25x^3 - 30x + 100 = \underline{\hspace{0.5cm}}(5x^2 + \underline{\hspace{0.5cm}}x + \underline{\hspace{0.5cm}})$

b. $12x^3 + 8x^2 + 4x = \underline{\hspace{0.5cm}}x(\underline{\hspace{0.5cm}}x^2 + 2x + \underline{\hspace{0.5cm}})$

c. $(x + 5)^2 = x^2 + \underline{\hspace{0.5cm}}x + \underline{\hspace{0.5cm}}$

d. $x^2 + \underline{\hspace{0.5cm}}x + 15 = (x + \underline{\hspace{0.5cm}})(x + 3)$

e. $2x^2 + \underline{\hspace{0.5cm}}x + 14 = 2(x + 1)(x + \underline{\hspace{0.5cm}})$

f. $4x^2 + 20x + \underline{\hspace{0.5cm}} = \underline{\hspace{0.5cm}}(x + 3)(x + 2)$

28 **a.**

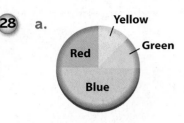

b. $\dfrac{1}{8}$

29 **a.** Triangular prism

b. Volume: $16\sqrt{33} \approx 91.9$ cubic units

c. The surface area of the solid is
$88 + 12\sqrt{33} \approx 156.9$ square units.

d. Student responses will vary.
One possible alternate net is
shown at the right.

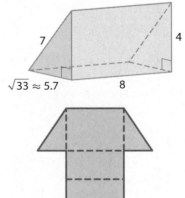

30 **a.** $10x^5y^6$

b. $\dfrac{3y^4}{x^2}$ or $3x^{-2}y^4$

c. $81x^{12}$

d. $16x^{12}$

31 **a.** $25x^3 - 30x + 100 = \underline{5}(5x^2 + \underline{-6}x + \underline{20})$

b. $12x^3 + 8x^2 + 4x = \underline{4}x(\underline{3}x^2 + 2x + \underline{1})$

c. $(x + 5)^2 = x^2 + \underline{10}x + \underline{25}$

d. $x^2 + \underline{8}x + 15 = (x + \underline{5})(x + 3)$

e. $2x^2 + \underline{16}x + 14 = 2(x + 1)(x + \underline{7})$

f. $4x^2 + 20x + \underline{24} = \underline{4}(x + 3)(x + 2)$

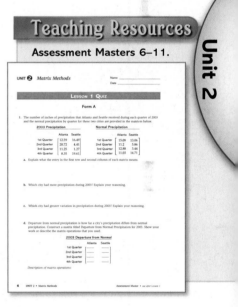

LESSON
2

Multiplying Matrices

I n Lesson 1, you constructed and interpreted matrices and operated on them in several different ways. You used matrices and their operations to analyze many different situations and solve problems in a variety of contexts. You have seen that matrices are particularly useful to businesses and manufacturers in tracking production levels and inventories of products.

LESSON 2 • Multiplying Matrices **103**

Multiplying Matrices

I n this lesson, students learn standard matrix multiplication in a sense-making way using the contexts of brand switching, tracking pollution through an ecosystem, and ranking players in tournaments. In the first investigation, students learn how to multiply a one-row matrix by another matrix, using the context of brand switching. This is generalized in the second investigation to larger matrices, other contexts, and noncontextual situations. Investigation 2 also helps students develop an understanding of which sizes of matrices can be multiplied and when the multiplication makes sense. Applications that employ multiplying a matrix by itself (powers of matrices) are explored in Investigation 3.

Lesson Objectives

- Understand, carry out, and interpret matrix multiplication
- Use matrix multiplication, including powers of matrices, to solve problems in a variety of settings
- Represent a vertex-edge graph as a matrix and use powers of that matrix to analyze the situation modeled by the vertex-edge graph

Think About This Situation

a A brief discussion of students' experience with athletic shoe brand switching will help engage students in the context of Investigation 1.

b Knowing the trends in brand switching would help companies decide what kinds of shoes to order and what advertising to design. Companies gather information about brand-switching trends by in-store surveys or by hiring a market research firm. They analyze brand-switching trends using statistics, matrices, or other methods.

c Students should suggest organizing sales information in matrices to allow for analyzing the data. Analyzing may involve adding the row or column entries, multiplying all of the entries by a single number, or comparing two rows and counting differences (e.g., in the pottery matrix in Lesson 1, Inv. 2). In the case of two matrices, analyzing may involve combining the matrices by adding (or subtracting) entry-by-entry, by using some comparison methods, or by entry-by-entry multiplication (e.g., to get the trustworthy friend matrix in Lesson 1, Inv. 2).

PROMOTING MATHEMATICAL DISCOURSE

Teaching Resources

Transparency Master 12.

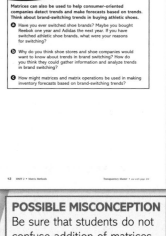

POSSIBLE MISCONCEPTION
Be sure that students do not confuse addition of matrices with summing rows or columns.

Matrices can also be used to help consumer-oriented companies detect trends and make forecasts based on trends. Think about brand-switching trends in buying athletic shoes.

a Have you ever switched shoe brands? Maybe you bought Reebok one year and Adidas the next year. If you have switched athletic shoe brands, what were your reasons for switching?

b Why do you think shoe stores and shoe companies would want to know about trends in brand switching? How do you think they could gather information and analyze trends in brand switching?

c How might matrices and matrix operations be used in making inventory forecasts based on brand-switching trends?

In this lesson, you will learn about an important new matrix operation—matrix multiplication. You will use matrix multiplication, including powers of matrices, to solve a variety of problems. You will also discover an important connection between paths in digraphs and powers of the corresponding adjacency matrices.

Investigation 1 Brand Switching

Manufacturers and big shoe stores carry out market research to gather information about brand switching. Suppose that the results of such market research at one large shoe store are shown in the following matrix. You can use this matrix to estimate how many customers will buy each shoe brand in the future. As you work on the problems in this investigation, look for answers to this question:

How can you multiply matrices to help make predictions based on trend data?

Brand-Switching Matrix

		Next Brand		
		Nike	Reebok	Fila
	Nike	40%	40%	20%
Current Brand	Reebok	20%	50%	30%
	Fila	10%	20%	70%

1 Each entry in the brand-switching matrix is the percentage of customers who will buy a certain brand of shoe, given the brand they currently own. We can use this information to make estimates about future purchases. For example, the entry in the second row and third column means that we can estimate that 30% of the people who now own Reebok will buy Fila as their next pair of shoes.

Think About This Situation, *page 104*

Teacher: *(The teacher chooses to introduce the TATS with a couple of questions rather than have students read the introductory paragraph. Asking questions about the Lesson 1 mathematics should prompt more students to recall themselves the information in the introductory paragraph.)* We have completed Lesson 1 of this unit, and you will be having your quiz tomorrow. Today, we will do some initial work on Lesson 2 in class. Thinking back to your work in Lesson 1, what types of situations lent themselves to using matrices?

Ashur: Sports statistics.

Susan: The information about pottery at different sites and who you wanted to go to a movie with or lend money to.

Dalila: Shoe information—well, lots of different business information.

Teacher: And what operations did you use to analyze and solve problems in these contexts?

Adam: We added and subtracted matrices and sometimes used row or column sums.

Sara: We also multiplied every number in the matrix—like when there was a 10% increase in the number of cars and trucks sold.

Teacher: Sara, do you remember what we called that type of multiplication?

Sara: Scalar multiplication.

Teacher: Today, we are going to go back to the context of shoe business. Shoe manufacturers or stores that sell shoes might be interested in tracking trends in shoe-buying by the public. Think about brand-switching trends. Have you ever switched shoe brands from one purchase to the next? If so, what were your reasons for switching?

Jasmine: I really like how Adidas shoes fit me, but I wanted to get some red ones and they didn't make red shoes. I found some red high-tops, but I do not know what brand they are.

Geraldo: Yeah, sometimes you can find cool shoes in the off-brands.

Robert: I used to buy off-brands, but now I need shoes that have arch supports.

Teacher: Why do you think shoe stores and companies would want to know about trends in brand switching?

Kelsey: They want to have enough shoes in stock of each brand so people do not go to a different store to shop.

Ben: And if you are the factory, you want to try to predict how many shoes people will buy so you can supply the stores and not have too many shoes left over.

Teacher: And how do you think they could gather information and analyze trends in brand switching?

Dabir: They would have to keep track of the numbers of shoes sold over a few years. Kind of like what we saw in the car sales for different years. But then analyze if brands have increasing or decreasing sales numbers.

Teacher: Okay, let's brainstorm about how matrices and matrix operations might be used in making these types of inventory forecasts based on information on brand-switching trends.

Kayla: You could look at different years' data, like Dabir said, and subtract to find the difference from one year to the next.

Lateefah: You might look at row sums if you did not worry about the categories such as sizes of shoes or men's and women's shoes.

Dean: I bet you use multiplication somehow. See the title of this lesson: *Multiplying Matrices*. Maybe like scalar multiplication with a percent increase or decrease. That is what we did with the car and truck sales problem.

Teacher: Good ideas! Let's turn to Investigation 1 and consider the question "How can you multiply matrices to help make predictions based on trend data?" using the brand-switching matrix provided. You should try to complete Problems 1 and 2 before the end of the hour.

a. What percentage of people who now own Nike will buy Reebok next?

b. What percentage of people who now own Reebok will stay with Reebok on their next shoe purchase?

c. Based on these data, to which shoe brand do you think the customers are most loyal? Why?

2 Assume that buyers purchase a new pair of shoes every year; suppose that this year 700 people bought Nike, 500 people bought Reebok, and 400 people bought Fila. Answer the following questions by using those assumptions and the brand-switching matrix on page 104.

a. How many people will buy Nike next year? Explain your method.

b. How many people will buy Reebok next year?

3 One way to answer the questions in Problem 2 is to use a new matrix operation. A one-row matrix for this year's numbers is written to the left of the brand-switching matrix. A one-row matrix is often more simply called a **row matrix**.

Buyers This Year				Brand-Switching Matrix		
				N	R	F
N	R	F	N	40%	40%	20%
[700	500	400]	R	20%	50%	30%
			F	10%	20%	70%

a. Complete the computation below for the number of people who will buy Fila next year.

$$\begin{pmatrix} \textit{Number of people} \\ \textit{who will buy} \\ \textit{Fila next year} \end{pmatrix} = 700 \times (\underline{\quad}) + 500 \times (\underline{\quad}) + 400 \times (\underline{\quad}) = \underline{\quad}$$

b. To which column of the brand-switching matrix do the numbers in the blanks correspond?

c. Which column of the brand-switching matrix can you combine with the row matrix to get the number of people who will buy Reebok next year? Explain how the row and the column are combined.

4 You have just performed a new matrix operation. This method of combining the row matrix with the columns of the brand-switching matrix is called **matrix multiplication**. When the row matrix is combined with each column of the brand-switching matrix, the result can be written as another row matrix.

a. Using the computations you have already done, list the entries of the row matrix on the right below.

Buyers This Year				Brand-Switching Matrix				Buyers Next Year		
				N	R	F				
N	R	F	N	40%	40%	20%		N	R	F
[700	500	400] ×	R	20%	50%	30%	=	[__	__	__]
			F	10%	20%	70%				

Brand Switching

In this lesson, students learn the process of standard matrix multiplication by analyzing situations and seeing how matrix multiplication emerges as a useful procedure to help understand situations and solve problems. The developmental process begins with learning how to multiply a one-row matrix by another matrix. The initial context is examining trends in athletic-shoe brand switching. As students begin work on this investigation, it is important to let them find their answers in any way that makes sense to them. As the investigation proceeds, students will begin formally using matrix multiplication.

KEY IDEA In this investigation, students will learn how to multiply a one-row matrix by another matrix. This is the first step in the development of matrix multiplication.

Launch

Tell students that in this lesson, they will study a new type of matrix multiplication. They should be alert to see the differences between this new method and the previous methods they have used that involve multiplication.

1   **a.** 40%

     b. 50%

     c. The three entries on the diagonal from the top-left to the bottom-right corners of the matrix represent the percentage of people loyal to their shoe brand. The largest percentage on the diagonal of the matrix is 70%. Thus, Fila customers are the most loyal because 70% of Fila customers do not expect to switch to Nike or Reebok.

COMMON ERROR Be sure students are looking from row to column. This is another opportunity to point out the importance of matrix labels.

2   **INSTRUCTIONAL NOTE** In this problem, students are beginning to informally use the row-column procedure that characterizes matrix multiplication. This procedure emerges naturally in the process of answering questions about brand-switching. It will be formalized in Problem 3.

     a. According to the assumptions, 420 people will buy Nike next year.
$700 \times 0.40 + 500 \times 0.20 + 400 \times 0.10 = 420$
Make sure students can explain how they arrived at their answers.

     b. 610 people will buy Reebok next year.
$700 \times 0.40 + 500 \times 0.50 + 400 \times 0.20 = 610$

3   **a.** $700 \times \underline{0.20} + 500 \times \underline{0.30} + 400 \times \underline{0.70} = 570$ people

     b. The numbers in the blanks correspond to the Fila column, which is the third column.

     c. The Reebok column, column 2, can be combined with the one-row matrix to get the number of people who will buy Reebok next year.

       You multiply the first entry in the row of the left matrix with the first entry in the column of the right matrix; add that to the product of the second entry of the row and the second entry of the column; and so on. (Students should now be able to verbalize the row-column procedure for matrix multiplication.)

TERMINOLOGY NOTE The term *one-row matrix* is informal but nicely descriptive. The more formal term is *row matrix* or, even more formally, *row vector*. The situation is similar for the term *one-row column*.

4   **a. Buyers Next Year**

       N   R   F
     [420   610   570]

POSSIBLE MISCONCEPTION Students need to be clear that the term *matrix multiplication* applies only to the row-column combination procedure, not to multiplying a matrix by a number (scalar multiplication) or multiplying two matrices entry-by-entry.

Unit 2

We say that the row matrix for this year is *multiplied* by the brand-switching matrix to get the row matrix for next year. The term "matrix multiplication" always refers to this type of multiplication and not to any of the other multiplications that you have done.

b. Based on the matrix multiplication in Part a, describe the trend for shoe sales next year. If you were the store manager, would you adjust your shoe orders for next year from what you ordered this year? Explain.

 Now that you have learned how to multiply matrices, practice it a few times before you continue analyzing the brand-switching situation. Perform the indicated matrix multiplications.

a. $[2 \quad 3 \quad 5]\begin{bmatrix} 6 & 0 & 2 \\ 5 & 3 & 1 \\ 3 & 6 & 2 \end{bmatrix}$ **b.** $[8 \quad -2]\begin{bmatrix} 2 & 4 \\ 3 & -4 \end{bmatrix}$

 The brand-switching matrix can be used to estimate how many people will buy each brand of shoe farther into the future. In Problem 4, you found that:

$$\begin{bmatrix} \text{the row matrix} \\ \text{showing how many} \\ \text{people bought each} \\ \text{brand this year} \end{bmatrix} \times \begin{bmatrix} \text{the brand} \\ \text{switching} \\ \text{matrix} \end{bmatrix} = \begin{bmatrix} \text{the row matrix} \\ \text{showing how many} \\ \text{people will buy each} \\ \text{brand next year} \end{bmatrix}$$

a. How many people will buy each brand two years from now? Show which matrices you could multiply to estimate this answer.

b. Use matrix multiplication to estimate the number of people who will buy each brand three years from now.

The way you have been multiplying matrices in this investigation is so useful that all calculators and software with matrix capability are designed with this kind of multiplication built in. All you have to do is enter the matrices and then multiply using the usual multiplication key or command.

 This problem will help you become familiar with the matrix multiplication capability of your calculator or software to further analyze brand switching.

a. Enter the brand-switching matrix and the matrix for the number of buyers this year. When entering a matrix, the first thing you do is enter its size; that is, you enter (*number of rows*) × (*number of columns*). When entering the brand-switching matrix, enter all percentages as decimals.

b. Use your calculator or computer software to check your computations from Problems 4 and 6 for the number of people who are expected to buy each brand one, two, and three years from now.

b. Nike sales should decrease and Reebok and Fila sales should increase. Responses about whether or not to adjust the shoe orders may vary. A sample response might be: Yes, I would adjust my shoe orders because of the expected increases and decreases. If you purchase more Nikes than suggested by the projection, you probably will lose money.

5 **a.** [42 39 17]

b. [10 40]

6 **INSTRUCTIONAL NOTE** Certainly the brand-switching matrix has limitations when used to estimate numbers far in the future. Some students may express these limitations in their groups. Limitations should be addressed for the class during the STM discussion.

a. Multiply the one-row matrix for next year's numbers by the brand-switching matrix (call it matrix B).

$$\begin{array}{ccc} \text{N} & \text{R} & \text{F} \end{array} \qquad \begin{array}{ccc} \text{N} & \text{R} & \text{F} \end{array}$$
$$[\,420 \quad 610 \quad 570\,] \times B = [\,347 \quad 587 \quad 666\,]$$

You estimate that 347 people will buy Nike shoes; 587 people will buy Reebok shoes; 666 people will buy Fila shoes.

b. Multiply the one-row matrix for the numbers two years from now by the brand-switching matrix. Based on this, you estimate that 323 people will buy Nike; 566 people will buy Reebok; and 712 people will buy Fila.

7 **INSTRUCTIONAL NOTE** This problem introduces students to using the matrix capability of their calculators or computer software. It also highlights the universality and usefulness of this seemingly strange multiplication since it is one type of matrix multiplication that is built into all calculators that handle matrices. (Scalar multiplication can also be done with these calculators.)

TECHNOLOGY NOTE You can use calculators or other software to work with matrices. Spreadsheets can also be used to do matrix multiplication but may be less intuitive than other software or calculators.

a–b. Be sure that students can enter a matrix into the calculator or software and carry out the multiplications.

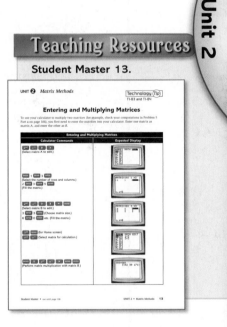

Teaching Resources

Student Master 13.

c. Let *NOW* represent the matrix showing how many people buy each brand this year and *NEXT* represent the matrix showing how many people will buy each brand next year. Write a rule that shows how *NOW* and *NEXT* are related.

d. Use this *NOW-NEXT* rule and the last-answer function on your calculator or computer software to estimate how many people will buy each brand four, five, ten, and twenty years from now.

    i. Describe the trend of sales over time.

    ii. If you were the shoe store manager, what would be your long-term strategy for ordering shoes? Explain.

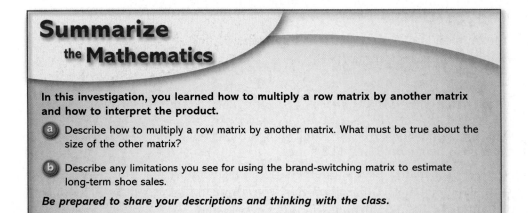

Summarize the Mathematics

In this investigation, you learned how to multiply a row matrix by another matrix and how to interpret the product.

a Describe how to multiply a row matrix by another matrix. What must be true about the size of the other matrix?

b Describe any limitations you see for using the brand-switching matrix to estimate long-term shoe sales.

Be prepared to share your descriptions and thinking with the class.

✓ Check Your Understanding

Use your understanding of matrix multiplication to complete these tasks.

a. To prepare for a dance, a school needs to rent 40 chairs, 3 large tables, and 6 punch bowls. There are two rental shops nearby that rent all of these items, but they have different prices as shown in the matrix below. Prices shown are per item.

Rental Prices

	U-Rent	Rent-All
Chairs	$2	$2.50
Tables	$20	$15
Bowls	$6	$4

    i. What is the size of the rental-prices matrix?

    ii. Put the information about how many chairs, tables, and bowls the school needs into a row matrix.

    iii. Use matrix multiplication to find a matrix that shows the total cost of renting all of the equipment from each of the two shops.

    iv. From which shop should the school rent?

Unit 2

c. $NEXT = NOW \times [brand\text{-}switching\ matrix] = NOW \times B$

              N   R   F   N   R   F

d. in 4 years: [313   554   732]   in 5 years: [309   549   742]

               N   R   F   N   R   F

in 10 years: [306   545   749]   in 20 years: [306   545   749]

    i. The rounded numbers become constant after about 10 years.

    ii. Responses will vary. Make sure that students support their reasoning.

        One possible response: The long-term customer buying distribution becomes constant, so order shoes according to the [306 545 749] matrix. Some students may argue that you cannot plan for ordering shoes 10 years from now, which is a reasonable statement.

INSTRUCTIONAL NOTE
Since matrix multiplication is not commutative, $B \times NOW$ is not a correct answer for Part c. Properties of matrices and operations on matrices, particularly matrix multiplication, are explicitly addressed in Lesson 3, Investigation 1.

Summary

Students do not need to understand the size of the product matrix at this time since this will be emphasized in the next investigation. However, if students make conjectures or raise questions, it would be a valuable use of time to pursue their ideas immediately. Students will be more inclined to ask questions and make conjectures in the future if discussions are not always postponed.

One way to prime the discussion for Part a is to have each group write their answer on the board. Then use these responses to formulate a good response.

INSTRUCTIONAL NOTE
In Part a of the STM, students should be encouraged to "wave their hands" (horizontal to vertical) in the way that indicates the matrix multiplication procedure.

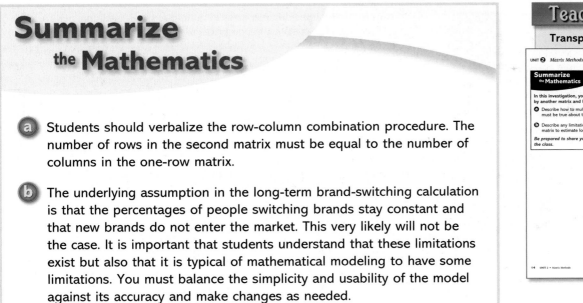

Summarize
the Mathematics

a Students should verbalize the row-column combination procedure. The number of rows in the second matrix must be equal to the number of columns in the one-row matrix.

b The underlying assumption in the long-term brand-switching calculation is that the percentages of people switching brands stay constant and that new brands do not enter the market. This very likely will not be the case. It is important that students understand that these limitations exist but also that it is typical of mathematical modeling to have some limitations. You must balance the simplicity and usability of the model against its accuracy and make changes as needed.

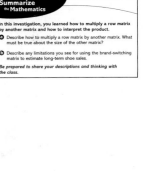

Teaching Resources

Transparency Master 14.

UNIT 2 *Matrix Methods*

Summarize
the Mathematics

In this investigation, you learned how to multiply a row matrix by another matrix and how to interpret the product.

a Describe how to multiply a row matrix by another matrix. What must be true about the size of the other matrix?

b Describe any limitations you see for using the brand-switching matrix to estimate long-term shoe sales.

Be prepared to share your descriptions and thinking with the class.

NOTE Solutions to Check Your Understanding are on page T108.

Unit 2

b. Perform the following matrix multiplications without using a calculator or computer. Then check your answers using technology.

i. $[-3 \quad 1] \begin{bmatrix} 4 & 5 & 2 \\ 0 & 6 & -2 \end{bmatrix}$

ii. $[3 \quad 6 \quad -5 \quad 9] \begin{bmatrix} 3 & 5 \\ 7 & 8 \\ 3 & -9 \\ 6 & 7 \end{bmatrix}$

iii. $[20 \quad 5 \quad 3] \begin{bmatrix} 1 & 2 & 4 \\ 1 & 0 & 4 \\ 1 & 3 & 5 \end{bmatrix}$

Investigation 2 More Matrix Multiplication

Matrix multiplication can be used to help analyze many different situations. As you work on the following problems, look for answers to these questions:

How do you multiply two matrices, each of which has several rows and columns?

Under what conditions is it possible and sensible to multiply two matrices?

Sports Uniforms Suppose that three Little League baseball teams are considering two suppliers for their team uniforms, Uniforms Plus and Sporting Supplies, Inc. Since they consider the quality and delivery from each supplier to be the same, their only objective is to spend the least amount of money.

Each team will order three different sizes of uniforms, small, medium, and large. Each supplier charges different prices for these three sizes, as shown in the matrix below.

Cost per Uniform

	S	M	L
Uniforms Plus	$28	$36	$41
Sporting Supplies	$34	$35	$36

All three of the Little League teams—the Kalamazoo Zephyrs, the Fairfield Fliers, and the Prescott Pioneers—have the same number of players. However, they need different quantities of small-, medium-, and large-size uniforms, as shown in the matrix below.

Quantity of Uniforms

	Zephyrs	Fliers	Pioneers
S	6	6	9
M	11	4	6
L	3	10	5

✓ Check Your Understanding

a. **i.** 3 × 2

   ii. Ch   Tab   Bo
   [40   3   6]

   iii. The total costs are given in the calculation below.

$$[40 \quad 3 \quad 6] \begin{bmatrix} \$2 & \$2.50 \\ \$20 & \$15 \\ \$6 & \$4 \end{bmatrix} = \begin{array}{cc} \text{U-Rent} & \text{Rent-All} \\ [\ \$176 & \$169 \ ] \end{array}$$

   iv. The school should rent from Rent-All.

b. **i.** [−12 −9 −8]

   ii. [90   171]

   iii. [28   49   115]

INSTRUCTIONAL NOTE
For Part aii, you might need to discuss the importance of the numbers being in the correct order and that the matrix is a row, not column, matrix.

Investigation ② More Matrix Multiplication

In this investigation, students learn:

- to multiply general matrices and interpret the results.
- about the sizes of matrices that can be multiplied and the size of the product matrix.
- whether or not the resulting matrix makes sense in a given context.

COLLABORATION SKILL
Stay on task.

Rather than explicitly prescribe the procedure for matrix multiplication at the beginning, it is intended that students will generate the procedure themselves as they work through the problems. It is important not to let students' work with this operation degenerate into an algorithm devoid of meaning. While students should become efficient with matrix multiplication, they also should see why it is sensible and be able to make sense of the outcome.

The sports uniforms problem is presented with more scaffolding than the roofing problem. The intent is to allow students to select the order they wish to multiply the matrices during the roofing problems. The order of multiplying matrices is explicitly addressed in Problem 7, so a class discussion of this concept can wait until the STM discussion.

1 Each team wants to choose a supplier so that they spend the least amount of money possible on their uniforms. Matrix multiplication can help them make the right decision.

   a. Recall how you multiplied the row matrix by the brand-switching matrix in Investigation 1. Use a similar method to multiply the cost matrix by the quantity matrix, as laid out below, without using the matrix feature of your calculator or computer software. Be prepared to explain your method.

$$
\begin{array}{c}
 \\
\text{Uniforms Plus} \\
\text{Sporting Supplies}
\end{array}
\begin{array}{cc}
\begin{array}{ccc} \text{S} & \text{M} & \text{L} \end{array} \\
\left[\begin{array}{ccc} \$28 & \$36 & \$41 \\ \$34 & \$35 & \$36 \end{array}\right]
\end{array}
\times
\begin{array}{c}
\begin{array}{ccc} \text{Zephyrs} & \text{Fliers} & \text{Pioneers} \end{array} \\
\begin{array}{c} \text{S} \\ \text{M} \\ \text{L} \end{array}
\left[\begin{array}{ccc} 6 & 6 & 9 \\ 11 & 4 & 6 \\ 3 & 10 & 5 \end{array}\right]
\end{array}
=
\left[\begin{array}{ccc} \rule{1cm}{0.4pt} & \rule{1cm}{0.4pt} & \rule{1cm}{0.4pt} \end{array}\right]
$$

   b. The entries in the product matrix provide very useful information. Explain what the number in the first row and second column of your product matrix means. What does the number in the second row and third column mean?

   c. Labels on matrices can help you interpret them more easily. Label the rows and columns of your product matrix. Describe how the row and column labels of the cost matrix, the quantity matrix, and the answer matrix are related.

   d. Give your product matrix a title.

   e. Now use your product matrix to solve the problem: Which supplier should each of the teams use in order to spend the least amount of money on uniforms?

2 Compare your answers and explanations in Problem 1 with those of other students in your class. Discuss and resolve any differences.

3 Call the cost matrix C and the quantity matrix Q. So far, you have multiplied $C \times Q$. Try multiplying $Q \times C$. Can you do it? Explain why or why not.

Roofing Crews A roofing contractor has three crews, X, Y, and Z, working in a large housing development of similar homes. The contractor wants to keep track of the crews' work. Matrices can help. Ultimately, the contractor wants to know the total labor cost for all three crews. To help find the total cost, the contractor organizes information on houses roofed, time, and cost in the following matrices.

1 **a. Total Cost of Uniforms**

	Zephyrs	Fliers	Pioneers
Uniforms Plus	$687	$722	$673
Sporting Supplies	$697	$704	$696

b. The number in the first row and second column of the answer matrix tells us that the Fliers would spend $722 if they bought their uniforms from Uniforms Plus. The $696 in the second row and third column tells us that if the Pioneers bought their uniforms from Sporting Supplies, Inc., they would spend $696.

c. INSTRUCTIONAL NOTE As students work through this part, it may help to ask how they know what the row and column labels of the answer matrix will be. Ask about the meaning of the new entries being created. Students should work hard on an explanation about why the "inner" labels seem to disappear. As one student said, "One row of entries and one column of entries are multiplied and totaled, so the answer only takes up one entry. The entry gets its meaning from the outer labels. Each entry in the answer has to mean some kind of total."

See Part a for row and column labels. The column labels of the cost-per-uniform matrix are the same as the row labels of the quantity-of-uniforms matrix. The row labels of the answer matrix and the cost-per-uniform matrix are the same. The column labels of the answer matrix and the quantity-of-uniforms matrix are the same.

d. The title of the answer matrix could be "Total Cost of Uniforms."

e. It would be less expensive for the Zephyrs to order their uniforms from Uniforms Plus. The Fliers would get a better deal if they ordered their uniforms from Sporting Supplies, Inc., and the Pioneers should order their uniforms from Uniforms Plus.

2 Students may have been doing this comparison with each other all along. Nevertheless, it is crucial that they compare and resolve differences explicitly here so that all students are multiplying and interpreting correctly.

KEY IDEA Problem 3 is designed to get students thinking about whether or not two matrices can be multiplied. In Problem 7 of this investigation, students will confront the issue that even if the sizes allow the multiplication procedure to be carried out, doing the multiplication may not make sense for the given context.

3 Students should see that when they attempt the row-column combination procedure on the indicated matrices, it does not work. Student explanations should focus on the fact that there are only two entries in the first column of C (cost matrix) to pair for multiplication with the three entries in the first row of Q (quantity matrix).

Unit 2

Teaching Resources

Student Master 15.

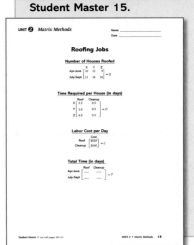

The first matrix below shows the number of houses roofed by each of the three crews during the second and third quarters of the year.

Number of Houses Roofed

	X	Y	Z	
Apr–June	10	12	9	$= Q$
July–Sept	11	14	10	

The following matrix shows the time required (in days) for each crew to roof one house and clean up.

Time Required per House (in days)

	Roof	Cleanup	
X	3.5	0.5	
Y	3.0	0.5	$= D$
Z	4.0	0.5	

The matrix below shows the total crew labor cost per day to apply the roof and clean up.

Labor Cost per Day

	Cost	
Roof	$520	$= C$
Cleanup	$160	

4 The total labor cost for the three crews depends on the total time spent by the crews to apply roofs and clean up during the second and third quarters.

a. What is the total time spent for all three crews combined to apply roofs from April through June?

b. Enter your answer from Part a into a total-time matrix like that below. Then complete the rest of the entries.

Total Time (in days)

	Roof	Cleanup	
Apr–June	____	____	$= T$
July–Sept	____	____	

c. What two matrices can be multiplied to give the total-time matrix?

5 In Problem 4, you created a matrix showing total labor *time* for the crews. Now consider labor *cost*.

a. Multiply the total-time matrix (T) by the labor-cost-per-day matrix (C).

b. Label the rows and columns of the product matrix. What information is given by the entries in the product matrix?

c. What do you notice about the labels of all three matrices? Compare your answers and labeling with those of your classmates and resolve any differences.

4

a. It took 107 days for all three crews to apply roofs from April to June. This is computed by using the first row of matrix Q and the first column of matrix D.

b. Total Time (in days)

$$\begin{array}{c} \\ \text{Apr–June} \\ \text{July–Sept} \end{array} \begin{array}{cc} \text{Roof} & \text{Cleanup} \\ \left[\begin{array}{cc} 107 & 15.5 \\ 120.5 & 17.5 \end{array}\right] \end{array}$$

c. $Q \times D = T$. (Students may note that it is possible to multiply Q and D in either order, but $D \times Q$ does not make sense in this situation. Students will further explore the notion of when you can multiply matrices and when the product makes sense in Problem 7 and in the next lesson.)

5

a. $T \times C = \begin{bmatrix} 107 & 15.5 \\ 120.5 & 17.5 \end{bmatrix} \begin{bmatrix} \$520 \\ \$160 \end{bmatrix} = \begin{bmatrix} \$58,120 \\ \$65,460 \end{bmatrix}$

b. The product matrix gives total cost. That is, each entry gives the total cost for applying the roofs and cleaning up for the houses during the indicated time period. See the matrix (and labels) below:

Total Cost

$$\begin{array}{c} \\ \text{Apr–June} \\ \text{July–Sept} \end{array} \begin{array}{c} \text{Cost} \\ \left[\begin{array}{c} \$58,120 \\ \$65,460 \end{array}\right] \end{array}$$

c. The labels for the rows of the product matrix (Total Cost) are the same as the labels for the rows of the Total Time matrix. The column label of the product matrix is the same as the column label for the Labor Cost per Day matrix.

INSTRUCTIONAL NOTE
Problems 4–7 refer to matrices C, D, and Q. It would be helpful to either write these matrices on the board or use the master provided.

Unit 2

6 What is the grand total labor cost of all three crews, for roofing all the houses and cleaning up, from April through September?

7 As you may have noticed, it does not always make sense to multiply two matrices. Consider the three roofing matrices on the previous page: Q, D, and C.

a. Can you multiply $C \times D$? Explain.

b. Consider $Q \times D$.

    i. Can you multiply $Q \times D$?

    ii. If so, does the information in the product matrix make sense? If possible, label the rows and columns and describe the information contained in the product matrix.

c. Try multiplying in the reverse order.

    i. Can you multiply $D \times Q$?

    ii. If so, what does the number in the first row and first column mean? If possible, label the rows and columns and describe the information contained in the product matrix.

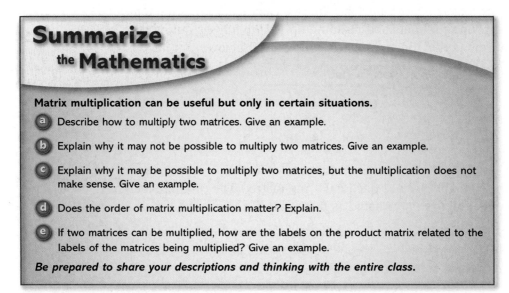

Summarize
the Mathematics

Matrix multiplication can be useful but only in certain situations.

ⓐ Describe how to multiply two matrices. Give an example.

ⓑ Explain why it may not be possible to multiply two matrices. Give an example.

ⓒ Explain why it may be possible to multiply two matrices, but the multiplication does not make sense. Give an example.

ⓓ Does the order of matrix multiplication matter? Explain.

ⓔ If two matrices can be multiplied, how are the labels on the product matrix related to the labels of the matrices being multiplied? Give an example.

Be prepared to share your descriptions and thinking with the entire class.

✓Check Your Understanding

Apply your understanding of matrix multiplication to help solve the following problems.

a. A toy company in Seattle makes stuffed toys, including crabs, ducks, and cows. The owner designs the toys, and then they are cut out, sewn, and stuffed by independent contractors. For the months of September and October, each contractor agrees to make the number of stuffed toys shown in the following matrix.

6 The grand total is $58,120 + $65,460 = $123,580.

7 **a.** It is not possible to multiply $C \times D$ because of a size mismatch. The number of columns in C does not match the number of rows in D.

    b. **i.** It is possible to multiply $Q \times D$. See Problem 4 on page 110.

        ii. Row and column labels should be as in Problem 4 Part b. Each entry in the matrix gives the total cost for all three crews applying roofs and cleanup for the indicated interval of months.

    c. **i.** $D \times Q$ is possible based on the sizes of the matrices.

        ii. The answer matrix does not make sense in this context. This becomes obvious when students try to interpret entries or label rows and columns.

INSTRUCTIONAL NOTE
In this problem, students notice again that matrix multiplication may not work because of a size mismatch. They also see that even if the sizes of matrices allow them to be multiplied, the product matrix may not make sense in the given context. (Students also may begin to notice that matrix multiplication is not commutative. This fact is pursued more explicitly in Lesson 3.)

Summary

As students discuss the STM questions, they should feel confident that:

- they can execute a matrix multiplication.
- they know when two matrices can be multiplied and when they cannot and if the product matrix makes sense in a given context.
- they are able to predict the labels of the product matrix.
- they can attach meaning to the entries of the product matrix.

Summarize
the Mathematics

Teaching Resources

Transparency Master 16.

UNIT 2 *Matrix Methods*

Summarize the Mathematics

Matrix multiplication can be useful but only in certain situations.

a Describe how to multiply two matrices. Give an example.

b Explain why it may not be possible to multiply two matrices. Give an example.

c Explain why it may be possible to multiply two matrices, but the multiplication does not make sense. Give an example.

d Does the order of matrix multiplication matter? Explain.

e If two matrices can be multiplied, how are the labels on the product matrix related to the labels of the matrices being multiplied? Give an example.

Be prepared to share your descriptions and thinking with the entire class.

16   UNIT 2 • Matrix Methods

a Students should explain the row-column combination procedure in their own words and provide an example.

b Matrices can't be multiplied when the sizes aren't compatible. For example, a 2×3 matrix can't be multiplied by a 2×3 matrix or a 4×5 matrix.

c It may be possible to multiply two matrices, but the answer matrix might not make sense in the context of the situation being studied. For example, students might use matrices $D \times Q$ from Problem 7, but you might challenge them to think of a different one to share with the class.

d Yes, students should have seen from Problem 3 that $Q \times C \neq C \times Q$. (Students will revisit this important fact in Lesson 3.)

e Thinking about the labels on the rows and columns can help find the correct matrices to multiply and correctly carry out the multiplication. If two matrices can be multiplied, then the labels on the columns of the left matrix must be the same as the labels on the rows of the right matrix. The row labels on the answer matrix are the same as the row labels of the matrix on the left. The column labels on the answer matrix are the same as the column labels of the matrix on the right.

MATH TOOLKIT After the full-class discussion has enabled students to clarify and extend their understanding of matrix multiplication, students should record their answers to Parts a, b, c, and e for the STM, including the examples. (Part d on commutativity will be studied in more depth in the next lesson.)

PROCESSING PROMPT On a scale of 1 to 5, with 5 the best score, today our group scored a _____ for staying on task. We could improve by ... .

Unit 2

Number of Toys Made

	Sept	Oct
Crabs	10	20
Ducks	25	30
Cows	10	30

Two of the contractors, Elise and Harvey, know from experience how many minutes it takes them to make each type of toy, as shown in this matrix:

Time per Toy (in minutes)

	Crab	Duck	Cow
Elise	55	60	90
Harvey	80	50	100

  i. Use matrix multiplication to find a matrix that shows the total number of minutes each of the two contractors will need in order to fulfill their contracts for each of the two months.

  ii. Convert the minute totals to hours. What matrix operation could you use to do this conversion? Does your calculator or computer software have the capability to perform this type of matrix operation?

b. Perform the following matrix multiplications without using a calculator or computer. Then check your answers using technology.

  i. $\begin{bmatrix} 2 & 3 \\ 4 & 5 \end{bmatrix}\begin{bmatrix} 6 \\ 7 \end{bmatrix}$

  ii. $\begin{bmatrix} 1 & 3 \\ 6 & 5 \end{bmatrix}\begin{bmatrix} 0 & 2 \\ 3 & 3 \end{bmatrix}$

  iii. $\begin{bmatrix} 1 & 0 & 2 \\ 2 & 3 & 0 \\ -4 & 1 & 1 \end{bmatrix}\begin{bmatrix} 2 & 3 \\ 4 & 0 \\ 1 & 2 \end{bmatrix}$

  iv. $\begin{bmatrix} 2 & 5 \\ 1 & 3 \end{bmatrix}\begin{bmatrix} x \\ y \end{bmatrix}$

  v. $\begin{bmatrix} 0 & 1 & 1 \\ 1 & 0 & 2 \\ 0 & 0 & 1 \end{bmatrix}\begin{bmatrix} 0 & 1 & 1 \\ 1 & 0 & 2 \\ 0 & 0 & 1 \end{bmatrix}$

Investigation 3   **The Power of a Matrix**

In this investigation, you will learn a new way to represent and analyze information using matrices. As you explore problems about ecosystems and tennis tournaments, look for answers to these questions:

> *How can you represent a vertex-edge graph with a matrix?*

> *If you multiply such a matrix by itself, what information do you get about the vertex-edge graph and the situation represented by the graph?*

✓ Check Your Understanding

a. **i.**

Time per Toy (in min)

	Crab	Duck	Cow
Elise	55	60	90
Harvey	80	50	100

×

Number of Toys Made

	Sept	Oct
Crabs	10	20
Ducks	25	30
Cows	10	30

=

Total Number of Minutes

	Sept	Oct
Elise	2,950	5,600
Harvey	3,050	6,100

INSTRUCTIONAL NOTE
The size of these matrices, 2 × 3 and 3 × 2, allow for multiplication in either order, but only one order makes sense. This can be seen by considering the row and column labels.

ii. The entries in the answer matrix below are rounded to the nearest tenth hour.

$$\begin{bmatrix} 2,950 & 5,600 \\ 3,050 & 6,100 \end{bmatrix} \times \frac{1}{60} \approx \begin{bmatrix} 49.2 & 93.3 \\ 50.8 & 101.7 \end{bmatrix}$$

Converting minutes to hours is a nice example of scalar multiplication—in this case, by $\frac{1}{60}$. Calculators and mathematical software will perform this multiplication. Simply enter $\frac{1}{60} \times A$.

TECHNOLOGY NOTE
Students may discover that implied multiplication is possible with many calculators. Interestingly, on some calculators **A*1/60** and **A(1/60)** will not compute while **[A]*(1/60)** will compute.

b. **i.** $\begin{bmatrix} 2 & 3 \\ 4 & 5 \end{bmatrix}\begin{bmatrix} 6 \\ 7 \end{bmatrix} = \begin{bmatrix} 33 \\ 59 \end{bmatrix}$

ii. $\begin{bmatrix} 1 & 3 \\ 6 & 5 \end{bmatrix}\begin{bmatrix} 0 & 2 \\ 3 & 3 \end{bmatrix} = \begin{bmatrix} 9 & 11 \\ 15 & 27 \end{bmatrix}$

iii. $\begin{bmatrix} 1 & 0 & 2 \\ 2 & 3 & 0 \\ -4 & 1 & 1 \end{bmatrix}\begin{bmatrix} 2 & 3 \\ 4 & 0 \\ 1 & 2 \end{bmatrix} = \begin{bmatrix} 4 & 7 \\ 16 & 6 \\ -3 & -10 \end{bmatrix}$

iv. $\begin{bmatrix} 2 & 5 \\ 1 & 3 \end{bmatrix}\begin{bmatrix} x \\ y \end{bmatrix} = \begin{bmatrix} 2x + 5y \\ x + 3y \end{bmatrix}$

v. $\begin{bmatrix} 0 & 1 & 1 \\ 1 & 0 & 2 \\ 0 & 0 & 1 \end{bmatrix}\begin{bmatrix} 0 & 1 & 1 \\ 1 & 0 & 2 \\ 0 & 0 & 1 \end{bmatrix} = \begin{bmatrix} 1 & 0 & 3 \\ 0 & 1 & 3 \\ 0 & 0 & 1 \end{bmatrix}$

INSTRUCTIONAL NOTE
In Part biv, students carry out a matrix multiplication that involves variables. This is a gentle preview of work they will do in Lesson 3 using matrices to solve systems of linear equations.

ASSIGNMENT NOTE
Review Task 20 on page 154 provides additional practice with matrix computation.

Unit 2

Investigation 3 — The Power of a Matrix

In this investigation, students will learn about powers of a matrix, that is, multiplying a matrix by itself. They will use powers of matrices to solve problems in a variety of contexts. They will examine powers of an adjacency matrix for a vertex-edge graph and interpret such a matrix in terms of the situation being modeled by the vertex-edge graph.

Pollution In an Ecosystem An ecosystem is the system formed by a community of organisms and their interaction with their environment. The diagram below shows the predator-prey relationships of some organisms in a willow forest ecosystem.

Willow Forest Ecosystem

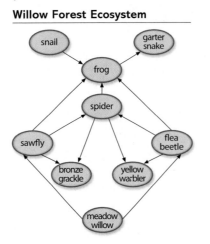

Such a diagram is called a **food web**. An arrow goes from one organism to another if one is food for the other. So, for example, the arrow from spider to yellow warbler means that spiders are food for yellow warblers.

Pollution can cause all or part of the food web to become contaminated. In the following problems, you will explore how matrix multiplication can be used to analyze how contamination of some organisms spreads through the rest of the food web.

① Using the willow forest ecosystem food web, discuss answers to the following questions.

    a. How are predator-prey relationships represented in the food web diagram? What do the arrows mean?

    b. Think about the effect on the ecosystem if a pollutant is introduced at some point in the forest. Assume the pollution does not kill any organisms, but the contamination is spread by eating.

        i. What might happen when a toxic chemical washes into a stream in which the frogs live?

        ii. What might happen if a pesticide contaminates the sawflies?

    c. The food web can be viewed as a vertex-edge graph, where the vertices are the organisms and the edges are the arrows. Since the edges have a direction, this type of vertex-edge graph is sometimes called a **directed graph**, or **digraph**.

       How can paths through the digraph help to analyze the spread of contamination? Illustrate your answer in the case where the contamination first effects the flea beetle.

TECHNOLOGY NOTE It will be helpful for students to use technology to facilitate Problems 1–5. For example, they could use the "Willow Forest Ecosystem" custom tool in the *CPMP-Tools* Discrete Math menu. Using this custom tool, students can load a partially-completed adjacency matrix and complete the matrix in the software. Then they can then use the software to investigate the adjacency matrix, operations on the adjacency matrix, and matrices that show the numbers of paths of length *n*. Alternatively, students could use the matrix functionality of a graphing calculator.

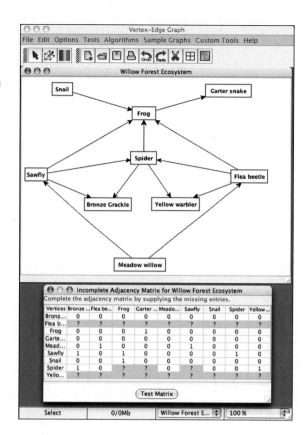

DIFFERENTIATION It is recommended to do both main parts of this investigation. However, for some students or classes, depending on their interest, ability, and pace, you may decide to do only the first part of the investigation on tracking pollution in an ecosystem. The second part, on tournament rankings, can be used for extra practice or for developing deeper understanding, as needed.

1 **a.** The arrows point to the predator in the predator-prey relationship. The arrow might be thought of as indicating what "goes into" what. That is, the arrow from spiders to yellow warblers could be thought of as spiders going into or being food for yellow warblers. So, for example, spiders are food for frogs, bronze grackles, and yellow warblers.

    b. **i.** The organisms that will be contaminated are those that eat frogs. In this ecosystem, only garter snakes eat frogs, so only garter snakes will be contaminated.

       ii. If sawflies are contaminated, the bronze grackles, spiders, frogs, garter snakes, and yellow warblers will all be in danger of contamination.

    c. The digraph can assist in the exploration of contamination since it reveals that once an organism is contaminated, all other organisms on all paths leading away from the source organism will also be contaminated. Thus, follow the paths to find the spread of contamination. Using the digraph and assuming the flea beetle is contaminated, the paths spreading the contamination are shown to the right.

POSSIBLE MISCONCEPTION
It is essential that students understand the phrase "are food for." This phrase is awkward, but it is needed in order to have the arrows point in the proper direction for the purpose of tracking the spread of pollution through the ecosystem. Some students may want to read an arrow from A to B as "A eats B" instead of "A is food for B." Be alert for this misinterpretation.

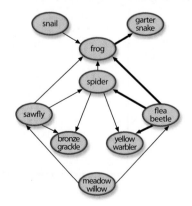

Matrices can be used to help find paths through digraphs. The first step in finding paths is to construct an *adjacency matrix* for the food web digraph. You may recall from *Core-Plus Mathematics* Course 1 that an adjacency matrix is constructed by using the vertices of the digraph as labels for the rows and columns of a matrix. Each entry of the matrix is a "1" or a "0" depending on whether or not there is an arrow in the digraph (directed edge) *from* the row vertex *to* the column vertex.

a. Below is a partially completed adjacency matrix for the food web digraph. Complete the adjacency matrix by filling in all the blank entries. For consistency in this investigation, we will always list the organisms alphabetically across the columns and down the rows.

Adjacency Matrix

	Bg	Fb	Fr	Gs	Mw	Sa	Sn	Sp	Yw	
Bronze grackle	0	0	0	0	0	0	0	0	0	
Flea beetle	—	—	—	—	—	—	—	—	—	
Frog	0	0	0	1	0	0	0	0	0	
Garter snake	0	0	0	0	0	0	0	0	0	
Meadow willow	0	1	0	0	0	1	0	0	0	$= A$
Sawfly	1	0	1	0	0	0	0	1	0	
Snail	0	0	1	0	0	0	0	0	0	
Spider	1	0	—	—	0	—	0	0	1	
Yellow warbler	—	—	—	—	—	—	—	—	—	

b. Compare your matrix with the matrices constructed by other students. Discuss and resolve any differences in your matrices so that everyone agrees upon the same matrix. Label this adjacency matrix A.

3 The adjacency matrix tells you if there is an edge from one vertex to another. An edge from one vertex to another is like a path of length one. Now think about paths of length two. A **path of length two** from one vertex to another means that you can get from one vertex to the other by moving along two consecutive directed edges.

a. The partially completed matrix below shows the number of paths of length two in the food web digraph. Complete the matrix.

Number of Paths of Length Two

	Bg	Fb	Fr	Gs	Mw	Sa	Sn	Sp	Yw
Bronze grackle	0	0	0	0	0	0	0	0	0
Flea beetle	—	—	—	—	—	—	—	—	—
Frog	0	0	0	0	0	0	0	0	0
Garter snake	0	0	0	0	0	0	0	0	0
Meadow willow	1	0	2	0	—	—	—	—	—
Sawfly	1	0	1	1	0	0	0	0	1
Snail	0	0	0	1	0	0	0	0	0
Spider	0	0	0	1	0	0	0	0	0
Yellow warbler	0	0	0	0	0	0	0	0	0

(2) **a. INSTRUCTIONAL NOTE** In Problems 2 and 3, students see the connection between contamination and paths through the food web. In order for students to make this connection, be sure that they understand that we are assuming the pollution does not kill any organisms. However, a contaminated organism is tainted and will pass along the contamination to any other organism that eats it. The issue of how far down the food chain the contamination spreads may come up in Part b below, and this issue is explicitly addressed in Problem 5.

Adjacency Matrix

	Bg	Fb	Fr	Gs	Mw	Sa	Sn	Sp	Yw	
Bronze grackle	0	0	0	0	0	0	0	0	0	
Flea beetle	0	0	1	0	0	0	0	1	1	
Frog	0	0	0	1	0	0	0	0	0	
Garter snake	0	0	0	0	0	0	0	0	0	
Meadow willow	0	1	0	0	0	1	0	0	0	$= A$
Sawfly	1	0	1	0	0	0	0	1	0	
Snail	0	0	1	0	0	0	0	0	0	
Spider	1	0	1	0	0	0	0	0	1	
Yellow warbler	0	0	0	0	0	0	0	0	0	

TECHNOLOGY NOTE Students might use the "Willow Forest Ecosystem" custom tool from the *CPMP-Tools* Discrete Math menu to load a partially-completed adjacency matrix. Then they can complete the adjacency matrix in the software. See also page T113.

b. Students should agree on the same matrix.

(3) **a. Number of Paths of Length Two**

	Bg	Fb	Fr	Gs	Mw	Sa	Sn	Sp	Yw	
Bronze grackle	0	0	0	0	0	0	0	0	0	
Flea beetle	**1**	**0**	**1**	**1**	**0**	**0**	**0**	**0**	**1**	
Frog	0	0	0	0	0	0	0	0	0	
Garter snake	0	0	0	0	0	0	0	0	0	
Meadow willow	1	0	2	0	**0**	**0**	**0**	2	1	$= A$
Sawfly	1	0	1	1	0	0	0	0	1	
Snail	0	0	0	1	0	0	0	0	0	
Spider	0	0	0	1	0	0	0	0	0	
Yellow warbler	0	0	0	0	0	0	0	0	0	

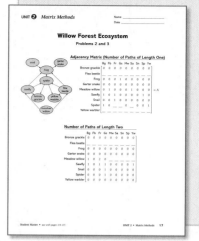
INSTRUCTIONAL NOTE Here, it is especially important to emphasize the matrix-reading convention: from the row to the column. Everyone needs to have identical matrices for the analysis that follows in Problem 3.

Unit 2

b. Compare your matrix to those constructed by others. Discuss and resolve any differences so that everyone has the same matrix.

4 What matrix operation(s) could be used to get the paths-of-length-two matrix from the paths-of-length-one matrix A? Make and test some conjectures. (You may find it helpful to use vertex-edge graph software or other technology for this problem.)

5 Suppose that the meadow willows are contaminated by polluted ground water. In turn, they contaminate other organisms that feed directly or indirectly on them. However, at each step of the food chain, the concentration of contamination decreases.

a. Suppose that organisms more than two steps from the meadow willow in the food web are no longer endangered by the contamination. Using the digraph, find one organism that is safe.

b. How can the matrices be used to help find all the safe organisms? Explain your reasoning.

c. Compare your methods for finding all the safe organisms with others.

Tournament Rankings You have seen that powers of an adjacency matrix give you information about paths of certain lengths in the corresponding vertex-edge graph. This connection between graphs and matrices is useful for solving a variety of problems. For example, it is often very difficult to rank players or teams in a tournament accurately and systematically. A vertex-edge graph can give you a good picture of the status of the tournament. The corresponding adjacency matrix can help determine the ranking of the players or teams. Consider the following tournament situation.

The second round of a city tennis tournament involved six girls, each of whom was to play every other girl. However, the tournament was rained out after each girl had played only four matches. The results of play were the following:

- Erina beat Keadra.
- Akiko beat Julia.
- Keadra beat Akiko and Julia.
- Julia beat Erina and Maria.
- Maria beat Erina, Cora, and Akiko.
- Cora beat Erina, Keadra, and Akiko.

6 Using the information above, can you decide anything about how the girls should be ranked at this stage of the tournament? Explain your reasoning.

b. Again, students need to have the matrix from Problem 3 Part a.

POSSIBLE MISCONCEPTION As students work with the matrix A^2, be sure that they understand A^2 is matrix A multiplied by itself, using standard matrix multiplication. Even though they may have learned matrix multiplication, they may still make the mistake here of thinking that A^2 is computed by squaring all of the entries of A. You may need to watch for this misconception and correct it by pointedly asking students. For example, it may help if you ask: "Why do we not just square each of the entries in matrix A to get A^2?" and "How is squaring a matrix like squaring a number? How is it different?".

4 **INSTRUCTIONAL NOTE** After students confirm their answers to Problem 3, this problem could be facilitated in a think-pair-share manner. Have students individually think about the matrix operation(s) that might be used to obtain the Number of Paths of Length Two matrix from the Number of Paths of Length One matrix (adjacency matrix). Then have students discuss with one other student their conjectures. Then as a whole class, discuss this item. The *CPMP-Tools* custom tool "Willow Forest Ecosystem" could be used for testing the squaring conjecture. This approach will eliminate the time-consuming task of entering the 9 × 9 adjacency matrix in calculators.

Students should quickly recognize that $A + A$ does not give the paths of length two. Another reasonable conjecture is A^2, the Number of Paths of Length Two matrix.

5 **a.** Snails and garter snakes are safe. All other organisms are one or two steps higher than the meadow willow vertex.

b. In order for an organism to be safe, it needs to be at least three steps higher than the contaminated organism. Some students might check the row of the contaminated organisms to find the organism from the column headings that have zeroes in both the adjacency matrix and the Number of Paths of Length Two matrix. Other students may move directly to operating on the matrices and determine that computing $A + A^2$ results in a single matrix that reveals the safe organisms. An entry of 0 in this matrix means that there are no paths of length one or two between the two vertices. Thus, 0 entries in the meadow willow row correspond to safe organisms.

c. INSTRUCTIONAL NOTE This part provides an opportunity for a class discussion of methods used. Allowing the thinking of those students who use A and A^2 (without expressing the safe organisms as $A + A^2$) to surface will provide insight into how and why the sum determines safe organisms. In addition, students who computed $A + A^2$ can help other students move toward the symbolic representation of the process that they used.

$$A + A^2 = \begin{array}{r} \\ \text{Bronze grackle} \\ \text{Flea beetle} \\ \text{Frog} \\ \text{Garter snake} \\ \text{Meadow willow} \\ \text{Sawfly} \\ \text{Snail} \\ \text{Spider} \\ \text{Yellow warbler} \end{array} \begin{array}{ccccccccc} \text{Bg} & \text{Fb} & \text{Fr} & \text{Gs} & \text{Mw} & \text{Sa} & \text{Sn} & \text{Sp} & \text{Yw} \\ \left[\begin{array}{ccccccccc} 0 & 0 & 0 & 0 & 0 & 0 & 0 & 0 & 0 \\ 1 & 0 & 2 & 1 & 0 & 0 & 0 & 1 & 2 \\ 0 & 0 & 0 & 1 & 0 & 0 & 0 & 0 & 0 \\ 0 & 0 & 0 & 0 & 0 & 0 & 0 & 0 & 0 \\ 1 & 1 & 2 & 0 & 0 & 1 & 0 & 2 & 1 \\ 2 & 0 & 2 & 1 & 0 & 0 & 0 & 1 & 1 \\ 0 & 0 & 1 & 1 & 0 & 0 & 0 & 0 & 0 \\ 1 & 0 & 1 & 1 & 0 & 0 & 0 & 0 & 1 \\ 0 & 0 & 0 & 0 & 0 & 0 & 0 & 0 & 0 \end{array}\right] \end{array}$$

INSTRUCTIONAL NOTE In Problems 6–8, students investigate one sensible method for ranking players in a tournament. This is another application of matrix powers. Note that there is no foolproof method for finding a completely fair and unambiguous ranking in all cases. Thus, in the ranking problems in this unit, students may feel a particular ranking outcome is not quite fair. If so, they should support any objections that they feel compelled to make. Allow for a variety of methods to surface. The method presented here works well, especially for this situation. This method also explicitly focuses on the process of mathematical modeling.

6 It looks like either Maria or Cora should be the winners because they each had 3 wins. It does not seem that there is a clear winner, but Maria beat Cora, so it would be reasonable to declare her the winner. A clear ranking of Julia and Keadra cannot be determined at this point because Julia and Keadra are tied in terms of number of wins (2 wins each). However, since Keadra defeated Julia, it seems reasonable that Keadra will be ranked above Julia. On the other hand, Julia beat Maria and Maria seems to be the champion. So, it is not clear how to rank Julia and Keadra. Erina and Akiko each have one win but have not played each other, so it is not clear which girl should be ranked above the other.

INSTRUCTIONAL NOTE Having students discuss their rankings in Problem 6 provides an initial examination that should generate some ambiguity and motivate the need for a deeper analysis, as follows in Problem 7.

7 **a.**

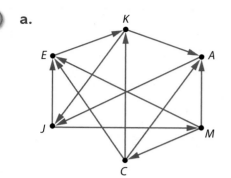

Tournament Results

	A	C	E	J	K	M
Akiko	0	0	0	1	0	0
Cora	1	0	1	0	1	0
Erina	0	0	0	0	1	0
Julia	0	0	1	0	0	1
Keadra	1	0	0	1	0	0
Maria	1	1	1	0	0	0

$= A$

b–c. Students may rank the girls as shown in the table at the right. They may argue to rank Julia above Keadra because Julia beat Maria (who has 3 wins as shown on the digraph). Each row sum reveals the number of players that particular player beat. A higher row sum would indicate a higher ranking. Based on the row sums, there appear to be the following ties: Maria-Cora, Julia-Keadra, and Erina-Akiko.

Adjacency Matrix Row Sums	
Akiko	1
Cora	3
Erina	1
Julia	2
Keadra	2
Maria	3

d.

Stage-two Wins

$A^2 =$

	A	C	E	J	K	M
Akiko	0	0	1	0	0	1
Cora	1	0	0	2	1	0
Erina	1	0	0	1	0	0
Julia	1	1	1	0	1	0
Keadra	0	0	1	1	0	1
Maria	1	0	1	1	2	0

Stage-two Row Sums	
Akiko	2
Cora	4
Erina	2
Julia	4
Keadra	3
Maria	5

Entries of the squared adjacency matrix tell how many paths of length two there are from one vertex to another. In the context of tournaments, the entries tell how many stage-two wins one player has over another. For example, there is 1 path of length two from Cora to Keadra, passing through Erina. Thus, Cora beat Erina who beat Keadra, and so Cora has 1 stage-two victory over Keadra. Another example: Cora has 2 stage-two wins over Julia, and so the Cora-Julia entry of the squared adjacency matrix is 2.

The row sums reveal the number of stage-two wins for each player. At this point the Maria-Cora tie seems to be resolved because Maria has 5 stage-two wins while Cora has only 4 stage-two wins. The Julia-Keadra tie is also resolved as Julia has 4 stage-two wins and Keadra has 3. (Students might use A^2 alone to do the ranking, or they might try to factor in the information from A in some way as well such as by using $A + A^2$. However students do it, there still will be a tie between Erina and Akiko.)

$A + A^2 =$

	A	C	E	J	K	M
Akiko	0	0	1	1	0	1
Cora	2	0	1	2	2	0
Erina	1	0	0	1	1	0
Julia	1	1	2	0	1	1
Keadra	1	0	1	2	0	1
Maria	2	1	2	1	2	0

$A + A^2$ Row Sums Excluding Diagonals	
Akiko	3
Cora	7
Erina	3
Julia	6
Keadra	5
Maria	8

Multiplying Matrices **T115B**

(7) A digraph and an adjacency matrix can be used to help rank the girls at this stage of the tournament with no ties.

a. Represent the status of the tournament by completing a copy of the digraph and adjacency matrix below.

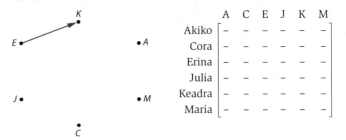

$$
\begin{array}{c}
\\
\text{Akiko} \\
\text{Cora} \\
\text{Erina} \\
\text{Julia} \\
\text{Keadra} \\
\text{Maria}
\end{array}
\begin{array}{c}
\begin{array}{cccccc}
\text{A} & \text{C} & \text{E} & \text{J} & \text{K} & \text{M}
\end{array} \\
\left[
\begin{array}{cccccc}
- & - & - & - & - & - \\
- & - & - & - & - & - \\
- & - & - & - & - & - \\
- & - & - & - & - & - \\
- & - & - & - & - & - \\
- & - & - & - & - & -
\end{array}
\right]
\end{array}
$$

b. Rank the girls as clearly as you can. Use the information shown in the digraph and adjacency matrix to explain your ranking.

c. If you did not use row sums of the adjacency matrix in Part b, what additional information do these sums provide?

d. Compute the square of the adjacency matrix and discuss what the entries tell you about the tournament. How could you use this information to help rank the girls?

e. Use further operations on the adjacency matrix to rank the players with no ties. Explain the ranking system you used. Compare your method and results with others.

Summarize the Mathematics

In this investigation, you explored how powers of an adjacency matrix for a digraph and sums of the powers could be used to analyze the digraph and the situation it models.

a Consider paths in a digraph.

   i. How do paths in a food web help you track the spread of contamination through the ecosystem?

   ii. What do paths in a tournament digraph tell you about the tournament?

b What do powers of the adjacency matrix tell you about paths in the digraph?

c Explain how you can use powers and sums of matrices to track pollution through an ecosystem and to rank the players in a tournament.

Be prepared to share your thinking and tournament-ranking plan with the class.

e. Students' methods may vary. They should recognize that the diagonal entries of A^3 should not be considered in row sums since we are not interested in counting wins over oneself. Checking the sums of the rows of the matrix formed by $A + A^2 + A^3$ (excluding nonzero diagonal entries) yields Maria-Cora-Julia-Keadra-Akiko-Erina.

NOTE Solutions to Problem 7 Parts a–d on page T115B.

$$A^3 = \begin{array}{c} \\ \text{Akiko} \\ \text{Cora} \\ \text{Erina} \\ \text{Julia} \\ \text{Keadra} \\ \text{Maria} \end{array} \begin{array}{cccccc} A & C & E & J & K & M \\ \left[\begin{array}{cccccc} 1 & 1 & 1 & 0 & 1 & 0 \\ 1 & 0 & 2 & 2 & 0 & 2 \\ 0 & 0 & 1 & 1 & 0 & 1 \\ 2 & 0 & 1 & 2 & 2 & 0 \\ 1 & 1 & 2 & 0 & 1 & 1 \\ 2 & 0 & 1 & 3 & 1 & 1 \end{array}\right] \end{array}$$

Stage-three Row Sums Excluding Diagonals	
Akiko	3
Cora	7
Erina	2
Julia	5
Keadra	5
Maria	7

$$A + A^2 + A^3 = \begin{array}{c} \\ \text{Akiko} \\ \text{Cora} \\ \text{Erina} \\ \text{Julia} \\ \text{Keadra} \\ \text{Maria} \end{array} \begin{array}{cccccc} A & C & E & J & K & M \\ \left[\begin{array}{cccccc} 1 & 1 & 2 & 1 & 1 & 1 \\ 3 & 0 & 3 & 4 & 2 & 2 \\ 1 & 0 & 1 & 2 & 1 & 1 \\ 3 & 1 & 3 & 2 & 3 & 1 \\ 2 & 1 & 3 & 2 & 1 & 2 \\ 4 & 1 & 3 & 4 & 3 & 1 \end{array}\right] \end{array}$$

$A + A^2 + A^3$ Row Sums Excluding Diagonals	
Akiko	6
Cora	14
Erina	5
Julia	11
Keadra	10
Maria	15

KEY IDEA It is worth pointing out that vertex-edge graphs give a nice picture of the situation when the problem is not too large; but in most real-world situations, the matrix representation, or some other computer-friendly representation, is more practical.

Summarize
the Mathematics

(a)
　i. The paths in the food-web digraph are the paths the contamination follows.

　ii. Paths in a tournament digraph correspond to multistage wins.

(b) The entries in A^n tell how many paths of length n there are from one vertex to another. (Since the reason behind the connection between the powers of the adjacency matrices and path lengths in the digraph are difficult and time-consuming to develop, do not expect students to give precise explanations for this connection. Interested students can be assigned Extensions Task 22.)

(c) By summing powers of the adjacency matrix corresponding to the food web, you can identify organisms that are in the path of the pollution and how far down the path they are. By summing powers of the adjacency matrix corresponding to the tournament digraph, you can see the direct and indirect wins for each player, which will help you rank the players.

Teaching Resources

Transparency Master 19.

UNIT **2** *Matrix Methods*

Summarize
the Mathematics

In this investigation, you explored how powers of an adjacency matrix for a digraph and sums of the powers could be used to analyze the digraph and the situation it models.

a Consider paths in a digraph.
　i. How do paths in a food web help you track the spread of contamination through the ecosystem?
　ii. What do paths in a tournament digraph tell you about the tournament?

b What do powers of the adjacency matrix tell you about paths in the digraph?

c Explain how you can use powers and sums of matrices to track pollution through an ecosystem and to rank the players in a tournament.

Be prepared to share your thinking and tournament-ranking plan with the class.

EQUITY Proposing alternate thoughtful plans here stimulates an interesting discussion. This practice promotes equity. See *Implementing Core-Plus Mathematics* for information on this research.

✓ Check Your Understanding

In any group of people, some are leaders and some are followers. This relationship of leaders and followers is called *social dominance*. The following digraph shows social dominance within a group of five people in an advertising agency. An arrow from one vertex to another means that the first person is socially dominant (is the "leader") over the other.

Social Dominance Graph

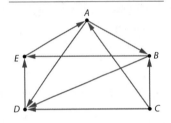

a. Describe and explain at least one interesting or unusual feature that you see in the dominance digraph.

b. Construct an adjacency matrix M for this digraph.

c. Using your adjacency matrix, identify an overall leader of this group. Can you rank, with no ties, all five people in terms of social dominance? Explain.

d. Compute M^3.

  i. Explain what the "1" for the *A-E* entry means in terms of social dominance.

  ii. Trace the paths in the digraph that correspond to the "2" for the *C-A* entry.

e. Use powers of your adjacency matrix and sums of rows to break any ties and rank the five people in terms of social dominance.

f. What do the arrows between *A*, *B*, and *E* indicate about these three people? Explain how this could be possible in a social group.

✓ Check Your Understanding

a. Some features are: the A-B-E cycle; nobody dominates C, that is, C seems to be an independent thinker; D is dominated by most people, that is, D seems to be a person whose opinions are easily shaped by others; E and C have no dominance relation, that is, these two people seem to act independently of each other's opinions.

b.

$$
\begin{array}{c c}
& \begin{array}{c c c c c} A & B & C & D & E \end{array} \\
\begin{array}{c} A \\ B \\ C \\ D \\ E \end{array} &
\left[\begin{array}{c c c c c}
0 & 1 & 0 & 1 & 0 \\
0 & 0 & 0 & 1 & 1 \\
1 & 1 & 0 & 1 & 0 \\
0 & 0 & 0 & 0 & 1 \\
1 & 0 & 0 & 0 & 0
\end{array}\right] = M
\end{array}
$$

c. Looking at row sums of M, there is no row sum of 4 (so no one directly dominates everyone else). C has the highest row sum of 3. Thus, C would seem to be the most dominant. A and B have row sums of 2 and A dominates B, so A appears to be the next in rank. Then B follows A.

It is harder to determine a ranking for D and E. D dominates E but D is also dominated by more people than E is.

d.

$$
\begin{array}{c c}
& \begin{array}{c c c c c} A & B & C & D & E \end{array} \\
\begin{array}{c} A \\ B \\ C \\ D \\ E \end{array} &
\left[\begin{array}{c c c c c}
2 & 0 & 0 & 0 & 1 \\
1 & 1 & 0 & 1 & 0 \\
2 & 0 & 0 & 1 & 3 \\
0 & 1 & 0 & 1 & 0 \\
0 & 0 & 0 & 1 & 2
\end{array}\right] = M^3
\end{array}
$$

    i. The A-E entry of 1 means that there is one path of length three from A to E. The path is A-B-D-E. This path means that A is dominant over B, who is dominant over D, who is dominant over E. Thus, A seems to have an indirect dominance over E.

    ii. Since the entries of M^3 show the number of paths of length three, students should trace the two paths of length three from C to A. They are C-D-E-A and C-B-E-A.

e.

$$
\begin{array}{c c}
& \begin{array}{c c c c c} A & B & C & D & E \end{array} \\
\begin{array}{c} A \\ B \\ C \\ D \\ E \end{array} &
\left[\begin{array}{c c c c c}
0 & 0 & 0 & 1 & 2 \\
1 & 0 & 0 & 0 & 1 \\
0 & 1 & 0 & 2 & 2 \\
1 & 0 & 0 & 0 & 0 \\
0 & 1 & 0 & 1 & 0
\end{array}\right] = M^2
\end{array}
\qquad
\begin{array}{c c}
& \begin{array}{c c c c c} A & B & C & D & E \end{array} \\
\begin{array}{c} A \\ B \\ C \\ D \\ E \end{array} &
\left[\begin{array}{c c c c c}
0 & 1 & 0 & 2 & 2 \\
1 & 0 & 0 & 1 & 2 \\
1 & 2 & 0 & 3 & 2 \\
1 & 0 & 0 & 0 & 1 \\
1 & 1 & 0 & 1 & 0
\end{array}\right] = M + M^2
\end{array}
$$

Sums of the rows of M^2 still show a tie, but sums of the rows of $M + M^2$ show a ranking of C-A-B-E-D.

f. The arrow from A to B means that A dominates B. The one from B to E indicates that B dominates E. The arrow from E to A means that E dominates A. The puzzling thing about this situation is that since A dominates B, who in turn dominates E, we might expect A to dominate E. But this is not true. This shows that in the case of social relations, direct relations are different from indirect relations. (Mathematically, this says that social dominance is not transitive.)

On Your Own

Applications

1 The Fairfield Hobbies and Games store sells two types of ping-pong sets. A Standard Set contains two paddles and one ball, and a Tournament Set contains four paddles and six balls. This information is summarized in the matrix below.

Ping-Pong Sets

$$\begin{array}{c} \\ \text{Tourn} \\ \text{Std} \end{array} \begin{array}{cc} \text{Balls} & \text{Paddles} \\ \left[\begin{array}{cc} 6 & 4 \\ 1 & 2 \end{array}\right] \end{array}$$

a. This month, the store orders 35 Tournament Sets and 50 Standard Sets. Organize this information in a row matrix. Label the columns of the matrix.

b. Use matrix multiplication to find another matrix that shows the total number of balls and paddles in all of the ping-pong sets ordered this month. Label the rows and columns.

2 Matrix multiplication can be used to help rank choices. For example, suppose that in your Social Studies class during an election year you are supposed to rank four U.S. presidential candidates based on three issues—environment, gun control, and minimum wage. Based on this ranking, you will choose who you would vote for.

| John Kerry | George W. Bush | Ralph Nader | Michael Badnarik |

You, like most voters, probably care more about some of these issues than others. Here's one way to do the ranking. First, rate each candidate on a scale of 1 to 5 on each issue where 5 is the best and the rating indicates your opinion of the candidate's strength on that issue. The ratings for one student, Tonya, are shown in the following matrix. (The rows correspond to the candidates, A, B, C, D, and the columns correspond to the issues, environment (E), gun control (G), and minimum wage (M).)

Applications

1 **a.** $\begin{array}{cc} \text{Tourn} & \text{Std} \\ [\ 35 & 50\ ] \end{array}$

b. $\begin{array}{cc} \text{Tourn} & \text{Std} \\ [\ 35 & 50\ ] \end{array} \times \begin{array}{c} \\ \text{Tourn} \\ \text{Std} \end{array}\begin{array}{cc} \text{Balls} & \text{Paddles} \\ \begin{bmatrix} 6 & 4 \\ 1 & 2 \end{bmatrix} \end{array} = \begin{array}{cc} \text{Balls} & \text{Paddles} \\ [\ 260 & 240\ ] \end{array}$

Unit 2

$$\begin{array}{c} \\ A \\ B \\ C \\ D \end{array}\begin{array}{ccc} E & G & M \end{array}\\ \left[\begin{array}{ccc} 4 & 5 & 2 \\ 1 & 5 & 3 \\ 3 & 3 & 4 \\ 4 & 2 & 4 \end{array}\right] = S$$

a. Based on the information shown so far, which candidate is top rated by Tonya? Explain your reasoning.

b. Tonya cares more about some issues than others. For her, the environment is twice as important as gun control, and minimum wage is three times as important as gun control. Thus, she would really rate a candidate based on this formula: R = 2E + G + 3M. Use this formula to compute Tonya's rating for candidate A.

c. Consider the following one-column matrix that shows the "weight" of Tonya's concern for each issue. (A one-column matrix is often simply called a **column matrix**.)

$$W = \left[\begin{array}{c} 2 \\ 1 \\ 3 \end{array}\right]$$

Multiply $S \times W$. What information is contained in the product matrix? Which candidate does Tonya rate the highest?

d. Adjust W to show your relative weight of concern for each issue. Then multiply $S \times W$ to examine the resulting candidate ratings.

3 The owners of a local gas station want to evaluate their business. They decide to examine sales, prices, and gross profits for the first two weeks in each of the last two years. This information is summarized in the following matrices.

Number of Gallons Sold in 1st Two Weeks of Year 1

	Regular	Super	Ultimate
Week 1	3,410	850	870
Week 2	3,230	810	780

= Q1

Revenue and Profit per Gallon in 1st Two Weeks of Year 1

	Rev/gal	Profit/gal
Regular	$2.80	$0.17
Super	$2.95	$0.19
Ultimate	$3.03	$0.20

= P1

Number of Gallons Sold in 1st Two Weeks of Year 2

	Regular	Super	Ultimate
Week 1	3,350	870	850
Week 2	3,240	780	790

= Q2

Revenue and Profit per Gallon in 1st Two Weeks of Year 2

	Rev/gal	Profit/gal
Regular	$2.86	$0.17
Super	$3.01	$0.18
Ultimate	$3.12	$0.21

= P2

a. What information would be provided by the product $Q1 \times P1$?

b. Multiply $Q1 \times P1$. Label the rows and columns of the product matrix.

c. Use matrix multiplication to find the total revenue and profit for all three types of gasoline combined for each of the two weeks in Year 2.

2 **a.** Candidate A is top-rated by Tonya since A has the greatest row sum, and the row sum is the sum of the candidate's rating on all three issues.

b. Tonya's rating for A is $2(4) + 5 + 3(2) = 19$.

c. $S \times W = \begin{bmatrix} 4 & 5 & 2 \\ 1 & 5 & 3 \\ 3 & 3 & 4 \\ 4 & 2 & 4 \end{bmatrix} \begin{bmatrix} 2 \\ 1 \\ 3 \end{bmatrix} = \begin{bmatrix} 19 \\ 16 \\ 21 \\ 22 \end{bmatrix}$

The product matrix represents Tonya's weighted rankings for the candidates. Now Tonya's top-rated candidate is D.

d. Responses will vary depending on the students' choices for W.

3 **a.** The entries would represent total revenue and total profit for each of the first two weeks of Year 1.

b. **Year 1 Total**

	Revenue	Profit
Week 1	$14,691.60	$915.20
Week 2	$13,796.90	$859.00

c. **Year 2 Total**

	Revenue	Profit
Week 1	$14,851.70	$904.60
Week 2	$14,079.00	$857.10

d. Were the first two weeks of Year 2 better than the first two weeks of Year 1? Explain.

e. Consider $P2 \times Q2$. Is it possible to carry out this matrix multiplication? If so, what do the entries in the product matrix tell you, if anything, about sales, prices, and profits at the gas station?

4 Perform the following matrix multiplications without using a calculator or computer. Then check your answers using technology.

a. $\begin{bmatrix} 2 & 3 \end{bmatrix} \begin{bmatrix} 4 & 1 & 0 \\ -5 & 3 & 1 \end{bmatrix}$

b. $\begin{bmatrix} 18 & -4 \\ 6 & -1 \\ \frac{1}{2} & 2 \end{bmatrix} \begin{bmatrix} 2 \\ 3 \end{bmatrix}$

c. $\begin{bmatrix} 6 & 5 \\ 4 & 3 \end{bmatrix} \begin{bmatrix} 2 \\ 7 \end{bmatrix}$

d. $\begin{bmatrix} 2 & 0 \\ 1 & 1 \end{bmatrix} \begin{bmatrix} 3 & -3 \\ 4 & 5 \end{bmatrix}$

e. $\begin{bmatrix} 2 & 1 & 2 \\ 3 & 5 & 4 \\ 1 & 0 & 3 \end{bmatrix} \begin{bmatrix} -1 & 0 \\ 2 & 4 \\ 3 & 3 \end{bmatrix}$

f. $A = \begin{bmatrix} 0 & 1 & 2 \\ 0 & 0 & 1 \\ 1 & 1 & 0 \end{bmatrix}$. Compute A^2.

5 Five students played in a round-robin ping-pong tournament. That is, every student played everyone else. The results were the following:

- Anna beat Darien.
- Bo beat Anna, Chan, and Darien.
- Chan beat Anna, Emilio, and Darien.
- Darien beat Emilio.
- Emilio beat Anna and Bo.

a. Represent the tournament results with a digraph by letting the vertices represent the players and drawing an arrow from one player to another if the first beats the second.

b. Construct an adjacency matrix for the digraph. Remember that you write "1" for an entry if there is an arrow from the player on the row to the player on the column.

c. Use sums and powers of the adjacency matrix to rank the five students in the tournament. Explain your method and report the rankings.

6 In Lesson 1, you investigated matrices that described friendship among a group of people. The friendship matrix below is for a different group of five people. Recall that an entry of "1" means that the person on the row considers the person on the column as a friend.

Friendship Matrix

	A	B	C	D	E
A	0	1	1	1	1
B	0	0	1	1	1
C	1	0	0	1	0
D	1	1	1	0	1
E	1	0	0	1	0

d. No. The first two weeks of Year 1 were better because the total profit ($1,774.20) was higher than in Year 2 ($1,761.70). If students consider total revenue, they will answer that Year 2 was the better time period. You might need to discuss the ideas of profit and revenue.

e. Yes, it is possible to multiply the matrices in this order because the number of rows of $Q2$ is the same as the number of columns of $P2$. However, the entries in the product matrix do not convey any useful information. For example, the entry in the first row and first column is the sum of the revenue from regular gas the first week and the profit from regular gas the second week.

4 **a.** $[-7 \quad 11 \quad 3]$ **b.** $\begin{bmatrix} 24 \\ 9 \\ 7 \end{bmatrix}$ **c.** $\begin{bmatrix} 47 \\ 29 \end{bmatrix}$

d. $\begin{bmatrix} 6 & -6 \\ 7 & 2 \end{bmatrix}$ **e.** $\begin{bmatrix} 6 & 10 \\ 19 & 32 \\ 8 & 9 \end{bmatrix}$ **f.** $A^2 = \begin{bmatrix} 2 & 2 & 1 \\ 1 & 1 & 0 \\ 0 & 1 & 3 \end{bmatrix}$

5 **a.**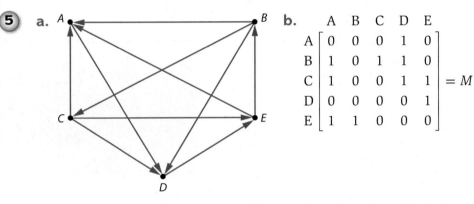

b.

	A	B	C	D	E	
A	0	0	0	1	0	
B	1	0	1	1	0	
C	1	0	0	1	1	$= M$
D	0	0	0	0	1	
E	1	1	0	0	0	

c. The rankings (from 1st to 5th) are: Bo, Chan, Emilio, Darien, and Anna. By looking individually at M, M^2, and M^3, a tie is present. $M + M^2$ has no ties, so the ranking can be made.

NOTE $M^2 + M^3$ and $M + M^2 + M^3$ also produce matrices with the same ranking as $M + M^2$.

	A	B	C	D	E	
A	0	0	0	0	1	
B	1	0	0	2	2	
C	1	1	0	1	1	$= M^2$
D	1	1	0	0	0	
E	1	0	1	2	0	

	A	B	C	D	E	
A	1	1	0	0	0	
B	2	2	0	1	2	
C	2	1	1	2	1	$= M^3$
D	1	0	1	2	0	
E	1	0	0	2	3	

	A	B	C	D	E	
A	0	0	0	1	1	
B	2	0	1	3	2	
C	2	1	0	2	2	$= M + M^2$
D	1	1	0	0	1	
E	2	1	1	2	0	

	A	B	C	D	E	
A	1	1	0	1	1	
B	4	2	1	4	4	
C	4	2	1	4	3	$= M + M^2 + M^3$
D	2	1	1	2	1	
E	3	1	1	4	3	

Two people are *mutual friends* if they consider each other friends. Thus, person A and person B are not mutual friends, but C and D are.

In this task, you will investigate *cliques*. A *clique* is a group of people who are all mutual friends of each other. (For this problem, consider only three-person cliques.)

a. Find one other pair of mutual friends and one clique.

b. To use powers of a matrix to find cliques, first build a *mutual-friends matrix M* by listing the five people across the top and down the side of a new matrix. Then write a "1" for each entry where the two people represented by that entry are mutual friends. If the people are not mutual friends, enter a "0".

c. Think of M as an adjacency matrix for a digraph and construct the digraph.

d. Compute M^3. What do the entries of M^3 tell you about mutual friends?

e. What do the entries in the main diagonal of M^3 tell you about cliques? Explain.

f. Consider the three-person cliques of each person.

    i. List all of the cliques of C. List all of the cliques of A.

    ii. How many cliques is B in? How many cliques is D in?

7 For any given case that comes before the Michigan Supreme Court, one judge is designated to write an opinion on the case (although any judge can choose to write an opinion on any case). All of the judges then sit together, discuss the case, and each written opinion is passed around and signed by all who approve of it. A case is decided when a majority of judges sign one opinion. The information in the following matrix, taken from historical court records, shows how often judges on the court from 1958–60 agreed with (and signed) one another's written opinions. As always, the matrix is read from row to column. For example, Judge Carr agreed with 61% of Judge Black's opinions.

Judge Agreements

	Ka	V	D	S	C	E	B	Ke
Kavanagh	—	76%	80%	85%	81%	88%	83%	77%
Voelker	81%	—	60%	90%	59%	86%	99%	63%
Dethmers	66%	65%	—	75%	99%	77%	72%	95%
Smith	78%	79%	63%	—	57%	81%	84%	64%
Carr	63%	58%	100%	66%	—	70%	61%	100%
Edwards	61%	68%	66%	76%	65%	—	70%	65%
Black	75%	84%	48%	77%	44%	68%	—	55%
Kelly	60%	53%	86%	63%	91%	61%	62%	—

Source: Leadership in the Michigan Supreme Court. *Judicial Decision Making.* New York: Free Press of Glencoe, 1963.

There are several ways you could analyze these data. Complete the analysis that follows.

6 **a.** Responses may vary. A-C, A-D, A-E, B-D, C-D, and D-E are the mutual-friends pairings. A-C-D and A-D-E are the only three-person cliques.

b. Note that this matrix is symmetric since x and y are mutual friends if and only if y and x are mutual friends. The matrix is shown below.

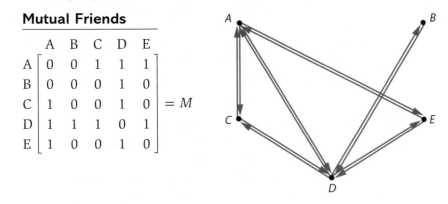

Mutual Friends

$$M = \begin{array}{c|ccccc} & A & B & C & D & E \\ \hline A & 0 & 0 & 1 & 1 & 1 \\ B & 0 & 0 & 0 & 1 & 0 \\ C & 1 & 0 & 0 & 1 & 0 \\ D & 1 & 1 & 1 & 0 & 1 \\ E & 1 & 0 & 0 & 1 & 0 \end{array}$$

c. See the digraph above. For each arrow going one way, there is a corresponding arrow going the opposite way.

d. In general, M^3 tells how many paths of length 3 there are between pairs of vertices. In the case of this mutual-friend digraph and matrix, M^3 tells how many mutual-friend paths of length 3 exist between any two people. A mutual-friend path of length 3 between X and Y means X is a friend of W, who is a friend of V, who is a friend of Y. For example, C is "connected" to D by mutual-friend paths of length 3 in six different ways: C-A-C-D, C-D-C-D, C-D-E-D, C-A-E-D, C-D-B-D, and C-D-A-D.

$$M^3 = \begin{array}{c|ccccc} & A & B & C & D & E \\ \hline A & 4 & 2 & 5 & 6 & 5 \\ B & 2 & 0 & 1 & 4 & 1 \\ C & 5 & 1 & 2 & 6 & 2 \\ D & 6 & 4 & 6 & 4 & 6 \\ E & 5 & 1 & 2 & 6 & 2 \end{array}$$

e. Entries in the diagonal correspond to mutual-friend paths of length 3 between a person and himself or herself. That is, the paths are like X-W-V-X. Such a path indicates a group of three people, all of whom are mutual friends, that is, a clique. Since it does not matter in which direction the friendships go, paths are duplicated. X-W-V-X and X-V-W-X are paths but not two different cliques. Thus, a main diagonal entry divided by 2 tells how many three-person cliques in which that person is a member.

f. **i.** Person C is in one clique: A-C-D. Person A is in two cliques: A-C-D and A-D-E.

ii. Person B is in no cliques. Person D is in two cliques: A-C-D and A-D-E.

7 **INSTRUCTIONAL NOTE** The Judge Agreements "matrix" is not technically a matrix since it is not an array of *numbers*. The entries on the diagonal are dashes. Thus, this is a table but not a matrix. For more on tables versus matrices, see Reflections Task 13 in Lesson 1. You may or may not decide to emphasize this fine point with your students. Most of the work in this task is done with the Ally Matrix, which is a matrix (a rectangular array of numbers).

TECHNOLOGY NOTE
Students might use *CPMP-Tools* to load the Friendship Matrix and invesigate using the software. Choose Algebra → CAS → Matrices → Sample Matrices → Friendship Matrix.

TECHNOLOGY NOTE
Students might use *CPMP-Tools* to load the Ally Matrix and invesigate using the software. Choose Algebra → CAS → Matrices → Sample Matrices → Ally Matrix.

Unit 2

a. Examine the matrix and write down two interesting statements about this particular Michigan Supreme Court.

b. Now, convert all the entries into 0s and 1s according to this rule:

Whenever a judge agrees with 75% or more of another judge's opinions, say that the one judge "agrees with" the other judge, and that entry should be a "1". Otherwise, enter a "0".

c. Interpret the new matrix by answering the following questions.

   i. Does Kavanagh agree with Dethmers?

   ii. Does Dethmers agree with Kavanagh?

   iii. Which judge agrees with the most other judges?

   iv. Which judge is agreed with by the most other judges?

d. Two judges who agree with each other are called *allies*.

   i. Find two allies among the judges.

   ii. Examine the *ally matrix* below. How are the two allies you found in part i indicated in the matrix? Identify another pair of allies.

Ally Matrix

	Ka	V	D	S	C	E	B	Ke
Kavanagh	0	1	0	1	0	0	1	0
Voelker	1	0	0	1	0	0	1	0
Dethmers	0	0	0	0	1	0	0	1
Smith	1	1	0	0	0	1	1	0
Carr	0	0	1	0	0	0	0	1
Edwards	0	0	0	1	0	0	0	0
Black	1	1	0	1	0	0	0	0
Kelly	0	0	1	0	1	0	0	0

   iii. Think of the ally matrix as an adjacency matrix for a digraph and then construct the digraph.

e. A group of three judges who are all allies with each other is called a *coalition*.

   i. Find one coalition.

   ii. Call the ally matrix A and compute A^3. What do the entries of A^3 tell you about allies?

   iii. What do the entries in the main diagonal of A^3 tell you about coalitions? Explain.

   iv. Describe some similarities and differences between coalitions and cliques. (See Applications Task 6.)

f. Three of these judges were Republicans and five were Democrats. Can you pick out the Republicans and Democrats from these data? Explain your reasoning.

a. Statements will vary. For example, Carr always agreed with Dethmers and Kelly; Carr and Dethmers almost always agreed with each other; any judge agreed with any other judge most (at least one half) of the time, except Black agreed with Carr only 44% of the time and Dethmers only 48% of the time.

b.

	Ka	V	D	S	C	E	B	Ke
Kavanagh	0	1	1	1	1	1	1	1
Voelker	1	0	0	1	0	1	1	0
Dethmers	0	0	0	1	1	1	0	1
Smith	1	1	0	0	0	1	1	0
Carr	0	0	1	0	0	0	0	1
Edwards	0	0	0	1	0	0	0	0
Black	1	1	0	1	0	0	0	0
Kelly	0	0	1	0	1	0	0	0

(Students may question why the diagonal entries of this 0-1 version of the judge-agreements matrix are 0s, and not 1s, since it seems feasible to consider that a judge agrees with himself. This is a reasonable question, and the data could have been represented with 100% in the diagonal entries of the judge-agreements matrix and a 1 in the diagonal entries of the corresponding 0-1 matrix. This would also lead to putting 1s in the diagonal entries of the ally matrix (see Part d). So, why use 0s in the diagonal? One part of the answer is that it is reasonable to use 0s in the diagonal since it seems rather pointless to say that a judge agrees with himself or is an ally of himself. However, the more important reason is because we want use the ally matrix for a specific purpose, and 0s work better for that purpose. We want to use the ally matrix to analyze *coalitions* (see Parts e and f). We will count the coalitions by using the A^3 matrix, which counts paths of length 3 in the ally matrix. In order to get a clean count, and no superfluous paths of length 3, we need 0s in the diagonal, not 1s.)

c. i. Yes, Kavanagh agrees with Dethmers.

  ii. No, Dethmers does not agree with Kavanagh.

  iii. Kavanagh agrees with everyone. (Examine the Kavanagh row.)

  iv. Smith is the judge with whom the most other judges agree. (Examine the Smith column.)

Unit 2

d. i. All the allies are Ka-V, Ka-S, Ka-B, V-S, V-B, D-C, D-Ke, S-E, S-B, and C-Ke.

ii. Allies are indicated by an entry of 1 in the ally matrix. (See Part b, above, for a discussion of why we put 0s in the diagonal of the ally matrix.)

iii.

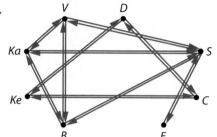

e. i. All of the coalitions are Ka-V-S, Ka-V-B, Ke-D-C, V-B-S, and Ka-B-S. Look for the triangles in the diagram.

ii. A^3 tells how many paths of length 3 exist between any 2 judges. Since a path of length 1 indicates an ally, A^3 shows for each judge who is an ally of an ally of an ally. If a judge is an ally, then that judge's allies might also be allies, but this connection gets more tenuous as the path length increases. Therefore, A^3 gives some information about the far extent of a judge's sphere of influence.

iii. If you divide the entries along the main diagonal by 2, then that quotient will tell you of how many coalitions that person is a member. The entries along the main diagonal work because there must be a circuit to determine a coalition; that is, the path must start and stop with the same person (the entries on the main diagonal). You must divide by 2 because a circuit of length 3, which indicates a coalition, could be traversed in either order.

iv. Both cliques and coalitions are groups of three, and the number of those are found by dividing the entries on the A^3 diagonal by 2. However, cliques refer to friendship, and coalitions represent similar judicial opinion.

f. The digraph of allies has two separate parts. It is reasonable that the three Republicans are Carr, Dethmers, and Kelly. Since these three are a coalition (and are members of only this coalition), it is possible that they agree on many issues. Therefore, they are "like-minded." The other five judges would likely be Democrats.

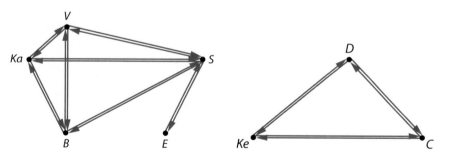

Teacher Notes

Connections

8 Recall that the size of a matrix is number of rows m by number of columns n, written $m \times n$. Suppose you want to multiply two matrices, $A \times B$, and suppose the size of A is $m \times n$.

  a. State the size of B as completely as you can.

  b. Given the size of B from Part a, state the size of the product matrix, $A \times B$.

9 There are at least two different types of multiplication that involve matrices:

  - multiplying two matrices using the standard row-by-column method that you learned in this lesson (matrix multiplication), and

  - multiplying each entry in a matrix by the same number (scalar multiplication).

  Each method is useful in certain contexts. For each method, find one situation from this lesson where that multiplication method can be used to better understand the situation.

10 Two matrix operations that you have used quite often are matrix multiplication and finding row sums. There is a connection between these two operations. Consider the following square matrix.

$$A = \begin{bmatrix} 0 & 1 & 0 & 0 \\ 0 & 0 & 1 & 0 \\ 1 & 0 & 0 & 1 \\ 1 & 1 & 0 & 0 \end{bmatrix}$$

  a. Multiply A on the right by a column matrix filled with 1s. That is, multiply:

$$\begin{bmatrix} 0 & 1 & 0 & 0 \\ 0 & 0 & 1 & 0 \\ 1 & 0 & 0 & 1 \\ 1 & 1 & 0 & 0 \end{bmatrix} \begin{bmatrix} 1 \\ 1 \\ 1 \\ 1 \end{bmatrix}$$

  Compare the product matrix to the row sums of A. Explain why this makes sense.

  b. What matrix multiplication would have the same effect as summing the rows of A^2? Summing the rows of A^3?

  c. Let E be the 4×1 matrix filled with 1s, and suppose that A represents the results of a tournament with four players. Explain the meaning of the following expression in terms of ranking the tournament:

$$AE + \frac{1}{2}A^2E + \frac{1}{3}A^3E$$

Connections

8 **a.** For $A \times B$, if A is an $m \times n$ matrix, then B must be $n \times r$. That is, the number of columns in A must be the same as the number of rows in B. B can have any positive integer r number of columns.

b. $A \times B$ must have size $m \times r$.

9 Responses will vary. Most of the problems in this lesson use standard matrix multiplication. One example of multiplying each entry in a matrix by the same number is converting minutes to hours in the Check Your Understanding Part a on page 111.

10 **a.** The product matrix is shown at the right. Its entries are the same as the row sums of A. Since each row is made up of 0s and 1s, multiplying each row entry by 1 and summing these 4 numbers is counting the number of 1s.

$$\begin{bmatrix} 1 \\ 1 \\ 2 \\ 2 \end{bmatrix}$$

b. To sum the rows of A^2 (or A^3), simply multiply A^2 (or A^3) by the column matrix filled with 1s.

c. This expression represents a 4×1 matrix whose entries are a weighted sum of row sums of powers of A. Thus, if A is a tournament matrix, then the entries of the 4×1 matrix $AE + \frac{1}{2}A^2E + \frac{1}{3}A^3E$ give a ranking of the four players where direct wins are given more weight than stage-two wins, which in turn are given more weight than stage-three wins. (This is, in fact, one method used to rank tournaments.)

11. In music, a change of key sounds more natural if only a few notes are changed. If two keys differ by too many notes, then a change from one key to the other is "remote" and sounds "unnatural" to people in our culture. Each key has five closely related keys, that is, keys that do not differ by very many notes. A vertex-edge graph can be used to model this situation, as follows. (The symbol ♭ is read "flat." For example, B♭ is read "B flat.")

Related Key Graph

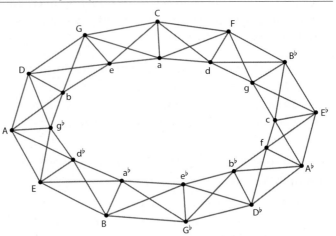

The twelve vertices in the outer circle represent the major keys: C, F, B flat, E flat, A flat, D flat, G flat, B, E, A, D, G. The vertices in the inner circle represent the twelve minor keys (written in lower-case letters): a, d, g, c, f, b flat, e flat, a flat, d flat, g flat, b, e. Each vertex is joined to the five vertices that represent the five closely related keys.

a. Suppose that key changes between keys that are one or two edges apart on the graph are thought to sound "natural," but key changes between keys that are farther apart sound "unnatural."

   i. Does a key change from C to g♭ sound natural? How about from G to A?

   ii. How many natural key changes are there from B?

b. What would be the size of an adjacency matrix for this graph?

c. How could you use operations on the adjacency matrix to answer Part a? Explain your thinking.

11 **a.** **i.** To move from C to g^b on the graph requires a path of length 3. Thus, this key change does not sound natural. Since the shortest path from G to A has length 2, the key change from G to A does sound natural.

   ii. There are 9 natural key changes from B.

b. 24 × 24

c. You would have to find the square of the matrix and then add this to the original matrix since you are looking for the number of one-step or two-step key changes. The non-diagonal entries that are zero correspond to key changes that do not sound natural. The number of nonzero entries corresponds to the number of natural key changes.

CULTURAL ISSUE Whether a sequence of notes seems natural or unnatural is influenced by culture. There may be students in your classroom who find European/American sounds unnatural.

Unit 2

Reflections

12 In Investigation 2, you learned how to multiply matrices using a specific "row-column procedure." Think about this multiplication procedure.

a. Show with hand movements how this procedure works.

b. Reflect on your experience learning this procedure and then write a few sentences explaining your answer to the following questions: Did you find this procedure easy or difficult to learn? Was it surprising or strange in any way? Did you at first think about multiplying matrices in a different way?

13 What must be true about the size of matrix A to allow you to compute $A \times A$?

14 Think about the matrix analysis of the ecosystem in Investigation 3.

a. What happens if you keep computing powers of the adjacency matrix for the food web digraph? What does this mean in terms of paths through the food web?

b. What do the entries in the last matrix, before you reach all 0s, tell you about path lengths? About the possible spread of contamination?

Willow Forest Ecosystem

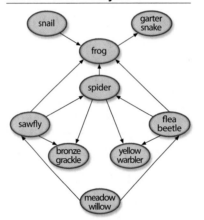

c. Explain how to compute a single matrix that will show, for each organism, all the organisms that are farther up the food chain. Compute the matrix and check it by examining the graph.

d. Contamination of which organisms has the potential to impact the ecosystem most? What matrix computation addresses this question?

e. Do you think that the adjacency matrix for any digraph will eventually have a power for which all of its entries are 0s? Explain why or why not.

Reflections

12 **a.** Students may demonstrate using a horizontal movement with the left hand and a simultaneous vertical movement with the right hand.

b. Student responses will vary. This is often a difficult and strange procedure for students to learn (although perhaps the approach used in this lesson will make it sensible and neither difficult nor strange for students). Students may comment that they first thought about multiplying matrices entry by entry since this is similar to the procedure used for adding matrices.

13 A must be an $n \times n$, or square, matrix. This is true because the number of columns of the first matrix in the product must be the same as the number of rows of the second matrix.

14 **a.** Eventually, some power of A will be all zeroes. This is because there are not any circuits in the digraph, so all paths have finite length. At some point, the lengths of the paths corresponding to a power of the matrix A will be longer than the length of any path in the digraph, so all entries will be zero. In the food web, the longest paths are of length 4, so A^5 and all higher powers will contain all zeroes.

b. The power of the matrix just before you reach all zeroes gives information about the length of the longest paths in the digraph. In the food web, A^4 is the highest power of A before all entries are zero, and the longest path length in the digraph is 4. In terms of possible spread of contamination, if the contamination will affect organisms that are 4 or fewer steps apart, then all organisms will be contaminated (assuming all organisms that do not feed on other organisms are contaminated directly).

c. Compute $A + A^2 + A^3 + A^4$. Compute up to the fourth power because 4 is the longest path length in the digraph. Thus, entries in $A + A^2 + A^3 + A^4$ show the number of paths of all possible lengths from one vertex to any other (see the matrix at the right). For each organism, look at the nonzero entries in the row corresponding to the organism. The organism corresponding to the column of the nonzero entry is farther up the food chain than the organism represented by the row.

	Bg	Fb	Fr	Gs	Mw	Sa	Sn	Sp	Yw
Bronze grackle	0	0	0	0	0	0	0	0	0
Flea beetle	1	0	2	2	0	0	0	1	2
Frog	0	0	0	1	0	0	0	0	0
Garter snake	0	0	0	0	0	0	0	0	0
Meadow willow	3	1	4	4	0	1	0	2	3
Sawfly	2	0	2	2	0	0	0	1	1
Snail	0	0	1	1	0	0	0	0	0
Spider	0	1	1	1	0	0	0	0	1
Yellow warbler	0	0	0	0	0	0	0	0	0

d. Contamination of the meadow willows will have the most impact on the ecosystem because there is a path of some length from the meadow willow to every other vertex except snails. Thus, all organisms except snails could become contaminated either directly or indirectly from the meadow willows. You can see this in the matrix $A + A^2 + A^3 + A^4$ because the meadow-willow row of that matrix has the most nonzero entries.

e. No, the adjacency matrix A for a digraph that contains circuits will never have a power that is all zeroes. This is because by going around the circuit over and over, you can get paths of any length. Thus, powers of A will always have some nonzero entries.

(15) Describe a situation, different from those in this lesson, where matrix multiplication would be useful. Write and answer two questions about the situation that involve using matrices.

(16) Look back at your work for Applications Task 7. Compare the judge-agreements matrix with the matrix you constructed in Part b of that task. What useful information is lost in the matrix you prepared?

Extensions

(17) Sometimes it is useful to interchange the rows and columns of a matrix. For a matrix M, the matrix obtained by interchanging the rows and columns of M is called the **transpose of M**, denoted M^T.

For example, if $M = \begin{bmatrix} 3 & 4 & 5 \\ 6 & 7 & 8 \end{bmatrix}$, then $M^T = \begin{bmatrix} 3 & 6 \\ 4 & 7 \\ 5 & 8 \end{bmatrix}$. Consider some

of the matrices you have studied—see the cost and quantity matrices from Investigation 2, reproduced below.

Cost per Uniform

$$C = \begin{array}{cc} & \begin{array}{ccc} S & M & L \end{array} \\ \begin{array}{c} \text{Uniforms Plus} \\ \text{Sporting Supplies} \end{array} & \begin{bmatrix} \$28 & \$36 & \$41 \\ \$34 & \$35 & \$36 \end{bmatrix} \end{array}$$

Quantity of Uniforms

$$Q = \begin{array}{cc} & \begin{array}{ccc} \text{Zephyrs} & \text{Fliers} & \text{Pioneers} \end{array} \\ \begin{array}{c} S \\ M \\ L \end{array} & \begin{bmatrix} 6 & 6 & 9 \\ 11 & 4 & 6 \\ 3 & 10 & 5 \end{bmatrix} \end{array}$$

a. Consider multiplication of matrices C and Q.

  i. Which multiplication is possible: $C \times Q$ or $Q \times C$? Why?

  ii. Carry out the possible multiplication.

b. Now consider the transpose matrices.

  i. Compute C^T and Q^T. Label the rows and columns of the two transpose matrices. Are the matrix titles still appropriate?

  ii. Think about which multiplications are possible: $C^T \times Q^T$ and $Q^T \times C^T$? Check your thinking by carrying out the possible multiplication(s).

c. Compare the product matrices from Parts a and b. Do the two product matrices contain the same information? Explain.

15 Student responses will vary. Students should select situations from their own experiences or from ideas from their parents.

16 The actual percentages give more information than the 0s and 1s. For example, Carr agreed with 61% of Black's opinions, and Black agreed with 44% of Carr's opinions; but in the 0s-and-1s matrix, both of the entries are 0. It now seems that the level of agreement between Black and Carr is the same both directions. This is typical of what happens in mathematical modeling. You may gain some power in terms of the usefulness of the model, but you may lose some of the detailed information.

Extensions

17 **a.** **i.** $C \times Q$ is possible. The sizes of the matrices makes this multiplication possible. $Q \times C$ is not possible since the number of columns of Q is not the same as the number of rows of C.

ii. $C \times Q =$

	Zephyrs	Fliers	Pioneers
Uniforms Plus	$687	$722	$673
Sporting Supplies	$697	$704	$696

b. **i.** $C^T =$

	Uniforms Plus	Sporting Supplies
S	$28	$34
M	$36	$35
L	$41	$36

$Q^T =$

	S	M	L
Zephyrs	6	11	3
Fliers	6	4	10
Pioneers	9	6	5

The matrix titles are still appropriate and can remain the same since each matrix still contains the same information, just slightly rearranged.

ii. $C^T \times Q^T$ is not possible.

$Q^T \times C^T =$

	Uniforms Plus	Sporting Supplies
Zephyrs	$687	$697
Fliers	$722	$704
Pioneers	$673	$696

c. $C \times Q$ and $Q^T \times C^T$ contain the same information, just arranged slightly differently with respect to rows and columns.

d. Consider the brand-switching matrix equation on page 105, reproduced below.

Buyers This Year   **Brand-Switching Matrix**   **Buyers Next Year**

$$
\begin{array}{c}
\begin{matrix} N & R & F \end{matrix} \\
\begin{bmatrix} 700 & 500 & 400 \end{bmatrix}
\end{array}
\times
\begin{array}{c}
\begin{matrix} & N & R & F \end{matrix} \\
\begin{matrix} N \\ R \\ F \end{matrix}
\begin{bmatrix} 40\% & 40\% & 20\% \\ 20\% & 50\% & 30\% \\ 10\% & 20\% & 70\% \end{bmatrix}
\end{array}
=
\begin{array}{c}
\begin{matrix} N & R & F \end{matrix} \\
\begin{bmatrix} \underline{\quad} & \underline{\quad} & \underline{\quad} \end{bmatrix}
\end{array}
$$

Sometimes, equations like this are written with column matrices (see Applications Task 2 Part c) instead of row matrices. Using *transpose matrices*, rewrite this equation as an equivalent equation with column matrices.

18 The most general definition of an adjacency matrix for a digraph is that it is a matrix with entries that indicate *how many* edges there are from the vertex on the row to the vertex on the column. In this lesson, an adjacency matrix was defined as a matrix with entries that indicate *if* there is an edge from the vertex on the row to the vertex on the column. Thus, the adjacency matrices in this lesson always had entries that were 1s or 0s. Using the more general definition of an adjacency matrix, an adjacency matrix can have entries that are larger than 1.

a. Draw a digraph that has an adjacency matrix in which some entries are larger than 1.

b. Describe the kinds of digraphs that have adjacency matrices with only 1s and 0s as entries.

19 Consider the brand-switching matrix from Investigation 1, reproduced below.

Brand-Switching Matrix

		Next Brand		
		Nike	Reebok	Fila
	Nike	40%	40%	20%
Current Brand	Reebok	20%	50%	30%
	Fila	10%	20%	70%

This matrix models a type of process called a *Markov process*, named after the Russian mathematician A. A. Markov. There are two key components of a Markov process: *states* and a *transition matrix*. In the brand-switching example, the states are the row matrices that show how many people buy each shoe brand in a given year. The transition matrix is the brand-switching matrix, which shows how the states change from year to year. Powers of this matrix give you information about the long-term behavior of the Markov process.

a. Call the brand-switching matrix B. Enter B into your calculator or computer software, entering the percents as decimals, and use the last answer function to compute all the powers of B up to B^{20}. Describe what happened. Explain the meaning of the entries of B^{20}.

d. $\begin{bmatrix} 40\% & 20\% & 10\% \\ 40\% & 50\% & 20\% \\ 20\% & 30\% & 70\% \end{bmatrix} \begin{bmatrix} 700 \\ 500 \\ 400 \end{bmatrix} = \begin{bmatrix} \_ \\ \_ \\ \_ \end{bmatrix}$

18 **a.** One possible digraph and its adjacency matrix are shown below.

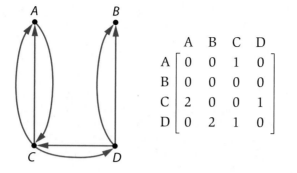

$$\begin{array}{c} \\ A \\ B \\ C \\ D \end{array} \begin{array}{cccc} A & B & C & D \\ \begin{bmatrix} 0 & 0 & 1 & 0 \\ 0 & 0 & 0 & 0 \\ 2 & 0 & 0 & 1 \\ 0 & 2 & 1 & 0 \end{bmatrix} \end{array}$$

b. A digraph whose adjacency matrix has only 1s and 0s will have at most one edge from any vertex to any other vertex. These matrices can model situations where a relationship exists or does not exist. For example, an animal is food for another, or it is not.

19 **a.** Eventually, every number in the first column is essentially the same, every number in the second column is the same, and every number in the third column is the same. Or, we could say that each row of the resulting matrix is the same. B^{20} shows the approximate percentages of shoes of each brand that will be sold 20 years later.

The matrix is: $B^{20} \approx \begin{bmatrix} 0.19 & 0.34 & 0.47 \\ 0.19 & 0.34 & 0.47 \\ 0.19 & 0.34 & 0.47 \end{bmatrix}$

The entries have reached a steady state. About 19% of customers will either stay with or change to Nike; about 34% will either stay with or change to Reebok; and about 47% will either stay with or change to Fila.

> **TECHNOLOGY NOTE** On some calculators, the last answer function works differently for matrices than usual. On *any* calculator with matrix operations, however, you should be able to simulate the "last answer" by storing the answer into a new matrix and using that new matrix.

Unit 2

b. In Investigation 1, you assumed that the numbers of people buying each brand of shoe this year were as follows: 700 people bought Nike, 500 people bought Reebok, and 400 people bought Fila. Do the following matrix multiplications using powers of B:

$$[700 \quad 500 \quad 400] \times B^4$$
$$[700 \quad 500 \quad 400] \times B^{10}$$
$$[700 \quad 500 \quad 400] \times B^{20}$$

c. Explain the meaning of $[700 \quad 500 \quad 400] \times B^n$ for a positive integer n.

20 Look back at the information on the extent of agreement among Michigan Supreme Court judges in Applications Task 7. The matrix summarizing that information is reproduced below. In Task 7, you looked for allies and coalitions among the judges. In this task, you will rank the judges according to how much influence they exert upon one another.

Judge Agreements

	Ka	V	D	S	C	E	B	Ke
Kavanagh	—	76%	80%	85%	81%	88%	83%	77%
Voelker	81%	—	60%	90%	59%	86%	99%	63%
Dethmers	66%	65%	—	75%	99%	77%	72%	95%
Smith	78%	79%	63%	—	57%	81%	84%	64%
Carr	63%	58%	100%	66%	—	70%	61%	100%
Edwards	61%	68%	66%	76%	65%	—	70%	65%
Black	75%	84%	48%	77%	44%	68%	—	55%
Kelly	60%	53%	86%	63%	91%	61%	62%	—

a. Look at the data for Kavanagh and Edwards. If you were to choose one of these judges as being dominant over the other, who would you pick as the dominant judge? Why?

b. Judge X is said to *dominate* Judge Y if Y agrees with X more than X agrees with Y. The goal now is to rank the judges according to dominance. To begin, think of a way to construct a *dominance matrix* using 0s and 1s. Construct the dominance matrix.

b. The product is approximately [313 554 732].
The product is approximately [306 545 749].
The product is approximately [306 545 749].

c. The entries in the product matrix will show how many pairs of each brand are estimated to be sold *n* years later. (You may want to discuss how reliable this estimation is.)

20 **a.** Kavanagh agrees with Edwards 88% of the time while Edwards only agrees with Kavanagh 61% of the time. Edwards appears to be the dominant judge over Kavanagh.

b. A 1 is placed in the matrix if the row judge dominates the column judge. For example, Kavanagh agrees with Voelker 76% of the time, and Voelker agrees with Kavanagh 81% of the time.

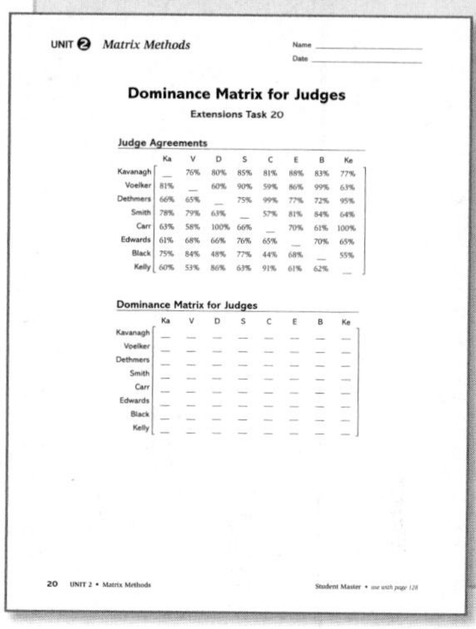

So, Kavanagh dominates Voelker, and a 1 is placed in the Ka-V position of the matrix.

Dominance Matrix

	Ka	V	D	S	C	E	B	Ke
Kavanagh	0	1	0	0	0	0	0	0
Voelker	0	0	1	0	0	0	0	0
Dethmers	1	0	0	0	1	0	0	0
Smith	1	1	1	0	1	0	0	0
Carr	1	1	0	0	0	0	0	0
Edwards	1	1	1	1	1	0	0	0
Black	1	1	1	1	1	1	0	1
Kelly	1	1	1	1	1	1	0	0

$= D$

Unit 2

Call the dominance matrix D. Direct dominance, as shown in D, is more powerful than the indirect dominance of second-stage, third-stage, or further-removed dominance, as shown in powers of D. The powers of D can be *weighted* with an appropriate multiplier to reflect the degrees of dominance.

c. Use weighted powers of the dominance matrix, along with row sums and matrix sums, to rank the eight judges according to dominance. Give the entries in D full weight (multiply by 1) and the entries in D^2 half weight (multiply by $\frac{1}{2}$). Continue in this manner. Multiply the entries in D^3 by $\frac{1}{3}$ and so on up through D^7, which would be multiplied by $\frac{1}{7}$.

(You may not need powers of D up through D^7 to get a clear ranking. A general rule, however, is to include powers up through D^{n-1}, where n is the number of vertices. The reason for stopping at $n - 1$ is that the longest possible path from a vertex without returning to that vertex has length $n - 1$.)

d. Use this weighted ranking method to rank the players in the tennis tournament in Investigation 3 (pages 115–116). How does this ranking compare with your previous ranking?

21 You have seen that matrices have some properties that are similar to properties of real numbers. Consider the idea of square root. Every non-negative real number has a square root. For example, to find a square root of 7, you must find a number x such that $x^2 = 7$. Consider a similar matrix situation. Find a matrix A that satisfies the matrix equation below.

$$A^2 = \begin{bmatrix} 1 & 1 & 0 \\ 0 & 0 & 1 \\ 1 & 0 & 1 \end{bmatrix}$$

Hints: You might find A by thinking how to multiply a matrix by itself, just as you can find the square root of 9 by thinking about how to multiply a number by itself to get 9. Another way to find A is to think of A as an adjacency matrix for a digraph. Given the information in matrix A^2, what does the diagraph for matrix A look like?

22 In Investigation 3, you found the number of paths of length two in the food web digraph by squaring the adjacency matrix for the digraph.

a. Explain as precisely as you can why multiplying the adjacency matrix by itself gives you information about the number of paths of length two.

b. In general, how could you use an adjacency matrix to find paths of length n ($n \geq 1$) in a digraph?

c. The row sums of $D + \frac{1}{2}D^2 + \frac{1}{3}D^3 + \frac{1}{4}D^4 + \frac{1}{5}D^5 + \frac{1}{6}D^6$ are shown in the table below. The ranking of the eight judges is now clear.

Dominance Ranking

Judge	Row Sum	Ranking
Kavanagh	4.35	8
Voelker	6.08	7
Dethmers	8.85	5
Smith	19.28	4
Carr	7.78	6
Edwards	31.15	3
Black	79.05	1
Kelly	49.78	2

d. The rows of $T + \frac{1}{2}T^2 + \frac{1}{3}T^3 + \frac{1}{4}T^4 + \frac{1}{5}T^5$, along with resulting rankings, are shown in the table below. This yields the same ranking as in Investigation 3.

Tournament Results

$$\begin{bmatrix} 0 & 0 & 0 & 1 & 0 & 0 \\ 1 & 0 & 1 & 0 & 1 & 0 \\ 0 & 0 & 0 & 0 & 1 & 0 \\ 0 & 0 & 1 & 0 & 0 & 1 \\ 1 & 0 & 0 & 1 & 0 & 0 \\ 1 & 1 & 1 & 0 & 0 & 0 \end{bmatrix} = T$$

Weighted Ranking

Player	Row Sum	Ranking
Akiko	7.28	5
Cora	15.38	2
Erina	6.7	6
Julia	13.08	3
Keadra	11.85	4
Maria	16.87	1

21 Students could try to find A by setting up two empty matrices, each one representing A, and then analyzing how to fill in the entries so that the multiplication of A by itself will yield the given matrix for A^2. Using an entirely different approach, we could think of A as an adjacency matrix. If A is an adjacency matrix for a digraph, then a 1 in A^2 means that there is one path of length two between the associated vertices in the digraph. Using this information, we can construct a digraph, as shown below and find A.

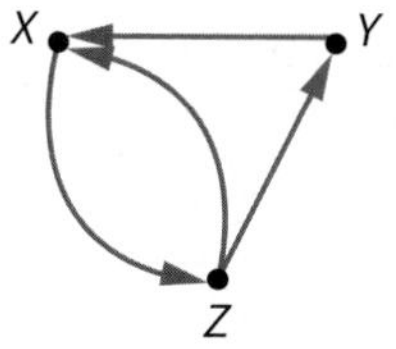

$$\begin{array}{c} \\ X \\ Y \\ Z \end{array} \begin{array}{ccc} X & Y & Z \\ \begin{bmatrix} 0 & 0 & 1 \\ 1 & 0 & 0 \\ 1 & 1 & 0 \end{bmatrix} \end{array} = A$$

22

a. The key to this correspondence is the row-column nature of matrix multiplication combined with the convention of reading matrices *from* rows *to* columns. Also, keep in mind that a path of length 2 starts *from* the start, goes *to* a connecting vertex, then goes *from* the connecting vertex *to* the end.

Imagine standing on a large copy of the food web. When multiplying the adjacency matrix by itself, you have a copy of the matrix on the left and another copy of the matrix on the right. You work with the *rows* of the left matrix. These rows represent where a path starts *from*. Imagine standing on the vertex for a row. As you move along that row in the matrix, an entry of 1 indicates a path *to* the vertex that column represents. You can step onto that vertex.

Now the question in creating two-stage paths is whether the new vertex is a connecting vertex. That is, can you go *from* that vertex *to* somewhere else? That happens only if you have also hit a 1 as you have simultaneously been coming down a column in the right-hand copy of the matrix. If you do simultaneously hit a 1 in a row of the left-hand matrix and a column of the right-hand matrix, then you have found a connecting vertex, and thus a path of length 2.

For example, suppose you are working with the flea-beetle row and the garter-snake column. There is a 1 in the *third* entry in the flea-beetle row; so, there is a path from flea beetle to frog. But the *third* entry in the garter-snake column also concerns the frog: a 1 there indicates a path from the frog to the garter snake.

So, you have found a path of length 2 (that is, a path with 2 edges): flea beetle → frog → garter snake.

Thus, whenever you find a matching pair of 1s as you do the row-column multiplication, you have found a connecting vertex. The path goes from the row vertex to the connecting vertex and then from the connecting vertex to the column vertex.

In summary, whenever you hit a nonzero entry simultaneously in the left and right copies of the adjacency matrix as you multiply, then you have a path of length 2. Since you multiply 1s and add the products as you go, you will get the total number of paths of length 2 as a final result.

b. To find the paths of length n, you compute the adjacency matrix to the power n. The number of paths of length n from row to column is the row sum, excluding the diagonal entry.

Teacher Notes

Review

23 Sketch graphs of the following linear equations.

   a. $3x + 4y = 12$

   b. $x - 3y = 5$

   c. $5x + y = 7$

24 Rewrite each of the following expressions in simplest equivalent form.

   a. $3(4x - 5) + 10x - 1$

   b. $4 + (x + 9)x + 5x$

   c. $7n(2n + 4) - 6(3n - 12)$

   d. $15 - 4(2p + 1) - (6 - p)$

25 Without using a protractor, try to draw an angle with each given measure. Then use a protractor to check your angle estimates.

   a. $45°$

   b. $120°$

   c. $30°$

   d. $170°$

   e. $135°$

26 Sketch a rectangular prism that has edges of length 3 cm, 5 cm, and 8 cm.

   a. Find the volume of the rectangular prism you sketched.

   b. Find the surface area of the rectangular prism you sketched.

   c. Find the volume and surface area of a prism that is similar to the one you sketched but has been enlarged by a scale factor of 3.

27 Solve each system of equations.

   a. $\begin{cases} y = 4x + 1 \\ 2x + 5 = y \end{cases}$

   b. $\begin{cases} 4x + y = 10 \\ 14x - y = -1 \end{cases}$

   c. $\begin{cases} 10x + 2y = 46 \\ 3x - 3y = 21 \end{cases}$

28 Place the following in order from smallest to largest.

   a. $\frac{1}{3}$, 0.33, 30%, 0.033, $\frac{303}{1,000}$

   b. $\frac{3}{4}$, 50%, 0.7, $\frac{6}{9}$, 0.25

Review

Just in Time

23 The axes intercepts are indicated on the graphs.

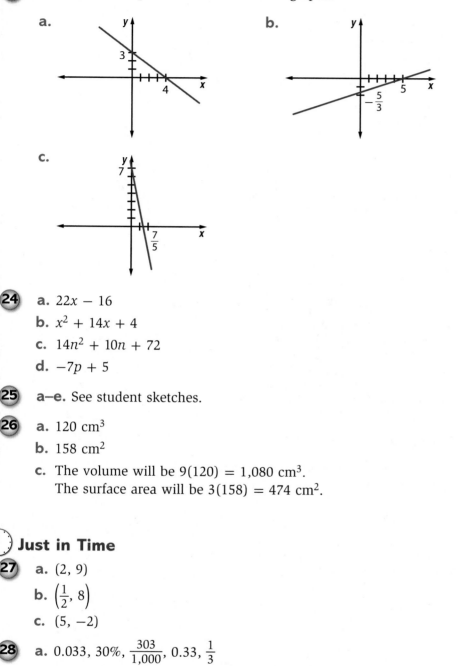

a.

b.

c.

24 a. $22x - 16$

b. $x^2 + 14x + 4$

c. $14n^2 + 10n + 72$

d. $-7p + 5$

25 **a–e.** See student sketches.

26 a. 120 cm^3

b. 158 cm^2

c. The volume will be $9(120) = 1{,}080 \text{ cm}^3$.
The surface area will be $3(158) = 474 \text{ cm}^2$.

Just in Time

27 a. $(2, 9)$

b. $\left(\frac{1}{2}, 8\right)$

c. $(5, -2)$

28 a. 0.033, 30%, $\frac{303}{1{,}000}$, 0.33, $\frac{1}{3}$

b. 0.25, 50%, $\frac{6}{9}$, 0.7, $\frac{3}{4}$

29 The shaded triangle below has been used to create a pattern. For each of the positions 1–4, describe the transformation that will map the shaded triangle onto that position.

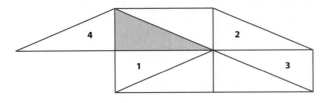

30 Fill in each blank with the appropriate number.

a. 1.5 ft = _____ in. = _____ yd

b. 3,750 mm = _____ cm = _____ m

c. 360 minutes = _____ seconds = _____ hours = _____ days

31 Mr. Hernandez gave each of his students a 20-item test. The table below gives some statistics associated with the number of items answered correctly by the students in his class.

Mean	15.5
Median	17
Standard Deviation	2.4

a. After returning the tests, Mr. Hernandez found an error on his answer key and so decided to add one point to each person's score. What would the new mean, median, and standard deviation be?

b. The scores on this test can be turned into percentages by multiplying each score by 5. What are the mean and median percentages of the original test results? What would the standard deviation of those percentages be?

32 Real numbers and operations on real numbers satisfy certain properties.

a. What real number x satisfies each equation below? (The variable a represents any real number.) Illustrate your answers for some sample values of a.

   i. $a + x = a$

   ii. $a \cdot x = a$

b. What real number x satisfies each equation? Illustrate your answers for some sample real number values of a.

   i. $a + x = 0$

   ii. $a \cdot x = 1$

29 To move to position 1, use a reflection across the line containing the longest leg of the shaded triangle.

To move to position 2, use a horizontal translation the length of the longest leg of the triangle. (Students may refer to this translation as a "slide.")

To move to position 3, use a 180° rotation about the point common to both triangles. (Students may refer to this as a half-turn.)
To move to position 4, use a vertical line reflection.

30 **a.** 1.5 ft = 18 in. = 0.5 yd

b. 3,750 mm = 375 cm = 3.75 m

c. 360 minutes = 21,600 seconds = 6 hours = 0.25 days

31 **a.**

Mean	16.5
Median	18
Standard Deviation	2.4

b.

Mean	77.5%
Median	85%
Standard Deviation	12%

Just in Time

32 Students should supply specific examples as well as the solutions below.

a. **i.** $x = 0$

ii. $x = 1$

b. **i.** $x = -a$

ii. $x = \dfrac{1}{a}$

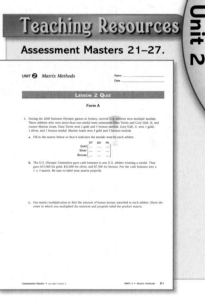

Teaching Resources

Assessment Masters 21–27.

Unit 2

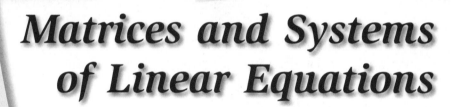

LESSON
3

$$X + 2y = 8 \qquad X = 8 - 2y$$
$$2x + y = 4 \implies 2x + y = 4$$
$$\Downarrow$$
$$2(8 - 2y) + y = 4$$
$$16 - 4y + y =$$

Matrices and Systems of Linear Equations

In previous lessons, you learned about matrices and matrix operations, and you used matrix methods to solve a variety of problems. One of the most common uses of matrices is to solve systems of linear equations. You already know several methods for solving a system of two linear equations. Using matrices will be another powerful method to add to your toolkit.

132   UNIT 2

Matrices and Systems of Linear Equations

This lesson continues the study of solving systems of linear equations. Students first encountered linear systems in Course 1, Unit 3, *Linear Functions*. They studied these systems in some detail in the previous unit in Course 2, *Functions, Equations, and Systems*. In this unit, students learn a matrix method for solving linear systems. Systems of linear equations will be revisited and used in later units and courses.

To begin learning how to use matrices to solve a system of linear equations, students first examine some important properties of matrices and compare them to properties of real numbers. Then, in Investigation 2, students learn how to apply those properties to solve a system of linear equations by setting up and solving a matrix equation. In Investigation 3, students review, analyze, and compare all of the methods they now know to solve linear systems.

Lesson Objectives

- Examine properties of operations with matrices
- Compare properties of matrices with those of real numbers
- Use matrices and their properties to solve systems of linear equations
- Review, analyze, and compare various methods for solving systems of linear equations

Lesson Launch

It is not necessary to review linear-system solution methods now since Investigation 3 focuses on reviewing the methods students learned in previous units and comparing to the new matrix method they will learn in this lesson.

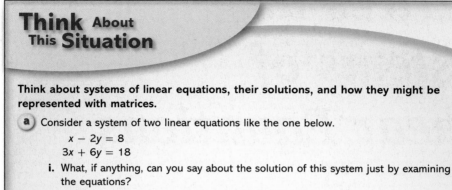

Think About
This Situation

Think about systems of linear equations, their solutions, and how they might be represented with matrices.

a Consider a system of two linear equations like the one below.

$$x - 2y = 8$$
$$3x + 6y = 18$$

i. What, if anything, can you say about the solution of this system just by examining the equations?

ii. What are some methods you know for solving such a system?

iii. Which method would you use? Why?

b Can you think of a way you might represent the system of equations above with matrices and matrix multiplication?

The first step in learning how to use matrices to solve linear systems is to examine more closely some properties of matrices. In Investigation 1, you will learn about some important properties of matrices and compare those properties to properties of real numbers. In Investigation 2, you will learn how to represent a system of two linear equations as a matrix equation and then how to solve the matrix equation. Finally, in Investigation 3, you will compare this matrix method for solving linear systems to methods you have previously learned.

Investigation 1 Properties of Matrices

Matrices and matrix operations obey certain properties. The matrix methods you use to solve problems often depend upon these properties. As you investigate properties of matrices, look for answers to these questions:

> *What are some important properties of operations with matrices?*

> *How are these properties similar to, and different from, properties of operations with real numbers?*

In arithmetic, you studied numbers and operations on numbers. In algebra, you have studied expressions and operations on expressions. In both settings, you found that certain properties were obeyed. For example, one such property is the *Associative Property of Addition:* $a + (b + c) = (a + b) + c$.

In this unit, you have been studying matrices and matrix operations, including matrix addition and matrix multiplication. You will now investigate properties of matrices and their operations. This situation occurs frequently in mathematics—certain mathematical objects (like numbers or matrices) along with operations on those objects are studied and then their properties are examined.

Think About This Situation

a. **i.** By examining the coefficients of *x* and *y* for this system, you see that the lines are not parallel and thus the system has one solution.

ii. Methods for solving systems are graphing, substitution, and elimination.

iii. Students should offer their ideas for the method of their choice for this particular system.

b. Students will not likely be able to answer this part. If someone remembers doing $\begin{bmatrix} 2 & 5 \\ 1 & 3 \end{bmatrix}\begin{bmatrix} x \\ y \end{bmatrix}$ from the Check Your Understanding on page 111, they might get started on this answer. Leave the answer open for this lesson to resolve.

Investigation 1   Properties of Matrices

In this investigation, students will learn about some important properties of matrices and their operations, and they will compare these properties to those of real numbers.

Matrix properties in the problems of this investigation include:

Problem 1: Matrix size conditions for adding matrices

Problem 2: Commutativity of matrix addition

Problem 3: Additive identity (zero matrix)

Problem 4: Additive inverse matrix

Problem 5: Matrix size conditions for multiplying matrices

Problem 6: Noncommutativity of matrix multiplication

Problem 7: Identity matrix (multiplicative identity)

Problems 8–10: Inverse matrix (multiplicative inverse)

DIFFERENTIATION
Depending on your students' middle-school background, you may decide that students would benefit from some review of properties of real numbers. If so, you can assign Review Task 32 from Lesson 2, if not yet assigned, or other problems that you create.

COLLABORATION SKILL
Make collaboration productive.

Unit 2

1 **Matrix Addition** To begin this exploration of properties of matrices, first consider matrix addition.

a. Suppose $A = \begin{bmatrix} 3 & 4 & 2 \\ 1 & 0 & 9 \end{bmatrix}$. To which of the following matrices can A be added?

$$B = \begin{bmatrix} 1 & 9 & 8 \\ 6 & 5 & 4 \end{bmatrix} \quad C = \begin{bmatrix} 2 & 3 & 4 \\ 1 & 5 & 6 \\ 8 & 5 & 6 \end{bmatrix} \quad D = \begin{bmatrix} 4 & 2 \\ 3 & 5 \\ 8 & 7 \end{bmatrix} \quad E = \begin{bmatrix} -7 & 798 & 87.9 \\ 0 & 0 & \frac{2}{3} \end{bmatrix}$$

b. Under what conditions can two matrices be added? State the conditions as precisely as you can and explain your reasoning.

2 **Commutative Property of Addition** You know from your previous studies that the order in which you add two numbers does not matter. That is, for all real numbers a and b, $a + b = b + a$.

a. Give three examples of the Commutative Property of Addition for real numbers.

b. Suppose $A = \begin{bmatrix} 3 & 4 & 2 \\ 1 & 0 & 9 \end{bmatrix}$ and $B = \begin{bmatrix} 1 & 9 & 8 \\ 6 & 5 & 4 \end{bmatrix}$. Is it true that

$A + B = B + A$?

c. Do you think $A + B = B + A$ for all matrices A and B (assuming that A has the same number of rows and columns as B)? Defend your answer.

3 **Additive Identity** The number 0 has a unique property with respect to addition: adding 0 to any real number leaves the number unchanged. That is, $a + 0 = a$, for all real numbers. The number 0 is called the *additive identity*. Consider a similar situation for matrices.

a. Suppose $A = \begin{bmatrix} 4 & 2 \\ -3 & 5 \\ 8 & 7 \end{bmatrix}$. Find a matrix C so that $A + C = A$.

b. Suppose matrix B has 4 rows and 3 columns. Find a matrix E such that $B + E = B$.

c. Look at the matrices you found in Parts a and b. Write a description (definition) of the **additive identity matrix** for $m \times n$ matrices. Such a matrix is also called a **zero matrix**.

4 **Additive Inverse** Every real number has an *additive inverse*. A number and its additive inverse sum to zero.

a. What is the additive inverse of 17? Of $\frac{3}{4}$? Of -356.76?

b. A matrix and its *additive inverse matrix* sum to the zero matrix.

Let $C = \begin{bmatrix} 2 & 4 & -3 \\ 3 & -5 & -7 \end{bmatrix}$. Find the additive inverse matrix for C by

filling in the blanks for the matrix below:

$$C + \begin{bmatrix} - & - & - \\ - & - & - \end{bmatrix} = \begin{bmatrix} 0 & 0 & 0 \\ 0 & 0 & 0 \end{bmatrix}$$

c. For any matrix A, describe (define) the **additive inverse matrix** for A.

①　**a.** Matrix A can be added to matrices B and E.

POSSIBLE MISCONCEPTION If you assigned the task about matrix transposes in the previous lesson (Extensions Task 17 on page 126), then students might have the misconception that matrix A can be added to matrix D by transposing D and then adding A and D. This, of course, is not true since the transpose of a matrix is not the same as the matrix itself.

b. Two matrices can be added together only if they have the same number of rows and the same number of columns. This is because you add the numbers from the corresponding entries.

②　**a.** Two examples are: $3 + 7 = 10$ and $7 + 3 = 10$; also $-12 + 8 = -4$ and $8 + (-12) = -4$.

b. Yes, $A + B = B + A$ for these matrices A and B.

c. Arguments will vary.

Commutativity of matrix addition (assuming the entries are real numbers) is based upon commutativity of real-number addition.

③　**a.** $C = \begin{bmatrix} 0 & 0 \\ 0 & 0 \\ 0 & 0 \end{bmatrix}$

b. $E = \begin{bmatrix} 0 & 0 & 0 \\ 0 & 0 & 0 \\ 0 & 0 & 0 \\ 0 & 0 & 0 \end{bmatrix}$

c. For an $m \times n$ matrix, the additive identity matrix (or zero matrix) will have m rows and n columns with a zero in every entry.

④　**a.** The additive inverse of:

17 is -17

$\frac{3}{4}$ is $-\frac{3}{4}$

-356.76 is 356.76

b. The additive inverse of C is the matrix $\begin{bmatrix} -2 & -4 & 3 \\ -3 & 5 & 7 \end{bmatrix}$.

c. The additive inverse matrix has the same number of rows and columns as the original matrix, and each entry is the opposite of the original entry in the same position.

⑤ Matrix Multiplication Another important matrix operation is matrix multiplication. As you discovered in Lesson 2, only matrices of "compatible" sizes can be multiplied.

a. Suppose *A* is a matrix that has 4 rows and 2 columns, and matrix *B* has 3 rows and 4 columns. Is it possible to multiply *A* × *B*? How about *B* × *A*? Explain.

b. Suppose *C* is a matrix that can be multiplied on the right by a 3×2 matrix, *D*. That is, you can multiply *C* × *D*. What could be the size of *C*? What would be the size of the product matrix?

c. Suppose matrix *A* has size $m \times n$. What must be the size of *B* so that it is possible to multiply *A* × *B*? What must be the size of the product matrix?

d. Sometimes it is possible to multiply two matrices in either order. What are the conditions on the sizes of two matrices *A* and *B* so that it is possible to multiply *A* × *B* and also *B* × *A*?

⑥ Commutative Property of Multiplication In the case of real numbers, you know that the order of multiplication of numbers does not matter. That is, $ab = ba$, for all real numbers *a* and *b*.

a. Give three examples illustrating the Commutative Property of Multiplication for real numbers.

b. Check to see if the commutative property is true for multiplication of 2×2 matrices. Explain your reasoning. Compare with other students and resolve any differences.

c. In Part d of Problem 5, you found a condition on the sizes of two matrices *A* and *B* so that it is possible to multiply both *A* × *B* and also *B* × *A*. But just because it is possible to multiply in both orders, do you necessarily get the same answer? You just explored this question with 2×2 matrices in Part b. Check it out for some other size matrices of your choice. For example, construct a 2×3 matrix and a 3×2 matrix, then multiply in both orders and see if you get the same answer.

d. Based on your work above, is the commutative property true for matrix multiplication? Explain.

Recall that a matrix with the same number of rows and columns is called a *square matrix*. Square matrices have several important properties with respect to matrix multiplication.

⑦ Multiplicative Identity The number 1 has the unique property that multiplying any real number by 1 does not change the number. That is, $a \times 1 = 1 \times a = a$, for all real numbers *a*. The number 1 is called the *multiplicative identity*. A square matrix that acts like the number 1 in this regard is called an *identity matrix* (or *multiplicative identity matrix*). Multiplying a matrix by the identity matrix does not change the matrix. That is, an **identity matrix** *I* has the property that $A \times I = I \times A = A$. Identity matrices are always square.

5 **a.** It is impossible to multiply $A \times B$ since the number of columns of A (2) is not the same as the number of rows of B (3). It is possible to multiply $B \times A$ since the number of columns of B (4) is the same as the number of rows of A (4).

b. The size of matrix C would be $n \times 3$, where n is an element of the natural numbers (a positive integer). This is because the number of columns of the first matrix and the number of rows in the second matrix must be the same if they are to be multiplied together. The size of the product matrix will be $n \times 2$.

c. For $A \times B$ to be possible, the number of columns in A must be equal to the number of rows in B; this number is n. The number of columns of B can be anything, say p. Thus, if matrix A has size $m \times n$, then for $A \times B$ to be possible, matrix B must have size $n \times p$, and the product will have size $m \times p$.

d. For $A \times B$ to be possible, the number of columns in A must be equal to the number of rows in B; say this number is n. For $B \times A$ to be possible, the number of columns in B must equal the number of rows in A; say this number is m. Thus, A will be an $m \times n$ matrix, and B will be an $n \times m$ matrix.

6 **a.** Two examples are: $(5)(6) = (6)(5)$; also $(-4)(7) = (7)(-4)$.

b. Using almost any randomly chosen matrices, students can easily verify that multiplication of 2×2 matrices is not commutative. Note that, of course, this is not limited to only 2×2 matrices since matrix multiplication is not commutative. Be aware, however, that some students might get "lucky" and find two matrices that commute, so be on the lookout for this unlikely situation. For example, square matrices in which the diagonal entries are the only nonzero entries do commute (such matrices are often called *diagonal matrices*).

c. Choosing any 2×3 matrix and any 3×2 matrix and multiplying in both orders will result in products that are not equal because the product matrices will be different sizes.

d. No, the Commutative Property of Multiplication is not true for matrices. In Part b, we showed that 2×2 matrices are not commutative and indicated that square matrices are not commutative. In Part c, we saw that nonsquare matrices may allow multiplication in both orders, but the products are not equal, and thus commutativity fails.

DIFFERENTIATION
Students who think visually can support their thinking by recognizing that geometrically the "shape" of matrices that can be multiplied in either order are 90° rotations of each other.

INSTRUCTIONAL NOTE
You may need to remind students that in order to show something is not true, only one counterexample needs to be found.

KEY IDEA It is important for students to realize that matrix multiplication is not commutative, not only because size conditions may not be met, but also because even when both orders of multiplication are possible, the product matrices may not be equal.

a. Find the identity matrix for 2×2 square matrices by filling in the blanks for the matrix below.

$$\begin{bmatrix} 5 & 4 \\ 2 & 6 \end{bmatrix} \begin{bmatrix} - & - \\ - & - \end{bmatrix} = \begin{bmatrix} 5 & 4 \\ 2 & 6 \end{bmatrix}$$

Compare your answer with those of other students. Resolve any differences.

b. Multiply $\begin{bmatrix} 5 & 4 \\ 2 & 6 \end{bmatrix}$ on the left by the identity matrix you found in Part a. Check that you get $\begin{bmatrix} 5 & 4 \\ 2 & 6 \end{bmatrix}$ as the answer.

c. Suppose matrix A has 3 rows and 3 columns. Find the identity matrix I such that $A \times I = A$.

d. Write a description of an identity matrix.

8 **Multiplicative Inverse** The product of a number and its *multiplicative inverse* is 1. Every nonzero number has a multiplicative inverse. For example, the multiplicative inverse of 5 is $\frac{1}{5}$ since $5 \times \frac{1}{5} = 1$.

a. What is the multiplicative inverse of 3? Of $\frac{1}{2}$? Of $\frac{5}{3}$?

b. Just as the product of a number and its multiplicative inverse is 1, the product of a matrix and its multiplicative inverse matrix is I. That is, the **multiplicative inverse matrix** for the square matrix D is the matrix written D^{-1}, such that $D \times D^{-1} = I$, where I is the identity matrix.

Suppose $D = \begin{bmatrix} 5 & 3 \\ 3 & 2 \end{bmatrix}$. Make and test a conjecture about the entries of D^{-1}.

c. There are several systematic methods for finding the entries of D^{-1}. One way is to use the fact that if D^{-1} is a matrix $\begin{bmatrix} a & b \\ c & d \end{bmatrix}$ such that $D \times D^{-1} = I$, then

$$\begin{bmatrix} 5 & 3 \\ 3 & 2 \end{bmatrix} \begin{bmatrix} a & b \\ c & d \end{bmatrix} = \begin{bmatrix} 1 & 0 \\ 0 & 1 \end{bmatrix}.$$

Test the following strategy for finding numbers a, b, c, and d that make this matrix equation true.

Step 1: Perform the indicated matrix multiplication to create a system of four linear equations.

$$\begin{bmatrix} 5 & 3 \\ 3 & 2 \end{bmatrix} \begin{bmatrix} a & b \\ c & d \end{bmatrix} = \begin{bmatrix} 1 & 0 \\ 0 & 1 \end{bmatrix}$$

One equation is $5a + 3c = 1$. Write down the other three equations.

(7) **a.** $\begin{bmatrix} 1 & 0 \\ 0 & 1 \end{bmatrix}$

b. Yes. Multiplying on the left by the identity matrix will give $\begin{bmatrix} 5 & 4 \\ 2 & 6 \end{bmatrix}$ as the answer.

c. The identity matrix for a 3 × 3 matrix is $\begin{bmatrix} 1 & 0 & 0 \\ 0 & 1 & 0 \\ 0 & 0 & 1 \end{bmatrix}$.

d. An identity matrix is a square matrix that has 1s on the diagonals from the upper-left corner to the lower-right corner (the main diagonal) and 0s everywhere else.

(8) **a.** The multiplicative inverse of 3 is $\frac{1}{3}$, of $\frac{1}{2}$ is 2, and of $\frac{5}{3}$ is $\frac{3}{5}$.

b. Students will likely suggest D^{-1} use reciprocals to create $\begin{bmatrix} \frac{1}{5} & \frac{1}{3} \\ \frac{1}{3} & \frac{1}{2} \end{bmatrix}$.

Calculating $D \times D^{-1}$ and finding that it does not produce the identity matrix should motivate learning the methods in Part c.

c. **Step 1:** $3a + 2c = 0$

$5b + 3d = 0$

$3b + 2d = 1$

Step 2: Solve the system of two equations involving a and c for a and c. Then solve the other system of two equations for b and d.

Step 3: Use the results from Step 2 to write D^{-1}. Check that $D \times D^{-1} = I$.

9 A multiplicative inverse matrix is often simply an **inverse matrix**. Other methods for finding an inverse matrix include using technology, using a formula, and using special matrix manipulations. A particular method using technology is provided below. (Other methods are examined in the On Your Own tasks.)

a. Consider again the matrix $D = \begin{bmatrix} 5 & 3 \\ 3 & 2 \end{bmatrix}$. Compute the inverse matrix for D using your calculator or computer software. On most calculators, this can be done by entering matrix D into your calculator and then pressing the $\boxed{x^{-1}}$ key. Compare this matrix with what you found in Problem 8. Resolve any differences.

b. An inverse matrix should work whether multiplied from the right or the left. That is,

$$D \times D^{-1} = D^{-1} \times D = I.$$

   i. For matrix D from Part a, check that $D^{-1} \times D = I$.

   ii. Also check that $D \times D^{-1} = I$.

c. Use your calculator or computer software to find A^{-1}, where

$$A = \begin{bmatrix} -8 & -10 \\ 2 & 3 \end{bmatrix}.$$

   Check that $A^{-1} \times A = A \times A^{-1} = I$.

10 Every real number (except 0) has a multiplicative inverse. Check to see if square matrices have this property.

a. Consider $A = \begin{bmatrix} 0 & 9 \\ 0 & 4 \end{bmatrix}$. Without using your calculator or computer software, try to find entries a, b, c, and d that will make the matrix equation true.

$$\begin{bmatrix} a & b \\ c & d \end{bmatrix}\begin{bmatrix} 0 & 9 \\ 0 & 4 \end{bmatrix} = \begin{bmatrix} 1 & 0 \\ 0 & 1 \end{bmatrix}$$

   Does A have an inverse? That is, does the matrix A^{-1} exist?

b. Find a square matrix with all nonzero entries that does not have an inverse.

Step 2: $\left.\begin{array}{l}5a + 3c = 1\\3a + 2c = 0\end{array}\right\} \Rightarrow 5\left(\frac{-2c}{3}\right) + 3c = 1$

$-10c + 9c = 3$

$c = -3$

$a = 2$

$\left.\begin{array}{l}5b + 3d = 0\\3b + 2d = 1\end{array}\right\} \Rightarrow 3\left(\frac{-3d}{5}\right) + 2d = 1$

$-9d + 10d = 5$

$d = 5$

$b = -3$

Step 3: $D^{-1} = \begin{bmatrix} 2 & -3 \\ -3 & 5 \end{bmatrix}$

9 **a.** $D^{-1} = \begin{bmatrix} 2 & -3 \\ -3 & 5 \end{bmatrix}$

b. **i.** $D^{-1} \times D = \begin{bmatrix} 2 & -3 \\ -3 & 5 \end{bmatrix}\begin{bmatrix} 5 & 3 \\ 3 & 2 \end{bmatrix} = \begin{bmatrix} 1 & 0 \\ 0 & 1 \end{bmatrix} = I$

ii. $D \times D^{-1} = \begin{bmatrix} 5 & 3 \\ 3 & 2 \end{bmatrix}\begin{bmatrix} 2 & -3 \\ -3 & 5 \end{bmatrix} = \begin{bmatrix} 1 & 0 \\ 0 & 1 \end{bmatrix} = I$

c. $A^{-1} = \begin{bmatrix} -0.75 & -2.5 \\ 0.5 & 2 \end{bmatrix}$

$A^{-1} \times A = \begin{bmatrix} -0.75 & -2.5 \\ 0.5 & 2 \end{bmatrix}\begin{bmatrix} -8 & -10 \\ 2 & 3 \end{bmatrix} = \begin{bmatrix} 1 & 0 \\ 0 & 1 \end{bmatrix} = I$

$A \times A^{-1} = \begin{bmatrix} -8 & -10 \\ 2 & 3 \end{bmatrix}\begin{bmatrix} -0.75 & -2.5 \\ 0.5 & 2 \end{bmatrix} = \begin{bmatrix} 1 & 0 \\ 0 & 1 \end{bmatrix} = I$

10 **a.** Matrix A does not have an inverse. To see this, let the left-hand matrix be $\begin{bmatrix} a & b \\ c & d \end{bmatrix}$. Multiplying the matrices together, we get $a \cdot 0 + b \cdot 0$ for the first entry of the product, which must be equal to 1. But there is no solution to this equation, and thus it is impossible for A^{-1} to exist.

b. Not all square matrices have inverses. For example, $\begin{bmatrix} 3 & 6 \\ 1 & 2 \end{bmatrix}$ does not have an inverse. (If $A = \begin{bmatrix} a & b \\ c & d \end{bmatrix}$, then A will *not* have an inverse if and only if $ad - bc = 0$. Do not expect students to find this general rule, although they should find a particular matrix that does not have an inverse.)

TECHNOLOGY NOTE When attempting to use a calculator or software to find the inverse of a matrix that does not have one, an error message will likely be displayed. Also, since inverse matrices may result in many decimal places, you may wish to have students change the display to fractions. This feature on TI calculators is under the **MATH** menu.

Unit 2

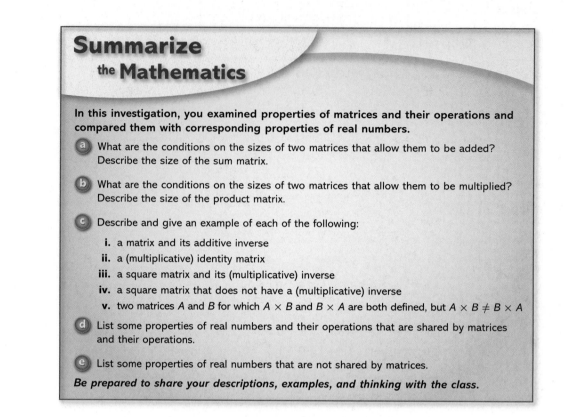

Summarize
the Mathematics

In this investigation, you examined properties of matrices and their operations and compared them with corresponding properties of real numbers.

a What are the conditions on the sizes of two matrices that allow them to be added? Describe the size of the sum matrix.

b What are the conditions on the sizes of two matrices that allow them to be multiplied? Describe the size of the product matrix.

c Describe and give an example of each of the following:

    i. a matrix and its additive inverse
    ii. a (multiplicative) identity matrix
    iii. a square matrix and its (multiplicative) inverse
    iv. a square matrix that does not have a (multiplicative) inverse
    v. two matrices A and B for which $A \times B$ and $B \times A$ are both defined, but $A \times B \neq B \times A$

d List some properties of real numbers and their operations that are shared by matrices and their operations.

e List some properties of real numbers that are not shared by matrices.

Be prepared to share your descriptions, examples, and thinking with the class.

✓ Check Your Understanding

Investigate other similarities and differences between operations on real numbers and the corresponding operations on matrices.

a. An important property of multiplication of numbers concerns products that equal zero. If x and y are real numbers and if $xy = 0$, what can you conclude about x or y? Is it possible that $xy = 0$, and yet $x \neq 0$ and $y \neq 0$?

b. Do you think the property in Part a is true for matrix multiplication? Make a conjecture, and then consider Part c below.

c. Suppose

$$A = \begin{bmatrix} 2 & 3 \\ 4 & 6 \end{bmatrix} \text{ and } B = \begin{bmatrix} 6 & 9 \\ -4 & -6 \end{bmatrix}.$$

Compute $A \times B$. Is it true for matrices that if $A \times B = 0$, then either $A = 0$ or $B = 0$?

d. Think of another property of addition or multiplication of real numbers, and investigate whether matrices also have this property. Prepare a brief summary of your findings.

When the terms "identity matrix" and "inverse matrix" are used, we are referring to the multiplication of matrices. When the inverse or identity for addition are referenced, the additional word "additive" will be used. Students may give examples for Part civ at this time. But by the end of this lesson, students should be able to recognize that a matrix that represents the coefficients of equations of parallel lines will have no inverse. For example, $\begin{bmatrix} 4 & -2 \\ -6 & 3 \end{bmatrix}$ has no inverse.

Summarize the Mathematics

Teaching Resources

Transparency Master 29.

UNIT ② *Matrix Methods*

Summarize the Mathematics

In this investigation, you examined properties of matrices and their operations and compared them with corresponding properties of real numbers.

ⓐ What are the conditions on the sizes of two matrices that allow them to be added? Describe the size of the sum matrix.

ⓑ What are the conditions on the sizes of two matrices that allow them to be multiplied? Describe the size of the product matrix.

ⓒ Describe and give an example of each of the following:
  i. a matrix and its additive inverse
  ii. a (multiplicative) identity matrix
  iii. a square matrix and its (multiplicative) inverse
  iv. a square matrix that does not have a (multiplicative) inverse
  v. two matrices A and B for which A × B and B × A are both defined, but A × B ≠ B × A

ⓓ List some properties of real numbers and their operations that are shared by matrices and their operations.

ⓔ List some properties of real numbers that are not shared by matrices.

Be prepared to share your descriptions, examples, and thinking with the class.

Transparency Master • *Use with page 138*   UNIT 2 • Matrix Methods   29

Unit 2

ⓐ Two matrices can be added if and only if their sizes are the same. The size of the sum matrix will be the same as the size of the two matrices being added.

ⓑ Matrix A can be multiplied by matrix B if the number of columns in A equals the number of rows in B. The product matrix will have the same number of rows as A and the same number of columns as B.

ⓒ i. The additive inverse of matrix A is a matrix of the same size, where each entry is the negative of the corresponding entry in matrix A. One example of a matrix and its additive inverse is
$$\begin{bmatrix} 1 & -2 & 4.5 \\ 0 & 3 & -0.7 \end{bmatrix} \text{ and } \begin{bmatrix} -1 & 2 & -4.5 \\ 0 & -3 & 0.7 \end{bmatrix}.$$

  ii. An identity matrix is a square matrix with 1s along the main diagonal and Os everywhere else. The 2×2 identity matrix is $\begin{bmatrix} 1 & 0 \\ 0 & 1 \end{bmatrix}$.

  iii. The multiplicative inverse of matrix A (if it exists) is the matrix A^{-1} such that $A \times A^{-1}$ gives the identity matrix. For example, if
$$A = \begin{bmatrix} 5 & 3 \\ 4 & 2 \end{bmatrix}, \text{ then } A^{-1} = \begin{bmatrix} -1 & 1.5 \\ 2 & -2.5 \end{bmatrix}.$$

  iv. See the solution to Problem 11 on the previous page. (Students are not expected to give a rigorous description of matrices that do not have inverses. They may use the examples in Problem 10, e.g., $\begin{bmatrix} 0 & 9 \\ 0 & 4 \end{bmatrix}$ has no inverse.)

  v. For example, see Problem 6 on page 135. Students may give two square matrices whose products in both orders are not equal, or they may give two nonsquare matrices that can be multiplied in either order but whose products cannot be equal since they have different sizes.

d Some properties that real numbers and matrices and their respective operations have in common are commutativity of addition, an additive inverse, the existence of a zero element (additive identity), and a multiplicative identity (for square matrices only).

e Multiplication of numbers is commutative, but multiplication of matrices is not. While all numbers (except 0) have multiplicative inverses, there are many matrices (particularly non-square matrices) that do not have multiplicative identities or inverses.

✓ Check Your Understanding

a. If x and y are real numbers and $xy = 0$, then at least one of x or y must be zero.

b. Opinions may vary. Students should state a conjecture, then do Part c.

c. $A \times B = \begin{bmatrix} 0 & 0 \\ 0 & 0 \end{bmatrix}$

The number property in Part a is not true for matrix multiplication. It is possible for $A \times B$ to be a zero matrix without either A or B being a zero matrix, as shown by this example.

d. Other properties that students should be familiar with are the Associative Properties of Addition and Multiplication and the Distributive Property of Multiplication over Addition. All of these properties hold for matrices. (Note that the distributive property is examined in Applications Task 1; the Associative Property of Multiplication is examined in Connections Task 8.)

Teacher Notes

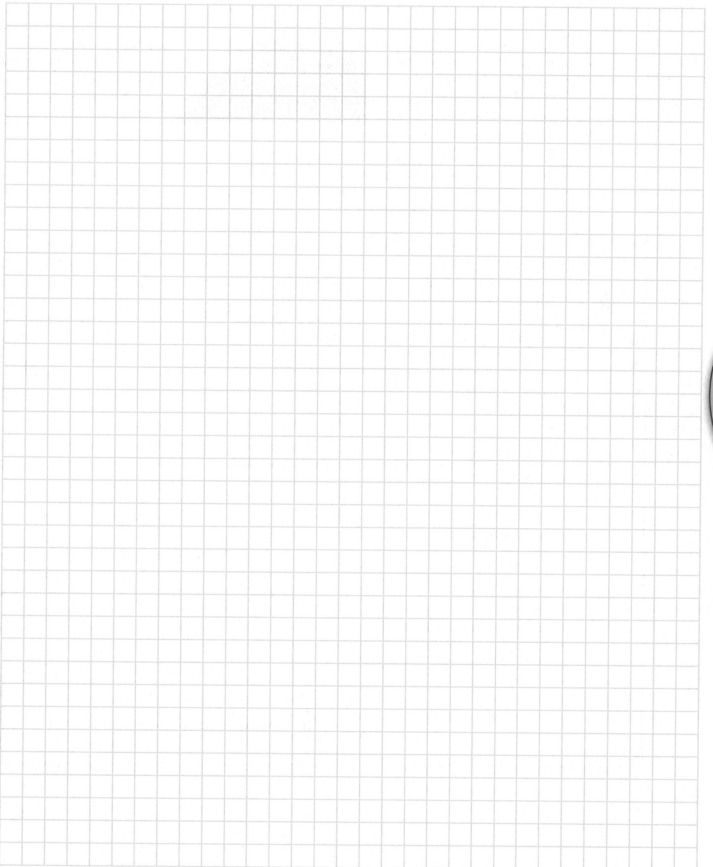

Smart Promotions, Smart Solutions

An expansion baseball team is planning a special promotion at its first game. Fans who arrive early will get a team athletic bag or a cap, as long as supplies last. Suppose the promotion manager for the team can buy athletic bags for $9 each and caps for $5 each. The total budget for buying bags and caps is $25,500. The team plans to give a bag or a cap, but not both, to the first 3,500 fans. The promotion manager wants to know: *How many caps and bags should be given away?* As you solve this problem, look for answers to this question:

> *How can a system of linear equations be represented and solved using matrices?*

1 First, solve the problem any way you can. That is, find the number of bags and caps that can be given away to 3,500 fans so that the entire budget of $25,500 is spent.

2 If you have not done so already, set up and solve a system of linear equations to solve this problem.

3 A system of linear equations like you used in Problem 1 or 2 can be represented with matrices. The matrix representation leads to another useful method for solving this problem.

a. Write the two equations, one above the other, in a form like that below.

$$\_\, b + \_\, c = 3{,}500$$
$$\_\, b + \_\, c = 25{,}500$$

b. This system of equations can be represented by a single matrix equation. Determine the entries of the matrix below so that when you do the matrix multiplication, you get the two equations in Part a.

$$\begin{bmatrix} \_ & \_ \\ \_ & \_ \end{bmatrix} \begin{bmatrix} b \\ c \end{bmatrix} = \begin{bmatrix} 3{,}500 \\ 25{,}500 \end{bmatrix}$$

c. Your matrix equation is of the form $A \times X = D$, or simply $AX = D$.

  i. Which matrix corresponds to A? This matrix is called the *matrix of coefficients*. Explain why that is a sensible name for the matrix.

  ii. Which matrix corresponds to X?

  iii. Which matrix corresponds to D?

d. Compare the matrix equation $AX = D$ to the linear equation $3x = 6$. How are these equations similar? How are they different?

Investigation 2 **Smart Promotions, Smart Solutions**

In this investigation, students learn a matrix method for solving systems of linear equations. In particular, they learn to translate a system of two linear equations into a matrix equation of the form $AX = D$ and solve the matrix equation by multiplying by A^{-1} on the left.

1 In this problem, students use whatever method they like, including guess-and-check, to solve the bags-and-caps problem. This helps remind them that they already know how to solve this type of problem. The solution is that 2,000 bags and 1,500 caps should be given away.

2 Students may have set up and solved a system of linear equations in Problem 1 above. If not, they should do so now. It will be crucial to have the system of equations set up in order to move to the matrix solution below. The two linear equations are $b + c = 3,500$ and $9b + 5c = 25,500$. Students may solve this system using tables, graphs, substitution, or elimination.

3   **a.** $1b + 1c = 3,500$
$9b + 5c = 25,500$

   b. $\begin{bmatrix} 1 & 1 \\ 9 & 5 \end{bmatrix} \begin{bmatrix} b \\ c \end{bmatrix} = \begin{bmatrix} 3,500 \\ 25,500 \end{bmatrix}$

   c.   i. $\begin{bmatrix} 1 & 1 \\ 9 & 5 \end{bmatrix}$ corresponds to A. It contains the coefficients of b and c.

   ii. $\begin{bmatrix} b \\ c \end{bmatrix}$ corresponds to X.

   iii. $\begin{bmatrix} 3,500 \\ 25,500 \end{bmatrix}$ corresponds to D.

   d. The matrix equation and the equation $3x = 6$ both have the same general form, but one involves matrices and the other integers.

> **INSTRUCTIONAL NOTE**
> In Problem 3 Part d, students are encouraged to see similarities to linear equations with which they are familiar. These similarities will be exploited in Problem 4 to help motivate and explain a matrix method for solving this linear system.

Unit 2

4 Thinking about how to solve the linear equation $3x = 6$ can help you figure out how to solve the matrix equation $AX = D$.

  a. Solve the equation $3x = 6$. Describe your method and explain why it works.

  b. Many students solve this equation by dividing both sides by 3, which is a good method. Juan solved it slightly differently. Here is his explanation:

  > I solved $3x = 6$ by multiplying both sides by $\frac{1}{3}$.
  >
  > This is essentially the same as dividing by 3.

  Explain what Juan means and why his method works.

  c. When solving $3x = 6$, you can divide both sides by 3 or multiply both sides by $\frac{1}{3}$. To solve similar matrix equations like $AX = D$, we use the multiplication method, since we know how to multiply matrices. Explain each step of the following comparison. Supply any missing details.

Solving a Linear Equation	Solving a Matrix Equation
$3x = 6$	$AX = D$
(*inverse of 3*) × $3x$ = (*inverse of 3*) × 6	(*inverse of A*) × AX = (*inverse of A*) × D
x = (*inverse of 3*) × 6	X = (*inverse of A*) × D
$x = \frac{1}{3} \times 6$	$X = A^{-1} \times D$

5 Now you are ready to solve the matrix equation you completed in Problem 3 Part b:

$$\begin{bmatrix} 1 & 1 \\ 9 & 5 \end{bmatrix} \begin{bmatrix} b \\ c \end{bmatrix} = \begin{bmatrix} 3{,}500 \\ 25{,}500 \end{bmatrix}$$

  a. What matrices should you multiply to solve the matrix equation?

  b. Solve the matrix equation. Record the matrix solution. What values for b and c do you get? How many bags and how many caps should the team give away?

  c. Compare your values for b and c with your solutions in Problems 1 and 2. Resolve any differences.

  d. To solve the matrix equation as above, you needed to find an inverse matrix. What method did you use to find the inverse matrix?

6 As usual, it is a good idea to check your solution.

  a. Use your equations in Part a of Problem 3 to check your solution.

  b. Use the matrix equation in Problem 5 to check your solution.

  c. When checking your solution, you should always check it against the original problem. Reread the original problem in the introduction to this investigation. Verify that your solution solves this problem.

4 a. Students may divide both sides by 3. They might justify this method by saying that it keeps the equation in balance or that they did the same thing to both sides. Students might also solve by multiplying both sides by $\frac{1}{3}$.

b. Since $\frac{1}{3} \cdot 3 = 1$, the left-hand side reduces to x when multiplied by $\frac{1}{3} \cdot \frac{1}{3} \cdot 6 = 2$, so the solution is $x = 2$. Multiplying by $\frac{1}{3}$ means to take $\frac{1}{3}$ of the amount. This is done by cutting the number into 3 equal parts (dividing by 3) and using one part for the result.

c. Students should explain each step of the comparison to each other so that they all understand the parallel being drawn. This is essential so that they will be able to add solving with inverse matrices to their toolkit of methods. They should be encouraged to supply any missing details they notice. Some details they may discuss include inserting a new second step that explicitly shows multiplication by the inverse on the left side of the equation as well as on the right side; or they may discuss why it is important that A^{-1} is multiplied on the left of D.

5 a. $A^{-1}D$ or $\begin{bmatrix} 1 & 1 \\ 9 & 5 \end{bmatrix}^{-1} \begin{bmatrix} 3{,}500 \\ 25{,}500 \end{bmatrix}$

b. $X = (A^{-1})D = \begin{bmatrix} -1.25 & 0.25 \\ 2.25 & -0.25 \end{bmatrix} \begin{bmatrix} 3{,}500 \\ 25{,}500 \end{bmatrix} = \begin{bmatrix} 2{,}000 \\ 1{,}500 \end{bmatrix}$

The matrix solution is $\begin{bmatrix} 2{,}000 \\ 1{,}500 \end{bmatrix}$. That is, $b = 2{,}000$ and $c = 1{,}500$. So, the team should give away 2,000 bags and 1,500 caps.

c. Students should see that the answers for b and c are the same as what they got before. (This comparison, along with the checks, is important so that students know that the solution using matrix inverses really does work.)

d. Students may find A^{-1} on a calculator or other technology by solving a system of equations or by using the method in Connections Task 7 on page 147. (This will also help remind them that they carefully studied the meaning of inverse matrices in the previous investigation. You should discuss with students the method(s) they use for this unit.)

6 a. $b = 2{,}000$ and $c = 1{,}500$ satisfies $b + c = 3{,}500$ and $9b + 5c = 25{,}500$.

b. The matrix solution, when substituted for X in the matrix equation, makes that equation true.

c. Students should verify that the entries in matrix X and the values of b and c do indeed solve the original problem about bags and caps.

POSSIBLE MISCONCEPTION
Students who try to multiply the inverse matrix on the right, when solving the matrix equation, should see the importance of multiplication on the left because the sizes will not be compatible. Reflections Task 13 on page 151 directs students to think more carefully about this restriction.

INSTRUCTIONAL NOTE
There are three statements of the solution in Part b: as a matrix, as values for b and c, and as quantities of bags and caps. Students should see that the solution can be stated in all ways.

Unit 2

7 The two equations below could represent the relationship between quantities of other promotional items.

$$x + y = 5{,}000$$
$$8x + 12y = 42{,}000$$

a. Using the context of promotional products for a team, describe a situation that could be modeled by this system of equations.

b. Represent the two equations with a matrix equation. Then solve the matrix equation. Check that your values for x and y satisfy the original system of equations and the matrix equation.

c. Interpret your solution in terms of the situation you described in Part a.

Summarize
the Mathematics

In this investigation, you learned how to solve a system of two linear equations using matrices. For a given system of two linear equations:

a Describe how to represent the system as a matrix equation.

b Describe how to use inverse matrices to solve the corresponding matrix equation $AX = C$. Explain how this inverse-matrix method is similar to how you solve equations like $5x = 20$.

c Describe at least two ways to check the solution.

Be prepared to share your descriptions and thinking with the entire class.

✔ Check Your Understanding

Cultivating the good will of fans is important for professional sports teams. Suppose that the promotions manager of the baseball team in Problem 1 decides to enhance the promotion by giving better prizes to more fans. The team owner agrees to increase the promotion budget to $37,500 and give a cap or jacket to the first 4,500 fans. The caps still cost $5 each; the jackets now cost $10 each.

a. Write a system of linear equations that represents this situation.

b. Write and solve the matrix equation representing this situation.

c. How many caps and how many jackets should be given away?

d. Show at least one way to check your answer.

(7) **a.** Students should describe a situation where a total of 5,000 items are given away. Two different items will be given away. The total budget for the promotion is $42,000. One of the items costs $8 and the other costs $12.

b. $AX = D = \begin{bmatrix} 1 & 1 \\ 8 & 12 \end{bmatrix} \begin{bmatrix} x \\ y \end{bmatrix} = \begin{bmatrix} 5,000 \\ 42,000 \end{bmatrix}$. Multiplying both sides of the

equation by A^{-1} on the left gives $\begin{bmatrix} x \\ y \end{bmatrix} = \begin{bmatrix} 4,500 \\ 500 \end{bmatrix}$. So, the solution

$x = 4,500$ and $y = 500$ satisfies both equations.

c. Responses should indicate that students can connect the solution of the matrix equation with their problem situations.

Summarize
the Mathematics

a If you have a system of equations $ax + by = c$ and $dx + ey = f$, then you can represent the system by the matrix equation

$$\begin{bmatrix} a & b \\ d & e \end{bmatrix} \begin{bmatrix} x \\ y \end{bmatrix} = \begin{bmatrix} c \\ f \end{bmatrix}.$$

(If students do not mention it themselves, you may want to point out that this matrix equation is of the general form $AX = C$. You then can ask, "How can you describe the entries of A? Of X? Of C?")

b You can solve a matrix equation $AX = C$ by multiplying both sides on the left by A^{-1}. That is, the solution is $X = A^{-1}C$. This works because, analogous to solving simple linear equations, you multiply both sides of the equation by the same thing; in this case, by the inverse of matrix A.

Since the product of a matrix and its inverse is the identity matrix I, on the left side of the equation you simply have the variable matrix IX or X, whose entries are equal to those of the matrix on the right side of the equation. (Note that there are, of course, limitations to this method, such as when A does not have an inverse. This is explored in the next investigation.)

c The solution could be checked using tables, graphs, substituting the values in the original equations, or substituting the values into the column matrix and performing the matrix multiplication.

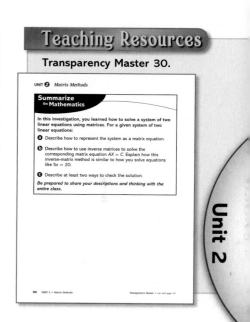
Unit 2

MATH TOOLKIT Students should summarize the process of representing a system of linear equations as a matrix equation, solving the equation, and checking the solution. An example should be included.

NOTE The solutions to the Check Your Understanding are on page T142.

LOOKING AHEAD The inverse-matrix method has some limitations, and there are other methods for solving systems using matrices. These points are pursued in the next investigation and in the OYO section. Students learn the inverse-matrix method here because it connects strongly with their previous work solving linear equations. The row-reduction, or Gaussian elimination, method is more efficient and versatile in general but is more complicated and beyond the scope of this text, although it is briefly explored in Extensions Task 18.

e. The matrix equation you solved in Part b relates to a particular context. For practice, solve the following matrix equations which do not relate to a particular context.

i. $\begin{bmatrix} 6 & 3 \\ 1 & 2 \end{bmatrix} \begin{bmatrix} x \\ y \end{bmatrix} = \begin{bmatrix} 4 \\ 5 \end{bmatrix}$

ii. $\begin{bmatrix} -2 & 4 \\ 0 & 3 \end{bmatrix} \begin{bmatrix} x \\ y \end{bmatrix} = \begin{bmatrix} 7 \\ -1 \end{bmatrix}$

 Investigation 3 **Analyzing and Comparing Methods**

Setting up and solving a matrix equation is a useful method for solving a system of linear equations. However, there are some limitations to this method, and there are other methods that might be better depending on the situation. As you work through this investigation, look for answers to these questions:

For solving systems of linear equations:

What are some limitations of the inverse-matrix method?

What are some advantages and disadvantages of each of the other methods you know?

1 **Getting Equations in the Right Form** In order to represent a system of linear equations as a matrix equation, as you did in the last investigation, the linear equations must be in the form $ax + by = c$. Consider the following linear system:

$$3x = 4 - 2y$$
$$x + 7 = 6y$$

a. Rewrite each of these equations in the form $ax + by = c$.

b. Solve this system of linear equations by setting up and solving a matrix equation.

2 **Limitations of the Inverse-Matrix Method** Setting up a matrix equation and then multiplying by the inverse of a matrix is a very useful method for solving a system of linear equations. But there are some limitations!

a. Try the method on each of the systems below. What happens when you try to calculate the inverse matrix?

$$2x + 5y = 10 \qquad\qquad 6x + 4y = 12$$
$$2x + 5y = 20 \qquad\qquad 3x + 2y = 6$$

✓ Check Your Understanding

a. Let c represent the number of caps given away and j represent the number of jackets given away. The system of equations is:

$$c + j = 4{,}500$$
$$5c + 10j = 37{,}500$$

b. $\begin{bmatrix} 1 & 1 \\ 5 & 10 \end{bmatrix} \begin{bmatrix} c \\ j \end{bmatrix} = \begin{bmatrix} 4{,}500 \\ 37{,}500 \end{bmatrix}$; $\begin{bmatrix} c \\ j \end{bmatrix} = \begin{bmatrix} 1{,}500 \\ 3{,}000 \end{bmatrix}$

c. 1,500 caps and 3,000 jackets

d. To check their answers, students may substitute the values for c and j into the original equations or the matrix equation.

e. **i.** Multiply both sides on the left by the inverse of $\begin{bmatrix} 6 & 3 \\ 1 & 2 \end{bmatrix}$. This yields the solution $\begin{bmatrix} x \\ y \end{bmatrix} = \begin{bmatrix} -0.7\overline{7} \\ 2.8\overline{8} \end{bmatrix}$.

ii. $\begin{bmatrix} x \\ y \end{bmatrix} = \begin{bmatrix} -4.16\overline{6} \\ -0.3\overline{3} \end{bmatrix}$

Investigation 3 — Analyzing and Comparing Methods

In this investigation, students will take a closer look at the inverse-matrix method which they learned in the last investigation and they will review and compare all the methods they now know for solving systems of linear equations.

① **a.** $3x + 2y = 4$ and $x - 6y = -7$

b. This system is equivalent to the matrix equation $\begin{bmatrix} 3 & 2 \\ 1 & -6 \end{bmatrix} \begin{bmatrix} x \\ y \end{bmatrix} = \begin{bmatrix} 4 \\ -7 \end{bmatrix}$.

The solution is $\begin{bmatrix} x \\ y \end{bmatrix} = \begin{bmatrix} 3 & 2 \\ 1 & -6 \end{bmatrix}^{-1} \begin{bmatrix} 4 \\ -7 \end{bmatrix} = \begin{bmatrix} 0.5 \\ 1.25 \end{bmatrix}$.

② **a.** For both systems, one graphing calculator response upon trying to use the inverse-matrix method is "ERR: SINGULAR MATRIX." A singular matrix is one that does not have an inverse. Thus, this calculator message is saying that the matrix of coefficients does not have an inverse. Therefore, the inverse-matrix method does not work.

b. Think about connections among the graph of a linear system, the number of solutions, and the inverse-matrix method.

    i. The inverse-matrix method fails for both of the linear systems in Part a. What does the graph of each linear system look like? How many solutions are there for each system?

    ii. What would the graph look like for a system in which calculating the inverse matrix is possible? How many solutions would such a system have?

c. Describe at least two patterns in the equations of a system of linear equations that indicate you will not be able to use an inverse matrix to solve the system. Check your conjecture by writing and solving systems of linear equations that exhibit these patterns.

Comparing Methods You now have several methods for solving a system of two linear equations: matrices, graphs, tables, elimination (combining the equations in a way that eliminates one of the variables), and substitution (rewriting the system as a single equation). In addition, you can sometimes solve the system just by examining the symbolic forms of the equations (like in Problem 2).

3 Consider the systems of equations below. You could solve each system in several ways. Sometimes one solution strategy is better than another. It is important to develop skill in selecting an appropriate method.

    System I: $\quad y = x - 4$
               $2x - y = -2$

    System II: $\quad s + p = 5$
               $2s - p = 4$

    System III: $x + 3y = 12$
               $4x + 12y = 48$

    System IV: $y = 0.85 + 0.10x$
               $y = 0.50 + 0.15x$

    System V: $\quad 6x + 8y = 22$
               $40x + 30y = 100$

a. For each system above, identify one of these five methods for solving it: matrices, graphs, elimination, substitution, and examining the equations in the system. *Choose a different method for each system.* Explain why you think the method you chose is a good method for solving that particular system.

b. Solve each system using the method you identified in Part a.

b. **i.** The graphs of the lines for the first system are parallel; thus, there is no solution to the system. The graphs of the lines for the second system are identical; thus, there are infinitely many solutions.

   ii. If it is possible to calculate the inverse matrix for the matrix of coefficients, then there is a single unique solution to the system. This would be shown by graphs in which the two lines intersect at exactly one point.

c. Possible patterns that students may state, indicating that the inverse-matrix method will not work:

- The $ax + by$ part of both equations is identical, but the right-hand sides of the equations are not the same. (Such a system has no solution.)

- The $ax + by$ part of both equations is identical, and the right-hand sides of the equations are also the same. (Such a system has infinitely many solutions.)

- One equation is a constant multiple of the other equation. (Such a system has infinitely many solutions.)

- The $ax + by$ parts of both equations are constant multiples of each other, but one full equation is not a constant multiple of the other. (Such a system has no solution.)

3 **a.** Students will likely identify the methods below for each system. They should provide a good reason why each method they choose works particularly well for the specific system.

System I: Substitution looks good since one equation is already solved for one variable in terms of the other.

System II: Elimination looks good here since adding the two equations will immediately eliminate p.

System III: In this system, we can see that the second equation is 4 times the first equation. Thus, by examining the symbolic forms of the equations and spotting a pattern, we can see that each equation describes the same line (and thus, there are infinitely many solutions).

System IV: Since both of these equations are in the "$y = ...$" form, it will be easy to enter them into a calculator, graph them, and find their intersection point. Finding a good window and "zooming" to find a solution with good accuracy may take some time.

System V: This system does not show any of the patterns above, it seems more "generic," and thus solving with matrices seems reasonable.

b. Students should solve each system with the method chosen in Part a.

System I: The solution is $x = -6$, $y = -10$.
System II: The solution is $s = 3$, $p = 2$.
System III: There are infinitely many solutions.
System IV: The solution is $x = 7$, $y = 1.55$.
System V: The solution is $x = 1$, $y = 2$.

> **INSTRUCTIONAL NOTE**
> Students should be able to determine the relationships between the lines by examining the equations. If not, they may choose to graph the systems.

> **INSTRUCTIONAL NOTE**
> Another pattern that students have not yet studied follows. The "diagonal products" of the coefficients in the two equations are equal. This condition captures all situations in which the inverse-matrix method will not work since this is exactly the situation in which the matrix of coefficients will not have an inverse. See Connections Task 7 on page 147.

Unit 2

Summarize
the Mathematics

In this investigation, you explored limitations of the inverse-matrix method for solving systems of linear equations. You also considered the question of choosing among the methods you know for solving such a system.

a Describe at least one limitation of the inverse-matrix method for solving a system of linear equations. Give an example illustrating this limitation.

b List all the methods you know for solving a system of linear equations. For each method:

   i. Describe the key steps in using the method.

   ii. Describe some advantages and disadvantages of the method.

c You have learned that for a system of two linear equations in two variables, there are 0 solutions, 1 solution, or infinitely many solutions. For each of these three possibilities for the number of solutions:

   i. Describe the graph of the linear system.

   ii. Describe what happens when you solve the system using elimination or substitution.

   iii. Describe what happens when you try to solve the system using the inverse-matrix method.

Be prepared to share your descriptions, examples, methods, and analysis with the class.

✔ Check Your Understanding

Set up and solve a matrix equation to solve each of the following systems of linear equations. Then check your solution by solving each system using one other method.

a. $y = 2x - 1$
    $3x - y = 1$

b. $x + y = -2$
    $6x + y = 0.5$

Summarize
the Mathematics

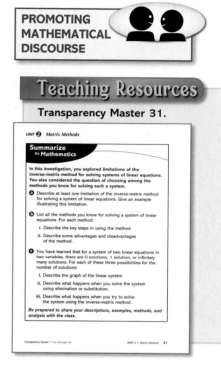

a The main limitation is that the matrix of coefficients may not have an inverse. For example, the following system cannot be solved by the inverse-matrix method since the matrix of coefficients does not have an inverse.

$$2x + 4y = 7$$
$$3x + 6y = 10.5$$

(Notice that the diagonal products are equal, and the second equation is 1.5 times the first equation. There are infinitely many solutions to this system.)

b **i–ii.** 1 Substitution method—quickly reduces two equations to one equation, but it may be hard to solve for one variable in terms of the other.

2 Elimination method—eliminates one variable so that only one equation in one variable needs to be solved, but it may be hard to figure out the right multiples to use before adding or subtracting the two equations to achieve the elimination.

3 Inverse-matrix method—quickly computes the solution, especially with the help of technology, but it may be hard to get both equations into the $ax + by = c$, form and the method will not work if the matrix of coefficients does not have an inverse.

4 Graphs method—gives a nice visual representation of the system and the solution(s), but it may be hard to graph and trace to find an accurate solution.

5 Table method—gives a nice numerical representation of the system and the solution(s), but it may be hard to build a detailed enough table to find an accurate solution.

6 "Examining the symbolic forms and spotting a pattern" method—gives a quick solution, but the patterns that are easy to spot, like when one equation is a constant multiple of the other, may not occur very often.

c **i–iii.** 1 0 solutions—The two lines are parallel. When solving using elimination or substitution, you get an impossible equation, like $0 = 2$. You cannot solve using the inverse-matrix method because the matrix of coefficients does not have an inverse.

2 1 solution—The two lines intersect at one point. The elimination and substitution methods yield the unique solution. The inverse-matrix method works since the inverse matrix exists in this case.

3 Infinitely many solutions—The two lines are in fact identical, so there are infinitely many points of intersection. The substitution and elimination methods yield an always-true equation, such as $0 = 0$. The inverse-matrix method does not work because the inverse matrix does not exist.

PROCESSING PROMPT
Today, _____ helped
          (name)
us recognize that … and make
the following changes … .

✓ Check Your Understanding

a. The matrix solution is $\begin{bmatrix} x \\ y \end{bmatrix} = \begin{bmatrix} -2 & 1 \\ 3 & -1 \end{bmatrix}^{-1} \begin{bmatrix} -1 \\ 1 \end{bmatrix} = \begin{bmatrix} 0 \\ -1 \end{bmatrix}$.

Using substitution, you get $3x - (2x - 1) = 1$. Thus, $x = 0$ and $y = -1$.

b. The matrix solution is $\begin{bmatrix} x \\ y \end{bmatrix} = \begin{bmatrix} 1 & 1 \\ 6 & 1 \end{bmatrix}^{-1} \begin{bmatrix} -2 \\ 0.5 \end{bmatrix} = \begin{bmatrix} 0.5 \\ -2.5 \end{bmatrix}$.

Subtracting the first equation from the second equation yields $5x = 2.5$. Thus, $x = 0.5$ and $y = -2.5$.

Summarize the Mathematics, *page 144*

Teacher: Okay, you have had some time to think about these questions in small groups. Let's talk about your summaries as a whole group. What did you describe as a limitation to using the inverse-matrix method for solving a system of linear equations, and what was your example illustrating the limitation? Group 1, will you share what your group said, please?

Aba: We talked about the problems in the investigations where the lines were parallel or where the two equations in the system actually represented the same line. The matrix didn't have an inverse. We just wrote down the problems on page 142 as our examples.

Teacher: Can you create a new example where a matrix wouldn't exist?

Elisa: Just do one where the two lines have the same slope, like $5x + 3y = 12$ and $5x + 3y = 23$.

Bryan: I was thinking of when two lines are actually the same line: like $4x + 6y = 18$ and $2x + 3y = 9$.

Teacher: Do other groups want to add anything else? *(Teacher waits for responses.)* No? All right, the next question asked you to list all of the methods you know for solving a system of linear equations, to describe the steps in the method, and to give some advantages and disadvantages to each method. Let's do some group presentations for this part. Choose a method you would like to present and include key steps of the method as well as advantages and disadvantages of the method in your presentation.

Student groups present their particular method. The teacher helps facilitate conversation about each method and pushes for clear and concise summaries.

Teacher: Good work! Let's continue with our summary. You have learned that for a system of two linear equations, there may be no solution, one solution, or infinitely many solutions. For each of those possibilities, what would the graph of the system look like?

Conner: Well, for no solutions, the two lines never intersect. They are parallel. And for one solution, the lines just cross once.

Julie: When there are infinitely many solutions, the two lines in the system are really the same line. They graph on top of each other.

Teacher: When a system has infinitely many solutions, does that mean that every point is a solution of that system?

James: Yeah. That's right. You can always find more pairs of numbers that solve the system by looking between two points. Like if $(1, 1)$ and $(2, 2)$ are solutions to the system, then $(1.5, 1.5)$ is another point on both lines of the system.

Teacher: Are we all agreed then that every point is a solution to a system with infinitely many solutions?

Lana: Well, James is right that you can always find more solutions between other solutions, but you better not go off the line.

Teacher: What do you mean, Lana?

Lana: Take James' example: the point $(0, 200)$ is not going to lie on his line going through $(1, 1)$ and $(2, 2)$. So, not all points are solutions to the system.

Teacher: The point of discussing this issue is that in mathematics, we need to be very careful with our language. When you have a linear system that has infinitely many solutions, you should not say "All points are solutions to this system." What should you say to be accurate? James, would you revise the statement: "When a linear system has infinitely many solutions, all points are solutions to this system," to make it accurate?

James: When a linear system has infinitely many solutions, all points on the two lines (that are really only one line) are solutions to this system.

Teacher: Are there any additional refinements needed to this statement? *(The teacher does not expect additional refinements but offers the opportunity to students and is also setting up the classroom norm that this type of question should be considered for all mathematical thinking. Students do not offer any suggestions.)*

Teacher: What happens for the three cases of 0 solutions, 1 solution, and infinitely many solutions when you solve the system using elimination or substitution?

Madison: When there is no solution, you end up with an equation that is never true, like $4 = 0$.

Ethan: And when there are infinitely many solutions, you end up with an equation that is always true, like $4 = 4$.

Teacher: What about the case of exactly one solution to a system?

Thomas: You just get a single point like $(5, 1)$.

Teacher: What does the final equation when solving the system look like in this case?

Hailey: You end with something like $x = 7$ or $y = 1.2$.

Teacher: Then what happens when you try to solve the system for these three cases using the inverse-matrix method?

Aiyana: You can only use the inverse-matrix method if there is exactly one solution; otherwise, the calculator gives an error message because there is no inverse matrix.

Teacher: You have generated a very thorough summary. Is there anything you would like to add to our summary?

Applications

1 In Investigation 1, you reviewed some properties of real numbers and their operations and investigated corresponding properties of matrices and their operations. The Distributive Property of Multiplication over Addition links multiplication and addition of numbers. That is, the distributive property guarantees that for all real numbers k, a, and b:

$$k(a + b) = ka + kb$$

a. Give two examples of the distributive property with numbers.

b. Suppose k is any number and A and B are any two matrices with the same size. Is it true that $k(A + B) = kA + kB$? Explain your reasoning.

2 In Investigation 1 Problem 7, you learned that the identity matrix for 2×2 matrices satisfies this equation:

$$\begin{bmatrix} 5 & 4 \\ 2 & 6 \end{bmatrix} \begin{bmatrix} a & b \\ c & d \end{bmatrix} = \begin{bmatrix} 5 & 4 \\ 2 & 6 \end{bmatrix}$$

a. Perform the matrix multiplication to create four linear equations.

b. Separate these four equations into two systems of two equations. Solve each system of two equations.

c. The results from Part b give you the entries for the identity matrix. Check that you get the same answer as when you found the identity matrix in Problem 7 on page 136.

3 At a school basketball game, the box office sold 400 tickets for a total revenue of $1,750. Tickets cost $6 for adults and $4 for students. In the rush of selling tickets, the box office did not keep track of how many adult and student tickets were sold. The school would like this information for future planning.

a. Let a represent the number of adult tickets sold and s represent the number of student tickets sold.

   i. Write an equation showing the relationship among a, s, and the number of tickets sold.

   ii. Write an equation showing the relationship among a, s, and the total revenue from ticket sales.

b. Write a matrix equation that represents the system of linear equations from Part a.

c. Solve the matrix equation. How many adult and student tickets were sold?

d. Check your solution using graphs.

e. Describe another way that you could check your solution.

On Your Own

Applications

1 **a.** Examples will vary.

b. Yes, it is true that $k(A + B) = kA + kB$. Notice that an entry in $k(A + B)$ will have the form $k(a + b)$, where a and b are the entries in matrices A and B, respectively. The corresponding entry in $kA + kB$ will be $ka + kb$. By the Distributive Property of Multiplication over Addition, $k(a + b) = ka + kb$, so we can see that corresponding entries in $k(A + B)$ and $kA + kB$ will be identical. (Students' explanations will likely be less formal.)

2 **a.** $5a + 4c = 5$
$5b + 4d = 4$
$2a + 6c = 2$
$2b + 6d = 6$

b. $\begin{cases} 5a + 4c = 5 \\ 2a + 6c = 2 \end{cases}$
The solution is $a = 1$ and $c = 0$.

$\begin{cases} 5b + 4d = 4 \\ 2b + 6d = 6 \end{cases}$
The solution is $b = 0$ and $d = 1$.

c. $\begin{bmatrix} 1 & 0 \\ 0 & 1 \end{bmatrix}$

3 **a.** **i.** $a + s = 400$

ii. $6a + 4s = 1{,}750$

b. $\begin{bmatrix} 1 & 1 \\ 6 & 4 \end{bmatrix} \begin{bmatrix} a \\ s \end{bmatrix} = \begin{bmatrix} 400 \\ 1{,}750 \end{bmatrix}$

c. Multiply both sides of the equation on the left by the inverse of the first (coefficient) matrix to find a and s:

$$\begin{bmatrix} a \\ s \end{bmatrix} = \begin{bmatrix} 1 & 1 \\ 6 & 4 \end{bmatrix}^{-1} \begin{bmatrix} 400 \\ 1{,}750 \end{bmatrix} = \begin{bmatrix} -2 & 0.5 \\ 3 & -0.5 \end{bmatrix} \begin{bmatrix} 400 \\ 1{,}750 \end{bmatrix} = \begin{bmatrix} 75 \\ 325 \end{bmatrix}$$

There were 75 adult and 325 student tickets sold.

d. Box Office Equations

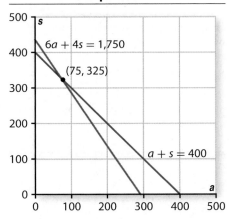

e. Students could substitute the solution into the matrix equation or system of equations.

4 A designer plans to inlay the brick design below into a concrete patio.

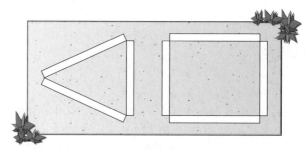

The design must meet the following specifications.

- The figures are outlined by rows of bricks, one brick wide (as represented in the drawing by the white strips).
- The rectangular design requires 50 bricks.
- The isosceles triangle design requires 40 bricks.
- The length of the longer sides of the rectangle is the same length as the longer sides of the triangle, and the length of the shorter sides of the rectangle is the same length as the shorter side of the triangle.

Find the number of bricks needed for each side of each figure by setting up and solving a system of linear equations.

5 A school principal and the local business community have devised an innovative plan to motivate better school attendance and achievement. They plan to give gift certificates to students who score high in each category. Students with high attendance will be awarded $25 gift certificates, and those with good grades will receive $20 gift certificates. The total budget for this plan is $1,500, and the planning committee would like to award 65 gift certificates. The next step is to determine the number of each type of gift certificate to be printed.

a. If x is the number of gift certificates for attendance and y is the number of gift certificates for good grades, write equations that model this situation.

b. Set up and solve a matrix equation that represents the system of linear equations from Part a. How many of each type of gift certificate can be awarded?

c. Verify your solution using a different method for solving a system of linear equations.

4 Let s represent the number of bricks in the short sides of the rectangle and triangle, and let ℓ represent the number in the long sides. Then the system of equations is as follows:

$$2s + 2\ell = 50$$
$$s + 2\ell = 40$$

Students may solve this system of equations by their preferred method. A matrix solution is given here.

The matrix equation is $\begin{bmatrix} 2 & 2 \\ 1 & 2 \end{bmatrix}\begin{bmatrix} s \\ \ell \end{bmatrix} = \begin{bmatrix} 50 \\ 40 \end{bmatrix}$. The inverse matrix is

$\begin{bmatrix} 1 & -1 \\ -0.5 & 1 \end{bmatrix}$, and so the solution is given by $\begin{bmatrix} s \\ \ell \end{bmatrix} = \begin{bmatrix} 1 & -1 \\ -0.5 & 1 \end{bmatrix}\begin{bmatrix} 50 \\ 40 \end{bmatrix} = \begin{bmatrix} 10 \\ 15 \end{bmatrix}$.

Each short side requires 10 bricks and each long side requires 15 bricks.

5 **a.** $x + y = 65$ and $25x + 20y = 1{,}500$

b. The matrix equation is $\begin{bmatrix} 1 & 1 \\ 25 & 20 \end{bmatrix}\begin{bmatrix} x \\ y \end{bmatrix} = \begin{bmatrix} 65 \\ 1{,}500 \end{bmatrix}$. Multiplying by the

inverse matrix on the left gives $\begin{bmatrix} x \\ y \end{bmatrix} = \begin{bmatrix} 1 & 1 \\ 25 & 20 \end{bmatrix}^{-1}\begin{bmatrix} 65 \\ 1{,}500 \end{bmatrix} = \begin{bmatrix} 40 \\ 25 \end{bmatrix}$.

Thus, 40 gift certificates will be awarded for attendance and 25 for good grades.

c. Solving the linear equations for y yields $y = 65 - x$ and $y = 75 - 1.25x$. The point of intersection of the two lines is $(40, 25)$. Students also could look at tables of values or solve the system algebraically.

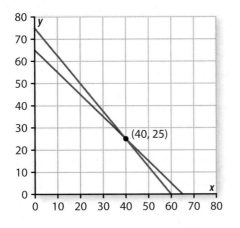

Unit 2

6 Solve the following matrix equations.

a. $\begin{bmatrix} 2 & 1 \\ 3 & 5 \end{bmatrix} \begin{bmatrix} x \\ y \end{bmatrix} = \begin{bmatrix} 8 \\ 7 \end{bmatrix}$

b. $\begin{bmatrix} -2 & 1 \\ 6 & -3.5 \end{bmatrix} \begin{bmatrix} x \\ y \end{bmatrix} = \begin{bmatrix} 12.75 \\ -6.5 \end{bmatrix}$

c. Choose one of the matrix equations above and rewrite it as a system of linear equations. Then solve the system using any nonmatrix method. Check that you get the same solution(s) as you found before.

Connections

7 In Investigation 1, you used two methods to find an inverse matrix: solving two systems of linear equations and using a calculator or computer software. Another method that works for 2×2 matrices is to use the following formula.

If $A = \begin{bmatrix} a & b \\ c & d \end{bmatrix}$, the inverse of A (when it exists) is given by:

$$A^{-1} = \frac{1}{ad - bc} \begin{bmatrix} d & -b \\ -c & a \end{bmatrix}$$

a. Use this formula to find the inverse of the following matrix. Then use matrix multiplication to check that the product of the inverse and the original matrix is the identity matrix.

$$\begin{bmatrix} 6 & 8 \\ 2 & 3 \end{bmatrix}$$

b. Use the formula to find the inverses of the following matrices. Check your answers.

i. $\begin{bmatrix} 5 & 3 \\ 3 & 2 \end{bmatrix}$

ii. $\begin{bmatrix} -8 & -10 \\ 2 & 3 \end{bmatrix}$

c. You discovered in Investigation 1 that not all matrices have an inverse.

i. Examine the formula for A^{-1} given above. What do you think will go wrong when you try to use the formula to compute the inverse of a 2×2 matrix that has no inverse?

ii. In Problem 10 (page 137), you discovered that $\begin{bmatrix} 0 & 9 \\ 0 & 4 \end{bmatrix}$ does not have an inverse. What happens when you try to use the formula above?

iii. Use what you've discovered about limitations of the formula to construct two matrices with all nonzero entries but no inverse.

6 **a.** $\begin{bmatrix} x \\ y \end{bmatrix} = \begin{bmatrix} 2 & 1 \\ 3 & 5 \end{bmatrix}^{-1} \begin{bmatrix} 8 \\ 7 \end{bmatrix} = \begin{bmatrix} 4.714 \\ -1.429 \end{bmatrix}$

b. $\begin{bmatrix} x \\ y \end{bmatrix} = \begin{bmatrix} -2 & 1 \\ 6 & -3.5 \end{bmatrix}^{-1} \begin{bmatrix} 12.75 \\ -6.5 \end{bmatrix} = \begin{bmatrix} -38.125 \\ -63.5 \end{bmatrix}$

c. For the matrix equation in Part b, you get

$$-2x + y = 12.75$$
$$6x - 3.5y = -6.5.$$

Multiply the first equation by 3 and add to the second equation to get

$$-0.5y = 31.75$$
$$y = -63.5.$$

Substituting into the first equation gives

$$-2x - 63.5 = 12.75$$
$$-2x = 76.25$$
$$x = -38.125.$$

This is the same solution as found in Part b above.

Connections

7 **a.** Using the formula, you get
$$\begin{bmatrix} 6 & 8 \\ 2 & 3 \end{bmatrix}^{-1} = \frac{1}{(6)(3)-(8)(2)} \begin{bmatrix} 3 & -8 \\ -2 & 6 \end{bmatrix} = \frac{1}{2}\begin{bmatrix} 3 & -8 \\ -2 & 6 \end{bmatrix} = \begin{bmatrix} \frac{3}{2} & -4 \\ -1 & 3 \end{bmatrix}.$$

b. **i.** $\begin{bmatrix} 5 & 3 \\ 3 & 2 \end{bmatrix}^{-1} = \frac{1}{(5)(2)-(3)(3)} \begin{bmatrix} 2 & -3 \\ -3 & 5 \end{bmatrix} = \begin{bmatrix} 2 & -3 \\ -3 & 5 \end{bmatrix}$

ii. $\begin{bmatrix} -8 & -10 \\ 2 & 3 \end{bmatrix}^{-1} = \frac{1}{(-8)(3)-(-10)(2)} \begin{bmatrix} 3 & 10 \\ -2 & -8 \end{bmatrix} = \frac{-1}{4}\begin{bmatrix} 3 & 10 \\ -2 & -8 \end{bmatrix} = \begin{bmatrix} \frac{-3}{4} & \frac{-5}{2} \\ \frac{1}{2} & 2 \end{bmatrix}$

c. **i.** Responses may vary. Whenever a 2 × 2 matrix does not have an inverse, the quantity $ad - bc$ will equal zero.

ii. When you try to use the formula, you get $(0)(4) - (9)(0) = 0$, which gives a zero in the denominator of the fraction in front of the matrix.

iii. Any matrix $\begin{bmatrix} a & b \\ c & d \end{bmatrix}$ where $ad - bc = 0$ will not have an inverse.

Example: $\begin{bmatrix} 1 & 2 \\ 3 & 6 \end{bmatrix}.$

8 The brand-switching matrix from Lesson 2 on page 105 is reproduced below with decimal entries instead of percents. This matrix provides information for projecting how many people will buy certain brands of athletic shoes on their next purchase given the brand they currently own. Matrix multiplication along with its properties can help you analyze this situation.

Brand-Switching Matrix

Next Brand

$$\text{Current Brand} \begin{array}{c} \\ N \\ R \\ F \end{array} \begin{array}{ccc} N & R & F \\ \left[\begin{array}{ccc} 0.4 & 0.4 & 0.2 \\ 0.2 & 0.5 & 0.3 \\ 0.1 & 0.2 & 0.7 \end{array}\right] \end{array} = B$$

a. Assume that buyers purchase a new pair of shoes every year. The following matrix shows the number of people who bought each of the three brands this year.

$$\begin{array}{ccc} N & R & F \\ [\,600 & 700 & 500\,] \end{array} = Q$$

How many people are projected to purchase each of the brands next year? Explain how to answer this question using matrix multiplication.

b. What would the brand-switching matrix look like if there is no change in the number of people buying each brand this year and next year?

c. You may recall the Associative Property of Multiplication for real numbers which guarantees that for all real numbers a, b, and c:
$a \times (b \times c) = (a \times b) \times c$.

For example, $3 \times (5 \times 2) = (3 \times 5) \times 2 = 30$.

Matrix multiplication also has this property, which can be used to project the number of people buying each brand several years into the future. From Part a, you know that

$$Q \times B = \left[\begin{array}{c} \text{the row matrix} \\ \text{showing how many} \\ \text{people will buy each} \\ \text{brand next year} \end{array}\right].$$

i. Compute and compare the results of $(Q \times B) \times B$ and $Q \times (B \times B)$. Explain why this is an example of the associative property. Explain the meaning of the resulting matrices.

ii. Describe the information obtained by computing $Q \times B^3$.

8 **a.** $[600 \quad 700 \quad 500] \begin{bmatrix} 0.4 & 0.4 & 0.2 \\ 0.2 & 0.5 & 0.3 \\ 0.1 & 0.2 & 0.7 \end{bmatrix} = [430 \quad 690 \quad 680]$

This model projects that 430 people will buy Nike shoes, 690 will buy Reebok shoes, and 680 will buy Fila shoes next year.

b. If everybody buys the same brand of shoe each year, the

brand-switching matrix is the identity matrix $\begin{bmatrix} 1 & 0 & 0 \\ 0 & 1 & 0 \\ 0 & 0 & 1 \end{bmatrix}$.

c. **i.** $(Q \times B) \times B = Q \times (B \times B) = [378 \quad 653 \quad 769]$

This is an example of the Associative Property for Matrix Multiplication since the parentheses associate different matrices. The answer matrix tells us this model projects that two years from now, 378 people will buy Nike shoes, 653 will buy Reebok shoes, and 769 will buy Fila shoes.

ii. $Q \times B^3$ tells the number of people projected to buy each brand three years from now.

d. The following matrix shows the number of people projected to buy each brand two years from now.

$$\begin{array}{ccc} \text{N} & \text{R} & \text{F} \\ [\,378 & 653 & 769\,] \end{array}$$

Using this matrix, find a matrix showing how many people will buy each brand one year from now. Compare with results from Part a.

9 A new nutrition plan that Antonio is considering restricts his drinks to water, milk, and fruit juice. The matrix below shows the amount of protein and calories per cup for skim milk and fruit juice.

Protein and Calories (per cup)

$$\begin{array}{c} \\ \text{Protein (g)} \\ \text{Calories (g)} \end{array} \begin{array}{cc} \text{Milk} & \text{Juice} \\ \left[\begin{array}{cc} 8 & 2 \\ 85 & 120 \end{array}\right] \end{array}$$

The plan recommends that Antonio drink enough milk and juice each day to get a total of 10 grams of protein and 180 calories from those sources. He wants to know how much milk and juice he must drink to meet these recommendations.

a. Construct a column matrix showing the recommended daily totals for protein and calories. Label the rows of the matrix.

b. Let x represent the number of cups of skim milk he should drink each day and y represent the number of cups of juice he should drink. Set up a matrix equation that models this situation.

c. Write a system of equations that represents this situation.

d. How many cups of milk and juice should Antonio drink daily to meet the recommended plan?

10 Sometimes a problem that involves two variables connected by linear relationships can be solved directly with matrices, rather than by first finding a system of linear equations and then using matrices.

a. The Fairfield Hobbies and Games store sells two types of ping-pong sets. A Standard Set contains two paddles and one ball, and a Tournament Set contains four paddles and six balls. Enter this information into the matrix below.

Ping-Pong Sets

$$\begin{array}{c} \\ \text{Balls} \\ \text{Paddles} \end{array} \begin{array}{cc} \text{Tourn} & \text{Std} \\ \left[\begin{array}{cc} \text{—} & \text{—} \\ \text{—} & \text{—} \end{array}\right] \end{array}$$

d. $[378 \quad 653 \quad 769] \begin{bmatrix} 0.4 & 0.4 & 0.2 \\ 0.2 & 0.5 & 0.3 \\ 0.1 & 0.2 & 0.7 \end{bmatrix}^{-1} = [430 \quad 690 \quad 680]$

This gives the same answer as in Part a. That is, this product matrix is equal to the product $Q \times B$.

9 **a.** $\begin{matrix} \text{Protein} \\ \text{Calories} \end{matrix} \begin{bmatrix} 10 \\ 180 \end{bmatrix}$

   b. The matrix equation is $\begin{bmatrix} 8 & 2 \\ 85 & 120 \end{bmatrix} \begin{bmatrix} x \\ y \end{bmatrix} = \begin{bmatrix} 10 \\ 180 \end{bmatrix}$.

   c. $\begin{cases} 8x + 2y = 10 \\ 85x + 120y = 180 \end{cases}$

   d. $\begin{bmatrix} x \\ y \end{bmatrix} = \begin{bmatrix} 8 & 2 \\ 85 & 120 \end{bmatrix}^{-1} \begin{bmatrix} 10 \\ 180 \end{bmatrix} \approx \begin{bmatrix} 1.06 \\ 0.75 \end{bmatrix}$

   So, Antonio should drink approximately 1.06 cups of milk and 0.75 cups of juice each day.

10 **a.**

	Tourn	Std
Balls	6	1
Paddles	4	2

b. The store receives a bulk shipment of ping-pong equipment consisting of 100 paddles and 110 balls. The owner wants to know how many of each type of ping-pong set she can make using this equipment. Let s represent the number of Standard Sets and t represent the number of Tournament Sets. Complete the following matrix equation so that it represents this situation.

$$\begin{bmatrix} 6 & 1 \\ 4 & 2 \end{bmatrix} \begin{bmatrix} - \\ - \end{bmatrix} = \begin{bmatrix} - \\ - \end{bmatrix}$$

c. Solve the matrix equation. How many sets of each type can the owner make using the balls and paddles in the bulk shipment?

d. Now, solve the problem another way. Write an equation that shows the relationship among s, t, and the total number of balls. Write another equation that shows the relationship among s, t, and the total number of paddles. Solve this system of equations. Check that you get the same answer as in Part c.

11 The owner of two restaurants in town has decided to promote business by allocating to each restaurant a certain amount of money to spend on restaurant renovation and community service projects. He has asked the manager of each restaurant to submit a proposal stating what percentage of their money they would like to spend in each of these two categories. The matrix below shows their proposals.

Funding Requests

	Rest. A	Rest. B
Renovation	70%	45%
Community Service	30%	55%

The owner has decided to allocate a total of $16,000 to renovations and $14,000 to community projects. The managers want to know how much money they will have to spend in each category.

a. Represent this situation with a matrix equation and with a system of linear equations.

b. Using a method of your choice, determine how much money each restaurant should be allocated.

Reflections

12 Think about the way matrices are added and multiplied.

a. Why should it not be surprising that matrix addition has the same properties as addition of numbers?

b. Why might it be reasonable to suspect that matrix multiplication would not have the same properties as multiplication of numbers?

b. The matrix equation is $\begin{bmatrix} 6 & 1 \\ 4 & 2 \end{bmatrix}\begin{bmatrix} t \\ s \end{bmatrix} = \begin{bmatrix} 110 \\ 100 \end{bmatrix}$.

c. $\begin{bmatrix} t \\ s \end{bmatrix} = \begin{bmatrix} 6 & 1 \\ 4 & 2 \end{bmatrix}^{-1}\begin{bmatrix} 110 \\ 100 \end{bmatrix} = \begin{bmatrix} 0.25 & -0.125 \\ -0.5 & 0.75 \end{bmatrix}\begin{bmatrix} 110 \\ 100 \end{bmatrix} = \begin{bmatrix} 15 \\ 20 \end{bmatrix}$

The owner can make 15 tournament sets and 20 standard sets.

d. The equation for the number of balls is $6t + s = 110$. The equation for the number of paddles is $4t + 2s = 100$. Students may solve the system of equations by their preferred method.

11 **a.** $\begin{bmatrix} 0.7 & 0.45 \\ 0.3 & 0.55 \end{bmatrix}\begin{bmatrix} a \\ b \end{bmatrix} = \begin{bmatrix} 16{,}000 \\ 14{,}000 \end{bmatrix}$ and $\begin{aligned} 0.7a + 0.45b &= 16{,}000 \\ 0.3a + 0.55b &= 14{,}000 \end{aligned}$

b. $\begin{bmatrix} a \\ b \end{bmatrix} = \begin{bmatrix} 0.7 & 0.45 \\ 0.3 & 0.55 \end{bmatrix}^{-1}\begin{bmatrix} 16{,}000 \\ 14{,}000 \end{bmatrix} = \begin{bmatrix} 2.2 & -1.8 \\ -1.2 & 2.8 \end{bmatrix}\begin{bmatrix} 16{,}000 \\ 14{,}000 \end{bmatrix} = \begin{bmatrix} 10{,}000 \\ 20{,}000 \end{bmatrix}$

So, Restaurant A should get $10,000 and Restaurant B should get $20,000.

Reflections

12 **a.** Matrix addition involves adding entries, which are real numbers, entry-by-entry. Thus, it is not surprising that matrix addition has the same properties as addition of real numbers.

b. Matrix multiplication is not done entry by entry. Instead, it is a rather complicated process of combining rows and columns using multiplication and addition of entries. Thus, it seems reasonable that matrix multiplication would not have the same properties as multiplication of real numbers.

Unit 2

13 Reproduced below is the comparison of methods for solving a linear equation and solving a matrix equation from Investigation 2 (page 140).

Solving a Linear Equation	**Solving a Matrix Equation**

$3x = 6$

$(inverse\ of\ 3) \times 3x = (inverse\ of\ 3) \times 6$

$x = (inverse\ of\ 3) \times 6$

$x = \frac{1}{3} \times 6$

$AX = D$

$(inverse\ of\ A) \times AX = (inverse\ of\ A) \times D$

$X = (inverse\ of\ A) \times D$

$X = A^{-1} \times D$

  a. For the equation $3x = 6$, the third line of the comparison could have been written:

$x = 6 \times (inverse\ of\ 3)$

  Explain why the corresponding matrix equation could *not* have been written:

$X = D \times (inverse\ of\ A)$

  b. How do you know that D must be multiplied *on the left* by the inverse of A?

14 If you were advising a friend who is about to learn the inverse-matrix method for solving systems of linear equations, what would you tell your friend about things to watch out for, easy parts, shortcuts, or other tips?

15 You have solved systems of linear equations using graphs, tables, the substitution method, the elimination method, and the inverse-matrix method. When solving a system of linear equations, how do you decide which method to use?

Extensions

16 Matrix equations and inverse matrices can be useful for solving systems of equations involving more than two variables. For example, Isabelle is considering a nutrition plan that restricts her drinks to skim milk, orange juice, tomato juice, and water. The matrix below shows the amount of protein, carbohydrate, and calories per cup for each beverage except water.

Protein, Carbohydrate, and Calories (per cup)

	M	OJ	TJ
Protein (g)	8	2	2
Carbohydrate (g)	12	29	10
Calories	85	120	45

The plan recommends that Isabelle drink enough milk and juice each day to get a total of 15 grams of protein, 46 grams of carbohydrate, and 246 calories from these sources. She wants to know how much of each beverage she must drink to meet these recommendations exactly.

13 **a.** Students should point out that sizes will not "fit" or that since matrix multiplication is not commutative, you cannot change the order.

b. Students should respond with reasoning similar to the following. Two general rules for solving equations are to "do the same thing to both sides" and "undo" something by "doing the opposite." Applying these rules to the equation $AX = D$, we see that in order to find X, we have to undo the multiplication by matrix A.

To do that, we multiply on the left by A^{-1} since $A^{-1} \cdot A = I$ and $I \cdot X = X$. Since we multiplied one side of the equation on the left by A^{-1}, we now have to do the same process to the other side of the equation. This yields $A^{-1} \cdot D$ (and not $D \cdot A^{-1}$). Some students may respond by noting that you cannot multiply on the right by A^{-1} since $A \cdot X \cdot A^{-1} \neq X$. Even in a situation where the sizes are compatible, $A \cdot X \cdot A^{-1}$ does not necessarily equal X since matrix multiplication is not commutative.

14 Possible suggestions are:

- Be sure that the equations are in the right form with the variables in the same order and with the equations neatly arranged on top of each other so the matrix form can be seen readily.

- Be sure that the numbers are entered in the calculator correctly and that the inverse matrix is multiplied on the left of the other matrix (e.g., for $AX = B$, $A^{-1} \cdot B = X$).

- Watch out for linear systems that will not be able to be solved with this method.

15 The choice of which method to use depends on how accurate the solution needs to be (graphing the equations and using a table of values may not be exact), the form of the original equation in the system, one's access to technology, and personal preference.

Unit 2

a. Set up a matrix equation that models this situation. Use multiplication by an inverse matrix to solve this equation. How much skim milk, orange juice, and tomato juice must Isabelle drink each day?

b. Write a system of three linear equations that represents this situation.

 Consider systems of equations with more than two variables.

a. The graph of an equation in the form $ax + by + cz = d$ is a plane in three-dimensional space. Consider a system of three such equations in three variables.

$$x - y + 2z = 1$$
$$2x + y + z = 1$$
$$4x - y + 5z = 5$$

   i. In what ways can three planes intersect?

   ii. Suppose you solve such a system of three linear equations and you find a single solution, (x, y, z), with specific values of x, y, and z. How would this situation be represented by the graphs of the three equations?

b. Try using an inverse matrix to solve the linear system in Part a. Do these three planes intersect in a single point? (You may wish to check your solution by using graphing software that can graph the three planes, if available.)

c. Solve the linear system below using matrix methods.

$$12w - 5x + y + 7z = 8$$
$$8w - 3x + 2y + 7z = 3$$
$$10w - 2x + 2y + 7z = 7$$
$$13w + x + 2y + 8z = 13$$

18 There is another matrix method for solving systems of linear equations, called *row reduction*, that is actually more efficient for a computer to implement than the inverse-matrix method which you learned in this lesson, and it works more generally. You will learn more about the row reduction method in later courses. To get an idea of how this method works, consider the following system of linear equations.

$$2x - y = 7$$
$$3x + 4y = -6$$

a. Solve this system using the elimination method.

b. As you carried out the elimination method in Part a, you multiplied the equations by constants and you added or subtracted equations. When doing these operations, you were essentially just operating on the coefficients of x and y and the constants on the right side of the equations. This suggests that these operations could be done just as well on a matrix with entries that are the coefficients and constants. Such a matrix is sometimes called the **augmented matrix**. Using such an augmented matrix, you can represent the above system as follows:

$$A = \begin{bmatrix} 2 & -1 & 7 \\ 3 & 4 & -6 \end{bmatrix}$$

Extensions

16 **a.** The matrix equation is

$$\begin{bmatrix} 8 & 2 & 2 \\ 12 & 29 & 10 \\ 85 & 120 & 45 \end{bmatrix}\begin{bmatrix} M \\ OJ \\ TJ \end{bmatrix} = \begin{bmatrix} 15 \\ 46 \\ 246 \end{bmatrix}.$$

Isabelle must drink approximately 0.93 cups of tomato juice TJ, 0.65 cups of orange juice OJ, and 1.48 cups of skim milk M.

b. $8M + 2OJ + 2TJ = 15$
$12M + 29OJ + 10TJ = 46$
$85M + 120OJ + 45TJ = 246$

17 **a.** **i.** Three planes could intersect in the following ways: not at all (at least two planes are parallel); two at a time, forming three lines that will not intersect; or all three together, forming a point, a single line, or a plane (if the three planes are identical).

ii. If by solving you find a single solution (x, y, z), then the planes all must intersect in a single point.

b. When we try to solve this system by using an inverse matrix, we get an error message: the matrix of coefficients does not have an inverse. This indicates that these planes do not have a unique point as their intersection. (In fact, they intersect two at a time, forming three lines.)

c. The solution to the linear system is $(1.627, 0.745, 0.020, -1.118)$.

18 **a.** $\begin{cases} 2x - y = 7 \\ 3x + 4y = -6 \end{cases}$

$$\begin{array}{rl} 8x - 4y &= 28 \\ 3x + 4y &= -6 \\ \hline 11x &= 22 \\ x &= 2 \\ y &= -3 \end{array}$$

b. **Step 1:** $\begin{bmatrix} 6 & -3 & 21 \\ 3 & 4 & -6 \end{bmatrix}$

Step 2: $\begin{bmatrix} 6 & -3 & 21 \\ -6 & -8 & 12 \end{bmatrix}$

Step 3: $\begin{bmatrix} 6 & -3 & 21 \\ 0 & -11 & 33 \end{bmatrix}$

DIFFERENTIATION
Extensions Tasks 18 and 19 could replace Applications Tasks 5 and 6 for advanced students.

Unit 2

The first two columns contain the coefficients of the variables, and the last column contains the constants on the right side of the equations. Now, carry out the operations you may have used in the elimination method, but just apply them to the entries in the matrix A, as follows.

Step 1: Rewrite the first row of matrix A so that it represents the system with the first equation replaced by 3 times the first equation.

Step 2: Rewrite the modified matrix so that it represents the system with the second equation replaced by -2 times the second equation.

Step 3: Finally, rewrite this modified matrix so that row 2 is replaced by the sum of modified rows 1 and 2.

  c. Write the system of equations represented by the final matrix in Part b.

  d. Use the results of Part c to solve the original system of equations. Check that you get the same solution(s) as in Part a.

  e. Compare the methods in Part a and Part b. Did you use the same multipliers in Parts a and b? If not, modify your elimination method in Part a so that it more closely corresponds to the row reduction method in Part b.

19 In Extensions Task 18, you learned about the row reduction matrix method for solving a system of linear equations. This method will work when the inverse-matrix method fails. For example, consider the following system:

$$2x + y = 7$$
$$4x + 2y = 10$$

  a. Solve this system using the elimination method. What is the solution?

  b. Try to solve this system using the inverse-matrix method. What happens?

  c. Study this application of the row reduction method.

Step 1: Form the augmented matrix: $\begin{bmatrix} 2 & 1 & 7 \\ 4 & 2 & 10 \end{bmatrix}$

Step 2: Multiply the top row by 2 and replace the top row with the result: $\begin{bmatrix} 4 & 2 & 14 \\ 4 & 2 & 10 \end{bmatrix}$

Step 3: Subtract the bottom row from the top row and replace the bottom row with the result: $\begin{bmatrix} 4 & 2 & 14 \\ 0 & 0 & 4 \end{bmatrix}$

Step 4: Write the system represented by the above matrix.

Step 5: Since $0 = 4$ is a contradiction, conclude there are no solutions to this system.

Compare this solution to the solution you found using the elimination method in Part a.

c. $6x - 3y = 21$
$-11y = 33$

d. $-11y = 33$
$y = -3$
Substitute into the first equation to get $6x - 3(-3) = 21$, or $x = 2$.

e. Students' multipliers may or may not match Part b. The elimination method matching Part b would involve multiplying the first equation by 3 and the second equation by -2 and adding to get:

$$\begin{array}{r} 6x - 3y = 21 \\ \underline{-6x - 8y = 12} \\ -11y = 33 \end{array}$$

Thus, $y = -3$. Then substitution gives $x = 2$.

19 **a.** Multiply the first equation by 2 and subtract the second equation to get $0 = 4$. This false equality (contradiction) shows that there are no solutions. The lines must be parallel.

b. If we try to use the inverse-matrix method, we need an inverse for the matrix of coefficients. But this matrix does not have an inverse. So, the inverse-matrix method does not work in this case. (We know there is not a single solution, but just from the fact that the inverse matrix does not exist, we do not know whether this is a system with no solutions or infinitely many solutions.)

c. We see that this matrix row-reduction method did yield the same answer as the elimination method. So, we see that the row-reduction method is a more general matrix method than the inverse-matrix method.

Unit 2

d. Use the row reduction method to solve each of the following systems of equations.

    i. $-2x + y = -1$
        $3x - y = 1$

    ii. $x - y = 3$
        $4x + y = 32$

    iii. $3x + y = -2$
        $6x + 2y = 0.5$

    iv. $3x - y = 2$
        $9x - 3y = 6$

Review

20 Consider the two matrices below.

$$M = \begin{bmatrix} 3 & 4 & 5 \\ 6 & 7 & 8 \\ 9 & -4 & 16 \end{bmatrix} \qquad N = \begin{bmatrix} 1 & 0 & 2 \\ 1 & 1 & 1 \\ 3 & 5 & 10 \end{bmatrix}$$

a. Compute $M \times N$.
b. Compute $M + N$.
c. Compute $M \times 2N$.
d. Compute $2M - 3N$.

21 Find the length of the third side of each right triangle.

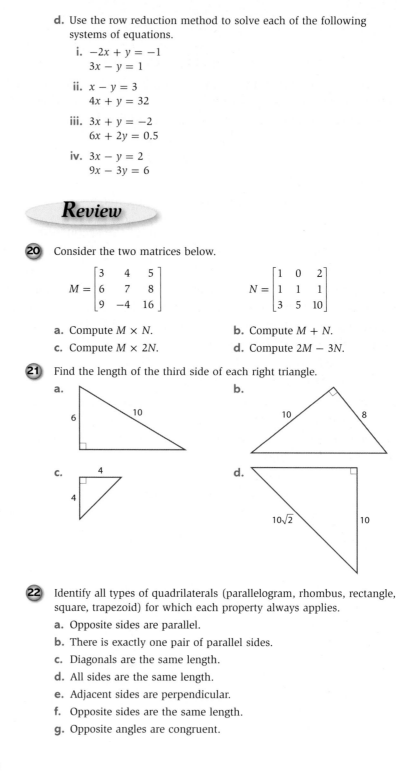

a.

6   10

b.

10   8

c.

4
4

d.

$10\sqrt{2}$ 10

22 Identify all types of quadrilaterals (parallelogram, rhombus, rectangle, square, trapezoid) for which each property always applies.

a. Opposite sides are parallel.

b. There is exactly one pair of parallel sides.

c. Diagonals are the same length.

d. All sides are the same length.

e. Adjacent sides are perpendicular.

f. Opposite sides are the same length.

g. Opposite angles are congruent.

d. i. $\begin{bmatrix} -2 & 1 & -1 \\ 3 & -1 & 1 \end{bmatrix} \rightarrow \begin{bmatrix} -2 & 1 & -1 \\ 1 & 0 & 0 \end{bmatrix} \Rightarrow x = 0$ and $y = -1$

ii. $\begin{bmatrix} 1 & -1 & 3 \\ 4 & 1 & 32 \end{bmatrix} \rightarrow \begin{bmatrix} 1 & -1 & 3 \\ 5 & 0 & 35 \end{bmatrix} \Rightarrow 5x = 35$, or $x = 7$ and $y = 4$

iii. $\begin{bmatrix} 3 & 1 & -2 \\ 6 & 2 & 0.5 \end{bmatrix} \rightarrow \begin{bmatrix} 6 & 2 & -4 \\ 6 & 2 & 0.5 \end{bmatrix} \rightarrow \begin{bmatrix} 6 & 2 & -4 \\ 0 & 0 & -4.5 \end{bmatrix} \Rightarrow 0 = -4.5$, so
there are no solutions.

iv. $\begin{bmatrix} 3 & -1 & 2 \\ 9 & -3 & 6 \end{bmatrix} \rightarrow \begin{bmatrix} 9 & -3 & 6 \\ 9 & -3 & 6 \end{bmatrix} \rightarrow \begin{bmatrix} 9 & -3 & 6 \\ 0 & 0 & 0 \end{bmatrix} \Rightarrow 0 = 0$, so there are
infinitely many solutions.

Review

20
a. $M \times N = \begin{bmatrix} 22 & 29 & 60 \\ 37 & 47 & 99 \\ 53 & 76 & 174 \end{bmatrix}$

b. $M + N = \begin{bmatrix} 4 & 4 & 7 \\ 7 & 8 & 9 \\ 12 & 1 & 26 \end{bmatrix}$

c. $M \times 2N = \begin{bmatrix} 3 & 4 & 5 \\ 6 & 7 & 8 \\ 9 & -4 & 16 \end{bmatrix} \times \begin{bmatrix} 2 & 0 & 4 \\ 2 & 2 & 2 \\ 6 & 10 & 20 \end{bmatrix} = \begin{bmatrix} 44 & 58 & 120 \\ 74 & 94 & 198 \\ 106 & 152 & 348 \end{bmatrix}$
Note that $M \times 2N = 2(M \times N)$.

d. $2M - 3N = \begin{bmatrix} 6 & 8 & 10 \\ 12 & 14 & 16 \\ 18 & -8 & 32 \end{bmatrix} - \begin{bmatrix} 3 & 0 & 6 \\ 3 & 3 & 3 \\ 9 & 15 & 30 \end{bmatrix} = \begin{bmatrix} 3 & 8 & 4 \\ 9 & 11 & 13 \\ 9 & -23 & 2 \end{bmatrix}$

Just in Time

21
a. 8

b. $\sqrt{164} = 2\sqrt{41} \approx 12.81$

c. $\sqrt{32} = 4\sqrt{2} \approx 5.66$

d. 10

Just in Time

22
a. parallelogram, rhombus, rectangle, square
b. rectangle, square
c. kite, rhombus, square
d. rhombus, square
e. rectangle, square
f. parallelogram, rhombus, rectangle, square
g. parallelogram, rhombus, rectangle, square

23 Write an equation for the line that fits each set of conditions.

  a. has y-intercept of $(0, 7)$ and slope of $\frac{1}{3}$

  b. contains $(-3, -2)$ and has slope 3

  c. contains $(-2, 6)$ and $(2, 14)$

  d. contains $(6, 5)$ and $(9, -5)$

24 Draw a graph that matches each equation.

  a. $y = -\frac{2}{3}x + 6$

  b. $y = 4x - 9$

  c. $3x + 9y = 18$

  d. $5x - 3y = 30$

  e. $y = -2$

  f. $x = 5$

25 Evaluate each of the following expressions when $x = -3$, $y = 5$, and $z = -1$.

  a. $xyz - 10$

  b. $x^2 + y^2 + z^2$

  c. $2z^3 - x^2y$

  d. $y - 7x - z + xy$

  e. $(x + y)^{-1}$

  f. $-3(x + 3z)^2$

26 The box plots below give the distributions of heights (in inches) for the Denver Nuggets and the Houston Rockets at the beginning of the 2006–2007 basketball season.

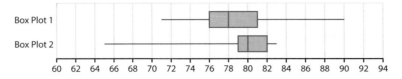

Heights of Players (in inches)

  a. The shortest player in the NBA during the 2006–2007 season played for the Denver Nuggets, and the tallest player played for the Houston Rockets. Use this information to match each box plot with the correct team.

  b. How tall was the shortest player in the NBA? How tall was the tallest player?

  c. Approximately what percentage of the Denver Nuggets players were at least 82 inches tall?

  d. Which team had the greater median height? Explain your reasoning.

  e. Does either team have a player whose height is an outlier? Explain your reasoning.

LESSON 3 • Matrices and Systems of Linear Equations   **155**

Just in Time

23   **a.** $y = \frac{1}{3}x + 7$ **b.** $y = 3x + 7$

　　c. $y = 2x + 10$ **d.** $y = \frac{-10}{3}x + 25$

Just in Time

24   **a–f.**

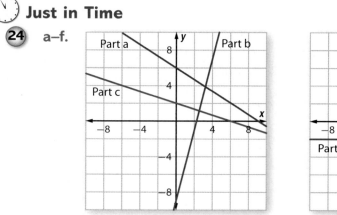 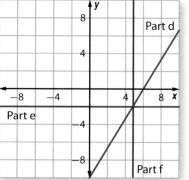

25   **a.** $(-3)(5)(-1) - 10 = 5$

　　b. $(-3)^2 + (5)^2 + (-1)^2 = 35$

　　c. $2(-1)^3 - (-3)^2(5) = -47$

　　d. $5 - 7(-3) - (-1) + (-3)(5) = 12$

　　e. $(-3 + 5)^{-1} = \frac{1}{2}$

　　f. $-3(-3 + 3(-1))^2 = -108$

26   **a.** Box Plot 1—Houston Rockets
　　　Box Plot 2—Denver Nuggets

　　b. 65"; 90"

　　c. 25%

　　d. The median height for the Denver Nuggets (80") is greater than the median height for the Houston Rockets (78").

　　e. Both teams have an outlier. This can be seen visually by measuring one and one-half boxes up and down from the third and first quartiles, respectively. The Denver Nuggets plot has at least one outlier, the minimum. The Houston Rockets plot has at least one outlier, the maximum.

　　　Houston Rockets:　$1.5(\text{IQR}) = 1.5(5) = 7.5$
　　　　　　　　　　　$Q_3 + 7.5 = 81 + 7.5 = 88.5$
　　　　　　　　　　　There is at least one Houston player whose height exceeds 88.5".

　　　Denver Nuggets:　$1.5(\text{IQR}) = 1.5(3) = 4.5$
　　　　　　　　　　　$Q_1 - 4.5 = 79 - 4.5 = 74.5$
　　　　　　　　　　　There is at least one Denver player whose height is below 74.5".

Unit 2

27 Complete the chart below to show equivalent fraction, decimal, and percent representations.

Fraction	Decimal	Percent
$\frac{1}{4}$		
	0.20	
		15
	1.75	

28 Solve each equation or inequality.

a. $5x + 4 = 2(x - 1)$

b. $6(2x - 10) = -4(4 - x)$

c. $2x + 8(12 + 3x) = 20x$

d. $2 - 4x \geq 20$

e. $x + 8 < 5 - 2x$

f. $15x + 120 > 0$

29 Maria knows that the definition of a rectangle is a parallelogram with one right angle. But, she wonders how this guarantees that all of the angles are right angles. Quadrilateral *ABCD* is a parallelogram and $\angle D$ is a right angle.

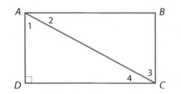

Maria wrote the following argument to convince herself that all of the angles of quadrilateral *ABCD* are right angles. Provide a justification for each numbered statement.

(1) $\overline{AB} \cong \overline{CD}$ and $\overline{AD} \cong \overline{CB}$.

(2) $\triangle ACD \cong \triangle CAB$

(3) $\angle B$ is a right angle.

(4) $m\angle 1 + m\angle 4 = 90°$ and $m\angle 2 + m\angle 3 = 90°$.

(5) $m\angle 2 = m\angle 4$

(6) $m\angle 1 + m\angle 2 = 90°$ and $m\angle 4 + m\angle 3 = 90°$.

(7) $\angle DAB$ is a right angle and $\angle BCD$ is a right angle.

(8) $\square ABCD$ is a rectangle.

30 Rewrite each expression as a product of linear factors.

a. $18x^2 - 6x$

b. $210x + 370$

c. $86 - 43x$

d. $-30x^2 - 8x$

27

Fraction	Decimal	Percent
$\frac{1}{4}$	0.25	25
$\frac{1}{5}$	0.20	20
$\frac{3}{20}$	0.15	15
$\frac{7}{4}$	1.75	175

28 a. $x = -2$

b. $x = 5.5$

c. $x = -16$

d. $x \leq -4.5$

e. $x < -1$

f. $x > -8$

Just in Time

29 (1) Definition of parallelogram—opposite sides congruent

(2) $\overline{AC}$ is not common to both triangles, so SSS Triangle Congruence condition

(3) $\angle D$ is a right angle and $m\angle B = m\angle D$

(4) Since the sum of the measures of the angles of a triangle is $180°$, the sum of the measures of the acute angles of a right triangle is $90°$.

(5) CPCTC

(6) $\angle 2 \cong \angle 4$ by CPCTC. Substitute equal angle measures.

(7) Definition of right angle

(8) Definition of a rectangle

30 a. $6x(3x - 1)$

b. $10(21x + 37)$

c. $43(2 - x)$

d. $-2x(15x^2 + 4)$ or $2x(-15x^2 - 4)$

INSTRUCTIONAL NOTE
Students should be able to remember this property that ensures that a parallelogram is a rectangle because of their visual experiences with quadrilateral linkages in Course 1 Unit 6.

Unit 2

Teaching Resources

Assessment Masters 32–37.

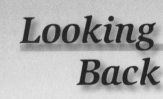

Looking Back

LESSON 4

In this unit, you learned about matrices, matrix operations, and properties of matrices. You learned how to use matrix methods to solve a wide variety of problems. In addition, you extended your understanding of vertex-edge graphs and systems of linear equations.

Matrices are rectangular arrays consisting of rows and columns of numbers. Operations on matrices include row sums, column sums, matrix addition and subtraction, multiplication of a matrix by a number, matrix multiplication, and finding the inverse of a matrix. Properties of matrices and matrix operations are often similar to, yet sometimes different from, the corresponding properties of real numbers and their operations. Matrices can be used to organize and display data, and to represent, analyze, and solve problems in diverse situations ranging from tracking inventories to ranking tournaments.

The tasks in this final lesson will help you review, pull together, and apply what you have learned about matrices and matrix methods.

1. **Tracking Physical Fitness** The U.S. Department of Education collects data on the physical fitness of American youths. The information below shows the average time, in minutes, for students 10–11 years old to run three-quarters of a mile and for students 12–17 years old to run one mile.

Boys

	1980	1989	
	6.5	7.3	10–11 year olds
	8.4	9.1	12–13 year olds
	7.2	8.6	14–17 year olds

Girls

	1980	1989
	7.4	8.0
	9.8	10.5
	9.6	10.7

Source: *Youth Indicators 1991: Trends in the Well-being of American Youth.* Washington, DC: U.S. Government Printing Office, 1991.

a. Write down two trends you see in the data. Write down one fact that you find surprising and explain why it surprises you.

b. The data as given are organized in two matrices titled "Boys" and "Girls." Reorganize the data into two different matrices titled "1980" and "1989." Don't change the row labels.

1   **a.** Responses will vary. Some possible trends: times increase from 1980 to 1989; older kids run faster (except for the 14–17 year-old girls in 1989); the average time for boys is less than the average time for girls; girls' times from 12–13 year olds to 14–17 year olds do not change much. One possible surprise is that in 1989, the 14–17 year-old girls were slower than the 12–13 year-old girls.

b. 1980   **1989**

$$\begin{array}{cc} B & G \\ \begin{bmatrix} 6.5 & 7.4 \\ 8.4 & 9.8 \\ 7.5 & 9.6 \end{bmatrix} \end{array} \begin{array}{c} \text{10–11 year olds} \\ \text{12–13 year olds} \\ \text{14–17 year olds} \end{array} \begin{array}{cc} B & G \\ \begin{bmatrix} 7.3 & 8.0 \\ 9.1 & 10.5 \\ 8.6 & 10.7 \end{bmatrix} \end{array}$$

> **POSSIBLE MISCONCEPTION**
> Because the distances run by the youngest students are shorter than the distances run by the others, care must be taken when working with these matrices. This is particularly relevant in Parts d and e.

c. Combine the 1980 matrix and the 1989 matrix, from Part b, to construct a single matrix that shows the change in average times from 1980 to 1989.

   i. What matrix operation did you use to combine the 1980 and 1989 matrices into this new matrix?

   ii. What are the column labels of this new matrix?

d. Think about the total time for three-person races, where the first leg of the race is three-quarters of a mile run by 10–11 year olds, the second leg is one mile run by 12–13 year olds, and the third leg is one mile run by 14–17 year olds.

   i. What do you think would have been the typical total time for such a race in 1989 if all three legs were run by girls?

   ii. What matrix operation did you use to answer this question?

e. Enrique claimed that in 1980, the 10–11 year-old boys ran faster than the 14–17 year-old boys, since 6.5 is less than 7.5. Do you agree? Explain. If you disagree, describe a method for making a more accurate comparison between the younger and older boys.

2 **Analyzing Flight Options** The vertex-edge graph below shows the direct flights between seven cities for a major airline.

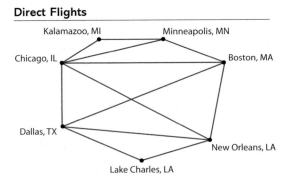

Direct Flights

a. Construct the adjacency matrix for the graph. List the vertices in alphabetical order.

b. How many cities can be flown to directly from Chicago? What matrix operation can be used to answer this question?

c. What is the fewest number of stops at intermediate cities needed to fly from Kalamazoo to Lake Charles?

d. It is tiring and time-consuming to have more than one stopover, that is, more than two segments on a flight. Use the adjacency matrix to construct a new matrix that shows which pairs of cities can be connected with a flight of two segments or less.

   i. What matrix operations did you perform to get the new matrix?

   ii. How can you use the new matrix to identify cities connected by a flight with no more than one stopover?

c. The "change" matrix is found by subtracting the 1980 matrix from the 1989 matrix.

Change in Times

	B	G
10–11 year olds	0.8	0.6
12–13 year olds	0.7	0.7
14–17 year olds	1.1	1.1

   i. Matrix subtraction was used.

   ii. Boys and Girls (or B and G)

d. i. 29.2 minutes

   ii. Find the column sum of the 1989 girls' column.

e. Enrique is incorrect because the distance for the youngest group was less than that for the others. A more accurate comparison could be made by scaling one group; for example, by multiplying the times for the 14–17 year-old boys by 0.75. (Although note that this scaling would not yield completely accurate times since speed varies when running a given distance as part of differing total distances.)

2 a.

	B	C	D	K	LC	M	NO
B	0	1	1	0	0	1	1
C	1	0	1	1	0	1	1
D	1	1	0	0	1	0	1
K	0	1	0	0	0	1	0
LC	0	0	1	0	0	0	1
M	1	1	0	1	0	0	0
NO	1	1	1	0	1	0	0

$= A$

b. 5; compute the row (or column) sum for Chicago in the matrix.

c. The minimum number of stopovers needed to fly from Kalamazoo to Lake Charles is 2. The route would be Kalamazoo-Chicago-Dallas (or New Orleans)-Lake Charles.

d. Construct $A + A^2$. Each entry in this matrix is the number of paths of length 2 or less between the respective vertices.

	B	C	D	K	LC	M	NO
B	4	4	3	2	2	2	3
C	4	5	3	2	2	3	3
D	3	3	4	1	2	2	4
K	2	2	1	2	0	2	1
LC	2	2	2	0	2	0	2
M	2	3	2	2	0	3	2
NO	3	3	4	1	2	2	4

$= A + A^2$

   i. The operations needed are squaring and adding.

   ii. Two cities are connected by a flight with no more than one stopover if the corresponding entry in $A + A^2$ is not a zero.

INSTRUCTIONAL NOTE
In Part a, you may want to check that everyone lists the vertices in alphabetical order. This will avoid unnecessary confusion as students analyze the task and compare responses.

e. Is there anything about the vertex-edge graph that seems unusual or out of place? Is the graph an acceptable model for this particular problem? Explain.

③ Producing Manuals Marcus, the owner of a small software company, is producing two manuals for a new software product. One manual is a brief start-up guide, and the other is a larger reference guide.

He contracts to have the manuals bound and shrink-wrapped at a local printer. However, he is on a deadline to ship the manuals in two days, and the machines that do the jobs are only available for a limited time. For the next two days, the binding machine is available for a total of 18 hours, and the shrink-wrap machine is available at later times for 10 hours. The matrix below shows how many seconds each machine requires for each manual.

Time Required (in seconds)

	Start-up Guide	Reference Guide
Bind	30	45
Shrink-Wrap	15	30

Marcus wants to know how many of each type of manual will be ready to ship in two days, if the printer uses all the available time on each machine for his job.

a. Represent this situation in four ways:

  i. using a system of linear equations

  ii. using a matrix equation

  iii. using graphs

  iv. using tables

b. Using one of the representations from Part a, determine how many of each type of manual will be ready to ship in two days.

c. Verify your answer using two of the other representations in Part a.

d. The next week, Marcus receives an unexpectedly large order. He needs 2,000 start-up guides and 800 reference guides bound and shrink-wrapped. Use matrix multiplication and scalar multiplication (multiplying a matrix by a number) to determine how many hours will be needed on each of the machines at the printer.

e. Students should notice that this graph is certainly not a geographically accurate map. For example, the placement of Kalamazoo between Chicago and Minneapolis is not geographically accurate. Yet the graph is still acceptable as a mathematical model for this problem since the only relevant feature is flight connections between cities.

3 **a.** Let s be the number of start-up guides completed and r be the number of reference manuals completed.

i. $30s + 45r = 64{,}800$ seconds
$15s + 30r = 36{,}000$ seconds

ii. $\begin{bmatrix} 30 & 45 \\ 15 & 30 \end{bmatrix} \begin{bmatrix} s \\ r \end{bmatrix} = \begin{bmatrix} 64{,}800 \\ 36{,}000 \end{bmatrix}$

iii.

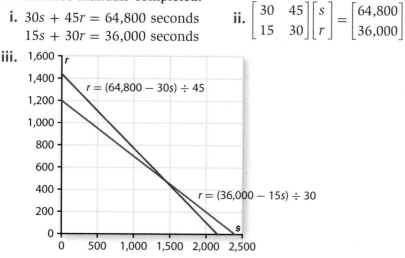

iv. Students could create a table for each of the linear equations in part i, and look for identical entries. An alternative table method is shown below. This table is constructed so that the shrink-wrap time used is always 36,000 seconds. You can see that the solution is somewhere between 1,200 and 1,600 start-up guides.

Production Time Requirements

Number of Start-up Guides	Number of Reference Guides	Shrink-wrap Time (in sec)	Binding Time (in sec)	Over or Under Binding Time
0	1,200	36,000	54,000	Under
400	1,000	36,000	57,000	Under
800	800	36,000	60,000	Under
1,200	600	36,000	63,000	Under
1,600	400	36,000	66,000	Over
2,000	200	36,000	69,000	Over
2,400	0	36,000	72,000	Over

b. Student methods will vary. 1,440 start-up guides and 480 reference manuals will be ready to ship in two days.

c. Students should use two representations different from that used in Part b to solve this system.

d. $\begin{bmatrix} 30 & 45 \\ 15 & 30 \end{bmatrix} \begin{bmatrix} 2{,}000 \\ 800 \end{bmatrix} = \begin{bmatrix} 96{,}000 \\ 54{,}000 \end{bmatrix}$

Making 2,000 start-up guides and 800 reference guides will require 96,000 seconds on the binding machine and 54,000 seconds on the shrink-wrap machine. To change these times into hours, use scalar multiplication: $\frac{1}{3{,}600} \begin{bmatrix} 96{,}000 \\ 54{,}000 \end{bmatrix} = \begin{bmatrix} 26.67 \\ 15 \end{bmatrix}$. So, this job will require $26\frac{2}{3}$ hours to bind and 15 hours to shrink-wrap.

TECHNOLOGY NOTE To carry out this method on a graphing calculator, you could solve each equation for r, enter each equation into the **Y=** menu, and then create a table. Most calculators will show one column for **X** (which is s in this case) and then columns for **Y1** (r in the first equation) and **Y2** (r in the second equation). Then you can scroll down and find an **X** where **Y1** = **Y2**. You may need to adjust the table start value and the table increment value to find the exact solution.

Unit 2

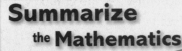

Summarize
the Mathematics

In this unit, you used matrix methods to analyze problem situations, and you examined properties of matrices.

a In order for information to be useful, it must be organized.

  i. Describe how matrices can be used to organize information.

  ii. Can the same information be displayed in a matrix in different ways? Explain.

  iii. What are some advantages of using matrices to organize and display information? What are some disadvantages?

b Sometimes a situation involves two variables that are linked by two or more conditions. These situations often can be modeled by a system of two linear equations. Describe how to use matrices to solve a system of linear equations.

c List all of the different operations on matrices that you learned about in this unit. For each operation:

  i. Give an example showing how to perform the operation using paper-and-pencil.

  ii. Describe how to perform the operation using your calculator or computer software.

  iii. Describe how the operation can be used to help you analyze some situation.

Be prepared to share your descriptions and examples with the class.

✔ Check Your Understanding

Write, in outline form, a summary of the important mathematical concepts and methods developed in this unit. Organize your summary so that it can be used as a quick reference in future units and courses.

You may want to have a different group share their response and thinking for each part. You can assess the extent of agreement of other groups by their questions or additions to the initial group's thinking. Facilitate resolutions of any disagreements before proceeding to the next part.

Summarize the Mathematics

a **i.** Student explanations could include a discussion of rows and columns, displaying information in a rectangular array, or organizing information related to two variables where the values of one variable are row labels and the values of a second variable are column labels (e.g., in Task 1, information about running time related to year and age).

ii. Yes. For example, you might transpose rows and columns, list the values of a variable in a different order along the rows or columns, or reorganize under different headings (e.g., in Task 1, reorganize running time data by using matrices titled by year instead of by gender).

iii. Advantages may include the following: Matrices are a straightforward, natural modification of tables, usable for data that depend on two variables, and easily stored in a computer. Matrices also can be operated on in a variety of ways, allowing you to analyze the information. Disadvantages may include the following: Matrices are only usable with two main categories and are not as visual as graphs.

b Students may give a description such as the following: Write the equations one above the other, each in the form $ax + by = c$. This makes it easy to see the matrix of coefficients and set up the matrix equation. Multiply the inverse of the matrix of coefficients times a matrix formed by the values on the right of the "equal to" sign to get the solution. Be sure that A^{-1} is on the left or comes first in the product.

c Possible operations are row and column sums, scalar multiplication (multiplying a matrix by a single number), multiplying two matrices using the row-column procedure, multiplying two matrices entry-by-entry, taking powers of matrices, adding matrices, and subtracting matrices. Students might even list things like finding the mean of a row. Students could also include finding the inverse of a matrix, when it exists, since this can be thought of in terms of the operation of inverting a matrix.

Students should be able to explain how to perform each operation by hand and on a calculator or with software. They should be able to find an example from this unit or another source of how that operation is used in a particular situation to yield additional information, a deeper analysis, or a solution.

Student Masters 40–42.

Assessment Masters 43–67.

Student Masters 68–69.

✓ Check Your Understanding

You may wish to have students use the Teaching Master, *Matrix Methods Unit Summary*, to help them organize the information. Above all, this should be something that is useful to the individual student.

Practicing for Standardized Tests

Each Practicing for Standardized Tests master presents 10 questions in the multiple-choice format of test items similar to how they often appear in standardized tests. Answers are provided below.

Answers to Practice Set 2

1. (c)   **2.** (e)   **3.** (c)   **4.** (a)   **5.** (a)

6. (c)   **7.** (d)   **8.** (c)   **9.** (c)   **10.** (b)

Teacher Notes

UNIT 3

Coordinate Methods

The use of coordinates to specify locations in two dimensions, as on a map, is familiar to you. The general idea of representing points in terms of coordinates has important mathematical applications in computer modeling. It enables designers and engineers to describe geometric ideas in algebraic language. Objects such as lines, circles, and other curves in two dimensions and surfaces in three dimensions can be expressed in terms of functions and equations. Transformations such as rotation or enlargement of these shapes and surfaces can be accomplished by operations on coordinates.

In this unit, you will study coordinate methods for representing, analyzing, and transforming two-dimensional shapes. Key ideas will be developed through your work on problems in three lessons.

Lessons

1 A Coordinate Model of a Plane

Use coordinates to represent points, lines, and geometric figures in a plane and on a computer or calculator screen and to analyze properties of shapes.

2 Coordinate Models of Transformations

Use coordinates to describe transformations of the plane and to investigate properties of shapes that are preserved under various types of transformations.

3 Transformations, Matrices, and Animation

Develop and use matrix representations of polygonal shapes and transformations to create computer animations.

Unit 3

COORDINATE METHODS

Unit Overview

This unit focuses on coordinate methods in geometry. Just as Rene Descartes' (1596–1650) work in coordinate geometry permitted the development of both algebra and geometry to move forward, the introduction of coordinate methods in Course 2 of the *Core-Plus Mathematics* curriculum advances and connects the algebra and geometry concepts begun in Course 1. The representations of shapes and transformations in a plane now are explored systematically using coordinates. Coordinate methods also lead to a simple, yet powerful, base for computer animations. The use of matrices as a representation tool is extended to describing shapes and transformations, thereby underscoring the connectedness of strands within the curriculum and the utility of matrices as a connector.

Technology as a Context for the Unit Using interactive geometry software in this unit allows students to raise questions about how the software is able to create, measure, and reposition shapes. Additionally, working in an interactive technology environment allows students to investigate text-provided questions as well as their own questions. The unit provides a gentle introduction to the use of interactive geometry software as a tool for exploring and applying important geometric ideas. In Unit 6, *Trigonometric Methods,* students will continue to use the geometry software. In Course 3 and Course 4 units, students will become more proficient with geometry software as a tool for discovering and applying geometric concepts. The time invested in becoming familiar with this tool will pay dividends in later units.

Therefore, it is valuable for all students to have individual computer time to explore the commands and functionality of interactive geometry software so they can flexibly interact with it in a variety of instructional settings. We realize that access to technology varies across schools and among classrooms. Some schools have chosen to support student learning with a classroom set of laptop computers. Other schools have more limited access to computers; consequently, teachers sign up to take their classes to the computer lab, use a single classroom computer for demonstration and shared student work, or provide a few computer stations within the classroom for groups to choose to use as they work on particular problems. Since *CPMP-Tools* is available on the *StudentWorks* CD-ROM and from the Internet (www.wmich.edu/cpmp/CPMP-Tools/), you may ask students to complete an investigation problem or two outside of class and be prepared to share results with classmates. This allows individual computer time and will be particularly helpful for students needing more time to investigate and process the material.

This unit can be effectively taught using one computer and a projection system. When a single classroom computer is used, we envision an interactive classroom setting in which all students are engaged in the exploration of mathematical situations—seeking patterns in displays, making and testing conjectures, and posing related questions. The computer operator can be a classroom teacher, a student, or a group of students. Using interactive geometry software, such as what resides on *CPMP-Tools*, on a single computer can provide the stage on which a problem situation is posed for the entire class, and classroom discourse can be the vehicle through which the mathematics emerges.

If a teacher is facilitating an investigation and acting as the computer operator, the exploration should still belong to the students. Hence, it will be important for the teacher to pose questions to both prompt and push student thinking. Alternatively, the teacher could facilitate an investigation allowing a student to act as the computer operator. In either case, when a problem indicates student choice of figures and/or transformations, the choice(s) should be solicited from students.

In this unit, students should consistently have access to grid or dot paper. Student Master 4 can be copied for this purpose. Using square dot paper and colored pencils will allow students to more easily identify shapes and their transformed images, particularly when horizontal and vertical segments are displayed.

Unit Objectives

- Use coordinates to represent points, lines, and geometric figures in a plane and on a computer or calculator screen
- Use coordinate representations of figures to analyze and reason about their properties
- Use coordinate methods and programming techniques as a tool to implement computational algorithms, to model rigid transformations and similarity transformations, and to investigate properties of shapes that are preserved under various transformations
- Build and use matrix representations of polygons and transformations and use these representations to create computer animations

CPMP-Tools

Although all investigations in this unit are written intending use of *CPMP-Tools* Interactive Geometry software, the investigations are easily adapted for use with commercial software such as *The Geometer's Sketchpad*, *Cabri Geometre*, or *Cinderella*. Recommendations and options for instruction when one or a few computers are available are at the beginning of investigations and at point of use.

When accessing *CPMP-Tools* software for use in this unit, be sure to select Course 2 from the Course menu on the left; then under the Geometry menu, select "Coordinate Geometry."

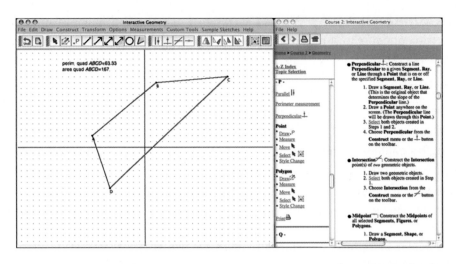

In addition to the general purpose interactive geometry tool, *CPMP-Tools* geometry software includes several custom tools: "Design by Robot," "Explore Angles in Circles," "Animate Shuttle," and "Roll Over." Lesson 1 Investigation 3 Problem 7 (page 178) uses the "Explore Angles in Circles" custom tool. This investigation does not call for other technology use, and thus lab access is not needed for this task. It can be facilitated, as suggested on page T161A, using a single class computer, having multiple computers available for student use as they reach Problem 7, or by student investigation individually outside of class time.

Ideally, for Lesson 1 Investigation 1, students will have access, in pairs, to computers and *CPMP-Tools* or other interactive geometry software. Doing so will enable students to become experienced using the software and better engage later in other whole-class discussions facilitated using one computer and projector. Selected investigation problems and homework tasks that require computer access can be done outside of class time. See page T164 for specific guidelines.

Lesson 2 Investigation 3, "Combining Transformations," can be completed using grid paper, but using the interactive geometry software in *CPMP-Tools* will allow students to quickly perform compositions (in both orders) and request lengths and areas from the Measurement menu to compare sizes of image and preimage polygons. In Lesson 3, students are asked to build transformation matrices and study planning algorithms and programs using a simplified programming language embedded in *CPMP-Tools*. Computer access during class time is not necessary for Lesson 3 unless you wish to provide students programming time during class. Students should complete Lesson 1 Extensions Task 27 (page 190) and Lesson 2 Extensions Task 31 (page 227) in preparation for developing their own animations in Lesson 3. See the introductory section on page T161 for other technology-related information.

Unit 3

STUDENT MASTERS The key geometric ideas listed here are on a student activity master with additional space to record key ideas as they are developed in this unit.

Student Masters 1–2.

Key Geometric Ideas from Course 1 This unit builds on important geometric concepts and relationships developed in the Course 1 unit, *Patterns in Shape*. Specifically:

Definitions

Isosceles triangle a triangle with at least two sides of equal length

Parallelogram a quadrilateral with opposite sides of equal length

Rectangle a parallelogram with one right angle

Kite a convex quadrilateral with two distinct pairs of consecutive sides the same length

Rhombus a quadrilateral with all four sides the same length

Congruent figures figures that have the same shape and size, regardless of position or orientation

Perpendicular bisector of a segment a line that is perpendicular to a segment and contains its midpoint

Square a rhombus with one right angle

Relationships

Pythagorean Theorem If the lengths of the sides of a right triangle are a, b, c, with the side of length c opposite the right angle, then $a^2 + b^2 = c^2$.

Converse of the Pythagorean Theorem If the sum of the squares of the lengths of two sides of a triangle equals the square of the length of the third side, then the triangle is a right triangle.

Triangle Inequality The sum of the lengths of any two sides of a triangle is always greater than the length of the third side.

Triangle Angle Sum Property The sum of the measures of the angles in a triangle is 180°.

Quadrilateral Angle Sum Property The sum of the measures of the angles in a quadrilateral is 360°.

Polygon Angle Sum Property The sum of the measures of the interior angles of a polygon with n sides is $(n - 2)180°$.

Base Angles of Isosceles Triangle Angles opposite congruent sides of an isosceles triangle are congruent.

Side-Side-Side (SSS) congruence condition If three sides of a triangle are congruent to the corresponding sides of another triangle, then the two triangles are congruent.

Side-Angle-Side (SAS) congruence condition If two sides and the angle between the sides of one triangle are congruent to the corresponding parts of another triangle, then the two triangles are congruent.

Angle-Side-Angle (ASA) congruence condition If two angles and the side between the angles of one triangle are congruent to the corresponding parts of another triangle, then the two triangles are congruent.

Opposite Angles Property of Parallelograms Opposite angles in a parallelogram are congruent.

Condition ensuring a parallelogram If the diagonals of a quadrilateral bisect each other, then the quadrilateral is a parallelogram.

Condition ensuring a rectangle If the diagonals of a parallelogram are the same length, then the parallelogram is a rectangle.

Condition ensuring a square If a rectangle has one pair of consecutive sides the same length, then the rectangle is a square.

30°-60° right triangle relationship For a right triangle with acute angles of measures 30° and 60°, the length of the side opposite the 30° angle is half the length of the hypotenuse. The length of the side opposite the 60° angle is $\sqrt{3}$ times the length of the side opposite the 30° angle.

45°-45° right triangle relationship For a right triangle with acute angles of measures 45°, the length of the hypotenuse is $\sqrt{2}$ times the length of a leg of the right triangle.

Lesson Objectives	On Your Own Assignments*	Suggested Pacing	Materials
Lesson 1 *A Coordinate Model of a Plane* • Use coordinates to represent points, lines, and geometric figures in a plane • Develop and use coordinate representations of geometric ideas such as distance, slope, and midpoint to analyze properties of lines and shapes • Design algorithms for programming calculators or computers to perform routine geometry-related computations • Develop and use equations for circles in a coordinate plane • Reason with general coordinates to establish properties of triangles, quadrilaterals, and circles	**After Investigation 1:** A1 or A2, A3, A4 or A5, A6, choose two of C12–C15, choose two of R20–R22, E27 or E28, Rv33–Rv35 **After Investigation 2:** choose two of A7–A10, C16, choose two of R23–R25, choose one of E29–E31, Rv36–Rv38 **After Investigation 3:** A11, C17–C19, R26, E32, Rv39–Rv42	10 days (including assessment)	• Internet access to site referred to on page T162A • *CPMP-Tools* interactive geometry software or similar software • Computer access for pairs of students • Computer and projection system • Grid or graph paper • Rulers • Unit resources
Lesson 2 *Coordinate Models of Transformations* • Use coordinates to develop function rules modeling translations, line reflections, and rotations and size transformations centered at the origin • Use coordinates to investigate properties of figures under one or more rigid transformations or under similarity transformations • Explore the concept of function composition using successive application of two transformations	**After Investigation 1:** A1, A3–A5, A6 or A7, R23, E29, Rv36–Rv38 **After Investigation 2:** A8–A10, C15, R24, R25, R26 or R27, E27, choose one of E30–E34, Rv39, Rv40 **After Investigation 3:** A11, A12 or A13, A14, choose one of C16–C19, C20, C21, C22, R28, E35, Rv41–Rv43	11 days (including assessment)	• Grid or graph paper • Rulers • *CPMP-Tools* interactive geometry software or similar software • Computer and projection system • Unit resources
Lesson 3 *Transformations, Matrices, and Animation* • Use coordinate rules for rotations about the origin to develop corresponding matrix representations • Use coordinate rules for size transformations centered at the origin to develop corresponding matrix representations • Use matrix representations of shapes and transformations to create simple animations involving rotations and size transformations	**After Investigation 1:** A1, A2, A3 or A4, C7, C8, C9 or C10, R12–R14, Rv22, Rv23 **After Investigation 2:** A5, A6, C11, R15, E16, choose one of E17–E21, Rv24, Rv25	6 days (including assessment)	• Grid or graph paper • Rulers • *CPMP-Tools* interactive geometry software or similar software • Computer and projection system • Unit resources
Lesson 4 *Looking Back* • Review and synthesize the major objectives of the unit		3 days (including assessment)	• Grid or graph paper • Rulers • *CPMP-Tools* interactive geometry software • Computer access for pairs of students • Unit resources

* *When choice is indicated, it is important to leave the choice to the student.*

Note: *It is best if Connections tasks are discussed as a whole class after they have been assigned as homework.*

Unit 3

A Coordinate Model of a Plane

Computer-generated graphics influence your world in striking ways. They are an important feature of Web sites where you search for information. They are also key elements of the video games you may play and the animated and special-effects films you enjoy.

Computer graphics are now the most commonly used tool in the design of automobiles, buildings, home interiors, and even clothing. And of course, computer or calculator graphics have been important tools in your study of mathematics. They have helped you produce, trace, and analyze graphs of data and functions. They have also helped you create geometric shapes and discover some of their properties.

Unit 3

A Coordinate Model of a Plane

Lesson 1 focuses on uses of coordinates to model two-dimensional space in the context of computer graphics using interactive geometry software such as the *CPMP-Tools* geometry software. Applications of coordinate models are investigated; in particular, students discover how to compute distances, slopes, and midpoints as well as how to use those calculations for identifying and reasoning about properties of certain quadrilaterals. The distance formula is also used to develop equations for circles in a coordinate plane. Throughout this lesson, students will have numerous opportunities to practice algebra skills.

During Investigation 1, students will develop formulas to find the distance between two points and the midpoint of a line segment. Students should note the central role played by the Pythagorean Theorem in this development. They will review the formula for calculating the slope of a line or a segment. They will explore writing algorithms that can be used to guide development of calculator or computer programs.

In Investigation 2, students will use the tools developed in Investigation 1 to further review the slope of a line and to discover the relationship between the slopes of perpendicular lines. Students will use distance between two points, the midpoint of a line segment, and the slope of a line to explore the characteristics of various quadrilaterals. In the process, students are introduced to matrix representations for polygons.

In the third investigation of this lesson, students focus on coordinate representations of circles. They use the distance formula to develop equations for circles first having center at the origin and then having center at any point with coordinates (h, k). Students also begin to develop the ability to use general coordinates of points to reason about the properties of shapes.

In this lesson, planning algorithms are introduced. These are simply sequences of steps that would need to be performed in order for a computer or calculator to do a task. Students are asked periodically to write such algorithms as new ideas arise. These algorithms may be translated into calculator programs by using the built-in commands on a programmable calculator. Many students enjoy programming and should be given the opportunity to do so. Some On Your Own tasks ask for calculator programs corresponding to the various planning algorithms. If students are using programmable calculators with computer links, a display capture (or "screen dump") is one way to obtain a quick copy for their Math Toolkits. Some students may wish to make a special section in their ring binders for programming notes.

Lesson Objectives

- Use coordinates to represent points, lines, and geometric figures in a plane
- Develop and use coordinate representations of geometric ideas such as distance, slope, and midpoint to analyze properties of lines and shapes
- Design algorithms for programming calculators or computers to perform routine geometry-related computations
- Develop and use equations for circles in a coordinate plane
- Reason with general coordinates to establish properties of triangles, quadrilaterals, and circles

Lesson Launch

To motivate an appreciation for the topics in this unit, it will be helpful for students to reflect briefly on the importance of coordinate systems in our world, particularly for computer graphics. One possibility is to ask students to cite an example of a coordinate system, then briefly discuss the enormous variety of ways in which we use coordinates to locate points in everyday life. For example, on a trip in which a student flies from his or her home to Washington, D.C., how many times might the student encounter a coordinate system? The home might be located by a coordinate (*house number, street name*); the airport might be located on a map by coordinates; the student might need to remember a parking place at the airport with a coordinate (*area, row*); the student might find the departure gate by a coordinate (*concourse, gate*) and his or her seat on the airplane by a coordinate (*row, seat*); and so on.

This unit will give students a sense of the creative and mathematical thinking that goes into the production of animated films and computer-aided design. Advances in computer animation allow companies to use virtual design when creating new products. This process saves time and money. A Web site showing the design and assembly of the new Boeing 787 aircraft can be found at blog.seattlepi.nwsource.com/aerospace/archives/109472.asp. Other sites such as www.pixar.com provide clips of animated films.

If you do not have classroom access to the Internet, then you might take an animated movie to class or ask if any students play computer or video games. Of course, many of them do, and you can extend the conversation with questions such as the following:

- Do any of the games involve guessing at the position of a hidden obstacle? Hitting a target? (Many games involve avoiding pitfalls or aiming at moving targets.)
- Are there animations to keep the visual display interesting? (Creative graphics are a major factor in keeping the player interested.)
- Do the obstacles or graphics stay in the same position for each game? (This depends somewhat on the game. Some follow patterns that will not change from game to game, but many will change.)
- How does the game know where "you" are on the screen and where the target is? How are the graphics created?

You will have many students who have played such games without ever thinking about the instructions that have to be in place to create the screen images.

Once you have discussed the broad applications of coordinate systems and computer animation, focus attention on computer graphics applications using the Think About This Situation.

Initially, students may depend on their experiences with computer drawing programs to answer the questions in the Think About This Situation. This lesson will push students to think about how interactive geometry software uses coordinate geometry, rules, and formulas to produce computer graphics. Students should be encouraged to think more deeply about location, shape, and size of the images.

How could you describe exactly where the figures are located in the coordinate plane? How could you get from one quadrilateral to another? How could you verify the lengths of segments?

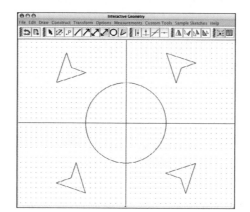

Examine the computer graphics screen shown above. The dots represent points with integer coordinates.

a How do you think the images are produced?

b How could you describe the location of the circle? Of each quadrilateral?

c How do the four quadrilaterals appear to be related? How could you check your claim?

d What equation could be used to describe the horizontal axis? A line 7 units above and parallel to the horizontal axis?

e What equation could be used to describe the vertical axis? A line 10 units to the left of and parallel to the vertical axis?

In this unit, you will study some of the mathematics, called **coordinate geometry**, that underlies computer graphics. As you complete the investigations in this first lesson, you will learn how to use coordinates to model points, lines, and geometric shapes in a plane and on a calculator or computer screen. You will also learn how to use coordinate representations of geometric ideas such as slope, distance, and midpoint to analyze properties of shapes.

Think About This Situation

(a) Students will most likely say that the images were created by connecting certain displayed points possibly through the Draw or Construct menus seen at the top of the screen. (You may need to point out the pull-down menus to keep ideas flowing.)

(b) The circle is centered at the origin and has a radius of 8 as counted by the dots. One way to describe the location of the quadrilaterals is to identify the coordinates of each vertex. Students may also refer to the location by the quadrant in which the quadrilateral lies. They might recognize that the quadrilaterals can be produced by repeatedly rotating one of the quadrilaterals 90° clockwise or counterclockwise about the origin.

(c) The four quadrilaterals seem to be congruent to each other. Students could check their claim by measuring the lengths of the sides and the angles of each quadrilateral. They might also think about calculating the lengths of sides by using the grid and the Pythagorean Theorem. They may suggest tracing or printing and cutting out one quadrilateral and placing it on each of the others. (You may wish to suggest that students draw the diagonals that form two triangles in each shape and show that all triangles formed are congruent.)

(d) The horizontal axis can be described by the equation $y = 0$. A line 7 units above and parallel to the horizontal axis can be described by the equation $y = 7$.

(e) The vertical axis can be described by the equation $x = 0$. A line 10 units to the left and parallel to the vertical axis can be described by the equation $x = -10$.

 **Representing Geometric Ideas with Coordinates**

Computer images on a screen are composed of lighted *pixels* (screen points) whose coordinates satisfy specific conditions. By specifying the conditions on pixels, CAD (computer-aided design) software and geometry drawing programs can be used to create all sorts of shapes and designs.

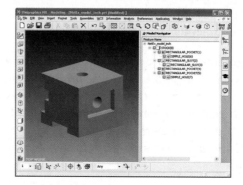

In this investigation, you will explore how a two-dimensional graphics program called *Interactive Geometry* uses coordinates in drawing and in calculating measures of geometric figures. Other software programs may work differently, but they are all based on the same mathematical ideas. As you work on the following problems, look for answers to these questions:

> *How can you create a polygon using interactive geometry software?*

> *What information and calculations are needed to find slopes, lengths, and midpoints of sides?*

Creating Shapes As a class or in pairs, experiment with the drawing capabilities of interactive geometry software.

1 Explore how each command in the Draw menu can be used to create examples of the objects listed.

   a. Draw commands can also be implemented by selecting the appropriate tool displayed on the software toolbar.

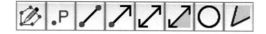

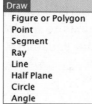

Draw
Figure or Polygon
Point
Segment
Ray
Line
Half Plane
Circle
Angle

   Match each icon in your software toolbar with the corresponding Draw command.

Representing Geometric Ideas with Coordinates

In this investigation, students will create shapes using interactive geometry software. They will develop formulas and write algorithms for finding slopes of lines, distances, and midpoints of segments.

One computer If you are using a single computer and a projection system, you can facilitate this investigation by having various students at the controls. Discussion would alternate between whole-class and think-pair-share discussion with student mathematical work and writing at several points in the investigation. One scenario for instruction in this manner follows.

(1) Begin by having a student experiment with the Draw menu. The student should tell the class what he or she is doing. Provide a second student time also. Students in the class might ask the computer operator to try a specific draw command.

(2) Next, ask students to match icons with the options in the Draw menu as shown in the student text. Then ask a student to accept directions to draw a circle congruent to the one in the TATS (Part b) from a fellow student. A different student could provide directions to the computer operator for drawing a quadrilateral congruent to the ones in the TATS. Shift the discussion back to groups to discuss how they know the quadrilateral drawn using *CPMP-Tools* is congruent to the one in the TATS (even if it is not congruent). Ask for a second method to draw the quadrilateral and repeat the congruent discussion.

(3) For Problem 2, switch to a different computer operator. A second student could be designated to publicly record the vertices of the rectangle and parallelogram that is drawn. (Turn the coordinates on using "Default Styles" in the Options menu.) Then ask pairs or groups of students to discuss how one knows that the figures in Part a and in Part b are a rectangle and a parallelogram, respectively. Follow with a teacher-facilitated discussion where student ideas are presented, clarified, and mathematically corrected if necessary.

Students would not write solutions to Problems 1 and 2.

(4) For Problems 3–5, use a similar method of providing instructions to a computer operator to draw the indicated rectangle and diagonals, and find the slopes and side lengths requested in Problems 3 and 4 using options in the Measurements menu. Move the labels as needed to improve the look of the display. Move this window to the right side of the monitor. Bring the main *CPMP-Tools* window to the front and open a new Coordinate Geometry window. Draw the rectangle and diagonals and report the lengths of the diagonals for Problem 5. Displaying the figures on a screen or projected on a white board will allow students to complete Problems 3–6 in their groups.

At this point or following Problem 7, students can do Reflections Task 20 for homework.

(5) Again, allow a student who receives instructions from others to draw the rectangle requested in Problem 8 and find the midpoints of the sides. Draw a second diagram and again display side by side for Problem 9. Student groups can then work on Problems 8–10.

  a. Here students will connect the toolbar icons to the Draw menu options.

COLLABORATION SKILL
Collaboration using technology requires making sure others can see or hear about the computer moves you use. During this investigation, practice verbalizing your interactive geometry constructions and asking others to clarify their constructions.

INSTRUCTIONAL NOTE
See the Unit Overview for information on technology use. Students can use grid paper to draw or record figures in this unit. When using *CPMP-Tools* select "Print" to obtain a copy of the screen.

Teaching Resources
Student Master 4.

UNIT 3 *Coordinate Methods*   Name
                                Date

Square Dot Paper

4   UNIT 3 • Coordinate Methods   Student Master

Unit 3

b. In a clear window, draw a circle congruent to the one on the computer screen shown on page 163. Explain how you know the two circles are congruent.

c. In a clear window, draw a quadrilateral congruent to the ones on the computer screen shown on page 163. Discuss how you know that the two quadrilaterals are congruent.

2 Now explore how to use interactive geometry software to create special quadrilaterals. First, clear the window.

a. Draw a rectangle. Record the coordinates of the vertices in the order in which you drew them. Discuss how you know that the displayed figure is a rectangle.

b. Clear the window and then find a different method to draw the same rectangle as in Part a. Describe your method.

c. Clear the window and then draw a parallelogram that is *not* a rectangle. Record the coordinates of the vertices in the order in which you drew them. Discuss how you know the displayed figure is a parallelogram.

d. By *clicking and dragging* a point, you can generate shapes for which some conditions remain the same and other conditions vary. Click and drag one of the vertices of your parallelogram in Part c. What types of shapes can you create?

Calculating Slopes and Lengths Next, explore some of the measurement capabilities of interactive geometry software.

3 Using a clear window, draw a rectangle *ABCD* with coordinates $A(2, 9)$, $B(10, 9)$, $C(10, -6)$, and $D(2, -6)$.

a. Draw the diagonals of the rectangle.

b. Use the "Slopes" command in the Measurements menu to find the slopes of the lines containing each side and the slopes of the two diagonals. Discuss why the reported slopes are reasonable.

Measurements
Coordinates
Lengths
Angles
Slopes
Perimeter/Circumference
Area
Calculation

c. How do you think the software calculates these slopes?

d. Calculate the slopes of the lines containing the diagonals without the use of technology. Compare your results to those in Part b. Explain any differences.

4 Delete the reported slopes. Then use the "Lengths" command in the Measurements menu to calculate the lengths of the sides of the rectangle you created in Problem 3.

a. How do you think the software calculates these lengths?

b. Suppose you have two points with coordinates (a, b) and (c, b) with $a < c$.

  i. How do you know that the points are on a *horizontal line*?

  ii. Write an algebraic expression for the length of the segment or distance between the points.

b. The radii of the circles are the same measure.

c. Methods will vary. Students might identify the exact coordinates of one of the quadrilaterals and reproduce it, indicating that this quadrilateral is a copy of an existing quadrilateral. Thus, the angle and side lengths are congruent. Alternatively, they might draw a quadrilateral in a different location than those on page 163. This can be done by setting one vertex on the coordinate grid, then counting the horizontal and vertical units to the next vertex of the quadrilateral on page 163 and duplicating that on their screen. Continuing in this manner, they can make a congruent copy of the quadrilateral. (To complete drawing shapes, you need to double-click as you place the last vertex of an open shape, or double-click the first vertex to close a polygon.)

2 **a.** Justifications that the figure is a rectangle should indicate that opposite sides are congruent (parallelogram) and that either one angle is a right angle or that the diagonals are the same length.

b. There are three methods students might use. One way is through the "Shape or Polygon" command under the Draw menu, a second way is using the "Segment" command under the Draw menu, and a third way is through a combination of the "Point" and "Segment" commands under the Draw menu. (Students can also access these commands through the icons.)

c. Students should indicate that pairs of opposite sides are congruent to justify that the figure is a parallelogram.

d. Moving only one vertex, different shapes can be created. For example, triangles, various general convex and nonconvex quadrilaterals, and general trapezoids (and an isosceles trapezoid) can be formed.

TECHNOLOGY NOTE
In *CPMP-Tools*, to select (or deselect) more than one feature of a shape, hold the Shift key while selecting (or deselecting). Encourage students to explore the Options menu and particularly the "Snap to Grid," "Default Styles" (for turning the labels and coordinates on/off as desired), and "Window Scale" options. Students will find that for most problems, it will be helpful to have the "Snap to Grid" option on.

3 **a–b.**

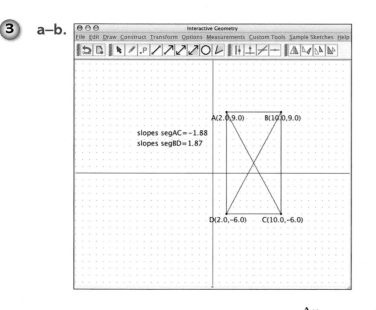

INSTRUCTIONAL NOTE
For Problems 3 Part b, 4 Part a, and similar items that indicate "discuss," students should not be expected to write responses.

c. The program applies the slope formula $\frac{\Delta y}{\Delta x}$ using the coordinates of the vertices.

d. The slopes of $\overline{AC}$ and $\overline{BD}$ are -1.875 and 1.875, respectively. *CPMP-Tools* rounds the slope to the nearest hundredth.

Unit 3

4 a.

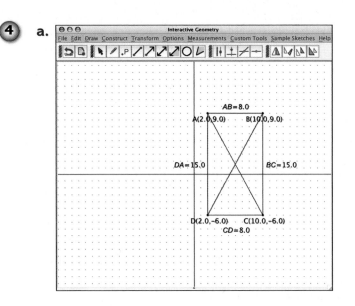

b. i. The points are on a horizontal line because they have the same *y*-coordinate.

ii. $c - a$ represents the length.

Lesson 1, Investigation 1, Problem 2

This dialogue box is modeled after the instructions for facilitating Investigation 1 with a single computer and a projection system as described on page T164. Various students have already explored how each command in the Draw menu can be used to create examples as indicated in Problem 1 and interactively discussed Parts a–c.

Teacher: Thanks to David for being willing to be the computer operator for Problem 1. Who would be willing to be the operator for Problem 2? Thank you, Serena. We also need a volunteer to be our recorder for some of the information we will be gathering from the geometry software. Thank you, Isaiah. Kalie, please read the directions for number 2 part a. Serena and Isaiah will execute the directions. Others should listen, observe, and advise Serena and Isaiah as needed.

Kalie: Draw a rectangle. Record the coordinates of the vertices in the order in which you drew them. I guess this means you can draw any rectangle you want, Serena. *(Serena begins drawing a rectangle.)*

Matthew: Wait, what were those coordinates? Isaiah is supposed to write them down. What were the coordinates of the first point, Serena?

Serena: I don't know. They are gone.

Teacher: The software allows you to display the coordinates. Serena, look under the Options menu. Select "Default Styles." Now select the box by "Coordinates." Let's start over with a new screen. *(Serena draws rectangle with coordinates A(0, 0), B(8, 0), C(8, 5), and D(0, 5), and Isaiah records the coordinates.)* Okay, how do we know that the shape that Serena drew is a rectangle? Think about this a minute by yourself and then discuss it in your groups. *(The teacher waits and listens.)* Okay, let's hear your thinking. Drew, what did your group decide?

Drew: We said that there were 4 right angles because the sides are horizontal and vertical.

Teacher: Drew, please state our definition of a rectangle more formally.

Drew: A rectangle is a quadrilateral with 4 right angles.

Teacher: Everyone agreed? *(Students indicate agreement.)* Okay, Serena, now draw a parallelogram that is not a rectangle. Again, tell Isaiah the coordinates so he can record them.

Serena: This time I am drawing $A(-5, -5)$ to $B(5, -5)$ to $C(8, 4)$ to $D(-1, 4)$. Got that Isaiah?

Isaiah: What was the last one?

Serena: D is $(-1, 4)$.

Quinn: But that is not a parallelogram.

Teacher: Why do you think that Quinn?

Quinn: You can see that side $\overline{BC}$ is not parallel to side $\overline{AD}$. If you move D over to $(-2, 4)$, it will be a parallelogram.

Teacher: Okay, Serena, click on the point D and drag it over to $(-2, 4)$. Isaiah, please change the coordinates of D. Now Serena and Isaiah, rejoin your groups; and everyone, discuss how you can verify mathematically that this quadrilateral is or is not a parallelogram. *(The teacher listens.)* Let's hear your thinking now. Marie, what did your group decide?

Marie: We said that $\overline{AB}$ and $\overline{CD}$ are both horizontal so they are parallel, then we checked the slopes of the other two sides. They are the same, 3.

Teacher: How did you decide that the slopes were 3?

Marie: We just counted from point A right 1 unit and noticed that if you went up 3 units, you hit the line. We did the same with point B.

Teacher: Is Marie's reasoning correct? *(Students agree.)* Think back a minute. What was the definition of a parallelogram that we used in Course 1? Sela?

Sela: A parallelogram is a quadrilateral that has opposite sides the same length.

Teacher: How would you use our definition to verify that the quadrilateral is a parallelogram?

Sela: We would have to measure or use the Pythagorean Theorem to find how long sides $\overline{BC}$ and $\overline{AD}$ are. But you can just count the lengths of $\overline{AB}$ and $\overline{CD}$ to see they are the same.

Teacher: Good thinking. In this unit, we will be expanding our knowledge of ways to represent slope, distance, and polygons on coordinate grids and use our knowledge to create animations such as the one we saw a little while ago. Antonette, please read Part d for us. *(She reads.)* Okay, would someone volunteer to try this with the geometry software? Ritchie, go ahead but please talk about what you are moving and what shape you have created. The job for the rest of you is to listen and consider if Ritchie's descriptions of the conditions that remain the same or change is accurate. Also, think about other shapes that might be created. *(An interactive discussion follows.)*

Unit 3

c. Suppose you have a *vertical line.*

   i. What is true of the coordinates of all points on the line?

   ii. Using variables, write coordinates for a point on the same vertical line as the point with coordinates (a, b).

   iii. Write an algebraic expression for the length of the segment or distance between the points.

5 Next, use the "Lengths" command to find the lengths of the diagonals of the rectangle you created in Problem 3.

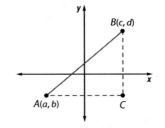

a. Explain how the software could use the coordinates of points A, C, and D to calculate the length of $\overline{AC}$. How could the software use the coordinates of points A, C, and B to calculate the length of $\overline{AC}$?

b. Test your ideas in Part a by calculating the length of $\overline{BD}$ and compare your answer to the software calculation.

c. What theorem justifies the method you used?

d. Now consider points $P(-1, 3)$ and $Q(2, 7)$ in a coordinate plane.

   i. Make a sketch on a coordinate grid showing points P and Q and $\overline{PQ}$.

   ii. Find the length of the segment $\overline{PQ}$ or distance between points P and Q. Compare your answer and method with those of your classmates. Resolve any differences.

e. Use similar reasoning to find the distance between points $S(-5, 4)$ and $T(3, -2)$.

6 To generalize the method you used for calculating distance between two points in a coordinate plane, consider general points $A(a, b)$ and $B(c, d)$ graphed below.

a. Make a copy of the diagram showing the coordinates of point C.

b. Write expressions for the distances AC and BC.

c. Write a formula for calculating the distance AB. Compare your formula with that of your classmates and resolve any differences.

d. When points A and B are on a horizontal or vertical line, will your formula calculate the correct distance AB? Why?

c. **INSTRUCTIONAL NOTE** Students will likely need to be encouraged to think about the size relationship between b and c in part iii. If your students studied distance represented as an absolute value in middle school, they may represent the length as $|c - b|$ or $|b - c|$.

    i. The coordinates of all points on a vertical line will have the same x-coordinate.

    ii. Students will likely use (a, c).

    iii. If $c > b$, $c - b$ represents the length.
       If $b > c$, $b - c$ represents the length.

5 Diagonals have lengths of 17 units.

  a. Since $\triangle ADC$ is a right triangle, the program could use the coordinates to find the lengths AD and DC. Then apply the Pythagorean Theorem to find the length of $\overline{AC}$. Similarly, since $\triangle ABC$ is a right triangle, the program could use the lengths AB and BC and the Pythagorean Theorem to find the length of $\overline{AC}$. (Students may want to use the "hide" command to temporarily remove diagonal $\overline{BD}$ making the right triangle $\triangle ADC$ more obvious.)

  b. $BD = 17$

  c. The Pythagorean Theorem justifies this method.

  d. **i.**

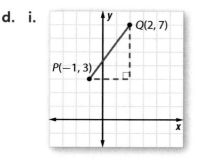

    ii. Students should find the horizontal and vertical distances between points P and Q, then use the Pythagorean Theorem to find PQ.
$$PQ = \sqrt{(-1 - 2)^2 + (3 - 7)^2} = \sqrt{25} = 5 \text{ units}$$

  e. $ST = \sqrt{(-5 - 3)^2 + (4 - (-2))^2} = \sqrt{100} = 10$ units

6 **a.**

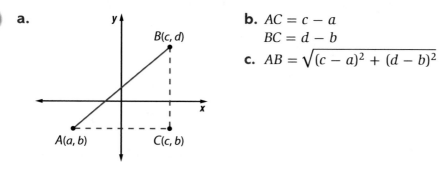

  b. $AC = c - a$
      $BC = d - b$

  c. $AB = \sqrt{(c - a)^2 + (d - b)^2}$

  d. Yes. If A and B are on a horizontal line, then the y-coordinate of B is equal to the y-coordinate of A. So, $AB = \sqrt{(c - a)^2 + (d - b)^2} = \sqrt{(c - a)^2 + (0)^2} = c - a$, if $c > a$.

  If A and B are on a vertical line, then the x-coordinate of B is equal to the x-coordinate of A. So, $AB = \sqrt{(c - a)^2 + (d - b)^2} = \sqrt{(0)^2 + (d - b)^2} = d - b$, if $d > b$.

Interactive geometry software uses a method equivalent to yours to calculate the distance between two points. In order to do this, the software needs information or *input* (in this case, the coordinates of two points); instructions for *processing* the information (in this case, a formula); and then instructions on what to do with the results or *output* (in this case, it displays the distance). Specifying such instructions is called **programming**.

Before writing a program, it is helpful to prepare an algorithm that lists the main sequence of steps needed to accomplish the task. The *Distance Between Two Points Algorithm* below could be used to guide program writing for any computer or calculator. In Applications Task 3, you will analyze a calculator program that implements this algorithm.

Distance Between Two Points Algorithm

Step 1: Input the coordinates of one point.
Step 2: Input the coordinates of the other point. } input

Step 3: Use the coordinates and the formula in Problem 6 Part c to calculate the desired distance. } processing

Step 4: Display and label the distance. } output

7 Use the questions below to help write a *Slope Algorithm*, similar to the Distance Between Two Points Algorithm, that could be used to prepare a program to calculate and display the slope of a line through the points $A(a, b)$ and $B(c, d)$.

- What information would you need to input?
- What formula could be used in the processing portion?
- What information should be displayed in the output?

Calculating Midpoints You now have a method for calculating the slope of a line and a method for calculating the distance between two points. Thus, you can compute the length and the slope of a segment in a coordinate plane. Coordinates also can be used by a graphics program to calculate the **midpoint** of a segment, that is, the point on a segment that is the same distance from each endpoint.

8 Use interactive geometry software to draw a rectangle $ABCD$ with vertices $A(2, 9)$, $B(10, 9)$, $C(10, -6)$, and $D(2, -6)$.

INSTRUCTIONAL NOTE To help students understand a program-planning algorithm, refer back to the algorithms studied in the *Vertex-Edge Graphs* unit in Course 1 and the compass and straight-edge constructions in *Patterns in Shape*. Then discuss the paragraph in the student text and the three parts to the distance-planning algorithm: input, processing, and output.

(7)
- You would need to input the coordinates for two points on the line.
- For points $A(a, b)$ and $B(c, d)$, $\dfrac{d - b}{c - a}$ or $\dfrac{b - d}{a - c}$ is the slope formula.
- The labeled slope would be displayed.

a. Use the "Midpoint" command in the Construct menu (or select the corresponding icon in the toolbar) to find the midpoint of each side of the rectangle.

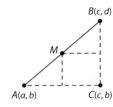

  i. Record the coordinates of the midpoints.

  ii. How do you think the software found these midpoints?

b. What should your software report as the midpoint of the segment with endpoints $P(-3, 2)$ and $Q(1, 2)$? With endpoints $S(3, 3)$ and $T(3, -2)$? Check your conjectures.

c. Suppose you have two points $P(a, b)$ and $Q(c, b)$. Write expressions for the coordinates of the midpoint of $\overline{PQ}$. Compare your expressions with others and resolve any differences.

d. Repeat Part c for the case of points $P(a, b)$ and $Q(a, c)$.

9 Use the "Midpoint" command to find the midpoint of diagonal $\overline{AC}$ of the rectangle in Problem 8. Of diagonal $\overline{BD}$. Record the coordinates.

a. What do you notice about the midpoints of the diagonals of the rectangle?

b. How do you think the software found these midpoints? Test your conjecture using a coordinate grid to find the midpoint of the segment joining the points $S(-3, -3)$ and $T(5, 5)$. Verify using your software.

c. Now consider a segment with general endpoints $A(a, b)$ and $B(c, d)$. Make a conjecture about the coordinates of the midpoint M of this segment.

  i. Test your conjecture using a coordinate grid and the points $V(2, -4)$ and $W(6, 8)$.

  ii. Check that your calculated point is the midpoint by verifying that:

   • it is on the line containing the points V and W, and

   • it is *equidistant* from points V and W.

10 Use the following questions to help write a *Midpoint Algorithm* that could be used to prepare a program to calculate and display the coordinates of the midpoint of a segment with endpoints $A(a, b)$ and $B(c, d)$.

• What information would you need to input?

• How will the processing portion of your algorithm differ from the algorithms to calculate distance and slope?

• What formula or formulas could be used in the processing portion?

• What information should be displayed in the output?

⑧ **a.** **i.**

Interactive Geometry

A(2.0,9.0) E(6.0,9.0) B(10.0,9.0)

H(2.0,1.5) F(10.0,1.5)

D(2.0,-6.0) G(6.0,-6.0) C(10.0,-6.0)

ii. Students will likely indicate that the horizontal (or vertical) midpoint coordinate was found by computing the average of the corresponding coordinates. Alternatively, some students may suggest that first the distance between the two horizontal (or vertical) points was found, then that value was cut in half and added (or subtracted) from the x-coordinate of one of the points. (This analysis is brought out in Connections Task 15 on page 186.)

b. The midpoint of $\overline{PQ}$ is $(-1, 2)$ and of $\overline{ST}$ is $(3, 0.5)$.

c. $\left(\dfrac{a + c}{2}, b\right)$

d. $\left(a, \dfrac{b + c}{2}\right)$

INSTRUCTIONAL NOTE
If students struggle with Problem 8 Part c, you could ask them to describe the location of the midpoint in words. Once they have done that, they should be focusing on "middle or average" values. They might also look back at Problem 8 Part aii.

⑨ The midpoint of $\overline{AC}$ is $(6, 1.5)$ and the midpoint of $\overline{BD}$ is $(6, 1.5)$.

a. The midpoints are the same.

b. The midpoint of $\overline{ST}$ is $(1, 1)$. (Students' conjectures will likely include finding the average of coordinates. They may have studied this in middle school.)

c. Conjecture: The midpoint of $\overline{AB}$ is $\left(\dfrac{a + c}{2}, \dfrac{b + d}{2}\right)$.

    i. The midpoint of $\overline{VW}$ is $\left(\dfrac{2 + 6}{2}, \dfrac{-4 + 8}{2}\right) = (4, 2)$.

    ii. • The equation of line $\overline{VW}$ is $y = 3x - 10$. Since $(4, 2)$ satisfies the equation, the point lies on the line.

      • The distance from both endpoints to the midpoint should be the same.
$$VM = \sqrt{(6 - 4)^2 + (8 - 2)^2} = \sqrt{40}$$
$$WM = \sqrt{(2 - 4)^2 + (-4 - 2)^2} = \sqrt{40}$$

INSTRUCTIONAL NOTE
As students complete Problem 9 Part cii, ask them why they needed to verify both bullets in this part to verify that the point $(4, 2)$ is the midpoint of $\overline{VW}$.

⑩ • You need to input the coordinates of the endpoints of the segment.

• The processing portion uses two formulas and needs to compute each coordinate of the midpoint separately.

• Using $A(a, b)$ and $B(c, d)$, the x-coordinate of the midpoint is $x = \dfrac{a + c}{2}$ and the y-coordinate is $y = \dfrac{b + d}{2}$.

• The labeled midpoint is the output.

Unit 3

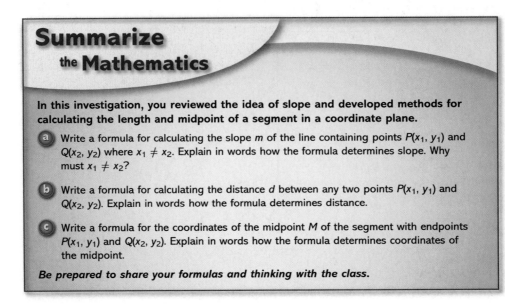

Summarize the Mathematics

In this investigation, you reviewed the idea of slope and developed methods for calculating the length and midpoint of a segment in a coordinate plane.

a Write a formula for calculating the slope m of the line containing points $P(x_1, y_1)$ and $Q(x_2, y_2)$ where $x_1 \neq x_2$. Explain in words how the formula determines slope. Why must $x_1 \neq x_2$?

b Write a formula for calculating the distance d between any two points $P(x_1, y_1)$ and $Q(x_2, y_2)$. Explain in words how the formula determines distance.

c Write a formula for the coordinates of the midpoint M of the segment with endpoints $P(x_1, y_1)$ and $Q(x_2, y_2)$. Explain in words how the formula determines coordinates of the midpoint.

Be prepared to share your formulas and thinking with the class.

✓ Check Your Understanding

In your previous studies, you saw that because triangles are rigid, they are often used in the design of complex structures such as the octagonal air control tower shown below.

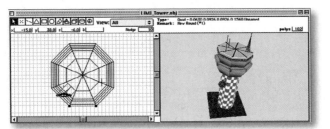

Suppose a triangular component in a CAD display of a different tower has vertices $A(0, 0)$, $B(4, -8)$, and $C(8, -4)$.

a. Make a drawing of $\triangle ABC$ on a coordinate grid. Then find the length of each side.

b. What kind of triangle is $\triangle ABC$? Explain your reasoning.

c. Find the coordinates of the midpoints of $\overline{AC}$ and $\overline{BC}$.

d. Find the slopes of $\overline{AB}$ and of the segment joining the midpoints found in Part c. How are these segments related?

e. Use the click-and-drag feature of interactive geometry software to test if the relationship you found in Part d holds in the case of other triangles, including obtuse triangles. Summarize your findings.

Summarize
the Mathematics

Teaching Resources
Transparency Master 5.

(a) $m = \dfrac{y_1 - y_2}{x_1 - x_2}$ or $\dfrac{y_2 - y_1}{x_2 - x_1}$

The formula determines the slope by finding the ratio of the vertical change to the horizontal change from one point to the other point. The restriction that $x_1 \neq x_2$ is necessary because otherwise the denominator of the slope ratio would be zero. This means the ratio is undefined.

(b) $d = \sqrt{(x_1 - x_2)^2 + (y_1 - y_2)^2}$ or $\sqrt{(x_2 - x_1)^2 + (y_2 - y_1)^2}$

The formula determines the distance by finding the horizontal change and the vertical change and then using these values as lengths of the legs of a right triangle. The distance between two points is the length of the hypotenuse of the right triangle.

(c) The midpoint of $\overline{PQ}$ is $\left(\dfrac{x_1 + x_2}{2}, \dfrac{y_1 + y_2}{2}\right)$. The formula finds the average of the x- and y-coordinates to determine the midpoint coordinates.

MATH TOOLKIT Record the general forms of the slope, distance, and midpoint formulas in your toolkit with examples, if needed.

✓ Check Your Understanding

COLLABORATION PROMPT
I could improve my collaboration while using technology by … .

a.

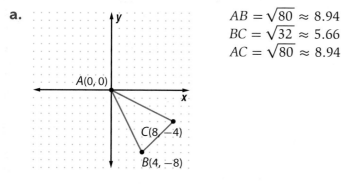

$AB = \sqrt{80} \approx 8.94$
$BC = \sqrt{32} \approx 5.66$
$AC = \sqrt{80} \approx 8.94$

b. $\triangle ABC$ is isosceles since two sides have equal lengths.

c. The midpoint of $\overline{AC}$ is $(4, -2)$. The midpoint of $\overline{BC}$ is $(6, -6)$.

d. The slope of $\overline{AB}$ is $\dfrac{8}{-4} = -2$. The slope of the segment joining the midpoints in Part c is $\dfrac{4}{-2} = -2$. The segments are parallel since they have the same slope.

e. Students' summaries should indicate that the segment connecting the midpoints of two sides of a triangle is parallel to the third (remaining) side.

Unit 3

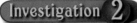

Reasoning with Slopes and Lengths

In the *Linear Functions* unit of Course 1, you discovered that nonvertical parallel lines have equal slopes. That is, if you know that two nonvertical lines are parallel, then you can conclude that they have equal slopes. Also, if the slopes of two lines are equal, then you can conclude that the two lines are parallel. These two facts are summarized in the statement:

Two nonvertical lines are parallel if and only if their slopes are equal.

All vertical lines are, of course, parallel. This fact and the fact that all horizontal lines are parallel are helpful in reasoning about shapes. To create rectangles in Investigation 1, you also likely used the fact that the coordinate axes are perpendicular to each other. As you work on the problems in this investigation, look for answers to the following questions:

How can you use slopes to create and reason about figures in a coordinate plane?

In general, how can you determine if two lines in a coordinate plane are perpendicular?

1 In the *Patterns in Shape* unit of Course 1, a **parallelogram** was defined as a quadrilateral with opposite sides the same length. You have probably discovered that when working with shapes in a coordinate plane, it is easier to calculate slopes than lengths of sides. Using coordinate methods, you can show that a quadrilateral with opposite sides parallel also has opposite sides the same length—so, it is a parallelogram.

a. Examine Diagram I below.

   i. Find the coordinates of point R so that opposite sides are parallel.

   ii. Calculate and compare the lengths of $\overline{PQ}$ and $\overline{SR}$. Of $\overline{PS}$ and $\overline{QR}$.

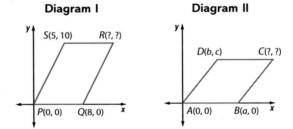

Diagram I   **Diagram II**

b. Now examine Diagram II that gives general coordinates.

   i. Find the coordinates of point C so that opposite sides are parallel.

   ii. Calculate and compare expressions for the lengths of $\overline{AB}$ and $\overline{DC}$. Of $\overline{AD}$ and $\overline{BC}$.

c. Based on your prior work in Course 1 and your work above, describe two ways to test if a quadrilateral is a parallelogram.

Reasoning with Slopes and Lengths

In this investigation, students use slopes and distances to create and reason about figures. Students investigate how slopes of perpendicular lines are related. In the process, the matrix representation of polygons is introduced.

In the opening paragraph, there is an italicized if-and-only-if statement. You may need to review this concept from Course 1 with students. Some students may wish to record this example of an "iff" statement in their math toolkits.

Be sure that students determine the coordinates of R in Problem 1 Part ai using the fact that opposite sides are parallel (not the same length). Problem 1 is reasoning that if opposite sides of a quadrilateral are parallel, then it is a parallelogram. That is, it satisfies the definition of **parallelogram** in Course 1 of *Core-Plus Mathematics*: a parallelogram is a quadrilateral with opposite sides the same length.

1 a. i. $R(13, 10)$; this result should be found using slopes of sides, *not* lengths of sides. (See the Launch above.) Note $\overline{SR}$ has slope 0 (since $\overline{PQ}$ has slope 0), so the y-coordinate of R must be 10. Since the slope of $\overline{PS}$ is 2, the slope of $\overline{RQ}$ is also 2. So, the x-coordinate of R is 13.

ii. $PQ = SR = 8$
$PS = QR = \sqrt{125} = 5\sqrt{5}$

b. i. $C(b + a, c)$. The y-coordinate of c means that the slope of $\overline{DC}$ will be the same as the slope of $\overline{AB} = 0$. The x-coordinate of $b + a$ means that the slope of $\overline{BC}$ will be the same as the slope of $\overline{AD} = \frac{c}{b}$.
Thus, the opposite sides are parallel.

Diagram II

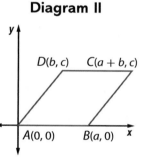

ii. $AB = a$
$DC = b + a - b = a = AB$
$AD = \sqrt{b^2 + c^2}$
$BC = \sqrt{(b + a - a)^2 + c^2} = \sqrt{b^2 + c^2} = AD$

c. A quadrilateral is a parallelogram if (1) both pairs of opposite sides are congruent, or if (2) both pairs of opposite sides are parallel.

> **MATH TOOLKIT** After completing Problem 1 students should add to their list of Key Geometric Ideas the condition that if opposite sides of a quadrilateral are parallel, then it is a parallelogram.

> **INSTRUCTIONAL NOTE** Any quadrilateral can be placed in a coordinate system so that one axis and the origin are determined by one edge of the given quadrilateral. This makes assignment of coordinates and calculations easier.

Unit 3

2 Consider quadrilateral *EFGH* shown below. Does quadrilateral *EFGH* appear to be a rectangle? Verify your conjecture by completing the following tasks.

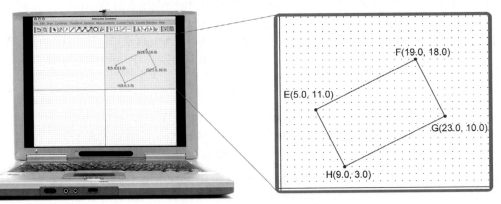

a. Use slopes to explain why quadrilateral *EFGH* is a parallelogram.

b. Based on your work in Problem 1, what can you conclude about the lengths of the sides of quadrilateral *EFGH*? Why?

c. Describe two ways you could use the distance formula to test if parallelogram *EFGH* (denoted □*EFGH*) is a rectangle.

d. Use one of the methods you described in Part c to show that □*EFGH* is a rectangle.

3 Calculating distances and using the converse of the Pythagorean Theorem is one way to show that two intersecting segments (and the lines containing them) are perpendicular. Interactive geometry software uses a less complex method to determine if two lines (segments) are perpendicular. By investigating the slopes of perpendicular segments, you can discover a simpler method. Share the work among your classmates.

a. For each set of points below, plot the points on a coordinate grid. Then verify the points represent vertices of a right triangle. In each case, identify the right angle.

    i. $A(4, 4)$, $B(8, -2)$, $C(14, 2)$ **ii.** $J(-3, 0)$, $K(0, 6)$, $L(3, -3)$

    iii. $P(8, -7)$, $Q(0, 1)$, $R(6, 7)$ **iv.** $X(2, 3)$, $Y(6, 19)$, $Z(10, 18)$

b. Identify the line segments that determine a right angle in each of the triangles in Part a. Then find the slopes of those segments. Write your slopes in reduced fraction form.

    i. What appears to be true about the slopes of perpendicular segments?

    ii. What appears to be true about the product of the slopes of perpendicular segments?

c. Check your observations in Part b using the slopes of the sides of rectangle *EFGH* in Problem 2.

2 **a.** The slope of $\overline{EH}$ is -2.
The slope of $\overline{FG}$ is -2.
Therefore, $\overline{EH} \parallel \overline{FG}$.
The slopes of $\overline{EF}$ and $\overline{HG}$ are $\frac{1}{2}$, so $\overline{EF} \parallel \overline{HG}$.
So, we can conclude that
$EF = HG$ and $EH = FG$.

b. Since opposite sides are parallel, *EFGH* is a parallelogram. By definition, the opposite sides of a parallelogram are congruent.

c. You could use the distance formula and the converse of the Pythagorean Theorem to determine if an angle of the parallelogram is a right angle. Or you could use the relationship that if the diagonals of a parallelogram are congruent, then it is a rectangle. (This was reviewed in Unit 2, Lesson 3, Problem 22.)

INSTRUCTIONAL NOTE
Students may need help in recalling what conditions ensure that a quadrilateral is a rectangle before they attempt this problem.

d. Using the converse of the Pythagorean Theorem:
$HE = \sqrt{(5-9)^2 + (11-3)^2} = \sqrt{80}$
$EG = \sqrt{(23-5)^2 + (10-11)^2} = \sqrt{325}$
$HG = \sqrt{(23-9)^2 + (10-3)^2} = \sqrt{245}$
Since $(\sqrt{80})^2 + (\sqrt{245})^2 = (\sqrt{325})^2$, $\triangle EHG$ is a right triangle with $\angle EHG$ a right angle.
Since $\square EFGH$ has a right angle, it is a rectangle.

Using, "If the diagonals of a parallelogram are congruent, then it is a rectangle": The distance formula gives $EG = FH = \sqrt{245}$.
So, *EFGH* is a rectangle.

INSTRUCTIONAL NOTE
Help students recognize that they are using the *converse* of the Pythagorean Theorem.

3 **INSTRUCTIONAL NOTE** In Problem 3, students are using inductive reasoning to conjecture that the slopes of perpendicular lines are opposite reciprocals. In Problem 4, they will discover the converse: if two lines have slopes that are opposite (or negative reciprocals), then the lines are perpendicular. Problem 5 has students summarize these findings in if-and-only-if form.

a. **i.** $(AB)^2 = 52$, $(BC)^2 = 52$, $(AC)^2 = 104$

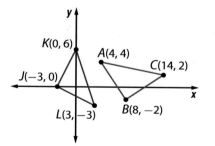

Since $(AB)^2 + (BC)^2 = (AC)^2$,
$\triangle ABC$ is a right triangle with $\angle B$ the right angle.

Unit 3

ii. $(JK)^2 = 45$, $(KL)^2 = 90$, $(JL)^2 = 45$

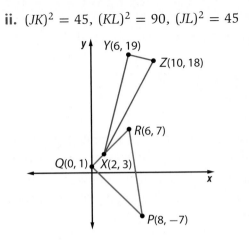

Since $(JK)^2 + (JL)^2 = (KL)^2$,
$\triangle JKL$ is a right triangle with $\angle J$ the right angle.

iii. $(PQ)^2 = 128$, $(QR)^2 = 72$, $(PR)^2 = 200$
Since $(PQ)^2 + (QR)^2 = (PR)^2$,
$\triangle PQR$ is a right triangle with $\angle Q$ the right angle.

iv. $(XY)^2 = 272$, $(YZ)^2 = 17$, $(XZ)^2 = 289$
Since $(XY)^2 + (YZ)^2 = (XZ)^2$,
$\triangle XYZ$ is a right triangle with $\angle Y$ the right angle.

b. $\triangle ABC$: $\overline{AB}$ and $\overline{BC}$ determine a right angle.
The slope of $\overline{AB}$ is $-\frac{3}{2}$; the slope of $\overline{BC}$ is $\frac{2}{3}$.

$\triangle JKL$: $\overline{JK}$ and $\overline{JL}$ determine a right angle.
The slope of $\overline{JK}$ is 2; the slope of $\overline{JL}$ is $-\frac{1}{2}$.

$\triangle PQR$: $\overline{PQ}$ and $\overline{QR}$ determine a right angle.
The slope of $\overline{PQ}$ is -1; the slope of $\overline{QR}$ is 1.

$\triangle XYZ$: $\overline{XY}$ and $\overline{YZ}$ determine a right angle.
The slope of $\overline{XY}$ is 4; the slope of $\overline{YZ}$ is $-\frac{1}{4}$.

i. It appears that the slopes of the perpendicular segments are reciprocals of each other with one positive and one negative slope.

ii. The product of the slopes is -1.

c. Slope of $\overline{EF}$ is $\frac{1}{2}$, of $\overline{FG}$ is -2, of $\overline{GH}$ is $\frac{1}{2}$, and of $\overline{EH}$ is -2.
$\overline{EF}$ and $\overline{FG}$ are perpendicular and the product of their slopes is -1.
$\overline{FG}$ and $\overline{GH}$ are perpendicular and the product of their slopes is -1.
$\overline{GH}$ and $\overline{EH}$ are perpendicular and the product of their slopes is -1.
$\overline{EH}$ and $\overline{EF}$ are perpendicular and the product of their slopes is -1.

Teacher Notes

4. Now, using a coordinate grid, draw and label two intersecting segments with the indicated conditions. Check if the segments are perpendicular by measuring the angle formed with the square corner of a sheet of paper.

   a. slope of $\overline{AB}$ is -2; slope of $\overline{BC}$ is $\frac{1}{2}$

   b. slope of $\overline{DE}$ is $\frac{3}{4}$; slope of $\overline{DF}$ is $-\frac{4}{3}$

   c. slope of $\overline{GH}$ is $-\frac{5}{6}$; slope of $\overline{HI}$ is $\frac{6}{5}$

   d. slope of $\overline{JK}$ is $\frac{3}{2}$; slope of $\overline{JL}$ is $-\frac{2}{3}$

5. Look back at your results in Problem 4.

   a. What appears to be true about pairs of nonvertical lines (or intersecting segments) with slopes whose product is -1? That is, with slopes that are **opposite reciprocals**?

   b. Check your conjecture with another pair of intersecting segments whose slopes are opposite reciprocals.

   c. Write a statement summarizing your discoveries in Problems 3 and 4 about perpendicular lines. Write your statement in an "if-and-only-if" form like the statement for parallel lines on page 170.

6. Computer-aided design makes extensive use of simple polygons in creating meshes that outline more complex shapes.

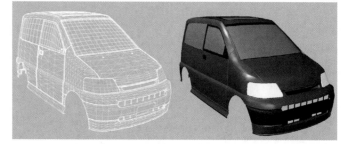

   Coordinates of consecutive vertices of different triangles and quadrilaterals are given below. In each case, carefully draw the figure on a coordinate grid and answer as precisely as possible the following questions.

   • If it is a triangle, is it a right triangle, an isosceles triangle, or an equilateral triangle?

   • If it is a quadrilateral, is it a square, rectangle, rhombus, parallelogram, or kite?

   Then describe the properties you used to determine your classifications. *Your analysis of at least three of the cases should be done without the use of interactive geometry software or calculator programs.*

   a. $A(-2, 2)$, $B(8, 6)$, $C(4, -4)$

   b. $D(6, 3)$, $E(-3, 9)$, $F(-6, 3)$, $G(3, -3)$

   c. $J(6, -3)$, $K(3, 9)$, $L(-6, -6)$

   d. $P(-4, 0)$, $Q(8, 0)$, $R(4, 8)$, $S(-4, 12)$

   e. $T(-5, 6)$, $U(-1, 8)$, $V(3, 0)$, $W(-1, -2)$

4 **a–d.** All angles are 90°.

5 **a.** Nonvertical lines whose slopes are opposite reciprocals appear to be perpendicular.

b. Students should select an example to check. They can use the converse of the Pythagorean Theorem to show that the segments are perpendicular.

c. Two nonvertical lines are perpendicular if and only if their slopes are opposite reciprocals.

NOTE In the Course 3 unit *Similarity and Congruence*, students will prove that two nonvertical lines are perpendicular if and only if their slopes are opposite reciprocals.

6 **a.** △*ABC* is an isosceles triangle since the lengths of the sides are $AB = \sqrt{116}$, $BC = \sqrt{116}$, $AC = \sqrt{72}$.

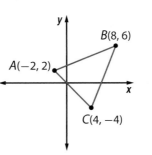

INSTRUCTIONAL NOTE Students should have square grid or dot paper for this problem. See Student Master 4 for dot paper.

b. *DEFG* is a parallelogram. This can be justified by confirming that pairs of opposites sides have equal lengths, $\sqrt{117}$ and $\sqrt{45}$, or that pairs of opposite sides have equal slopes, $-\frac{2}{3}$ and 2. Since *DF* ≠ *EG*, *DEFG* is not a rectangle.

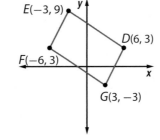

c. △*JKL* is an isosceles right triangle. Since the slope of $\overline{JL}$ is $\frac{1}{4}$ and the slope of $\overline{JK}$ is −4, $\overline{JL} \perp \overline{JK}$. Also, the lengths of $\overline{JL}$ and $\overline{JK}$ are both $\sqrt{153}$.

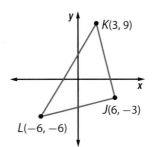

SCOPE AND SEQUENCE Students will prove necessary and sufficient conditions for classifying quadrilaterals in the Course 3 unit *Similarity and Congruence*.

d. *PQRS* is a kite since distinct pairs of consecutive sides are congruent $RS = QR$ and $PQ = QS$.

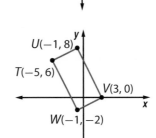

e. *TUVW* is a rectangle; since pairs of opposite sides have equal lengths, $\sqrt{20}$ and $\sqrt{80}$ or pairs of opposite sides are parallel with slopes of $\frac{1}{2}$ and −2, and a pair of consecutive sides are perpendicular.

Unit 3

7 Examine the measurements of side lengths and angles of quadrilateral *TUVW* from Part e of Problem 6 drawn with interactive geometry software. The information was produced by selecting the polygon and using the "Coordinates," "Lengths," and "Angles" commands in the Measurements menu.

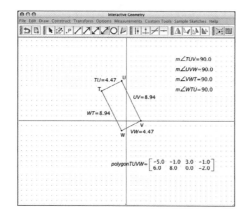

In addition to providing length and angle measure information, the window provides the matrix representation of quadrilateral *TUVW*.

$$TUVW = \begin{matrix} T & U & V & W \\ \begin{bmatrix} -5 & -1 & 3 & -1 \\ 6 & 8 & 0 & -2 \end{bmatrix} \end{matrix}$$

Matrices provide an efficient way for the computer to store and keep track of the vertices of polygons.

a. In the same manner, represent two of the other polygons in Problem 6 with a matrix.

b. Quadrilateral *WXYZ* is to be a rectangle.

$$WXYZ = \begin{bmatrix} 1 & 6 & 10 & ? \\ 2 & 0 & 10 & ? \end{bmatrix}$$

  i. Find the coordinates of the fourth vertex. Describe how you found the coordinates.

  ii. Draw quadrilateral *WXYZ* on a coordinate grid. Does *WXYZ* appear to be a rectangle?

  iii. Verify that *WXYZ* is a rectangle by giving evidence related to its sides and angles.

8 In Problem 5 of Investigation 1, you may have observed that the diagonals of rectangle *ABCD* were the same length.

a. Use graph paper or interactive geometry software to draw several other rectangles and calculate the lengths of the diagonals in each case. What did you find?

7 a. $ABC = \begin{bmatrix} -2 & 8 & 4 \\ 2 & 6 & -4 \end{bmatrix}$, $DEFG = \begin{bmatrix} 6 & -3 & -6 & 3 \\ 3 & 9 & 3 & -3 \end{bmatrix}$,

$JKL = \begin{bmatrix} 6 & 3 & -6 \\ -3 & 9 & -6 \end{bmatrix}$, and $PQRS = \begin{bmatrix} -4 & 8 & 4 & -4 \\ 0 & 0 & 8 & 12 \end{bmatrix}$.

b. i. The coordinates of Z are (5, 12). These can be found by counting the horizontal and vertical units needed to move from X to Y and using the same units from W to arrive at Z. Alternatively, students might compute the slopes of the sides.

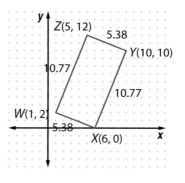

   ii. *WXYZ* appears to be a rectangle.

   iii. Opposite sides are congruent (or opposite sides are parallel), so *WXYZ* is a parallelogram.

   Slope of $\overline{WX} = -0.4$ Slope of $\overline{YZ} = -0.4$
   Slope of $\overline{XY} = 2.5$ Slope of $\overline{ZW} = 2.5$

   The product of the slopes of adjacent sides is -1, so right angles are formed at each vertex.

8 a. Students' specific rectangles will have diagonals of the same length.

> **HABIT OF MIND**
> In Problem 8, students again examine an idea by looking for patterns or relationships in specific examples, making a conjecture based on the examples, and then justifying the conjecture for the general case. This process should be explicitly discussed with students.

Unit 3

b. You can use general coordinates to justify that the two diagonals of *any* rectangle are the same length.

   i. Begin by placing a rectangle in a coordinate plane so that general coordinates are easy to work with as shown below. What are the coordinates of point *C*?

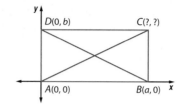

   ii. Show that $AC = BD$.

c. Without using coordinates, how could you use ideas of congruent triangles from Course 1 to justify that $AC = BD$?

d. In Problem 9 (page 168) of Investigation 1, you found that the diagonals of the rectangle intersected at their midpoints. That is, the diagonals of the rectangle *bisected* each other. Use the diagram and general coordinates above to justify that the diagonals of any rectangle bisect each other.

e. Explain why the diagonals of any square are congruent and bisect each other.

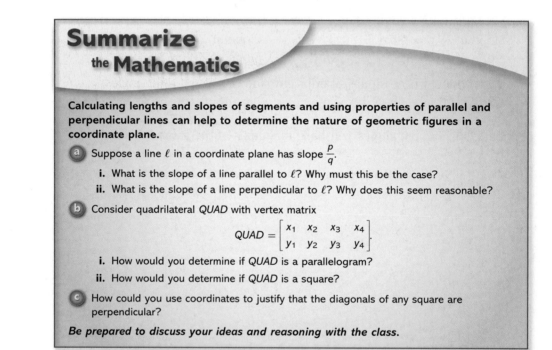

Summarize
the Mathematics

Calculating lengths and slopes of segments and using properties of parallel and perpendicular lines can help to determine the nature of geometric figures in a coordinate plane.

a Suppose a line ℓ in a coordinate plane has slope $\frac{p}{q}$.

   i. What is the slope of a line parallel to ℓ? Why must this be the case?

   ii. What is the slope of a line perpendicular to ℓ? Why does this seem reasonable?

b Consider quadrilateral *QUAD* with vertex matrix

$$QUAD = \begin{bmatrix} x_1 & x_2 & x_3 & x_4 \\ y_1 & y_2 & y_3 & y_4 \end{bmatrix}.$$

   i. How would you determine if *QUAD* is a parallelogram?

   ii. How would you determine if *QUAD* is a square?

c How could you use coordinates to justify that the diagonals of any square are perpendicular?

Be prepared to discuss your ideas and reasoning with the class.

b. **i.** $C(a, b)$

   ii. $AC = \sqrt{a^2 + b^2}$

       $BC = \sqrt{a^2 + b^2}$

c. $\triangle ADC$ is congruent to $\triangle ABC$ by the SAS congruence condition. Opposites sides of the rectangle are congruent, and $\angle B$ and $\angle D$ are both right angles. (In fact, $\triangle ABC \cong \triangle ADC \cong \triangle DCB \cong \triangle DAB$.)

d. The midpoint of $\overline{AC}$ is $\left(\frac{a}{2}, \frac{b}{2}\right)$. The midpoint of $\overline{BD}$ is $\left(\frac{a}{2}, \frac{b}{2}\right)$.

e. Since any square is a rectangle, the properties justified for rectangles apply to squares.

Summary

Prior to addressing the STM questions, ask students to report their responses to Problem 8 Part e. Students may have suggested using general coordinates to justify the statement. The point of asking this question is so that students recognize that when they prove a statement for one type of quadrilateral, it applies to others that are lower in the hierarchy of quadrilaterals. In Problem 8, they proved that the diagonals of a rectangle are congruent and bisect each other; thus, it is also true for any square.

Summarize
the Mathematics

a   **i.** The slope of a line parallel to ℓ is also $\frac{p}{q}$ because parallel lines have the same slope.

   ii. The slope of a line perpendicular to ℓ is $-\frac{q}{p}$ when $p \neq 0$. Otherwise, a line perpendicular to ℓ is vertical and the slope is undefined. The product of the slopes, when both exist, is -1. This makes sense because the perpendicular line must slope the opposite direction as ℓ and with the reciprocal rise/run relationship.

b Students should explain how they can use coordinates to find the criteria in Part b.

   i. QUAD is a parallelogram if: (1) both pairs of opposite sides are the same length, (2) both pairs of opposite sides are parallel or have the same slope, or (3) the diagonals bisect each other (Course 1 p. 376).

   ii. QUAD is a square if: (1) it is a rectangle with a pair of consecutive sides congruent, or (2) all four sides are the same length (a rhombus) and QUAD has a right angle.

c You could position the square with one vertex at the origin and two sides along the x- and y-axes. Then assign general coordinates to the vertices and compute the slopes of the diagonals. If the slopes are opposite reciprocals or their product is -1, then the diagonals are perpendicular.

Teaching Resources

Transparency Master 6.

UNIT ❸ *Coordinate Methods*

Summarize
the **Mathematics**

Calculating lengths and slopes of segments and using properties of parallel and perpendicular lines can help to determine the nature of geometric figures in a coordinate plane.

❶ Suppose a line ℓ in a coordinate plane has slope $\frac{p}{q}$.

  i. What is the slope of a line parallel to ℓ? Why must this be the case?

  ii. What is the slope of a line perpendicular to ℓ? Why does this seem reasonable?

❷ Consider quadrilateral QUAD with vertex matrix

$$QUAD = \begin{bmatrix} x_1 & x_2 & x_3 & x_4 \\ y_1 & y_2 & y_3 & y_4 \end{bmatrix}.$$

  i. How would you determine if QUAD is a parallelogram?

  ii. How would you determine if QUAD is a square?

❸ How could you use coordinates to justify that the diagonals of any square are perpendicular?

Be prepared to discuss your ideas and reasoning with the class.

6 UNIT 3 • Coordinate Methods   Transparency Master • see unit page 174

MATH TOOLKIT Students should add the conditions that ensure a quadrilateral is a square and parallelogram to their key geometric ideas. Some students may wish to give an example of two lines that are perpendicular and record the if-and-only-if statement from Problem 5.

Unit 3

✓ Check Your Understanding

Consider quadrilateral *PQRS* with vertex matrix

$$PQRS = \begin{bmatrix} 8 & 28 & 24 & 4 \\ 4 & 12 & 28 & 20 \end{bmatrix}.$$

a. Draw quadrilateral *PQRS* on a coordinate grid.

b. What special kind of quadrilateral is *PQRS*? Use coordinates to justify your answer.

Investigation 3 — Representing and Reasoning with Circles

In Investigations 1 and 2, you learned how to represent and analyze polygons in a coordinate plane. You can describe their sides using linear equations and study their properties using ideas of distance and slope. Polygons, particularly triangles and quadrilaterals, are the building blocks for architectural designs. Industrial, automotive, and aerospace designs often require that shapes have circular components.

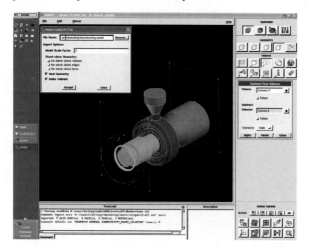

Your work on the problems in this investigation will help you answer these questions:

> *What information is needed to create a circle in a coordinate plane?*
>
> *How can you represent circles in a coordinate plane with equations?*
>
> *How can you use general coordinates of points to reason about special properties of circles?*

Unit 3

Check Your Understanding

a.

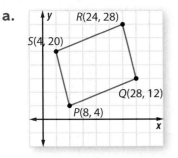

b. Students might check the lengths of opposite sides to determine the shape of the quadrilateral. A solution using mainly slope analysis follows.

The slope of $\overline{PQ}$ is $\frac{8}{20} = \frac{2}{5}$.

The slope of $\overline{RS}$ is $\frac{8}{20} = \frac{2}{5}$.

The slope of $\overline{QR}$ is $\frac{16}{-4} = -4$.

The slope of $\overline{SP}$ is $\frac{16}{-4} = -4$.

PQRS is a parallelogram since pairs of opposite sides are parallel. *PQRS* is not a rectangle or square since the slopes of consecutive sides are not opposite reciprocals. $PQ = \sqrt{20^2 + 8^2} = \sqrt{464}$ and $QR = \sqrt{4^2 + 16^2} = \sqrt{272}$, so *PQRS* is not a rhombus.

Investigation 3 Representing and Reasoning with Circles

In this investigation, students will learn to represent circles in a coordinate plane with equations. Students will use the distance formula and general coordinates to reason about special properties of shapes. They may need to refer to their Technology Tips from Investigation 1.

1. As a class, explore how interactive geometry software could be used to create the design shown at the right.

   a. What information was needed by the software to draw each circle? Why do you think that information is sufficient?

   b. Clear the window and redraw the square, centered at the origin, with side length 10 units.

   c. Draw a circle **inscribed in the square**, that is, a circle that touches each side of the square at one point. Describe the points of contact of the circle and square.

   d. Draw a circle **circumscribed about the square**, that is, a circle that passes through each vertex of the square.

   e. What is the radius of each circle in Parts c and d?

2. Here are two circles with center at the origin O and radius 10 drawn in a coordinate plane.

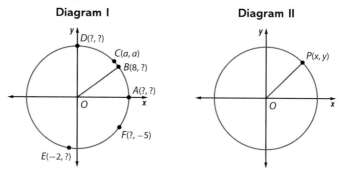

Diagram I

Diagram II

   a. What must be true about the distance from point O to any other point on the circle?

   b. Without the help of software, find the missing coordinate(s) of points A through F on the circle in Diagram I.

   c. Suppose $P(x, y)$ is any point on the circle in Diagram II.

      i. What must be true about the distance OP?

      ii. Write an equation showing the relationship between x, y, and the radius of the circle.

   d. Write an equation for a circle with its center at the origin and with radius 7. With radius $\sqrt{3}$. With radius r.

1 **a.** The center and radius are needed to draw the circles. Since the centers of the circles are the midpoints of the sides of the squares, these midpoints will need to be found. The radii for the circles can then be drawn from the centers to the vertices of the squares.

b. The square should have vertices $(5, 5)$, $(-5, 5)$, $(-5, -5)$, $(5, -5)$.

c. The midpoint of each edge of the square is where the circle is tangent to the square.

d.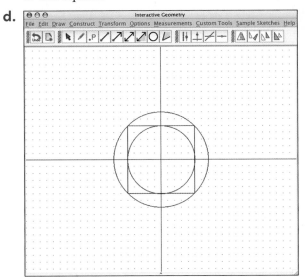

MATH TOOLKIT Sketch an example of a circle inscribed in a regular hexagon and a circle circumscribed about a regular hexagon. Label them.

e. The radius of the inscribed circles is 5, and the radius of the circumscribed circles is $\sqrt{50} = 5\sqrt{2}$.

2 **a.** The distance must be 10 units.

b. Students should use the distance formula to find the coordinates.

$A(10, 0)$
$B(8, 6)$
$C(\sqrt{50}, \sqrt{50})$
$D(0, 10)$
$E(-2, -\sqrt{96})$
$F(5\sqrt{3}, -5)$

c. **i.** $OP = 10$

ii. $\sqrt{(x - 0)^2 + (y - 0)^2} = OP = 10$ or
$(x - 0)^2 + (y - 0)^2 = 10^2$
$x^2 + y^2 = 10^2$

d. Radius 7: $x^2 + y^2 = 49$
Radius $\sqrt{3}$: $x^2 + y^2 = 3$
Radius r: $x^2 + y^2 = r^2$

INSTRUCTIONAL NOTE Students may struggle finding the coordinates in Part b. If necessary, focus their thinking on their response to Part c so that they use the distance formula.

Unit 3

3 A calculator-produced circle is shown below. The **Zsquare** window has a scale on both axes of 1 unit.

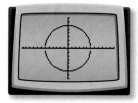

a. What is the radius of the circle?

b. Write an equation for this circle.

c. What expressions could be placed in the 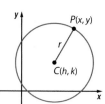 menu to produce the circle? Do your expressions produce a circle with the same radius?

d. Use your calculator to produce a copy of the circle shown in the computer display on page 163.

4 Some of the circles you created in Problem 1 did not have their centers at the origin. However, you can use reasoning similar to that in Problem 2 to find equations for these circles.

a. What is the center and radius of the circle whose center is on the positive *x*-axis?

   i. Suppose $P(x, y)$ is any point on that circle. Explain why it must be the case that $\sqrt{(x - 5)^2 + y^2} = 5$.

   ii. Use that information to write an equation for the circle that does not involve a radical symbol.

b. Write similar equations for:

   i. the circle whose center is on the positive *y*-axis.

   ii. the circle whose center is on the negative *x*-axis.

   iii. the circle whose center is on the negative *y*-axis.

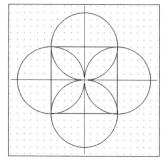

c. Verify that the coordinates of the vertices of the square satisfy your equations of the four circles that contain those vertices. Share the workload with your classmates.

5 Now try to generalize your work in Problems 2–4 to a circle whose center is not on an axis.

a. Use reasoning similar to that in Problem 4 to find the equation of a circle with center $C(h, k)$ and radius *r*.

b. Compare your equation with those of your classmates. Resolve any differences.

c. Rewrite your equation in Part b for the case when $C(h, k)$ is the origin. What do you notice?

3 **a.** The radius is 6.

  b. $x^2 + y^2 = 36$

    $y = \pm\sqrt{36 - x^2}$

  c. $y = \pm\sqrt{36 - x^2}$

  d. $y = \pm\sqrt{64 - x^2}$

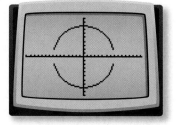

TECHNOLOGY NOTE If students do not know about the zoom function **ZSquare**, they will have an ellipse displayed instead of a circle.

4 **a.** The center is (5, 0) and the radius is 5.

    i. The equation is an application of the distance formula for points (5, 0) and (x, y) where the distance is 5 units from point (5, 0) to point (x, y).

    ii. Squaring both sides gives $(x - 5)^2 + y^2 = 25$.

  b. **i.** $x^2 + (y - 5)^2 = 25$

    ii. $(x + 5)^2 + y^2 = 25$

    iii. $x^2 + (y + 5)^2 = 25$

  c. Students should verify that the points (5, 5), (−5, 5), (−5, −5), and (5, −5) satisfy the appropriate equations.

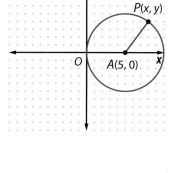

INSTRUCTIONAL NOTE
Again, students should be using the distance formula to find the equations. Be sure students recognize that when the ordered pair satisfies the equation, it is a point on the circle. Formally, if $A(a, b)$ satisfies $(x - h)^2 + (y - k)^2 = r^2$, then $(a - h)^2 + (b - k)^2 = r^2$. So, $A(a, b)$ is on a circle with center (h, k) and radius r by the definition of a circle.

5 **a–b.** $CP = r$ and $CP = \sqrt{(x - h)^2 + (y - k)^2}$.

    So, $\sqrt{(x - h)^2 + (y - k)^2} = r$.

    Thus, $(x - h)^2 + (y - k)^2 = r^2$.

  c. When the center is the origin, the equation is $x^2 + y^2 = r^2$. The equations for circles centered at the origin with radii of 8, $\sqrt{3}$, and 6 in Problems 2 and 3 were in this algebraic form.

6 Without using technology, determine which of the following equations describe a circle in a coordinate plane. For each equation that represents a circle, determine the center, the radius, and one point on the circle. For each equation that does *not* represent a circle, explain why not.

a. $x^2 + y^2 = 25$

b. $x^2 + y = 16$

c. $3x^2 + 3y^2 = 108$

d. $(x - 5)^2 + (y - 1)^2 = 81$

e. $3x^2 + y^2 = 9$

f. $x^2 + (y + 5)^2 = 1$

7 Coordinates as employed by interactive geometry software open new windows to geometry by allowing you to easily create figures and search for patterns in them. Complete Parts a–c using your software. You can create the figures yourself or use the "Explore Angles in Circles" custom tool.

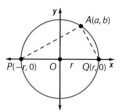

a. Draw a circle with center A and diameter with endpoint B. Label the other endpoint C.

b. Construct a new point D on the circle. Then draw $\overline{BD}$ and $\overline{CD}$.

c. Click and drag point D along the circumference of the circle.

  i. What appears to be true about $\angle CDB$ in all cases?

  ii. How is your conjecture supported by calculations from the Measurements menu?

d. State your conjecture in the form:
An angle inscribed in a semicircle ... .
Compare your conjecture with your classmates and resolve any differences.

8 As you saw in Investigation 2, coordinates can provide a powerful way to justify conjectures you make about geometric figures. The key is to position the figure in a coordinate plane so that general coordinates are easy to work with. A circle with center at the origin and radius r is shown below. Point $A(a, b)$ is a general point on the circle, different from points P and Q which are endpoints of a diameter on the x-axis.

6 Student-selected points on the circle will vary. One possible point is provided.

a. $C(0, 0)$; $r = 5$; $(0, 5)$

b. Not a circle because the y-term is not of degree 2. This equation is a quadratic function.

c. $C(0, 0)$; $r = 6$; $(6, 0)$

d. $C(5, 1)$; $r = 9$; $(5, 10)$

e. Not a circle since the equation cannot be written in the form $(x - h)^2 + (y - k)^2 = r^2$.

f. $C(0, -5)$; $r = 1$; $(0, -4)$

TECHNOLOGY NOTE When using *CPMP-Tools* or other interactive geometry software, the right triangle must be *constructed* so that the three vertices are on the circle. One way to achieve this is to construct a line containing the center of the circle and then find the intersection points of the circle and the line. Next, construct a new point on the circle for the vertex of the right angle and the two legs of the triangle.

When creating the figures using *CPMP-Tools*, it is sometimes beneficial to turn off "Snap to Grid." The "Explore Angles in Circles" custom tool provides a preconstructed angle inscribed in a semicircle. Students can drag the vertex of the right angle while observing that its measure remains 90°. They can also drag the diameter to examine circles of different sizes.

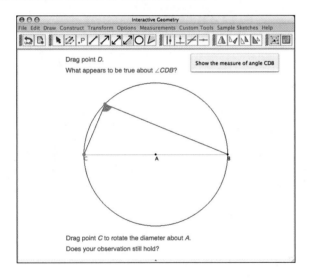

7 **a–c.** Students should find that m∠CDB = 90°.

d. An angle inscribed in a semicircle is a right angle.

Use these general coordinates and the following questions to help justify the conjecture you made in Problem 7:

An angle inscribed in a semicircle is a right angle.

a. What are some possible methods you could use to justify that $\angle PAQ$ is a right angle?

b. What are the coordinates of points P and Q?

c. Since point $A(a, b)$ is on the circle, what must be true about the distance OA? How is that distance related to the coordinates a and b?

d. Study Jack's argument below. He shows that $\triangle PAQ$ is a right triangle, and so $\angle PAQ$ is a right angle. Check the correctness of Jack's reasoning and give reason(s) justifying each step. If there are any errors in Jack's reasoning, correct them.

Jack's argument

The length of $\overline{PA} = \sqrt{(a+r)^2 + b^2}$, so $(PA)^2 = (a+r)^2 + b^2$.　　(1)

The length of $\overline{AQ} = \sqrt{(r-a)^2 + b^2}$, so $(AQ)^2 = (r-a)^2 + b^2$.　　(2)

The length of $\overline{PQ} = 2r$, so $(PQ)^2 = 4r^2$.　　(3)

$$(PA)^2 + (AQ)^2 = (a+r)^2 + b^2 + (r-a)^2 + b^2 \qquad (4)$$
$$= (a^2 + 2ar + r^2 + b^2) + (r^2 - 2ar + a^2 + b^2) \qquad (5)$$
$$= 2a^2 + 2r^2 + 2b^2 \qquad (6)$$
$$= 2(a^2 + b^2) + 2r^2 \qquad (7)$$
$$= 2r^2 + 2r^2 \qquad (8)$$
$$= 4r^2 \qquad (9)$$
$$= (PQ)^2 \qquad (10)$$

Therefore, $\triangle PAQ$ is a right triangle with $\angle PAQ$ a right angle.　　(11)

e. Now examine Malaya's argument justifying the conjecture that $\angle PAQ$ is a right angle. Check the correctness of Malaya's reasoning and give reason(s) justifying each step. Correct any errors in Malaya's reasoning.

Malaya's argument

The slope of $\overline{PA}$ is $\dfrac{b}{a+r}$.　　(1)

The slope of $\overline{QA}$ is $\dfrac{b}{a-r}$.　　(2)

The product of the slopes is $\left(\dfrac{b}{a+r}\right)\left(\dfrac{b}{a-r}\right) = \dfrac{-b^2}{a^2 - r^2}$.　　(3)

Since $a^2 + b^2 = r^2$, it follows that $a^2 - r^2 = -b^2$.　　(4)

This means that the product of the slopes is $\dfrac{b^2}{-b^2} = -1$.　　(5)

So, $\overline{PA} \perp \overline{AQ}$ and $\angle PAQ$ is a right angle.　　(6)

8 **a.** One possible method is to show that $(PA)^2 + (AQ)^2 = (PQ)^2$, the converse of the Pythagorean Theorem.

A second possible method is to show that the slopes of $\overline{PA}$ and $\overline{AQ}$ are opposite reciprocals, or equivalently that the product of the slopes is -1, and thus that $\overline{PA}$ and $\overline{AQ}$ are perpendicular.

b. $P(-r, 0)$; $Q(r, 0)$

c. $OA = r$; $a^2 + b^2 = r^2$, so $a = \sqrt{r^2 - b^2}$ and $b = \sqrt{r^2 - a^2}$.

d. Each statement is correct.

(1) The distance formula for $P(-r, 0)$ and $A(a, b)$
(2) The distance formula for $A(a, b)$ and $Q(r, 0)$
(3) The distance formula for $P(-r, 0)$ and $Q(r, 0)$
(4) Addition of two lengths in two different representations; Addition Property of Equality
(5) Expanding binomials
(6) Simplifying expressions
(7) Common factoring
(8) Substitution $r^2 = a^2 + b^2$
(9) Addition
(10) Substitution $PQ^2 = 4r^2$
(11) Converse of Pythagorean Theorem

e. Each statement is correct.

(1) Slope calculation for $P(-r, 0)$ and $A(a, b)$
(2) Slope calculation for $Q(r, 0)$ and $A(a, b)$
(3) Multiplication
(4) Equation of circle is $x^2 + y^2 = r^2$; so, using point (a, b) on the circle, $a^2 + b^2 = r^2$. Subtraction of b^2 and r^2 from both sides of the equation gives $a^2 - r^2 = -b^2$.
(5) Substitute equation in Step 4 into equation in Step 3
(6) When the product of two slopes is -1, the two lines are perpendicular. A is the point of intersection of the two lines, so $\angle A$ is a right angle.

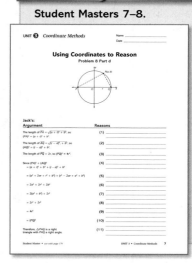
INSTRUCTIONAL NOTE
Having a classroom discussion around Problem 8 Part d is important. This problem is challenging for students. You may want to make an overhead of the master to fill in reasons.

Summary

In the process of discussing the Summarize the Mathematics, be sure students recognize the value in generalizing and justify statements for all cases using general coordinates. You may also wish to have students look back at the placement of the circles in Problems 2 and 8 that helped make reasoning with general coordinates easy.

In this investigation, you discovered how to write equations for circles in a coordinate plane and used coordinates to make general arguments.

(a) What is the equation of a circle with center at the origin and radius r?

(b) What is the equation of a circle with center at (h, k) and radius r?

(c) What formula was the key to deriving the equation of a circle?

(d) How can you tell by looking at an equation whether its graph is a circle?

(e) Why are general coordinates such as (a, b) used in reasoning about geometric properties?

Be prepared to share your equations and thinking with the class.

✔ Check Your Understanding

A circle with center at $(3, -4)$ is drawn so that it is **tangent** to the x-axis. That is, the circle touches the x-axis at only one point called the *point of tangency*.

a. Draw the circle on a coordinate plane.

b. What are the coordinates of the point of tangency?

c. Write an equation for the circle.

d. Write an equation for a congruent circle with center at the origin.

e. Graph the circle in Part d on your graphing calculator.

Summarize
the Mathematics

ⓐ $x^2 + y^2 = r^2$

ⓑ $(x - h)^2 + (y - k)^2 = r^2$

ⓒ The distance formula

ⓓ An equation (that can be) expressed in the form $(x - h)^2 + (y - k)^2 = r^2$ when graphed is a circle with center (h, k) and radius r.

ⓔ General coordinates allow you to prove a statement for all points rather than only specific points. The variable represents *any* numbers, not just specific choices. The use of variables makes statements that hold for all choices of numbers that can replace the variables.

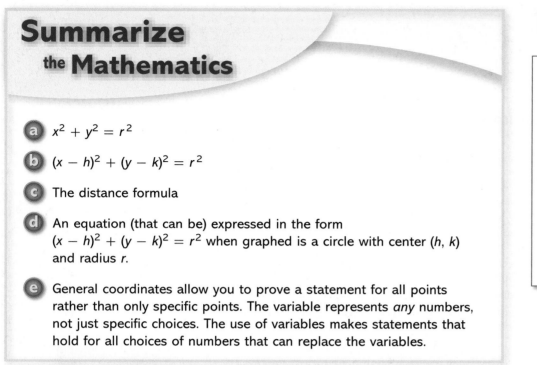
✔Check Your Understanding

a.

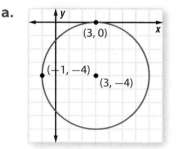

b. $(3, 0)$

c. $(x - 3)^2 + (y + 4)^2 = 16$

d. $x^2 + y^2 = 16$

e. To graph this circle, students can use the equations $y = \sqrt{16 - x^2}$ and $y = -\sqrt{16 - x^2}$.

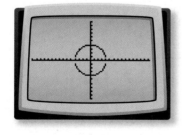

Applications

1. Use graph paper, the **Line(** command from the DRAW menu of your graphing calculator, or interactive geometry software to draw a model of a kite with vertices $A(5, -6)$, $B(7, -2)$, $C(5, 2)$, and $D(-9, -2)$.

   a. Does your drawing appear to be that of a kite? Use careful reasoning with the coordinates to justify that $ABCD$ is a kite, that is, a quadrilateral with exactly two pairs of congruent adjacent sides.

   b. Draw the cross braces of the kite and find their lengths using coordinates.

   c. Use coordinates to find the midpoints of $\overline{AC}$ and $\overline{BD}$.

   d. Justify that the midpoint of $\overline{AC}$ is on $\overline{BD}$. How is this fact seen in your drawing?

2. Use graph paper, the **Line(** command from the DRAW menu of your graphing calculator, or interactive geometry software to draw a model of a school crossing sign. Assume the height is the same as the width of the base, and the length of the vertical edges is half that of the base. Locate the shape on the coordinate axes so that one side of the shape is on the x-axis and the y-axis is a line of symmetry.

   a. Give the coordinates of each vertex.

   b. Determine the length of each side using coordinates. Which pairs of sides are the same length?

   c. Use coordinates to find the height of your model sign.

   d. Find the area of your model sign.

3. The following program, designed for one type of graphing calculator, computes the distance between two points in a coordinate plane. The left-hand column is the program; the right-hand column describes the function of the commands.

DIST Program	
Program	**Function in Program**
ClrHome	Clears display screen
Input "X COORD",A	
Input "Y COORD",B	Enters x- and y-coordinates
Input "X COORD",C	of two points
Input "Y COORD",D	
$\sqrt{((A{-}C)^2+(B{-}D)^2)}{\rightarrow}L$	Calculates distance and stores value in memory location L
Disp "DISTANCE IS",L	Outputs calculated distance with label

Applications

1 **a.** If students use uniform x and y scales or **ZSquare**, they should have a shape that looks like a kite. Using the distance formula, $DC = AD = \sqrt{212}$ and $BC = BA = \sqrt{20}$.

b. $AC = 8$ units
$BD = 16$ units

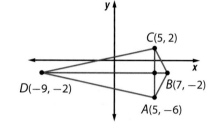

c. The coordinates of the midpoint of $\overline{AC}$ are $(5, -2)$.

The coordinates of the midpoint of $\overline{BD}$ are $(-1, -2)$.

d. The equation for $\overleftrightarrow{BD}$ is $y = -2$.
Since the coordinates of the midpoint of $\overline{AC}$ are $(5, -2)$, it lies on $\overline{BD}$.

This is seen in the drawing by noticing that the midpoint of $\overline{AC}$, B, and D are all on the same line.

2 Student choices of coordinates may vary. One example using a base of length 16 is provided.

a. The coordinates are $A(8, 0)$, $B(8, 8)$, $C(0, 16)$, $D(-8, 8)$, and $E(-8, 0)$.

b. Pairs of sides as shown in the photo are the same length.

$AE = 16$, $AB = DE = 8$,
$BC = CD = \sqrt{128} = 8\sqrt{2}$

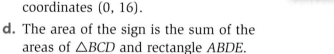

c. The height is 16 since C has coordinates $(0, 16)$.

d. The area of the sign is the sum of the areas of $\triangle BCD$ and rectangle $ABDE$.

$Area\ of\ sign = \frac{1}{2}(16)(8) + (16)(8) = 192$ square units

3 **INSTRUCTIONAL NOTE** Students should enter the program in their calculators as a time-saver since they will regularly need to find distances. It is also recommended, but not required, that students enter the slope and midpoint programs into their calculators.

Some students have difficulty getting a program to run because of syntax errors. Those students may need extra help by the teacher or a group member. Troubleshooting can be very educational.

> **DIFFERENTIATION**
> Problems 3, 4, and 5 have students create three separate programs. Challenge students to write *one* program that finds all three—distance, slope, and midpoint.

a. Describe how this program uses the Distance Between Two Points Algorithm on page 167.

b. What does the program call the coordinates of the two points?

c. Explain how the processing portion actually calculates the distance.

d. Enter the program DIST in your calculator (modified as necessary for your particular calculator). Check your program for accuracy by testing several pairs of points.

4 Modify the program in Applications Task 3 so that it will compute the slope of a nonvertical segment determined by two points. Call your new program SLOPE. Check your program for accuracy by testing it with several points.

5 In Investigation 1, Problem 10 (page 168), you wrote a midpoint algorithm for calculating the coordinates of the midpoint of a segment. A program for a graphing calculator that will compute the midpoint of a segment is shown below.

MIDPT Program

Program	Function in Program
ClrHome	1. Clears display screen
Input "X COORD",A	2. _____
Input "Y COORD",B	3. _____
Input "X COORD",C	4. _____
Input "Y COORD",D	5. _____
$(A+C)/2 \rightarrow X$	6. _____
$(B+D)/2 \rightarrow Y$	7. _____
Disp "MIDPOINT COORDS"	8. Displays words, MIDPOINT COORDS
Disp X	9. _____
Disp Y	10. _____
Stop	11. _____

---

a. Analyze this program and explain the purpose of each command line as was done for lines 1 and 8.

b. Enter the program MIDPT in your calculator. (Depending on your calculator, you may need to modify the commands slightly.) Test the program on pairs of points of your choosing.

6 Drilling teams from oil companies search around the world for new sites to place oil wells. Increasingly, oil reserves are being discovered in offshore waters. The Gulf Oil Company has drilled two high-capacity wells in the Gulf of Mexico 5 km and 9 km from shore, as shown in the diagram on page 183. The 20 km of shoreline is nearly straight, and the company wants to build a refinery on shore between the two wells. Since pipe and labor cost money, the company wants to find the location that will serve both wells and uses the least amount of pipe when it is laid in straight lines from each well to the refinery.

a. This program uses the algorithm by inputting the coordinates of the two points, calculating the distance, and outputting the result of the calculation.

b. (A, B) and (C, D)

c. The formula in the processing adds the differences squared of the x-coordinates and y-coordinates and then takes the square root of that sum.

d. Students should enter the program and verify that it runs.

4

SLOPE Program

Program	Function in Program
ClrHome	Clears display screen
Input "X COORD",A	
Input "Y COORD",B	Enters x- and y-coordinates
Input "X COORD",C	of two points
Input "Y COORD",D	
(D–B)/(C–A)→M	Calculates slope and stores value in memory location M
Disp "SLOPE IS ",M	Outputs calculated slope with label

> **TECHNOLOGY TIP** For TI calculators, when entering the commands **ClrHome**, **Input**, and **Disp**, do not simply type them in, rather insert the commands from the **CATALOG** (scroll down in the list until you find them).

5 **a. Function in Program**
1. Clears display screen
2. Stores the x-coordinate of one point in A
3. Stores the y-coordinate of the same point in B
4. Stores the x-coordinate of the second point in C
5. Stores the y-coordinate of the second point in D
6. Calculates the x-coordinate of the midpoint and stores it in X
7. Calculates the y-coordinate of the midpoint and stores it in Y
8. Displays words, MIDPOINT COORDS
9. Displays the x-coordinate of the midpoint
10. Displays the y-coordinate of the midpoint
11. Ends the program

b. Students should enter the program and test it on pairs of points.

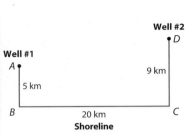

Well #1
A•

5 km

B

Well #2
•D

9 km

20 km
Shoreline

C

a. How can coordinates be used to model this situation?

b. What distance(s) should you try to minimize to use the least amount of pipe?

c. Do you think the refinery should be closer to *B*, to *C*, or at the midpoint of the shoreline? Make a conjecture.

d. Determine your best estimate for the location of the refinery. About how much pipe will be required?

e. There are several methods for solving this problem, including:

- Analyze tables or graphs of a function relating total length of pipe to distance of refinery from point *B*.
- Use point *D*, its reflection across $\overleftrightarrow{BC}$, and congruent triangles.
- Use the click-and-drag feature of interactive geometry software.

Select a method different from what you used in Part d and use that method to solve this problem. Compare your answer with that found in Part d.

7 A CAD face-view drawing of a building includes a quadrilateral *PQRS* whose vertices are given by the matrix:

$$\begin{array}{cccc} P & Q & R & S \end{array}$$
$$\begin{bmatrix} 4 & 8 & 14 & 10 \\ 4 & -2 & 2 & 8 \end{bmatrix}$$

a. Sketch the quadrilateral on a coordinate grid.

b. What kind of quadrilateral is *PQRS*? Give reasons to support your response.

8 $\overline{AB}$ has endpoints *A*(−5, 0) and *B*(4, 3). $\overline{CD}$ has endpoints *C*(−3, 9) and *D*(1, −3). The equations of the lines containing $\overline{AB}$ and $\overline{CD}$ are $x - 3y = -5$ and $3x + y = 0$, respectively.

a. How could you quickly check that these equations are correct?

b. Verify that the lines are perpendicular.

c. Find the point of intersection of $\overline{AB}$ and $\overline{CD}$ by solving the system of equations.

d. Find the midpoints of $\overline{AB}$ and $\overline{CD}$. Compare your results with Part c.

e. What kind of quadrilateral is *ACBD*? Explain your reasoning.

6 **a.** Each point on the model may be represented by an ordered pair. One convenient choice is to locate B at the origin.

b. The sum of the distances from the refinery on the shoreline to the two oil wells should be minimized.

c. The refinery should be closer to B. However, students' conjectures may vary.

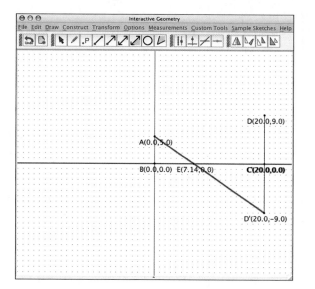

d–e. A reasonable estimate for the location of the refinery is at $E(7, 0)$. This location means about 24.4 km of pipe would be required. The exact location, $\left(\frac{50}{7}, 0\right)$, requires about 24.1 km of pipe. Various methods are shown below.

- Analyze a table of $y = \sqrt{x^2 + 5^2} + \sqrt{(20 - x)^2 + 9^2}$ or graph this function on the interval $0 \leq x \leq 20$. Locate the smallest y value.

- Using grid paper or geometry software, reflect $\overline{CD}$ across $\overleftrightarrow{BC}$. Then construct $\overline{AD'}$. Find the location of the refinery by solving the linear equation $y = -\frac{14}{20}x + 5 = 0$ or by using geometry software constructing the intersection of the x-axis and $\overline{AD'}$.

> **TECHNOLOGY NOTE**
> *CPMP-Tools* or other geometry software may be used in Parts d or e. If using *CPMP-Tools*, students will need to change the horizontal scale found under Options, Window Scale. Encourage them to turn on the coordinates under Options, Default Style Window.

- To use the click-and-drag feature of geometry software, construct the shape, construct a point E on $\overline{BC}$, construct $\overline{AE}$ and $\overline{DE}$. Measure the lengths of $\overline{AE}$ and $\overline{DE}$. Calculate the sum $AE + DE$. Click and drag point E to find the minimum value for $AE + DE$. A range of values around $x = 7.14$ will display the minimum pipe length of approximately 24.4 km.

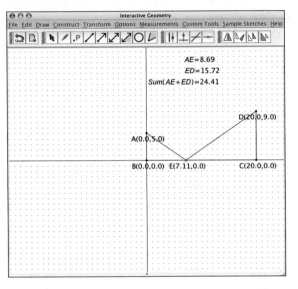

7. **a.**

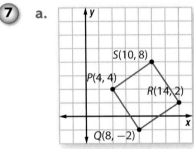

b. $PQRS$ is a square. Slope of $\overline{PQ}$ is $-\frac{3}{2}$. Slope of $\overline{SR}$ is $-\frac{3}{2}$. Slope of $\overline{PS}$ is $\frac{2}{3}$. Slope of $\overline{QR}$ is $\frac{2}{3}$. Since the opposite sides are parallel and consecutive sides have slopes that are opposite reciprocals, the quadrilateral is either a rectangle or a square. $PS = PQ = \sqrt{52} \approx 7.21$, so $PQRS$ is a square.

8. **a.** A quick check would involve substituting the coordinates for each point into its respective equation to see if the point is on the line.

b. These lines are perpendicular since the slopes are $\frac{1}{3}$ and -3, opposite reciprocals of each other.

c. Students might solve this system using matrices, substitution, or linear combinations. The point of intersection is $\left(-\frac{1}{2}, \frac{3}{2}\right)$.

d. The midpoint of $\overline{AB}$ is $\left(-\frac{1}{2}, \frac{3}{2}\right)$. The midpoint of $\overline{CD}$ is $(-1, 3)$. The midpoint of $\overline{AB}$ is the same as the intersection point of $\overline{AB}$ and $\overline{CD}$. But the midpoint of $\overline{CD}$ is not the same point of intersection.

e. Using the distance formula, $AC = CB \approx 9.22$ and $AD = BD \approx 6.71$; so by the definition, quadrilateral $ACBD$ is a kite.

Teacher Notes

Unit 3

9 In Check Your Understanding Part d (page 169), you discovered that the line segment connecting the midpoints of two sides of a particular triangle was parallel to the third side. You may have also noticed that the length of the *midsegment* was half the length of the third side. With coordinates, you can verify this is true for any triangle.

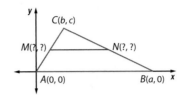

Using the above placement of $\triangle ABC$ in a coordinate plane:

a. Find the coordinates of the midpoint M of $\overline{AC}$. Of the midpoint N of $\overline{BC}$.

b. Use coordinates to explain why $\overline{MN} \parallel \overline{AB}$.

c. Show that $MN = \frac{1}{2}AB$.

10 Quadrilateral $ABCD$ is a rhombus with general coordinates.

a. Determine the coordinates of point C.

b. Show that $\overline{AC} \perp \overline{BD}$.

c. Show that $\overline{AC}$ bisects $\overline{BD}$ and that $\overline{BD}$ bisects $\overline{AC}$.

d. Write a statement that summarizes this general property of rhombuses.

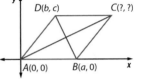

11 The circle shown below was produced from the DRAW menu of a graphing calculator using the command **Circle(0,0,6)**. It is displayed in the standard **ZSquare** window.

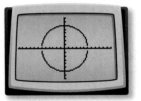

a. Write an equation for the displayed circle.

   i. Use your equation to find two points on the circle whose x-coordinate is 3.

   ii. What two expressions could be used in the [Y=] menu to produce a graph of the circle?

9 **a.** $M\left(\dfrac{b}{2}, \dfrac{c}{2}\right)$; $N\left(\dfrac{a+b}{2}, \dfrac{c}{2}\right)$

b. The slope of $\overline{MN}$ is $\dfrac{0}{\frac{a}{2}} = 0$ and the slope of $\overline{AB}$ is 0.

So, the lines are parallel.

c. $MN = \left|\dfrac{a+b}{2} - \dfrac{b}{2}\right| = \dfrac{a}{2}$

$AB = a$

So, $MN = \dfrac{1}{2}AB$.

10 **a.** $C(a + b, c)$

b. The slope of $\overline{AC}$ is $\dfrac{c}{a+b}$.

The slope of $\overline{BD}$ is $\dfrac{-c}{a-b}$.

The product of the slopes is
$\dfrac{c}{a+b} \cdot \dfrac{-c}{a-b} = \dfrac{-c^2}{a^2 - b^2}$.

Since $b^2 + c^2 = a^2$,

$\dfrac{-c^2}{a^2 - b^2} = \dfrac{-c^2}{b^2 + c^2 - b^2} = \dfrac{-c^2}{c^2} = -1$.

Thus, the diagonals are perpendicular.

c. The midpoint of $\overline{AC}$ is $\left(\dfrac{a+b}{2}, \dfrac{c}{2}\right)$.

The midpoint of $\overline{BD}$ is $\left(\dfrac{a+b}{2}, \dfrac{c}{2}\right)$.

Since this is the same point, the diagonals bisect each other.

d. The diagonals of a rhombus are perpendicular bisectors of each other.

11 **a.** $x^2 + y^2 = 36$

   i. When $x = 3$, $y^2 = 27$. $y = \pm\sqrt{27} = \pm 3\sqrt{3}$

   ii. $y = \pm\sqrt{36 - x^2}$

The figure for problem 10 shows a coordinate plane with points D(b, c), C(a + b, c), A(0, 0), B(a, 0), with the diagonals drawn and labels a, b, c.

b. Use the **Circle(** command to produce a circle with center at (2, 4) and radius 10. What might be a good window to use to display the circle?

   i. Write an equation for the circle.

   ii. Use your equation to find two points on the circle whose x-coordinate is 5.

c. Use the **Circle(** command to produce the circle defined by $(x + 5)^2 + (y - 8)^2 = 84$.

   i. Write an equation for a circle that has the same center and is tangent to the x-axis.

   ii. Write an equation for a circle that has the same center and is tangent to the y-axis.

   iii. Write an equation for a circle that is tangent to both the x- and y-axes and is congruent to the given circle that you graphed. How many circles are possible? How are their centers related?

Connections

12 In Course 1, you may have conducted an experiment in which you placed several equal weights at various positions on a yardstick and found the balance point or *center of gravity*. The balance point corresponded to the mean of the distances from zero on the yardstick.

Test a similar idea for two-dimensional shapes.

a. Cut out a triangle from a sheet of cardboard or tag board that is about the size of a $\frac{1}{2}$-sheet of notepaper.

   • Experiment with the cutout to try to find a point at which it will balance on the top of your finger or a pencil.

   • Now place the cutout on a coordinate grid and record the coordinates of its vertices.

   • Compute the mean of the x-coordinates and the mean of the y-coordinates. Locate this point on your coordinate grid and on the cardboard cutout.

   • Verify by balancing that the point you found is the center of gravity.

b. Repeat Part a for a rectangle. For a parallelogram that is not a rectangle. What do you notice?

c. Repeat Part a for a quadrilateral that is not a parallelogram. What do you notice?

LESSON 1 • A Coordinate Model of a Plane   **185**

b. Students should produce the circle using **Circle(2,4,10)**. One good window would be the standard **ZSquare** increased by a factor of 2. A window of Xmin = −30, Xmax = 30, Xscl = 5, Ymin = −20, Ymax = 20, Yscl = 5 works well.

  i. $(x - 2)^2 + (y - 4)^2 = 100$

  ii. When $x = 5$, $(y - 4)^2 = 91$, so $y \approx -5.54$ or $y \approx 13.54$.

c. Students should use **Circle(−5,8,√(84))**.

  i. $(x + 5)^2 + (y - 8)^2 = 64$

  ii. $(x + 5)^2 + (y - 8)^2 = 25$

  iii. There are four possibilities. Students should have one of the following equations.

$$(x + \sqrt{84})^2 + (y + \sqrt{84})^2 = 84$$
$$(x - \sqrt{84})^2 + (y - \sqrt{84})^2 = 84$$
$$(x + \sqrt{84})^2 + (y - \sqrt{84})^2 = 84$$
$$(x - \sqrt{84})^2 + (y + \sqrt{84})^2 = 84$$

Relationships that could be described are:

- The centers are reflections across x- or y-axes.
- The centers are rotations of 90°, 180°, or 270° of each other.
- The centers have $\pm \sqrt{84}$ for each coordinate.
- The centers are vertices of a square centered at the origin with side lengths $2\sqrt{84}$.

Connections

12 **a.** Students should conduct the experiment and verify that the center of gravity of a triangle with vertices $A(x_1, y_1)$, $B(x_2, y_2)$ and $C(x_3, y_3)$ is the point with coordinates $\left(\dfrac{x_1 + x_2 + x_3}{3}, \dfrac{y_1 + y_2 + y_3}{3} \right)$.

b. Students should notice that in the case of a rectangle and a parallelogram that is not a rectangle, the center of gravity is the point of intersection of the diagonals.

c. For quadrilaterals that are not parallelograms, the method outlined in Part a does not produce the center of gravity.

INSTRUCTIONAL NOTE
Task 12 requires students to have pieces of cardboard and grid paper. Attaching the grid paper to the triangle before cutting out the triangle allows students to cut out triangles with vertices that have integer coordinates.

INSTRUCTIONAL NOTE
Recall from Course 1 that parallelograms have half-turn symmetry about the point of intersection of the diagonals. Some students might be encouraged to show algebraically why the observation in Part b must be the case.

Unit 3

13 An engineering school offers a special reading and writing course for all entering students. Students are assigned to one of two sections based on performance on a placement test. Section A emphasizes reading skills; Section B stresses writing skills. The mean test scores for Section A are 64.2 (reading) and 73.8 (writing). For Section B, the mean reading and writing scores are 74.4 and 57.6, respectively. Placement test scores of five students are shown below.

Placement Test Scores

	Reading Score	Writing Score
Jim	68	64
Emily	67	67
Anne	70	62
Miguel	66	69
Gloria	60	60

a. Represent the reading and writing scores of each student listed in the table as a point on a coordinate grid. Label the points. On the same grid, also plot and label the points corresponding to the mean scores for Sections A and B.

b. Using only the visual display, assign students to Section A or B. What influenced your choices?

c. Suppose students are assigned to the section whose mean point is closest to their point.

i. Assign each student to a section. Compare your assignments to that in Part b.

ii. Why would this assignment criterion make sense for placement of students?

d. Are there any students for whom neither section appears appropriate? Explain your response.

14 How do you use the concept of mean in your procedure to calculate the coordinates of the midpoint of a segment?

15 Suppose (x_1, y_1) and (x_2, y_2) are given points with $x_2 > x_1$. Then the x-coordinate of the midpoint is half the distance from x_1 to x_2 added to x_1.

a. Show that the above statement is true when $x_1 = 6$ and $x_2 = 11$.

b. Explain why the above statement makes sense.

c. Rewrite the expression $x_1 + \dfrac{x_2 - x_1}{2}$ in a simpler equivalent form. Is this the x-coordinate of the midpoint?

13 a.

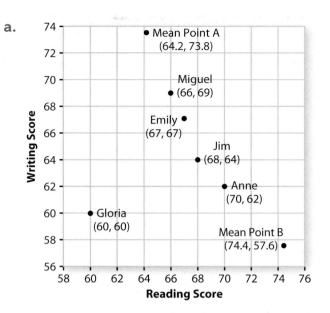

b. Visually, Emily and Miguel have scores closer to Section A's mean scores, whereas Jim and Anne have scores closer to Section B's mean scores. Students may choose to assign Gloria to either section since visually there seems to be little difference in the distances from her ordered pair to the mean points for Sections A and B.

c. i. To assign a student to one section or the other, simply choose the section whose ordered pair of mean placement test scores is closer to the student's own scores. Then Emily, Miguel, and Gloria would be in Section A, and Jim and Anne would be in Section B.

Student	Distance From A's Mean	Distance from B's Mean
Jim	10.51	9.05
Emily	7.35	11.96
Anne	13.15	6.22
Miguel	5.13	14.16
Gloria	14.42	14.60

ii. With these assignments, Section A would have students who need more work in reading than writing and the class could emphasize reading. Similarly, Section B could focus on writing since reading scores of students are higher than writing scores for this section.

d. Since Gloria's test score ordered pair is almost equidistant from both A and B, and this distance is relatively large, neither section seems particularly appropriate for her.

14 To calculate the coordinates of the midpoint, you find the mean (or average) of the x-coordinate and y-coordinate.

15 a. Using the indicated procedure, the x-coordinate of the midpoint is $\frac{11 - 6}{2} + 6 = 8\frac{1}{2}$. Using the midpoint formula, the x-coordinate of the midpoint is $\frac{11 + 6}{2} = 8\frac{1}{2}$. Since the given procedure produces the correct x-coordinate for the midpoint, the statement is true, at least in this case.

b. Yes, since the midpoint is halfway between the two endpoints.

c. $x_1 + \frac{x_2 - x_1}{2} = \frac{2x_1}{2} + \frac{x_2}{2} - \frac{x_1}{2} = \frac{x_1}{2} + \frac{x_2}{2} = \frac{x_1 + x_2}{2}$

It is the coordinate of the midpoint. (This shows the statement before Part a in the student text is true in all cases where $x_2 > x_1$.)

16 So far, you have been drawing polygons in a coordinate plane by plotting and connecting vertices in order. You can also think of polygons as being *enveloped* by a family of lines. Examine the lines below and the quadrilateral that is enveloped by them. The scale on both axes is 1 unit.

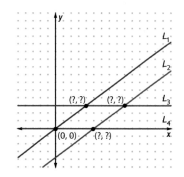

a. Without use of technology, match each equation given below with the line through the corresponding side of the quadrilateral. Describe clues you used to determine the matches.

Equation I $y = 0$ **Equation II** $3x - 4y = 15$

Equation III $y = 3$ **Equation IV** $3x - 4y = 0$

b. Determine the coordinates of the vertices of the quadrilateral.

c. Explain as precisely as possible how you can verify the quadrilateral is a rhombus.

d. The equations in Part a describe lines that contain the sides of the quadrilateral. The equations will describe only the points on the sides if you restrict the input values for x and y.

   i. In the case of the equation for the side determined by the vertices (0, 0) and (4, 3), explain why $0 \le x \le 4$ ($x \ge 0$ and $x \le 4$) and $0 \le y \le 3$.

   ii. For each of the remaining equations in Part a, describe the restrictions on x and y so that the equation describes just the side of the rhombus.

17 A circle with radius 3 and center at the origin is shown at the right.

a. Justify that the point with coordinates $(2, \sqrt{5})$ is on the circle.

b. Use symmetry to name the coordinates of three other points on the circle.

c. Without any calculations, identify the coordinates of four other points on the circle.

16 **a.** Students may use slopes and *y*-intercepts to help them match each equation to the appropriate line. Alternatively, they could solve the equations for *y* and have their calculators draw the graphs.

NOTE This task offers an opportunity to informally address restricted domains and ranges.

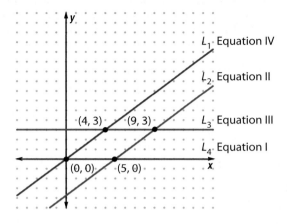

b. See the graph above.

c. The quadrilateral is a rhombus because it is a quadrilateral with opposite sides parallel (one pair of sides having slope 0 and the other pair having slope $\frac{3}{4}$) and all sides of equal length (5 units).

d. **i.** The *x*-coordinates of the points on that side of the rhombus are all between 0 and 4, inclusive, while the *y*-coordinates are between 0 and 3, inclusive. This gives $0 \le x \le 4$ and $0 \le y \le 3$.

ii. For the side determined by the vertices (5, 0) and (9, 3), $5 \le x \le 9$ and $0 \le y \le 3$.

For the side determined by the vertices (9, 3) and (4, 3), $4 \le x \le 9$ and $y = 3$.

For the side determined by the vertices (0, 0) and (5, 0), $0 \le x \le 5$ and $y = 0$.

17 **a.** $x^2 + y^2 = 9$; $(2)^2 + (\sqrt{5})^2 = 9$, so $(2, \sqrt{5})$ is on the circle.
b. $(-2, \sqrt{5})$, $(-2, -\sqrt{5})$, $(2, -\sqrt{5})$
c. $(\sqrt{5}, 2)$, $(-\sqrt{5}, 2)$, $(-\sqrt{5}, -2)$, $(\sqrt{5}, -2)$, $(0, 3)$, $(3, 0)$, $(0, -3)$, $(-3, 0)$

18. In this lesson, you saw how geometric figures and distance measurement in a plane can be represented using coordinates. Complete a table like the one below, which summarizes key features of a two-dimensional **coordinate model** of geometry. Then give a specific example of each idea from the coordinate model.

Geometric Idea	Coordinate Model	Example
Point	Ordered pair (x, y) of real numbers	
Plane	All possible ordered pairs (x, y) of real numbers	(No example needed)
Line	All ordered pairs (x, y) satisfying a linear equation $ax + by = c$	$2x + y = 8$
Segment length		
Midpoint		
Circle		
Parallel lines		
Perpendicular lines		

19. State Police radios can transmit up to 25 miles. Officer Jacobs patrols Highway 20 which runs straight north from the state police post to Driftwood, located 50 miles from the police post. Officer Kelley patrols Highway 45, which runs straight west from the police post to the state line, 50 miles west of the police post.

   a. This situation can be represented with a coordinate model as shown below.

      i. What does the 50 × 50 grid represent?

      ii. What does point O_1 represent? Point O_2? Point P?

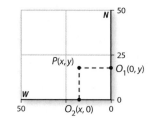

   b. Find the probability that the officers can talk to each other if calls can be relayed through the police post.

   c. Find the probability that the officers can talk to each other if calls are *not* relayed through the police post.

18

Geometric Idea	Coordinate Model	Example
Point	Ordered pair (x, y) of real numbers	$(3, -2)$
Plane	All possible ordered pairs (x, y) of real numbers	(No example needed.)
Line	All ordered pairs (x, y) satisfying a linear equation $ax + by = c$	$2x + y = 8$
Segment Length	Given two points $A(x_1, y_1)$ and $B(x_2, y_2)$, $AB = \sqrt{(x_1 - x_2)^2 + (y_1 - y_2)^2}$.	$A(3, 4)$ and $B(6, 0)$; $AB = \sqrt{(3 - 6)^2 + (4 - 0)^2}$ $= \sqrt{9 + 16} = \sqrt{25} = 5$
Midpoint	Given two points (x_1, y_1) and (x_2, y_2), the midpoint of the segment is $M = \left(\dfrac{x_1 + x_2}{2}, \dfrac{y_1 + y_2}{2}\right)$.	Midpoint of $A(3, 4)$ and $B(6, 0)$ is $M(4.5, 2)$.
Circle	Given a center $O(h, k)$ and a radius r, all ordered pairs (x, y) satisfying $(x - h)^2 + (y - k)^2 = r^2$	A circle with center $O(2, -8)$ and radius $= 10$, $(x - 2)^2 + (y + 8)^2 = 100$
Parallel lines	Any two lines of the form $y = mx + b$ and $y = mx + c$, where m, b, and c are real numbers and $b \neq c$; also $x = c$ and $x = d$	$y = 3x + 1$ and $y = 3x - 5$; $x = 1$ and $x = -3$; or $y = 7$ and $y = -3$
Perpendicular lines	Any two lines of the form $y = mx + b$ and $y = -\dfrac{1}{m}x + c$; also $x = c$ and $y = d$	$y = 2x - 7$; $y = -\dfrac{1}{2}x + 2$; $x = -1$ and $y = 0$

INSTRUCTIONAL NOTE
You may wish to have students place this page in their math toolkits.

19 **a.** **i.** The grid represents the pairs of numbers for the miles away from the police post traveled by the two officers. The horizontal axis represents Highway 45. The vertical axis represents Highway 20. $(0, 0)$ represents the state police post.

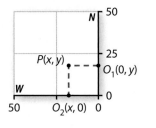

ii. Officer 1 is at point $O_1(0, y)$ and Officer 2 is at point $O_2(x, 0)$. Point P represents the officers' two locations: x-coordinate for Kelley and y-coordinate for Jacobs.

b. If the signal can be relayed through the police station, then any point in the shaded square indicates a point (O_2, O_1) where the officers can talk to each other.

$$P(less\ than\ 25) = 1 - \frac{50^2 - 25^2}{50^2} = 0.25$$

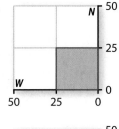

c. The officers' two locations are identified by the ordered pair (x, y). If $\sqrt{x^2 + y^2} \leq 25$ or $x^2 + y^2 \leq 625$, the distance between the two officers is less than 25 miles.

Thus, a point inside the quarter circle will indicate positions for Officer Jacobs and Officer Kelley such that they are less than 25 miles apart.

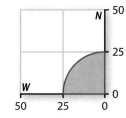

So, $P(less\ than\ 25) = 1 - \dfrac{50^2 - \frac{1}{4}\pi(25)^2}{50^2} \approx 0.196$

Reflections

20 How can you show that two triangles are congruent by calculating with the coordinates of the vertices?

21 In the first investigation, you invented formulas for calculating the distance between two points in a coordinate plane and finding coordinates of the midpoint of the segment determined by those points. You were asked to write your formulas for general points (x_1, y_1) and (x_2, y_2), that is, using *subscript notation*. What advantages or disadvantages do you see in using subscript notation in these cases?

22 In the definition of the midpoint of a segment on page 167, the phrase "on a segment" is included. Why is that phrase needed?

23 For points $P(x_1, y_1)$ and $Q(x_2, y_2)$ in a coordinate plane:

- the slope of line PQ is $\dfrac{\Delta y}{\Delta x}$ or $\dfrac{y_1 - y_2}{x_1 - x_2}$.
- the distance PQ is $\sqrt{(\Delta x)^2 + (\Delta y)^2}$ or $\sqrt{(x_1 - x_2)^2 + (y_1 - y_2)^2}$.

In each case, the differences of coordinates are calculated. When calculating the slope or calculating the distance, does the order in which you subtract the coordinates make any difference? Illustrate and explain your reasoning.

24 An equilateral triangle has two vertices at $(0, 0)$ and $(0, 8)$. What are the possible coordinates of the third vertex? Illustrate and explain your reasoning.

25 Quadrilateral *ABCD* has vertex *A* at the origin and adjacent sides of length 13 and 5 units. For each part below, illustrate and explain your reasoning.

a. Find coordinates for *B, C,* and *D* so that quadrilateral *ABCD* is a rectangle.

b. Find coordinates for *B, C,* and *D* so that quadrilateral *ABCD* is a parallelogram (but not a rectangle).

26 Suppose you are given the coordinates of three points in a plane. How can you use calculations on the coordinates:

a. to test whether or not the three points lie on a line?

b. to test whether or not the three points are the vertices of a right triangle?

c. to test whether or not one of the points is on the perpendicular bisector of the segment with the other two points as endpoints?

d. to test whether or not one of three points is the center of a circle containing the other two points.

Reflections

20 To show two triangles are congruent by using the coordinates of the vertices, you would use the distance formula to determine whether or not the corresponding sides were the same length.

21 Responses may vary. One advantage of using the subscript notation is that it is clear which variables refer to the x-coordinate and which refer to the y-coordinate. It is also clear to which point the coordinate refers. A disadvantage when handwriting is that x_2 may look like $x2$. (Until students get used to using the subscript notation, they may find it cumbersome.)

22 The phrase "on a segment" is included to ensure that there is only one possible midpoint. Given any two points A and B, there exist infinitely many points which are equidistant from A and B (namely, all points lying on the perpendicular bisector of $\overline{AB}$). However, if we require the midpoint to lie on the segment $\overline{AB}$, the midpoint is a unique ordered pair.

23 • For the slope, the order in which you subtract makes no difference as long as the first coordinate in each difference comes from the same point. If you mix points, the slopes computed are not correct.

• For the distance formula, it makes no difference whether you evaluate $x_1 - x_2$ or $x_2 - x_1$ since the square of each is the same. The same can be said for the y values.

24 There are two possible coordinates for the third vertex: approximately $(6.93, 4)$ and $(-6.93, 4)$. (If students are having difficulty, encourage them to draw a diagram. They should be able to see that the y-coordinate of the third point must be 4.)

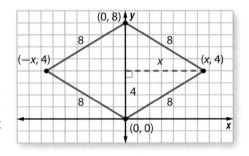

Using the Pythagorean Theorem,
$$4^2 + x^2 = 8^2$$
$$x^2 = \sqrt{48}$$
$$x \approx \pm 6.93.$$

NOTE Solutions to Task 26 are on page T190.

25 **a.** Since the orientation of rectangle $ABCD$ is not specified, there are infinitely many possibilities for the coordinates of B, C, and D. A natural choice would be $B(0, 5)$, $C(13, 5)$, and $D(13, 0)$. However, acceptable answers are any coordinates for B, C, and D which define a quadrilateral with opposite sides parallel, adjacent sides perpendicular, and of the specified dimensions.

b. B, C, and D may have any coordinates which ensure that a parallelogram of the required dimensions will be constructed, but the parallelogram is not a rectangle. One example is $B(3, 4)$, $C(16, 4)$, and $D(13, 0)$. (There *are infinitely many possibilities*. This can be thought about as rotating the quadrilateral about the origin.)

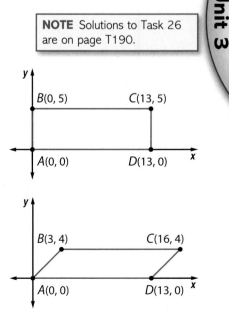

Unit 3

Extensions

27 In addition to the graphics window, interactive geometry software may also include a programming window that can be used to create both simple and complex figures by entering program commands. In Lesson 3, you will use the programming window to create animations.

To become familiar with the programming window, use the "Design by Robot" custom tool to complete the following tasks.

a. Enter the commands below in the programming window of your software. "Right 90" means "rotate the robot 90° clockwise" from its "home" position.

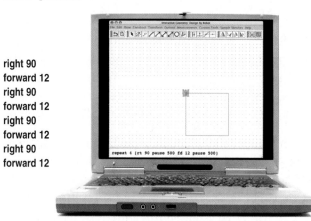

```
right 90
forward 12
right 90
forward 12
right 90
forward 12
right 90
forward 12
```

i. Compare the figure you created with that shown on the screen above.

ii. Compare the program you entered with that shown on the above screen. How are they similar and how are they different in execution? In structure?

iii. Use the clearscreen (**cs**) and **home** commands to clear the window and position the robot at the origin of the coordinate system. Then modify one of the programs so that the robot draws a rectangle that is *not* a square.

b. As you saw in Part a, blocks of the same instructions that are used in succession can be put into a single "repeat" statement. Predict the shape created by this repeat statement:

repeat 3 [fd 10 rt 120]

Check your prediction.

26 **a.** Two possible tests are:

   (1) Compute the distance between each pair of points. If the sum of the two smaller distances equals the largest distance, then the points lie on the same line. (If the sum of the two smaller distances is larger than the largest distance, a triangle is formed.)

   (2) Use the coordinates of two of the points to find the equation of the line through those points. Then substitute the coordinates of the third point into the equation to see if the point is on the line.

b. Two possible tests students might suggest:

   (1) find slopes of the sides to see if the slope of one side is the opposite reciprocal of another side, or

   (2) find the lengths of the sides and check to see if the three lengths are a Pythagorean triple.

c. Find the distance between pairs of points. If one point is the same distance from the other two, it is on the perpendicular bisector of the segment formed by those two points. This is the same as testing that the three points form an isosceles triangle.

d. Find the distance between pairs of points. If one point is the same distance r from the other two, it is the center of a circle with radius r. The circle will contain the other two points since they are the same distance r from the center.

Extensions

27 **a.** **i.** Shapes should be the same.

   ii. The program on the screen executes the same. It uses abbreviations for the commands and repeats with pauses.

   iii. Students' programs will vary but should draw a nonsquare rectangle.

b. An equilateral triangle with side lengths of 10 units is created.

> **TECHNOLOGY NOTE**
> These programming commands are modeled after Logo. Students may have some familiarity with this programming language from middle school experiences.

Unit 3

c. Use the programming window to direct the robot to draw each of the following shapes. Before beginning each part, use the clearscreen (**cs**) and **home** commands to clear the window and position the robot at the origin of the coordinate system.

    i. an isosceles right triangle with two sides of length 10

    ii. a parallelogram that is not a rectangle

    iii. a regular hexagon with side length of 8

d. Compare the shapes created by each repeat statement.

Shape I   **repeat 20 [fd 2 rt 18]**

Shape II **repeat 180 [fd 0.2 rt 2]**

e. Enter the following program. Describe the design produced and how it was created.

    cs home
    repeat 75 [fd 12 pause 250 rt 125 pause 250]

28 In Investigation 1, you discovered a formula for the midpoint of a segment in a coordinate plane. If you know the coordinates of the midpoint of a segment and the coordinates of one endpoint, how can you find the coordinates of the other endpoint? Illustrate your idea for the segment $\overline{AB}$ where A has coordinates $(8, -2)$ and the coordinates of the midpoint are $(11.5, 2)$.

29 The four lines with equations $x + y = 2$, $y = 1$, $x + y = -2$, and $x - 3y = 2$ envelop a quadrilateral.

a. Find the coordinates of its vertices.

b. Sketch the quadrilateral.

    i. For each equation, what restrictions on the input values for x and y are needed so the equation describes only the side of the figure?

    ii. What kind of quadrilateral is formed? How do you know?

c. Find equations for the lines containing the diagonals of the quadrilateral. What restrictions on the input values for x and y are needed for the lines to describe only the diagonals?

d. What are the coordinates of the point of intersection of the diagonals?

e. Verify your answer in Part d using a method different from the one you used to find that answer.

30 Look back at Applications Task 10. Write the converse of the statement you wrote in Part d.

a. Do you think the converse statement is always true? Test your conjecture using graph paper or interactive geometry software.

b. To prove your conjecture, would it be easier to use general coordinates or the idea of congruent triangles? Explain your reasoning and provide a sample proof.

c. Write the statement from Applications Task 10, Part d and its converse as a single "if and only if" statement.

Unit 3

c. Programs may vary. Pause commands are not necessary.

   i. **fd 10 rt 90 pause 250 fd 10 rt 135 fd 14.14** (approximately $10\sqrt{2}$)

  ii. **rt 30 repeat 2 [fd 5 pause 250 rt 60 pause 250 fd 10 pause 250 rt 120]**

 iii. **repeat 6 [fd 8 rt 60]**

d. Shape I is a regular dodecahedron. Shape II has 180 edges of length 0.2 and looks almost circular. The "circle" is a little smaller than the dodecahedron.

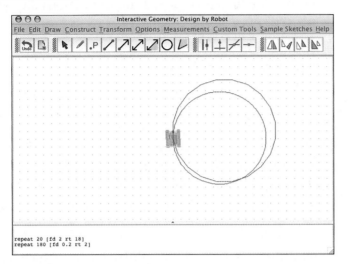

e. The design is a circle surrounded by 75 tangent segments. It was created by forming connected segments of length 12 units turning at an angle of 125° each time.

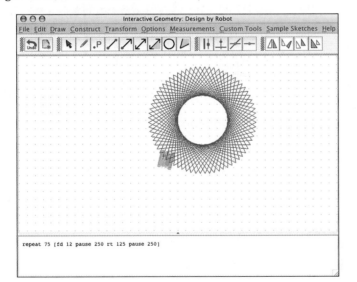

28 An algebraic way would be to note that $11.5 = \dfrac{8 + x}{2}$ and $2 = \dfrac{-2 + y}{2}$, and solve for x and y, the coordinates of B. Another way would be to note the change in x-coordinates and y-coordinates from the point to the midpoint and then use the same changes from the midpoint to find the other endpoint which in this case is $(15, 6)$. See the diagram at the right.

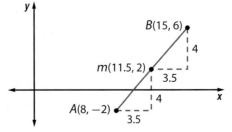

29 **a–b. i.** For the equation $x + y = 2$, the restrictions are $1 \leq x \leq 2$ and $0 \leq y \leq 1$.
For the equation $y = 1$, the restrictions are $-3 \leq x \leq 1$ and $y = 1$.
For the equation $x + y = -2$, the restrictions are $-3 \leq x \leq -1$ and $-1 \leq y \leq 1$.
For the equation $x - 3y = 2$, the restrictions are $-1 \leq x \leq 2$ and $-1 \leq y \leq 0$.

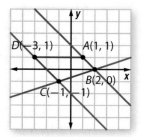

ii. *ABCD* is a trapezoid because two sides are parallel. Segments *AB* and *CD* are parallel because the slopes of lines *AB* and *CD* are both -1. $\overline{AD}$ and $\overline{BC}$ have slopes 0 and $\frac{1}{3}$, so are not parallel.

c. The equation of the diagonal joining $(-1, -1)$ and $(1, 1)$ is $y = x$ or $x - y = 0$, and the restrictions are $-1 \leq x \leq 1$ and $-1 \leq y \leq 1$. The equation of the diagonal joining $(-3, 1)$ and $(2, 0)$ is $x + 5y = 2$, and the restrictions are $-3 \leq x \leq 2$ and $0 \leq y \leq 1$.

d–e. Students might use substitution, elimination, or a matrix method for Part d. To check in Part e, they should use a different method. The diagonals intersect at the point $\left(\frac{1}{3}, \frac{1}{3}\right)$.

30 Conjecture: If the diagonals of a quadrilateral are perpendicular and bisect each other, then the quadrilateral is a rhombus.

a. Students should provide a few examples to test the conjecture.

b. It is easier to use congruent triangles. If the diagonals of *ABCD* bisect each other and are perpendicular, as shown in the diagram, four congruent right triangles are formed. The sides of the quadrilateral are the four congruent hypotenuses. Thus, *ABCD* is a rhombus.

c. A quadrilateral is a rhombus if and only if its diagonals are perpendicular bisectors of each other.

31 Streets in a city or neighborhood are often built in a rectangular grid. The street layout may be represented by a rectangular coordinate system. In this situation, distances can be measured along streets, as a car would drive, not diagonally across blocks. (Of course, there are no one-way streets!) The shortest street distance between two locations is called the **taxi-distance**. For example, on the following coordinate grid, the taxi-distance between points P and Q is 5.

a. Find the taxi-distance between the given points O and P, and between points T and R.

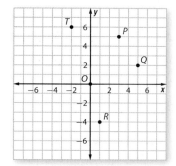

b. A Dial-a-Ride dispatcher receives a request for a pickup at point $X(-8, 20)$. Available vans are stationed at point $A(12, 8)$ and at point $B(-11, -7)$. Which van should make the pickup? Why?

c. Write a formula for computing the taxi-distance TD between points $P(a, b)$ and $Q(c, d)$.

d. Draw a graph of all points in the plane (not just points with integer coordinates) whose taxi-distance from $(0, 0)$ is 2. Do the same for all points whose taxi-distance from $(0, 0)$ is 4.

e. What would be a reasonable name for the figures you graphed in Part d?

f. In *taxi geometry*, what would be a reasonable value for π?

32 Use interactive geometry software to construct a triangle, $\triangle ABC$, segment by segment.

a. Using the "Midpoint" and "Perpendicular" commands, construct the lines that are the perpendicular bisectors of the sides of your triangle. What appears to be true about the three perpendicular bisectors of the sides?

b. Test your conjecture in Part a with several different types of triangles including right, obtuse, and acute by clicking and dragging a vertex of $\triangle ABC$. Write a summary of your findings.

c. Suppose P is the point where the perpendicular bisectors of the sides of $\triangle ABC$ meet. What seems to always be true about the lengths PA, PB, and PC? Explain carefully why that must be the case.

d. Given any triangle in the plane, is it possible to draw a circle that contains the three vertices? Explain.

INSTRUCTIONAL NOTE Taxi geometry is an example of a *non-Euclidean geometry*. Points and lines are the same as in Euclidean coordinate geometry, and angles are measured in the same way. Only the distance function is different. As a consequence, SAS and other congruence conditions fail in taxi geometry. Students will investigate why this is the case in the Course 3 unit, *Similarity and Congruence*. An excellent resource for this topic is Eugene Krause's book, *Taxicab Geometry* (Addison-Wesley Publishing Company, 1975). See also Krause's article "Taxicab Geometry" in December 1973's *Mathematics Teacher*. Interested students should be encouraged to complete the project on this topic in the unit resources.

31　**a.** The taxi-distance between points O and P is 8.
　　　The taxi-distance between points T and R is 13.

　　b. The closer van, at point $B(-11, -7)$, should make the pickup: taxi-distance from A to X is 32 and from B to X is 30.

　　c. Since taxi-distance is the sum of the horizontal distance and the vertical distance between two points, a possible formula is
　　　$TD = |a - c| + |b - d|$.

　　d. **INSTRUCTIONAL NOTE** If students continue to think contextually, they may graph only the lattice points of the grid representing the blocks. If so, have students consider finding the y-coordinates for $x = 1.5$, keeping the idea of moving only in horizontal or vertical directions.

Taxi-distance from $(0, 0)$ is 2.　　Taxi-distance from $(0, 0)$ is 4.

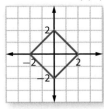　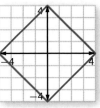

　　e. Since students are graphing the set of all points a fixed distance from the origin, a reasonable name for their figures might be "taxi-circles with centers at the origin." (Some students may identify the figures as squares. Part f should encourage them to rethink that response.)

　　f. In Euclidean geometry, π is the ratio of the circumference of a circle to its diameter. In the case of each taxi-circle in Part d,
　　$\dfrac{\textit{taxi-distance around taxi-circle}}{\textit{taxi-distance across figure (diameter)}} = 4$.

Unit 3

32 **TECHNOLOGY NOTE** To construct perpendicular bisectors in *CPMP-Tools*, select a segment that forms one side of the triangle and construct the midpoint. Then select both the side of the triangle and the midpoint to construct the perpendicular bisector. Once the three perpendicular bisectors are constructed, select them and construct the intersection point *G*. (See the screen on the left below.) Then construct $\overline{AG}$, $\overline{BG}$, and $\overline{CG}$ using the segment tool and find the lengths of these segments as shown on the second screen below.

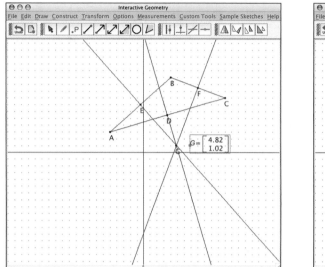   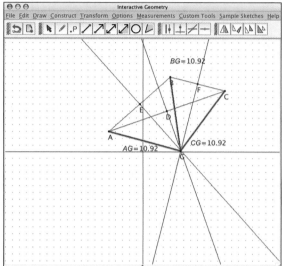

a. The three perpendicular bisectors appear to intersect at one point. (Click and drag a vertex of the triangle to quickly explore any cases.)

b. Students should indicate that the perpendicular bisectors of the sides intersect at a point and that sometimes the intersection point is outside of the triangle.

c. $\overline{PA}$, $\overline{PB}$, and $\overline{PC}$ seem to have the same length. See the screen below. $\overline{GA}$, $\overline{GB}$, and $\overline{GC}$ have the same length. Notice that since *G* is on the bisector of $\overline{AB}$, it is the same distance from the endpoints and $GA = GB$. The same reasoning applies to the other two sides of $\triangle ABC$. Some students may explain by using congruent triangles *AGD* and *CGD*.

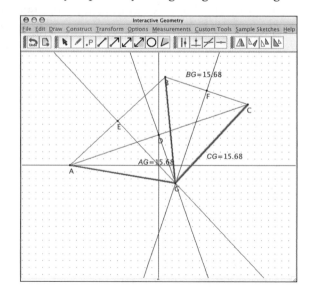

d. INSTRUCTIONAL NOTE This circle with center *G*, the common intersection point of the perpendicular bisectors of the sides of △*ABC* and going through the vertices of △*ABC*, is called the *circumcircle* of △*ABC*. *G* is called the *circumcenter* of △*ABC*. These concepts will be studied in Course 3, Unit 3, *Similarity and Congruence*.

If, for any triangle, Part c is true, then a circle with radius *PA* centered at *P* will contain the other two vertices. The definition of a circle ensures that all points a fixed distance from the center will lie on the circle.

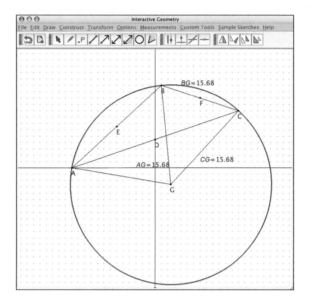

Review

33 Use your understanding of square roots to solve each of the following equations.

a. $5 = \sqrt{x}$

b. $9 = \sqrt{t - 100}$

c. $2\sqrt{y} = 14$

34 Suppose the strip pattern shown below extends indefinitely in both directions.

a. Describe all of the symmetries of the pattern that also preserve color.

b. Describe all of the symmetries of the pattern if color is ignored.

35 Write an equation for the line passing through the indicated pair of points.

a. $D(3, 2)$ and $E(9, 4)$

b. $S(3, 1)$ and $T(5, -2)$

36 Consider the lines $y = x$ and $y = -x$.

a. On the same coordinate grid, draw graphs of these lines.

b. What is the measure of the angle formed by the positive x-axis and the line $y = x$? Explain your reasoning as carefully as possible.

c. Are these two lines perpendicular? Explain your reasoning.

37 Expand each of the following products to an equivalent expression in standard quadratic form.

a. $(x + 3)^2$

b. $(5 + y)^2$

c. $(t - 8)^2$

d. $(p - 6)(p + 6)$

38 Suppose that Lauren randomly surveyed 150 students in her school and asked if they attended the school musical last year. Sixty of the students indicated that they had attended the school musical last year. Based upon this data, approximately how many of the 1,150 students in the school do you expect will attend the musical this year?

Review

Just in Time

33 **a.** $x = 25$

b. $t = 181$

c. $y = 49$

Just in Time

34 **a.** If color is preserved, there is horizontal translation symmetry of dark sections to dark sections and light sections to light sections. There is also 180° rotational symmetry about the points where the vertical and horizontal white bars intersect.

b. If color is ignored, then there are also line reflections as indicated by the lines below. (Glide reflections will be introduced in Connections Task 19 on page 224. If your students studied this transformation in middle school, they may mention it here.)

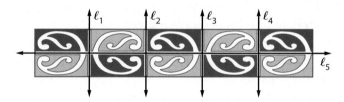

35 **a.** $y = \frac{1}{3}x + 1$

The slope of $\overline{DE}$ is $\frac{2}{6} = \frac{1}{3}$.

Using this rate of change and moving from D to the y-axis, the y-intercept is $(0, 1)$.

b. $y = -1.5x + 5.5$

The slope of $\overline{ST}$ is $-\frac{3}{2}$.

Using the slope-intercept form and $S(3, 1)$ to find the y-intercept:

$1 = -\frac{3}{2}(3) + b$

$b = 1 + \frac{9}{2} = \frac{11}{2} = 5.5$

Just in Time

36 **a.**

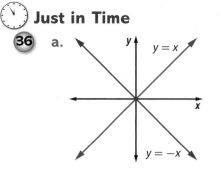

b. Pick any point *P* on the line. It has coordinates (*x, x*).

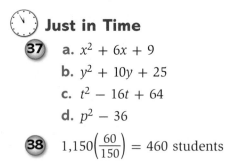

Then consider the triangle formed by the line, the positive *x*-axis, and the vertical line from *P* to the *x*-axis.
The lengths of the legs of this right triangle are the same length, so it is an isosceles right triangle. Therefore, the base angles must each have measure 45°.

c. Students might indicate that the slopes of $y = x$ and $y = -x$ are negative reciprocals. Alternatively, an argument similar to that in Part b can be made to show that the line $y = -x$ makes a 45° angle with the negative *x*-axis.
Therefore, the angle made by the lines must be $180° - 45° - 45° = 90°$. So, the lines are perpendicular. (Students might also reason using vertical angles formed by $y = x$ and $y = -x$.)

Just in Time

37 **a.** $x^2 + 6x + 9$

b. $y^2 + 10y + 25$

c. $t^2 - 16t + 64$

d. $p^2 - 36$

38 $1,150\left(\dfrac{60}{150}\right) = 460$ students

Teacher Notes

39 Solve each equation without using calculator graphs or tables of values.

a. $12 + 2(5x - 8) = 0$

b. $(x + 4)(7 - x) = 0$

c. $(3x + 9) - (5x - 8) = 0$

d. $6(2^x) - 48 = 0$

40 The cost of painting a wall is directly proportional to the area of the wall. A wall that is 22 feet long and 10 feet high costs $30 to paint.

a. How much will it cost to paint a wall that is 28 feet long and 12 feet high?

b. Find the constant of proportionality for this situation and explain what it means in terms of the context.

41 Examine the linear graphs shown below.

a. Match each equation with its graph.

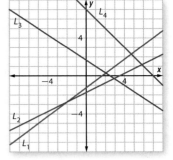

Equation I $y + x = 7$

Equation II $5 - 2x = 3y$

Equation III $4y - 2x = -7$

Equation IV $3x - 4y = 5$

b. Did you match equations to graphs by finding x- and y-intercepts from the equations? If not, try it.

c. Did you match equations to graphs by rewriting equations in the form $y = a + bx$ and finding slopes? If not, try it.

42 You may recall that if n is a positive integer, $x^{\frac{1}{n}}$ represents the number that when multiplied by itself n times equals x. For example, $16^{\frac{1}{4}} = 2$ because $2 \cdot 2 \cdot 2 \cdot 2 = 16$. The symbol $\sqrt[n]{x}$ is another way of representing $x^{\frac{1}{n}}$. The exponent properties that you have learned for integers also work for exponents that are fractional. Without use of technology, determine the value of each of the following. Then check your work using technology.

a. $\left(8^{\frac{1}{3}}\right)^2$

b. $36^{\frac{3}{2}}$

c. $3^{\frac{1}{3}} \, 3^{\frac{2}{3}}$

d. $30^{\frac{1}{2}} \, 3{,}000^{-\frac{1}{2}}$

39
a. $x = 0.4$

b. $x = -4$ or $x = 7$

c. $x = \dfrac{17}{2} = 8.5$

d. $x = 3$

40
a. $\dfrac{30}{(22)(10)} = \dfrac{C}{(28)(12)}$, so $C \approx \$45.82$.

b. $30 = k(22)(10)$, so $k = \dfrac{3}{22} \approx 0.136$.

   The constant of proportionality indicates that it costs 13.6¢ per square foot to paint the walls.

41
a.

	Equation	Line
I	$y + x = 7$	L_4
II	$5 - 2x = 3y$	L_3
III	$4y - 2x = -7$	L_2
IV	$3x - 4y = 5$	L_1

b–c. Students should try alternate methods to match equations and graphs.

42
a. 4

b. 216

c. 3

d. $\dfrac{1}{10}$

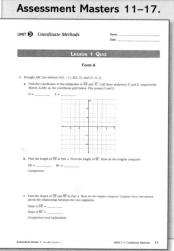

Teaching Resources

Assessment Masters 11–17.

Unit 3

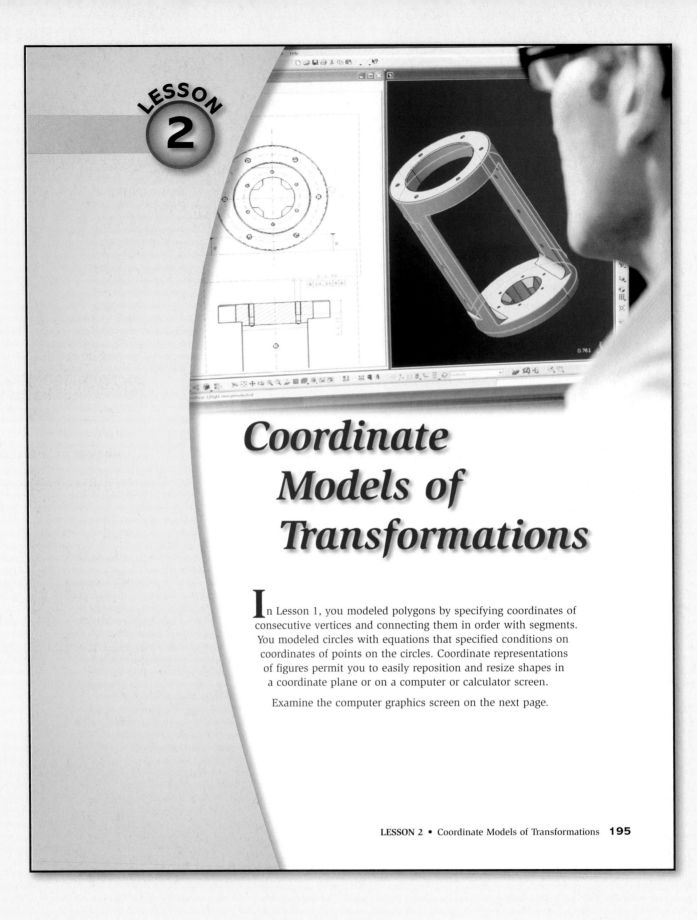

Coordinate Models of Transformations

In Lesson 1, you modeled polygons by specifying coordinates of consecutive vertices and connecting them in order with segments. You modeled circles with equations that specified conditions on coordinates of points on the circles. Coordinate representations of figures permit you to easily reposition and resize shapes in a coordinate plane or on a computer or calculator screen.

Examine the computer graphics screen on the next page.

Coordinate Models of Transformations

In Lesson 2, students are engaged in describing transformations of a plane using coordinates and function rules. Investigation 1 focuses on rigid transformations—transformations that reposition a figure. A figure and its image under a rigid transformation are congruent. Investigation 2 focuses on size transformations—transformations that enlarge or reduce the size of a figure but do not change its shape. A figure and its image under a size transformation are similar. Investigation 3 focuses on how transformations can be combined to produce new transformations, in particular, transformations that can both reposition and resize a figure.

Students begin by examining images of specific points under a particular transformation and generalize a coordinate rule for the transformation. From specific cases, students generalize the effects of various transformations on segment length, angle measure, and area. In some cases, they may verify their conjectures algebraically. Students also investigate composition of transformations, again making generalizations. In Problem 7 on page 214, students investigate composition of size transformations and translations. They discover that the order in which transformations are applied sometimes produces different results. Composition of transformations is not commutative.

It is important to check with your feeder middle schools to determine the extent of your students' previous experience with coordinate geometry and transformations. Many Standards-based programs now include an introduction to these mathematical topics. If this is the case, students may be able to generalize to coordinate rules without finding all of the images requested in the student text.

Lesson Objectives

- Use coordinates to develop function rules modeling translations, line reflections, and rotations and size transformations centered at the origin
- Use coordinates to investigate properties of figures under one or more rigid transformations or under similarity transformations
- Explore the concept of function composition using successive application of two transformations

Unit 3

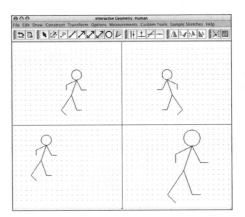

Think About This Situation

The computer graphics display above shows some of the ways in which a figure in a coordinate plane can be transformed in terms of position and/or size.

a How could you create the humanoid in the second quadrant using interactive geometry software? How could you describe the figure using coordinates?

b What transformation of the figure in Quadrant II would produce the image in Quadrant I? The image in Quadrant III? The image in Quadrant IV?

c How do you think coordinates might be used to describe these transformations?

In this lesson, you will learn how coordinates can be used to transform shapes. You will investigate coordinate representations of **rigid transformations** that provide a way to reposition figures in a plane without changing the shape or the size of the figures. You will also investigate coordinate representations of **similarity transformations** that can be used to resize figures while maintaining their shapes. Finally, you will explore some of the matrix algebra of transformations—how matrices are used to represent transformations and how they are combined to form new transformations.

As an introduction to this lesson, you might have students think about some of the key aspects of video games and animated films like *Ratatouille, Shrek 2, The Incredibles,* or *Cars*. At the top of this list will be action—the movement or repositioning of characters on the screen, often with an apparent change in size. In this lesson, students will examine how coordinate representations of figures make it relatively easy to describe how they can be repositioned or resized in a plane. As students respond to the Think About This Situation questions, you may need to connect the informal language of "flips" and "slides" to the idea of line reflections and translations previously studied in Course 1 in the context of symmetry.

Think About This Situation

a You could make a circle for the head and then draw segments for the body, arms, and legs. You could describe the figure by providing coordinates of the endpoints of the segments and the center and radius of the circle.

b A reflection across the *y*-axis would produce the figure in Quadrant I. A translation would produce the figure in Quadrant III. An increase in size and translation would produce the figure in Quadrant IV.

c Students may suggest adding a constant to the coordinates of a figure to move the figure over a certain number of units. They may suggest multiplying the coordinates of a figure as a way to resize the figure.

Investigation 1 • Modeling Rigid Transformations

Computer graphics enable designers to model two- and three-dimensional figures and to also easily manipulate those figures. For example, interior design software permits users to select images of various types and sizes of furniture and position them at different places in a room layout by sliding and rotating the shapes. Automotive design software permits users to create symmetric components of vehicles by reflecting and/or rotating basic design elements. Complete models of vehicles can be rotated and viewed from different angles.

In this investigation, you will explore how coordinates are used in computer graphics software to transform the position of shapes in a plane. As you work on the following problems, look for answers to these questions:

How can coordinates be used to describe a sliding motion or translation?

How can coordinates be used to describe a turning motion or rotation?

How can coordinates be used to describe a mirror or line reflection?

1. Interactive geometry software provides tools to reposition a shape by translation, rotation about a point, and reflection across a line. Other software will have similar commands. As a class or in pairs, experiment with the first three commands in the Transform menu and the corresponding functions in the menu bar.

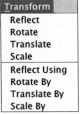

   a. Begin by exploring how the Translate command can be used to transform shapes in a plane. Draw a shape or select the "Humanoid" from Sample Sketches. Translate the shape to a different position. Observe how the original shape and its *image* appear to be related. Repeat for at least three other translations, including: one that slides the shape horizontally; one that slides the shape vertically; and one that slides the shape in a slanted direction.

   b. Next, explore how the Rotate command can be used to transform shapes in a plane. Draw a figure or select the "Humanoid" shape from Sample Sketches. Rotate the figure counterclockwise about the origin. Observe how the original figure and its image appear to be related. Repeat for at least three other counterclockwise rotations about the origin, including: a 90° rotation; a 180° rotation; and a 45° rotation.

Modeling Rigid Transformations

In this investigation, students develop coordinate rules and program planning algorithms for specific rigid transformations—translations, 90°, 180°, and 270° rotations about the origin, and reflections across the x- and y-axes and across the lines $y = x$ and $y = -x$. (In On Your Own Tasks 17 and 18, students will develop coordinate rules for reflections across other lines.)

As you move from group to group, support student use of the language of transformations, including the terms "preimage" and "image." In addition, you may want to check that students are keeping careful and complete notes as new rules and planning algorithms are developed.

INSTRUCTIONAL NOTE Problem 1 invites students to explore the transformation functionality of the interactive geometry software *CPMP-Tools* to set the context for the investigation. This problem could be done as an interactive launch with various students at the controls. Alternatively, you might ask students to explore these features outside of class time prior to beginning the investigation.

1 **a–c.** Students should explore the "Translate," "Rotate," and "Reflect" commands of *CPMP-Tools* interactive geometry. Rotations are about the origin.

c. Now, explore how the Reflect command can be used to transform a shape in a plane. Draw a shape or select the "Humanoid" shape from Sample Sketches. Reflect the shape across a line of your choice. Observe how the original shape and its image appear to be related. Repeat for at least three other line reflections, including: a reflection across the *x*-axis; a reflection across the *y*-axis; and a reflection across the line *y* = *x*. In each case, first clear the window and redraw your shape.

d. How do you think the software determines the position of the translated image of a shape? The rotated image of a shape? The reflected image of a shape?

Translating Shapes A **translation,** or sliding motion, is determined by distance and direction. By looking carefully at a simple shape and its translated image, you can discover patterns relating the coordinates of the shape and the coordinates of its image.

 On the screen below, a flag *ABCDE* and its translated image *A′B′C′D′E′* are shown.

Horizontal Translation

D *C*   *D′* *C′*
E *B*   *E′* *B′*
A   *A′*

a. Describe the translation as precisely as you can.

b. Explain how the translated image of the flag could be produced using only the translated images of points *A*, *B*, *C*, *D*, and *E*.

c. Under this translation, what would be the image of (0, 0)? Of (1, −5)? Of (−5, −4)? Of (*a*, *b*)?

d. Write a rule you can use to obtain the image of any point (*x*, *y*) in the coordinate plane under this translation. State your rule in words and in symbolic form (*x*, *y*) → (__, __).

d. Students may suggest that the program uses coordinates. (If they suggest the program moves the object a certain distance or about an angle, ask them how the program determines the exact location.)

2   **a.** The flag is translated 12 units to the right.b

b. If you know the translated images of points *A, B, C, D*, and *E*, then you can draw the image flag by connecting the image points in the same order as the corresponding preimage points. (This is true since, under a translation, the image of a line segment is a congruent line segment.)

c.

Preimage	Translated Image
(0, 0)	(12, 0)
(1, −5)	(13, −5)
(−5, −4)	(7, −4)
(a, b)	(a + 12, b)

d. To get the *x*-coordinate of the image of any point, add 12 to the *x*-coordinate of the point. The *y*-coordinate of the image is the same as the *y*-coordinate of the point. Symbolically, $(x, y) \rightarrow (x + 12, y)$.

3 The screens below show a flag *ABCDE* and its image under two other translations.

Vertical Translation

Oblique Translation

a. Describe the vertical translation as precisely as you can. The diagonal (oblique) translation.

b. Under the vertical translation, what would be the image of (0, 0)? Of (2, 5)? Of (4.1, −2)? Of (*a*, *b*)?

c. Write a rule you can use to obtain the image of any point (*x*, *y*) under the vertical translation. State your rule in words and in symbolic form (*x*, *y*) → (__, __).

d. Under the oblique translation, what would be the image of (0, 0)? Of (2, 5)? Of (4.1, −2)? Of (*a*, *b*)?

e. Write a rule you can use to obtain the image of any point (*x*, *y*) under the oblique translation. State your rule in words and in symbolic form.

4 Compare the transformation rules you developed for Part d of Problem 2 and for Parts c and e of Problem 3. Write a general rule that tells how to take any point (*x*, *y*) and find its translated image if the preimage is moved horizontally *h* units and vertically *k* units. Compare your rule with others and resolve any differences.

You now have a rule you can use to find the translated image of any point when you know the **components of the translation**—the horizontal and vertical distances and directions the point is moved (left or right, up or down). This is exactly the information a calculator or computer graphics program needs in order to display a set of points and their translated images.

5 Use the following questions to help write an algorithm that would guide a programmer in the development of a translation program that displays the original figure (called the **preimage**) and its translated image and connects corresponding vertices of the two figures.

• What information would you need to input?

• What formula or formulas could be used in the processing portion?

• What information should be displayed in the output?

3 **a.** The vertical translation moved the flag down 9 units. The oblique translation moved the flag right 10 units and down 4 units. (Students' descriptions at this point may be more general.)

b. **Vertical Translation**

Preimage	Translated Image
(0, 0)	(0, −9)
(2, 5)	(2, −4)
(4.1, −2)	(4.1, −11)
(a, b)	(a, b − 9)

c. To find the image of any point (x, y) under the vertical translation, leave the x-coordinate as it is and subtract 9 from the y-coordinate. Symbolically, $(x, y) \rightarrow (x, y - 9)$.

d. **Oblique Translation**

Preimage	Translated Image
(0, 0)	(10, −4)
(2, 5)	(12, 1)
(4.1, −2)	(14.1, −6)
(a, b)	(a + 10, b − 4)

e. To obtain the coordinates of any point (x, y) under the oblique translation, add 10 to the x-coordinate of the point and subtract 4 from the y-coordinate of the point. Symbolically, $(x, y) \rightarrow (x + 10, y - 4)$.

4 The general rule that tells how to take any point (x, y) and find its translation image if the preimage is moved horizontally h units and vertically k units is $(x, y) \rightarrow (x + h, y + k)$.

5

Translation Algorithm

Step 1. Get the coordinates of the vertices of the preimage figure.

Step 2. Enter horizontal translation h and vertical translation k.

} input

Step 3. Calculate the coordinates of the image points using the rule $(x, y) \rightarrow (x + h, y + k)$.

} processing

Step 4. Display and label original and image points. Connect image points to match preimage points.

} output

INSTRUCTIONAL NOTE
It is not expected that students distinguish between horizontal, vertical, and oblique translations as defined terms. The form of the coordinate rule is the same for all three types of translations:
$(x, y) \rightarrow (x + h, y + k)$.

DIFFERENTIATION If some students in your class are not able to move flexibly between subtraction and the corresponding thinking about adding a negative, this context provides an opportunity to address this. Focus their thinking on their language of subtraction and how this operation moves the figure left or down. The generalized rules in Parts c and e use subtraction. But the generalized rule for all transformations in Problem 4 implies that when h is negative, the figure moves left; and when k is negative, the figure moves down.

ASSIGNMENT NOTE
Applications Tasks 2, 6, and 7 can be assigned following Problem 5.

Unit 3

Rotating Shapes Rotations about the origin have similar coordinate models. A **rotation,** or turning motion, is determined by a point called the *center of the rotation* and a *directed angle of rotation*. A flag *ABCDE* and its images under counterclockwise rotations of 90°, 180°, and 270° about the origin are shown below.

Rotations About the Origin

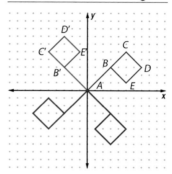

6. Consider flag *ABCDE* above and its image under a 90° counterclockwise rotation about the origin.

   a. On a copy of the table below, record the coordinates of the images of the five points on the flag under a 90° counterclockwise rotation about the origin. Explain why the rotated image of the flag could be produced using only the rotated images of points *A, B, C, D,* and *E*.

Preimage	90° Counterclockwise Rotated Image
A(0, 0)	A'(,)
B(3, 3)	B'(,)
C(5, 5)	C'(,)
D(7, 3)	D'(,)
E(5, 1)	E'(,)

   b. Use any patterns you see between preimage and image points in your completed table to help plot the points (−2, −5), (−4, 1), (5, −3), and their images under a 90° counterclockwise rotation about the origin on a new coordinate grid.

      i. For each preimage point, use dashed segments to connect the preimage to the origin and the origin to the image.

      ii. Connect each preimage segment to its image segment with a "turn" arrow that shows the directed angle of rotation.

   c. Write a rule relating the coordinates of any preimage point (*x, y*) and its image point under a 90° counterclockwise rotation about the origin. State your rule in words and in symbolic form.

6 **a.**

Preimage	90° Counterclockwise Rotated Image
A(0, 0)	A'(0, 0)
B(3, 3)	B'(−3, 3)
C(5, 5)	C'(−5, 5)
D(7, 3)	D'(−3, 7)
E(5, 1)	E'(−1, 5)

If you know the rotated images of points *A, B, C, D,* and *E,* then you can draw the image flag by connecting the image points in the same order as the corresponding preimage points. This is true since, under a rotation, the image of a line segment is a congruent line segment.

b. i–ii. The preimage points are indicated by * and the image points are indicated by •.

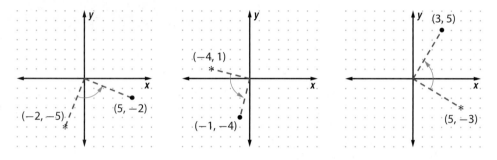

c. To obtain the coordinates of any point (*x, y*) under the 90° counterclockwise rotation about the origin, take the opposite of the *y*-coordinate of the preimage as the *x*-coordinate of the image and the *x*-coordinate of the preimage as the *y*-coordinate of the image. Students may use more informal language such as: To find the image coordinates, switch the coordinates and make the image *x*-coordinate the opposite sign. Symbolically, this is $(x, y) \rightarrow (-y, x)$.

UNIT ❸ *Coordinate Methods*   Name _____
   Date _____

90° Counterclockwise Rotation About the Origin
Problem 6

6. a.

Preimage	90° Counterclockwise Rotated Image
A(0, 0)	A'
B(3, 3)	B'
C(5, 5)	C'
D(7, 3)	D'
E(5, 1)	E'

b.

c. Symbolic rule: (x, y) →
Rule written in words:

d.

20   UNIT 3 • Coordinate Methods   Student Master • use with page 200

INSTRUCTIONAL NOTE
Check to be sure students are using a 90° counterclockwise rotation, not a clockwise rotation, for Problem 6.

d. According to your rule, what is the image of $(0, 0)$? Why does this image make sense?

e. How should the slope of the line through a preimage point and the origin be related to the slope of the line through the origin and the image point? Verify your idea by computing and comparing slopes.

f. Write an algorithm to guide the development of a program for a 90° counterclockwise rotation about $(0, 0)$ that displays the preimage and image figures.

(7) As you probably expect, counterclockwise rotations of 180° and 270° about the origin also have predictable coordinate patterns. Use a copy of the screen at the top of page 200 showing flag *ABCDE* and its images to explore these patterns.

a. Investigate patterns in the coordinates of the preimage and image pairs when points are rotated 180° about the origin.

b. Write a rule relating the coordinates of any preimage point (x, y) and its image point under a 180° rotation about the origin. State your rule in words and in symbols.

c. How is the slope of the line through two preimage points related to the slope of the line through the images of those points? What does this tell about a line and its image under a 180° rotation?

d. Similarly, search for patterns in the coordinates of the preimage and image pairs when points are rotated 270° counterclockwise about the origin.

e. Write a rule relating the coordinates of any preimage point (x, y) and its image point under a 270° counterclockwise rotation about the origin. State your rule in words and in symbols.

f. Describe how you could modify the algorithm in Part f of Problem 6 so that it would guide development of a program to rotate a point 180° or 270° counterclockwise about the origin instead of 90° counterclockwise.

Reflecting Shapes

Line reflections can also be expressed using coordinates. A **line reflection** is determined by a "mirror line" (or line of reflection) that is the perpendicular bisector of the segment connecting a point and its reflected image. A point on the line of reflection is its own image. In the following problems, you will build coordinate models for reflections across vertical and horizontal lines, as well as across the lines $y = x$ and $y = -x$.

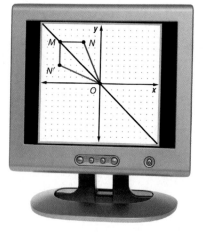

d. The image of $(0, 0)$ is $(0, 0)$. This makes sense because $(0, 0)$ is the center of rotation, and the center does not move in a rotation.

e. These lines should be perpendicular, so their slopes should be opposite reciprocals of one another. Students should have computations of slope comparisons to verify this relationship.

f.

Rotation 90° Counterclockwise Algorithm

Step 1. Get the coordinates of the vertices of the preimage figure. } input

Step 2. Calculate the coordinates of the image points using the rule $(x, y) \rightarrow (-y, x)$. } processing

Step 3. Display and label original and image points. Connect image points to match preimage connections. } output

---

(7)   **a.** Students might organize their investigation as follows:

Preimage	180° Counterclockwise Rotated Image
$A(0, 0)$	$(0, 0)$
$B(3, 3)$	$(-3, -3)$
$C(5, 5)$	$(-5, -5)$
$D(7, 3)$	$(-7, -3)$
$E(5, 1)$	$(-5, -1)$
$(-2, -5)$	$(2, 5)$
$(-4, 1)$	$(4, -1)$
$(5, -3)$	$(-5, 3)$

b. The x- and y-coordinates of the image of a point under a 180° counterclockwise rotation about the origin are the opposites of the x- and y-coordinates of the preimage. Symbolically, $(x, y) \rightarrow (-x, -y)$.

c. The slopes are the same. Thus, a line and its image under a 180° rotation about the origin are parallel.

d.

Preimage	270° Counterclockwise Rotated Image
$A(0, 0)$	$(0, 0)$
$B(3, 3)$	$(3, -3)$
$C(5, 5)$	$(5, -5)$
$D(7, 3)$	$(3, -7)$
$E(5, 1)$	$(1, -5)$
$(-2, -5)$	$(-5, 2)$
$(-4, 1)$	$(1, 4)$
$(5, -3)$	$(-3, -5)$

e. Under a 270° counterclockwise rotation about the origin, the x-coordinate of the image is equal to the y-coordinate of the preimage, and the y-coordinate of the image is the opposite of the x-coordinate of the preimage. Symbolically, $(x, y) \rightarrow (y, -x)$.

f. The symbolic rule in Step 2 should be $(x, y) \rightarrow (-x, -y)$ for a 180° counterclockwise rotation and $(x, y) \rightarrow (y, -x)$ for a 270° counterclockwise rotation about the origin. The rest of the algorithm remains the same.

ASSIGNMENT NOTE
Applications Task 3 could be assigned after Problem 7.

Unit 3

8 A flag *ABCDE* and its reflected image across the *y*-axis are shown on the screen below.

Reflected Across the *y*-axis

a. Investigate patterns in the coordinates of preimage and image pairs when points are reflected across the *y*-axis.

b. Explain why the reflected image of the flag could be produced using only the reflected images of points *A, B, C, D,* and *E*.

c. Write a rule which tells how to take any point (x, y) and find its reflected image across the *y*-axis. State your rule in words and in symbols.

d. On a copy of the diagram, use dashed segments to connect point *A* to point *A'* and point *D* to point *D'*. Use coordinates to verify that the *y*-axis is the perpendicular bisector of $\overline{AA'}$ and $\overline{DD'}$.

9 The table below shows coordinates of six preimage points and coordinates (a, b) of a general point. Plot each of the six points and its reflected image across the *x*-axis.

a. Record the coordinates of the image points in a table like the one below.

Preimage	Reflected Image Across *x*-axis
$(-4, 1)$	$(-4, -1)$
$(3, -2)$	
$(-2, -5)$	
$(4, 5)$	
$(0, 1)$	
$(-3, 0)$	
(a, b)	

b. What pattern relating coordinates of preimage points to image points do you observe? Use the pattern to give the coordinates of the image of (a, b).

8 a.

Preimage	Reflected Across the y-axis
A(−5, 2)	A′(5, 2)
B(−5, 5)	B′(5, 5)
C(−5, 7)	C′(5, 7)
D(−8, 7)	D′(8, 7)
E(−8, 5)	E′(8, 5)

Teaching Resources

Student Master 22.

UNIT 3 *Coordinate Methods* Name _____
Date _____

Line Reflections
Problems 8 and 9

b. If you know the reflected images of points *A, B, C, D,* and *E,* then you can draw the image flag by connecting the image points in the same order as the corresponding preimage points. This is true since, under a reflection, the image of a line segment is a congruent line segment.

c. The *x*-coordinate for the image of a point reflected across the *y*-axis is the opposite of the preimage *x*-coordinate. The *y*-coordinates are the same. Symbolically, $(x, y) \rightarrow (-x, y)$.

d. Since the pair of points $A(-5, 2)$ and $A'(5, 2)$ and the pair of points $D(-8, 7)$ and $D'(8, 7)$ have the same *y*-coordinates, $\overline{AA'}$ and $\overline{DD'}$ are horizontal segments. Since the *y*-axis is vertical, $\overline{AA'}$ and $\overline{DD'}$ are perpendicular to the *y*-axis. The *x*-coordinates of −5 and 5 (and −8 and 8) indicate that the points are the same distance |5| (and |8|) from the *y*-axis. So, the *y*-axis is the perpendicular bisector of $\overline{AA'}$ and $\overline{DD'}$.

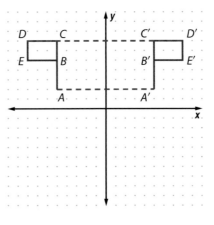

9 **INSTRUCTIONAL NOTE** In Problem 9, students should be plotting points (not just looking for numerical patterns) so they can relate the coordinate model to what they see happening on the graph.

a. The preimage points are indicated by * and the image points are indicated by •.

Preimage	Reflected Image Across x-axis
(−4, 1)	(−4, −1)
(3, −2)	(3, 2)
(−2, −5)	(−2, 5)
(4, 5)	(4, −5)
(0, 1)	(0, −1)
(−3, 0)	(−3, 0)
(a, b)	(a, −b)

b. The *x*-coordinates are the same and the *y*-coordinates are opposites.

c. Write a rule that tells how to take any point (x, y) and find its reflected image across the x-axis. State your rule in words and in symbols.

d. How is the x-axis related to the segment determined by any point (a, b) not on the x-axis and its reflected image? Justify your answer using coordinates.

10 Draw the graph of $y = x$. Plot each preimage point in the table below and its reflected image across that line. Connect each preimage/image pair with a dashed segment.

a. Record the coordinates of the image points in a copy of the table below.

Preimage	Reflected Image Across $y = x$
(−4, 1)	(1, −4)
(3, −2)	
(−2, −5)	
(4, 5)	
(0, 1)	
(−3, 0)	
(a, b)	

b. Describe a pattern relating coordinates of preimage points to image points.

c. Write a rule relating the coordinates of any preimage point (x, y) to its reflected image across the line $y = x$. State your rule in words and in symbols.

d. How is the line of reflection, $y = x$, related to the segment determined by any point (a, b) not on the line and its image? Justify your answer.

11 Next, investigate patterns in the coordinates of the preimage and image pairs when points are reflected across the line $y = -x$.

a. Draw the graph of $y = -x$. Then plot the six preimage points in the table in Problem 10 and their reflected images across the line.

b. Describe a pattern relating coordinates of preimage points to coordinates of image points.

c. Write a rule relating the coordinates of any preimage point (x, y) and its reflected image across the line $y = -x$. State your rule in words and in symbols.

d. How is the segment determined by a point and its reflected image related to the line $y = -x$?

c. The *x*-coordinates of the preimage and image are the same. The
y-coordinate of the image is the opposite of the *y*-coordinate of the
preimage. Symbolically, $(x, y) \rightarrow (x, -y)$.

d. The *x*-axis is perpendicular to and bisects the segment determined by
each point and its reflection image. This is true because each segment
formed from a point (a, b) and its image point is a vertical segment.
The *x*-axis is horizontal so each segment is perpendicular to the *x*-axis.
The opposite values of *y*-coordinates b and $-b$ show that the point
and its image point are the same distance from the *x*-axis.

10 The preimage points are indicated by * and the image points are
indicated by •.

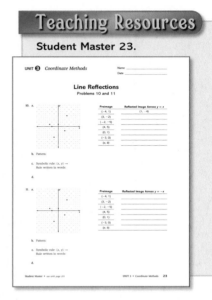
a.

Preimage	Reflected Image Across y = x
(−4, 1)	(1, −4)
(3, −2)	(−2, 3)
(−2, −5)	(−5, −2)
(4, 5)	(5, 4)
(0, 1)	(1, 0)
(−3, 0)	(0, −3)
(a, b)	(b, a)

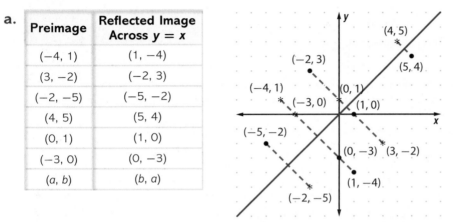

b. The *x*- and *y*-coordinates are interchanged for the image point.

c. The *x*-coordinate of the preimage is the *y*-coordinate of the image, and
the *y*-coordinate of the preimage is the *x*-coordinate of the image.
Symbolically, $(x, y) \rightarrow (y, x)$.

d. The line $y = x$ is the perpendicular bisector of the segment formed by
point (a, b) and its image under reflection across the line $y = x$. The
slope of each preimage/image segment is −1 and the slope of $y = x$ is
1. This indicates that the reflection line is perpendicular to each of the
segments. Any point (a, b) and its image (b, a) are the same distance
from the line $y = x$, so the midpoint of each segment lies on the
line $y = x$.

11 **a.**

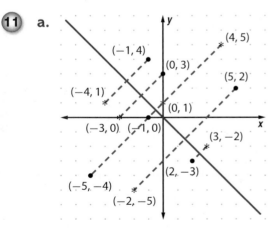

b. The image *x*- and
y-coordinates are interchanged
and both made the opposite
of the preimage coordinates.

c. The *x*-coordinate of the
image is the opposite of the
y-coordinate of the preimage.
The *y*-coordinate of the
image is the opposite of
the *x*-coordinate of the
preimage. Symbolically,
$(x, y) \rightarrow (-y, -x)$.

d. The line $y = -x$ is the perpendicular bisector of the segment formed
by a point and its image under reflection across the line $y = -x$.

Unit 3

12 You now have coordinate models for the following line reflections.

- reflection across the *x*-axis
- reflection across the *y*-axis
- reflection across the line $y = x$
- reflection across the line $y = -x$

Sharing the workload among your classmates, develop planning algorithms that would guide a programmer in the development of line reflection programs for each of these four line reflections. Identify the input, processing, and output portions of each of your algorithms.

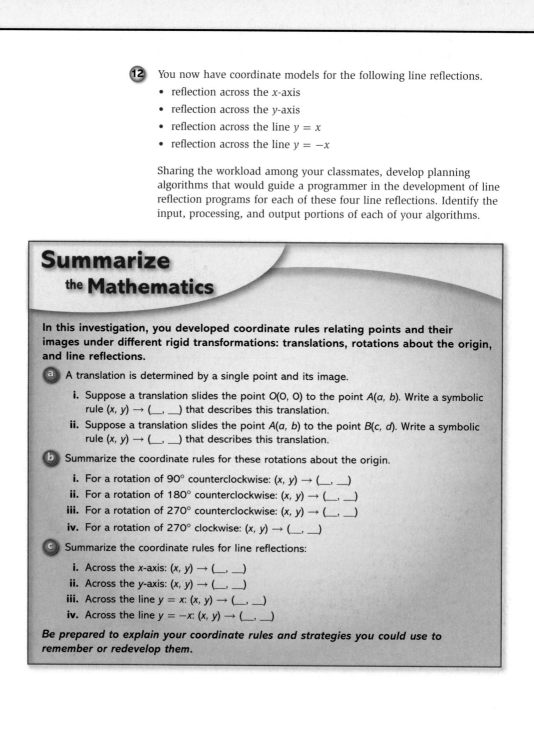

Summarize
the Mathematics

In this investigation, you developed coordinate rules relating points and their images under different rigid transformations: translations, rotations about the origin, and line reflections.

a A translation is determined by a single point and its image.

   i. Suppose a translation slides the point $O(0, 0)$ to the point $A(a, b)$. Write a symbolic rule $(x, y) \rightarrow (\_\_, \_\_)$ that describes this translation.

   ii. Suppose a translation slides the point $A(a, b)$ to the point $B(c, d)$. Write a symbolic rule $(x, y) \rightarrow (\_\_, \_\_)$ that describes this translation.

b Summarize the coordinate rules for these rotations about the origin.

   i. For a rotation of 90° counterclockwise: $(x, y) \rightarrow (\_\_, \_\_)$

   ii. For a rotation of 180° counterclockwise: $(x, y) \rightarrow (\_\_, \_\_)$

   iii. For a rotation of 270° counterclockwise: $(x, y) \rightarrow (\_\_, \_\_)$

   iv. For a rotation of 270° clockwise: $(x, y) \rightarrow (\_\_, \_\_)$

c Summarize the coordinate rules for line reflections:

   i. Across the *x*-axis: $(x, y) \rightarrow (\_\_, \_\_)$

   ii. Across the *y*-axis: $(x, y) \rightarrow (\_\_, \_\_)$

   iii. Across the line $y = x$: $(x, y) \rightarrow (\_\_, \_\_)$

   iv. Across the line $y = -x$: $(x, y) \rightarrow (\_\_, \_\_)$

Be prepared to explain your coordinate rules and strategies you could use to remember or redevelop them.

(12)

Line Reflection Algorithm

Step 1. Get x- and y-coordinates of point. } input

Step 2. Calculate the coordinates of the image
point using the appropriate rule below. } processing

Step 3. Display the graph of the points
with coordinates on. } output

This algorithm works for each line reflection transformation. The planning algorithms would differ only in the formula used for calculating the coordinates of the image point:

- reflection across x-axis: $(x, y) \rightarrow (x, -y)$
- reflection across y-axis: $(x, y) \rightarrow (-x, y)$
- reflection across the line $y = x$: $(x, y) \rightarrow (y, x)$
- reflection across the line $y = -x$: $(x, y) \rightarrow (-y, -x)$

You may wish to have students draw pictures of the transformations to help them see the relationship. Notice that the rules in Parts bi and biv are identical since a counterclockwise rotation of $x°$ is equivalent to a clockwise rotation of $360° - x°$. If students do not offer this observation, ask them why these rules are the same.

As a follow-up question to Part c, ask students how the rules relating preimage/image coordinates for line reflections differ from the rules for translations. A possible response follows.

For the line reflections students have studied so far, when a point (x, y) is reflected, the image point is found by some combination of $\pm x$ and $\pm y$. Thus, the absolute values of the coordinates of the two points are the same, although their order is possibly reversed. In the case of a translation, positive or negative values are added to the x- and y-coordinates to give the image coordinates.

Teaching Resources

Transparency Master 24.

MATH TOOLKIT If not already done, students should write symbolic rules for the rigid transformations in their toolkit.

Unit 3

Summarize
the Mathematics

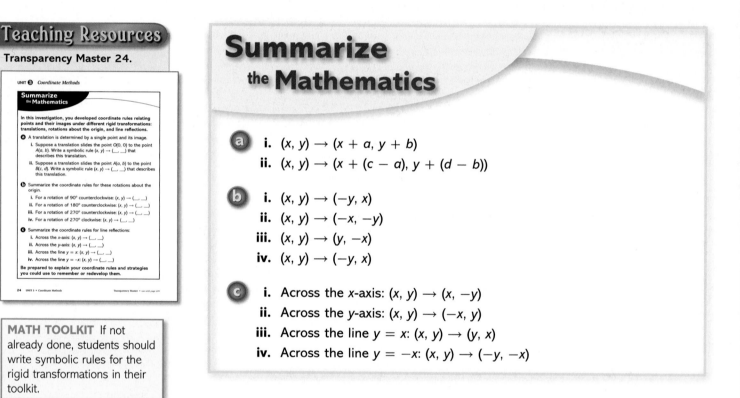

(a) i. $(x, y) \rightarrow (x + a, y + b)$

ii. $(x, y) \rightarrow (x + (c - a), y + (d - b))$

(b) i. $(x, y) \rightarrow (-y, x)$

ii. $(x, y) \rightarrow (-x, -y)$

iii. $(x, y) \rightarrow (y, -x)$

iv. $(x, y) \rightarrow (-y, x)$

(c) i. Across the x-axis: $(x, y) \rightarrow (x, -y)$

ii. Across the y-axis: $(x, y) \rightarrow (-x, y)$

iii. Across the line $y = x$: $(x, y) \rightarrow (y, x)$

iv. Across the line $y = -x$: $(x, y) \rightarrow (-y, -x)$

LANGUAGE NOTE Students were introduced to the term "rigid transformations" on page 196 and the term was again used in the introductory sentence to this Summarize the Mathematics. While doing this investigation, they have developed a concept image of this idea but may not have connected the concept to the term. This will be particularly true for English Language Learners (ELL) or students who struggle with reading.

It is not necessary to have students record the definition of this term in their Math Toolkits, but help students make the connection that rigid transformations are transformations for which the preimage and image figures have the same size and shape or are congruent. Following the discussion of the STM, ask questions such as the following:

- Notice that the translations, reflections, and rotations were called "rigid transformations" in the introductory sentence in the STM. What does "transformations" mean?

- How does that word relay the idea of what happens when translations, reflections, and rotations are applied to figures (or the plane)?

- What does the adjective "rigid" mean and why do you think it was used?

Then indicate that in Investigation 2, they will consider transformations that are not rigid called size transformations. (Other transformations that are not rigid are introduced in homework tasks in Lessons 2 and 3.)

✔ Check Your Understanding

Consider the following matrix representation of $\triangle ABC$.

$$\triangle ABC = \begin{bmatrix} -1 & 4 & 3 \\ 2 & -3 & 5 \end{bmatrix}$$

a. On separate grids, sketch and label $\triangle ABC$ and its image under each of the following transformations.

   i. Reflection across the y-axis

   ii. Translation with horizontal component -3 and vertical component 2

   iii. Reflection across the line $y = x$

   iv. Rotation of 180° about the origin

   v. Rotation of 90° counterclockwise about the origin

b. For one of the transformations in Part a, use coordinates to show that $\triangle ABC$ and its transformed image are congruent.

Investigation 2 · Modeling Size Transformations

In the previous investigation, you found patterns in the coordinates of preimage/image pairs for transformations with which you were familiar. For those transformations, the distance between any pair of preimage points was the same as the distance between their images. As a result, under these rigid transformations, a polygon and its image had the same size and shape—they were congruent.

In this investigation, you will reverse the procedure. You will start with a rule relating coordinates of any preimage and its image, and you will explore how the transformation affects familiar shapes.

As you complete the problems in this investigation, look for an answer to this question:

   How can coordinates be used to rescale or resize a shape?

✔ Check Your Understanding

a. **i.** Reflection across *y*-axis   **ii.** Translation with horizontal component −3 and vertical component 2

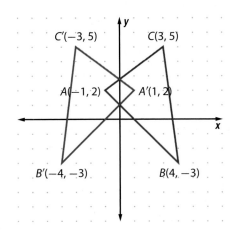

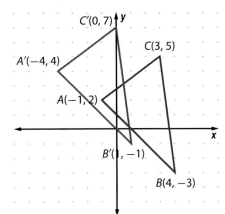

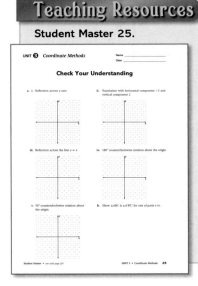

iii. Reflection across the line *y* = *x*

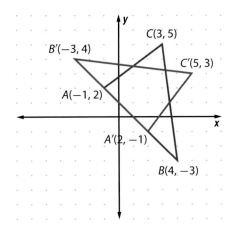

iv. 180° counterclockwise rotation about the origin   **v.** 90° counterclockwise rotation about the origin

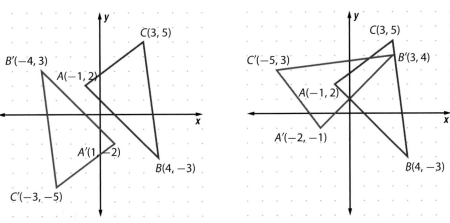

b. Students should use the distance formula to determine that the triangles are congruent by the SSS triangle congruence property.

Unit 3

1 Consider first the transformation defined by the following rule:

$$\begin{array}{ccc} \text{preimage} & & \text{image} \\ (x,\ y) & \rightarrow & (3x,\ y) \end{array}$$

This rule is read "the *x*-coordinate of the image is 3 times the *x*-coordinate of the preimage; the *y*-coordinate of the image is the same as the *y*-coordinate of the preimage."

a. Which of Figures II, III, or IV on the previous page appears to be the image of Figure I under this transformation? Explain your reasoning.

b. On a coordinate grid, plot the points $X(1, 1)$, $Y(5, 1)$, and $Z(5, 5)$. Draw $\triangle XYZ$ and its image under this transformation.

c. Examine your preimage and image shapes. What characteristics of $\triangle XYZ$ are also characteristics of its image? How do the shapes differ?

d. How do you think the perimeter of $\triangle XYZ$ will compare to the perimeter of its image? How do you think the area of $\triangle XYZ$ will compare to the area of its image? Test your conjectures.

e. Which of Figures II, III, or IV on the previous page could be the image of Figure I when transformed by the rule: $(x,\ y) \rightarrow (x,\ 3y)$? What clue(s) did you use?

Your work on Problem 1 has shown that even a simple transformation might not preserve all characteristics of the preimage shape. By modifying the transformation rule slightly, you can create a transformation which has many interesting and useful characteristics.

2 A **size transformation** (or **dilation**) of magnitude 3 centered at the origin is defined by the following rule:

$$\begin{array}{ccc} \text{preimage} & & \text{image} \\ (x,\ y) & \rightarrow & (3x,\ 3y) \end{array}$$

a. On a copy of the diagram shown here, draw the image of quadrilateral *ABCD* under this size transformation. Label image vertices A', B', C', and D'.

b. Examine your preimage and image shapes. Make a list of all of the properties of quadrilateral *ABCD* that seem to also be properties of quadrilateral $A'B'C'D'$. Also, describe how the two shapes seem to differ.

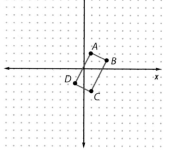

Unit 3

In this investigation, students will use coordinate methods to discover several characteristics of size transformations. These include:

- the effects of size transformations on length, area, and angle measure (extended to parallel and perpendicular lines) for various figures.
- the relation of the center and magnitude of a size transformation to pairs of preimage/image points.

Launch

To introduce this investigation, you might want to refer students back to the Think About This Situation questions on page 196. Ask them to describe in words, using appropriate vocabulary (or in symbols), how one human model was transformed into another.

As you circulate among groups, you can caution students that it will be helpful for them to make careful sketches for each of the figures in these problems before they try to generalize ideas about size transformations. However, for most problems, students should use coordinates to explain their responses and not rely solely on their sketches.

1 **a.** Figure III. Horizontally, the figure has been stretched, but it stayed the same height. This makes sense because the rule retains the same *y* values but increases the image *x* values by 3 times the preimage values. (Students may not select the correct figure or have well-articulated reasoning here but should have correct reasoning for Part e.)

b.

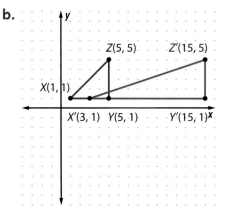

(This transformation is scaling in the *x*-direction only.)

c. $\triangle XYZ$ and $\triangle X'Y'Z'$ are both right triangles with the same height. The lengths of the bases and hypotenuses are different. Students may or may not mention the scale factor of 3.

d. Students may conjecture that:
(1) neither the perimeters nor the areas of the two triangles are equal (correct); that
(2) both the perimeter and area of $\triangle X'Y'Z'$ are 3 times those of $\triangle XYZ$ (incorrect); that
(3) the perimeter of $\triangle X'Y'Z'$ is 3 times the perimeter of $\triangle XYZ$ and the area of $\triangle X'Y'Z'$ is 9 times the area of $\triangle XYZ$ (incorrect); or that
(4) the area of $\triangle X'Y'Z'$ is 3 times that of the preimage (correct) and that the perimeter of $\triangle X'Y'Z'$ is greater than the perimeter of $\triangle XYZ$ but not 3 times greater (correct).

Testing: *Perimeter of* $\triangle XYZ = 4 + 4 + \sqrt{32} = 8 + 4\sqrt{2} \approx 13.7$ units

Perimeter of $\triangle X'Y'Z' = 12 + 4 + \sqrt{160} = 16 + 4\sqrt{10} \approx$ 28.6 units

Area of $\triangle XYZ = 8$ square units;
Area of $\triangle X'Y'Z' = 24$ square units

The area of $\triangle X'Y'Z'$ is 3 times that of $\triangle XYZ$, but the perimeters do not have this relationship.

e. Figure IV seems to be the image of Figure I because the rule indicates that the *y* value (or height) is increased by a factor of 3 while the *x* value (or width) remains the same.

2 **a.**

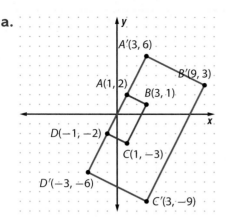

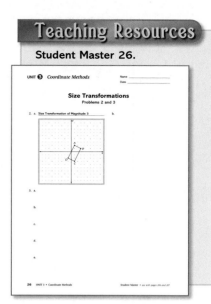

b. *ABCD* and *A'B'C'D'* each have 4 sides and 4 angles. Corresponding angles in the two quadrilaterals appear to have equal measure. Corresponding sides appear parallel, and the two figures have the same shape.

ABCD and *A'B'C'D'* seem to differ in that they are of different size. The side lengths of the image are proportionally 3 times larger than the side lengths of the preimage. This means that the perimeters and the areas are different. (In Problem 3, the relationship between the perimeter and area of figures and their images under a size transformation will be examined, so, the ideas need not be pursued here.)

Unit 3

(3) Making visual comparisons, as you did in Problem 2, is useful; but such comparisons should be made with some skepticism. You should always seek additional evidence to support or refute your visual conjectures. This is where coordinate representations and formulas for distance and slope can be very helpful. Use these ideas to examine more carefully quadrilateral *ABCD* and its image quadrilateral *A′B′C′D′* that you drew in Problem 2.

   a. Compare the length of $\overline{AB}$ with the length of $\overline{A'B'}$. Does the same relation hold for other preimage/image pairs of segments? Explain.

   b. How does $\overleftrightarrow{AB}$ appear to be related to $\overleftrightarrow{AD}$? Does the same relationship hold for their images? Give evidence to support your claim.

   c. How do the perimeters of quadrilateral *ABCD* and quadrilateral *A′B′C′D′* compare?

   d. How does $\overleftrightarrow{BC}$ appear to be related to $\overleftrightarrow{AD}$? Is this relationship true for their images? Justify your conclusion.

   e. What kind of quadrilateral is *ABCD*? Is the image quadrilateral *A′B′C′D′* the same kind of quadrilateral? Explain your reasoning.

   f. How do the areas of quadrilaterals *ABCD* and *A′B′C′D′* appear to be related? State a conjecture. Test your conjecture. How does the magnitude of the size transformation come into play here?

(4) Refer back to your drawing of quadrilateral *ABCD* and its image quadrilateral *A′B′C′D′* under the size transformation of magnitude 3.

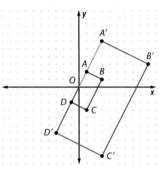

   a. Use a ruler to draw lines through *A* and *A′*, *B* and *B′*, *C* and *C′*, and *D* and *D′*. Extend the lines to intersect the axes. What do you notice about the intersection of these four lines?

   b. Find the equations of the four lines in Part a. Use these equations to verify your observation in Part a.

   c. The size transformation has its **center** at the origin since the lines in Part a intersect at (0, 0). What is the image of the center (0, 0) under this size transformation?

   d. Compare the distances from the center *O* to a point and to the image of that point. State a conjecture.

      i. Find the distance from *O* to *A* and from *O* to *A′*. From *O* to *B* and from *O* to *B′*. Do these distances confirm your conjecture?

      ii. Make similar comparisons for distances from point *O* to points *C* and *D* and to their images. What seems to be true? Modify your original conjecture, if necessary, based on the evidence.

   e. Now try to generalize your finding. How should the distances from *O*(0, 0) to *P*(*a*, *b*) and from *O*(0, 0) to *P′*(3*a*, 3*b*) be related? Show why this must be the case by calculating the distances *OP* and *OP′*.

   f. Complete the following statement:

     If O is the center of a size transformation with magnitude k and

     the image of P is P′, then OP′ = _____ and $\dfrac{OP'}{OP}$ = _____.

     Compare your general statement with that of others. Resolve any differences.

3 **a.** The length of $\overline{AB}$ is $\sqrt{5}$, or approximately 2.236 units, and the length of $\overline{A'B'}$ is $\sqrt{45} = 3\sqrt{5}$, or approximately 6.708 units.
The length of the image segment is three times the length of the preimage segment. This relationship holds for each of the other pairs of line segments. The image length is three times the length of the preimage.

b. $\overleftrightarrow{AB}$ and $\overleftrightarrow{AD}$ are perpendicular.
The slope of $\overleftrightarrow{AB}$ is $-\frac{1}{2}$ and the slope of $\overleftrightarrow{AD}$ is 2.
The same relationship holds for $\overleftrightarrow{A'B'}$ and $\overleftrightarrow{A'D'}$. The slope of $\overleftrightarrow{A'B'}$ is $-\frac{1}{2}$ and the slope of $\overleftrightarrow{A'D'}$ is 2.
The slopes of both sets of lines are opposite reciprocals of one another.

c. The perimeter of quadrilateral $A'B'C'D'$ is three times the perimeter of quadrilateral $ABCD$.

d. The slope of $\overleftrightarrow{BC}$ and the slope of $\overleftrightarrow{AD}$ are both 2, so the lines are parallel. $\overleftrightarrow{B'C'}$ and $\overleftrightarrow{A'D'}$ are also parallel with slopes of 2.

e. $ABCD$ is a rectangle. $A'B'C'D'$ is also a rectangle. Both quadrilaterals have two pairs of opposite sides that are parallel and consecutive sides that are perpendicular.

f. Conjecture: Students' conjectures may vary; but after computing areas, they should recognize that the image area is the scale factor squared times the preimage area.
The area of $ABCD$ is $(AB)(BC) = (\sqrt{5})(\sqrt{20}) = 10$ square units.
The area of $A'B'C'D'$ is $(A'B')(A'D') = (\sqrt{45})(\sqrt{180}) = 90$ square units.
The area of the image is 9 times the area of the preimage. This change is the magnitude of the size transformation squared.

4 **a.** When the lines are extended, they all intersect at the origin. (This characteristic always holds for size transformations centered at the origin. For any size transformation, the intersection point of these lines is the center of the transformation.)

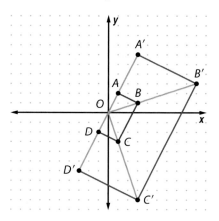

b. The line through B and B' has slope $\frac{3-1}{9-3} = \frac{1}{3}$ and the point
(3, 1) is on it. Substituting (3, 1) into $y = \frac{1}{3}x + b$ gives $y = \frac{1}{3}x$.
Similarly, the line through C and C' has equation $y = -3x$. The line through A and A' coincides with the line through D and D' and has equation $y = 2x$. All four lines go through the origin.

c. The image of (0, 0) is (0, 0).

INSTRUCTIONAL NOTE
This problem can be used to discuss that in some cases, such as for comparing and pattern searching, it is valuable to use exact square roots of numbers.

COMMON ERROR In Part b, students may say that AD is twice as long as AB, not paying careful attention to the difference in symbols $\overline{AB}$ and $\overleftrightarrow{AB}$.

NOTE Solutions to Problems 4 Parts d–f are on page T208.

5 Next, consider a size transformation with magnitude 0.5 and center at the origin.

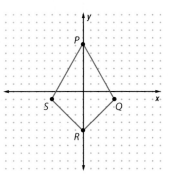

a. Write a rule for this size transformation.

b. On a copy of the diagram shown here, plot and label the image of quadrilateral *PQRS* under this size transformation. How do you think quadrilateral *PQRS* and its image are related in terms of shape? In terms of size?

c. Compare segment lengths in the image with corresponding lengths in quadrilateral *PQRS*. How does the magnitude 0.5 affect the relation between lengths? Between perimeters?

d. Find the area of the image quadrilateral. Compare it to the area of quadrilateral *PQRS*. How does the magnitude 0.5 affect the relation between areas?

6 Now, consider $\triangle PQR = \begin{bmatrix} 3 & -3 & -2 \\ 4 & 2 & -1 \end{bmatrix}$.

a. Sketch $\triangle PQR$ on a coordinate grid.

b. Sketch the image, $\triangle P'Q'R'$, resulting from transforming $\triangle PQR$ with a size transformation of magnitude 2.5 and center at the origin.

c. Compare lengths of corresponding preimage and image sides.

d. How are $\overleftrightarrow{PQ}$ and $\overleftrightarrow{QR}$ related? How are $\overleftrightarrow{P'Q'}$ and $\overleftrightarrow{Q'R'}$ related? Give evidence to support your claim.

e. Use the information in Parts c and d to help you determine the area of $\triangle PQR$ and $\triangle P'Q'R'$. Compare the areas and relate them to the magnitude 2.5.

7 Size transformations are used by interactive geometry software to resize figures in a coordinate plane. As a class or in pairs, experiment with the "Scale" (or similar) command.

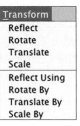

a. Draw $\triangle XYZ = \begin{bmatrix} 8 & 4 & -3 \\ 6 & -7 & -4 \end{bmatrix}$.

b. Find images of $\triangle XYZ$ when transformed with magnitudes 3, 1.5, and 2.5. In each case, compare side lengths and areas of the preimage and image triangles. Are the results of your comparisons consistent with what you would have predicted? Explain.

d. INSTRUCTIONAL NOTE This task is central to the concept of a size transformation. Students will observe that a size transformation alters each side of a shape by a certain factor. Through this task, students should progress beyond that idea to the more important, core idea: How is the expansion accomplished? Having students talk about a size transformation with its center at the origin should help to keep the issue in focus. In particular, as seen in Part e, the scale factor is the ratio of the distance of the image point from the origin to the distance of the preimage point from the origin.

Conjecture: The distance from O to the image point appears to be 3 times the distance from O to the preimage point.

  i. $OA = \sqrt{5} \approx 2.236$ units and $OA' = \sqrt{45} = 3\sqrt{5} \approx 6.708$ units.
  $OB = \sqrt{10} \approx 3.162$ units and $OB' = \sqrt{90} = 3\sqrt{10} \approx 9.487$ units.
  This confirms the conjecture given above.

  ii. $OC = \sqrt{10} \approx 3.162$ units and $OC' = \sqrt{90} = 3\sqrt{10} \approx 9.487$ units.
  $OD = \sqrt{5} \approx 2.236$ units and $OD' = \sqrt{45} = 3\sqrt{5} \approx 6.708$ units.
  In each case, the distance from the origin to the image point is 3 times the distance from the origin to the preimage point.

e. The length of the image segment would be 3 times as long as the length of the preimage segment. $OP = \sqrt{a^2 + b^2}$ and $OP' = \sqrt{9a^2 + 9b^2}$ that is, $3\sqrt{a^2 + b^2}$. OP' is 3 times OP.

f. $OP' = k \cdot OP$ and $\dfrac{OP'}{OP} = k$

INSTRUCTIONAL NOTE
You may want students to check in with their answer to Problem 4 Part f before moving on to Problem 5 to be sure they are correct.

5
  a. $(x, y) \rightarrow (0.5x, 0.5y)$

  b. The image quadrilateral is shown in the plot at the right. Conjectures may vary. The quadrilaterals are the same shape; the image is smaller (a shrunken version of the original).

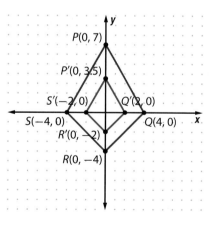

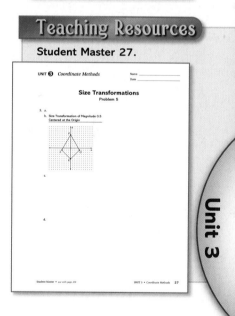

Teaching Resources

Student Master 27.

  c. Each image length is half the length of the preimage segment; the perimeter of the image is half that of the preimage.

Preimage	Length	Image	Approximate Length
PQ	$\sqrt{65} \approx 8.06$	P'Q'	4.03
QR	$\sqrt{32} \approx 5.66$	Q'R'	2.83
RS	$\sqrt{65} \approx 8.06$	R'S'	4.03
SP	$\sqrt{32} \approx 5.66$	S'P'	2.83

  d. The area of $PQRS$ is 44 square units. The area of $P'Q'R'S'$ is 11 square units. The area of the image kite is one-fourth the area of the preimage kite. This is the magnitude of the size transformation squared $0.5^2 = 0.25$ times the area of the preimage.

Unit 3

6 **a–b.**

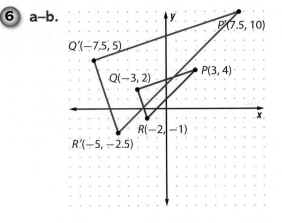

c. Image segments are 2.5 times the length of preimage segments. For example, $PQ = \sqrt{40} \approx 6.32$ while $P'Q' = \sqrt{250} \approx 15.81$.

d. The slope of $\overleftrightarrow{PQ}$ is $\frac{1}{3}$ and the slope of $\overleftrightarrow{QR}$ is -3; therefore, $\overleftrightarrow{PQ}$ is perpendicular to $\overleftrightarrow{QR}$. The same is true for $\overleftrightarrow{P'Q'}$ and $\overleftrightarrow{Q'R'}$.

e. *Area* $\triangle PQR = 0.5(QR)(QP) = 0.5(\sqrt{10})(\sqrt{40}) = 10$ square units
Area $\triangle P'Q'R' = 0.5(Q'R')(Q'P')$
$$= 0.5(\sqrt{62.5})(\sqrt{250}) = 62.5 \text{ square units}$$

The area of $\triangle P'Q'R'$ is 2.5^2, or 6.25 times the area of $\triangle PQR$.

7 **ONE COMPUTER** If you are using one computer and a projector, have a student draw △*XYZ*. To encourage class participation, other students could direct the next steps in the analysis. The "Scale By" option under the Transform menu allows you to choose the scale factor to perform a size transformation on the selected shape. Parts c and d could then be assigned as homework to allow each student time to experiment. The STM discussion can precede the completion of Parts c and d.

a. Students should draw △*XYZ* using *CPMP-Tools* or similar software.

b. All image lengths are the magnitude of the transformation times the length of the preimage.

All areas of the image triangles are the square of the scale factor times the area of the preimage.

$(3)^2 \cdot 51.5 \approx 463.5$ square units

$(1.5)^2 \cdot 51.5 \approx 115.885$ square units

$(2.5)^2 \cdot 51.5 \approx 321.875$ square units

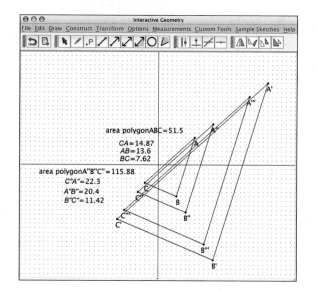

Unit 3

c. Select the "Humanoid" from Sample Sketches. Experiment with commands in the Transform menu to produce a series of images that suggests the figure is walking toward the front of the screen.

d. Clear the window. Experiment with commands in the Transform menu to produce a series of images that suggests the figure is walking toward the back of the screen.

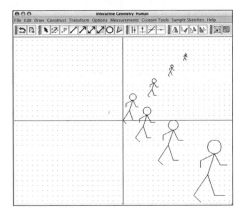

Summarize
the Mathematics

In this investigation, you explored properties of size transformations.

a Explain why the transformation in Problem 1 $(x, y) \rightarrow (3x, y)$ is or is not a size transformation.

b Suppose a size transformation with magnitude $k > 0$ and center at the origin O maps A onto A', B onto B', and C onto C'.

   i. Write a rule that can be used to obtain the image of any point (x, y) in the coordinate plane under this size transformation. State your rule in words and in symbolic form.

   ii. How is the length $A'B'$ related to the length AB?

   iii. If $\triangle ABC$ has an area of 25 square units, what is the area of $\triangle A'B'C'$? Why does this make sense in terms of the formula for the area of a triangle?

   iv. How is the distance from O to C' related to the distance from O to C?

   v. Where do $\overleftrightarrow{AA'}$ and $\overleftrightarrow{CC'}$ intersect? Does $\overleftrightarrow{BB'}$ intersect there too?

c How are size transformations similar to rigid transformations? How are they different?

d What is the magnitude of a size transformation that is also a rigid transformation? Describe such a transformation.

Be prepared to explain your conclusions to the entire class.

Unit 3

c. Use the "Scale By" command under the Transform menu to produce some larger humanoids. Then translate the progressively larger images toward the bottom-right corner of the screen. Translation can be accomplished using the "Translate By" command and choosing horizontal and vertical translation components. Translation can also be done by selecting the figure and then the Translate button on the toolbar. Then drag the figure to the desired location. Unwanted figures can be erased by selecting them and hitting the Delete key. See the screen at the right.

d. Similar methods can be used once the humanoid is reduced in size in order to give the impression that the figure is walking toward the back of the screen.

Summary

Following student responses to Part biii, it may be helpful for some students to provide a sketch of $\triangle ABC$ to support their reasoning as shown below.

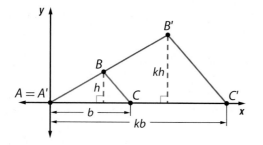

Area $\triangle ABC = \frac{1}{2}bh$

Area $\triangle A'B'C' = \frac{1}{2}(kb)(kh) = \frac{1}{2}k^2bh$

Summarize
the **Mathematics**

ⓐ The transformation is not a size transformation because only the x-coordinate was multiplied by a factor of 3. In a size transformation, both the x- and the y-coordinates of the preimage must be multiplied by the same constant to find the image.

ⓑ
  i. $(x, y) \rightarrow (kx, ky)$
    The coordinates of each image point are k times the coordinates of the original point.

  ii. $A'B' = kAB$

  iii. The area of $\triangle A'B'C'$ is $25k^2$ square units. The formula for the area of a triangle is $\frac{1}{2}$ *base* × *height*. In a size transformation, both of those lengths would be multiplied by the scale factor k. So, the area is changed by a factor of k^2:
$$\frac{1}{2} k \cdot base \times k \cdot height = k^2 \cdot \frac{1}{2} base \times height.$$

  iv. The distance OC' is k times the distance OC.

  v. $\overleftrightarrow{AA'}$ and $\overleftrightarrow{CC'}$ intersect at the center of the transformation (in this case, the origin O). $\overleftrightarrow{BB'}$ also passes through the origin.

ⓒ The image of a shape under size transformations or a rigid transformation is the same type of shape—angle measures are retained as is parallelism of segments. Size transformations, unlike rigid transformations, change lengths by the scale factor.

ⓓ Size transformations of magnitudes 1 (and −1) are also rigid transformations. With magnitude 1, the transformation is the identity transformation—every image point is the same as its preimage. (With magnitude −1, the transformation is a 180° rotation about the origin.)

✔Check Your Understanding

a. The length of the third side of the original triangle is $\sqrt{41} \approx 6.4$ units. The lengths of the sides of the image triangle are 3.5 times the preimage lengths: 14 units, 17.5 units, and approximately 22.4 units.

b. The area of the original triangle is 10 square units. The area of the image triangle is $10(3.5)^2$, or 122.5 square units.

c.

Size Transformation Algorithm	
Step 1. Get the coordinates of a point (x, y).	} input
Step 2. Get the magnitude k of the size transformation.	
Step 3. Compute the coordinates of the image point (kx, ky).	} processing
Step 4. Display the graphs of the point and its image.	} output
Step 5. Display the coordinates of the points.	

Lesson 2, Investigation 2,
Summarize the Mathematics, *page 209*

Teacher: *(Students have spent time on the STM in small groups. They have written their answers on large poster paper and have them displayed around the room. The teacher has randomly numbered the papers 1 through 6.)* In this investigation, you explored properties of size transformations. Take out your toolkits because we will now formalize some of the mathematics using your responses to this STM. Take a couple of minutes to look at the six different group responses. Pay particular attention to the similarities and differences in responses. Then we will decide together as a class what should be included in our final STM answers.

Teacher: Group 3, which response do you think best explains why $(x, y) \rightarrow (3x, y)$ is or is not a size transformation?

Carissa: Poster 5 because it tells it is *not* a size transformation but also explained that the y values needed to be multiplied by the same number as the x values to make it a size transformation.

Teacher: Joe, do you agree with them?

Joe: Yes, but we liked the example on Poster 2 showing that a triangle under this transformation did not produce a similar triangle.

Teacher: Did this make their explanation better?

Joe: Yes, because it gave us a picture to help us.

Teacher: Does anyone see the need to add anything else? *(Pauses for answers)* No? Okay, let's move on to Part b. Part b focuses on many of the properties of size transformations, so it would be a good idea to enter these into your toolkit. Let's begin by writing the conditions for our rule: "Suppose a size transformation with magnitude $k > 0$ and center at the origin O maps A onto A', B onto B', and C onto C', then ..."

Teacher: Look at the rules written for Part bi. Which response do you think is the best?

Shelby: The rules are all the same. The descriptions are all similar, but we decided that the one on Poster 4 best. It says, "Take the coordinates of the original point and multiply them by k."

Suki: We thought we should use the idea from our response along with that on Poster 4 in this way: "Take the coordinates of the original point and multiply them by k to get the coordinates of the image point."

Teacher: Suki, why did your group think your description was an improvement of the description on Poster 4?

Suki: A "best" answer would talk about the coordinates of both points and make it clear how to get from the original point to the transformed point.

Teacher: Thanks for clarifying your reasoning. It looks like we all agree that $(x, y) \rightarrow (kx, ky)$ is the rule. So, complete the sentence we started above including "the rule $(x, y) \rightarrow (kx, ky)$." If you wish to add the description, you may.

Teacher: Zach, what do you like about the answer on Poster 1 to the question of how the lengths of a segment and its image are related in Part bii?

Zach: We like the fact that they said the length $A'B'$ would be k times the length AB.

Teacher: Do you think there is anything missing?

Sally: You need to add that it is k times *larger* like Poster 5.

Seth: But what if k was equal to $\frac{1}{2}$?

Sally: Oh, we did not think of that.

Teacher: So, is the answer on Poster 1 complete? *(The class agrees.)*

Teacher: So for the record, let's add Group 1's response to our toolkit for Part bii; the length $A'B'$ is k times the length AB.

Teacher: Let's look at the question about areas. It looks like we have a couple different responses for this one. From the posters, it looks like the area of $\triangle A'B'C'$ is either $25k$ or $25k^2$.

Sheri: We had $25k$. We now agree with the other groups; we forgot that for area, it is the square of the magnitude.

Teacher: That sounds good, but what do the posters say about this making sense in terms of the area formula?

Zach: We like Poster 4's statement that the formula is one half base times height, so it is multiplied by k^2.

Seth: Look at Poster 3; they have a nice example of how the formula shows why the area is k^2 times as big as the original area. They showed the area calculations for a triangle and its image that was scaled by 3.

Marie: But look at Poster 6. They have a diagram explanation. The picture of the two triangles helps me understand better.

Teacher: So, let's summarize. Let's use the ideas from the posters, including the formula for the area of a triangle and the use of the symbols $\triangle ABC$ and $\triangle A'B'C'$ to explain this property of size transformations. Those who wish to add a diagram to their explanation may do so. *(Teacher gives students a few minutes to complete their toolkit. In addition, students are asked to indicate by diagrams that parallel segments and angle measures are retained under size transformations—Part c.)*

✓ *Check Your Understanding*

A size transformation with magnitude 3.5 and center at the origin is applied to a right triangle with legs of length 4 and 5 units.

a. What are the lengths of the three sides of the image triangle?

b. What is the area of the given triangle and of its image?

c. Write an algorithm for a program that will accept the coordinates of a point and the magnitude of this or any other size transformation (with center at the origin). The program should display the point, its image, and their coordinates.

Investigation 3 — Combining Transformations

Computer graphics software includes the creation, storage, and manipulation of figures that can be simple or complex. Translations, rotations, and size transformations are essential to many graphics applications to change the position, tilt, and size of shapes. You now have the basic tools for creating computer graphics images because you know the coordinate rules that define some of these key transformations.

What kinds of transformations do you think were needed to create the characters' walk from the back of the landscape to the front?

As you work on the problems of this investigation, look for answers to these questions:

> *How can rigid transformations and/or size transformations be combined to form new transformations?*
>
> *When combining two transformations, how can you predict what the new transformation will be and how it will affect the preimage?*

Investigation 3 — Combining Transformations

Now that students have examined several different transformations individually, this investigation asks them to explore combinations of transformations. It provides a good opportunity to cement understanding of the basic transformations from a coordinate geometry perspective and to relate transformations to ideas of similarity.

Students will use coordinate methods to explore the effects of various composite transformations on position, length and slope of segments, and area of closed figures. Finding the image of figures under a composition of transformations can be accomplished by applying the second transformation to the figure's image under the first transformation, or by determining the single transformation (if one exists) that is equivalent to the composition, then applying that single transformation.

Students will explore:

- combining two translations,
- combining two rotations,
- combining two line reflections, and
- combining two size transformations.

They will also consider combining a rotation with a line reflection, with a size transformation, and with a translation. Combinations of a size transformation with a translation and with a line reflection are also considered.

Students working in pairs at computers should be able to accomplish Problems 1, 2, and 3 with minimal assistance. As you circulate among the pairs, you can ask students questions that require them to use the new vocabulary they are acquiring. For example, ask: "What is the difference between the two types of transformations in Problems 2 and 3?" (Geometrically, they have different effects; translations are achieved symbolically by adding components to the coordinates of the original figure while size transformations centered at the origin work by multiplying each coordinate of the original figure by the same constant.)

Problem 4 might be more challenging than the first three problems. You might wish to choose a successful group to demonstrate Problem 4. This makes a good summary activity on the subject of simple compositions. All students should be able to demonstrate, both geometrically and symbolically, the composition of a 90° counterclockwise rotation and a rotation of 180°, each centered at the origin.

Problem 5 suggests that line reflections can be considered the building blocks for other rigid transformations. Students will discover that the composite of a reflection across the x-axis followed by a reflection across the line $y = x$ is a 90° counterclockwise rotation about the origin (the intersection of the two lines). Problem 5 also develops the result that a composite of a reflection across the x-axis followed by a reflection across the y-axis is a 180° rotation about the origin.

In Problems 6 through 9, students can use *CPMP-Tools* to check conjectures about compositions of transformations. However, it is important that they also write examples in symbolic form. This will help them algebraically see why some compositions give different results when the order is reversed.

NOTE The solution to the Check Your Understanding is on page T209A.

COLLABORATION SKILL
Respectfully listen and respond to others' conjectures and reasoning.

Unit 3

Use interactive geometry software or graph paper to complete the following problems. You should focus your attention on (1) preimage/image point coordinate patterns and (2) how the shape of the preimage and its image are related.

1 This first problem will help you experiment with combinations of transformations.

   a. Draw $\triangle ABC = \begin{bmatrix} 7 & 13 & 7 \\ 15 & 6 & 2 \end{bmatrix}$ in a coordinate plane.

   i. Draw the image of $\triangle ABC$ reflected across the y-axis. Find the coordinates of B', the image of B. Similarly, find the coordinates of A' and C'.

   ii. Next, draw the image of $\triangle A'B'C'$ rotated 90° counterclockwise about the origin. Find the coordinates of B'', the image of B'. What are the coordinates of A'' and C''?

   b. Now, examine $\triangle ABC$, $\triangle A'B'C'$, and $\triangle A''B''C''$.

   i. Are they congruent? Explain your reasoning.

   ii. What is the measure of $\angle B$? How do you know? What is the measure of $\angle B''$?

   iii. Compare the **orientation** (the clockwise or counterclockwise labeling of the vertices) of $\triangle ABC$ to the orientation of $\triangle A''B''C''$. What do you notice? Why does your observation make sense?

   c. If you first rotate $\triangle ABC$ 90° counterclockwise about the origin and then reflect that image across the y-axis, do you think you will get the same *final* image, $\triangle A''B''C''$? Try it! Explain what happens.

   d. Is the final image $\triangle A''B''C''$ in Part c related to $\triangle ABC$ by a single transformation? Is so, describe the transformation.

In the following problems, you will investigate more systematically the effects of various combinations of transformations.

2 **Combining Two Translations** Examine the effects of applying one translation followed by another. This two-step transformation is called a **composition of translations**.

   a. Draw $\triangle ABC$ with vertex coordinates $A(1, 5)$, $B(6, 2)$, $C(8, 11)$.

   b. Translate $\triangle ABC$ using the translation with horizontal component 6 and vertical component -10. Then apply the translation with horizontal component -8 and vertical component 2 to the image of $\triangle ABC$. What were the net horizontal and vertical distances that you translated the figure and in which directions?

   c. Compare the size, shape, and orientation of $\triangle ABC$ and the final image.

   d. Compare the coordinates of the vertices of the final image with those of $\triangle ABC$. What pattern do you observe?

ONE COMPUTER If you do not have access to a computer lab or laptops for pairs of students, one way to facilitate this investigation using a projection system follows.

(1) Problem 1: Have students draw $\triangle ABC$ and each of the images for the composite transformation using grid paper and discuss the results with classmates.

(2) Problems 2–7: As in Lesson 1 Investigation 1, have a student operate the computer based on instructions from other students. Someone should publicly record the vertices so everyone can examine them for patterns and determine a single transformation rule. When conjectures or predictions are to be made, students can discuss this in pairs before the transformations are generated on the computer.

(3) Problems 8 and 9 can be completed by groups or pairs of students without technology access.

1   **a. i–ii.**

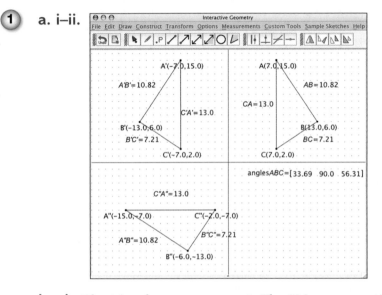

NO TECHNOLOGY Students can use *grid paper* for this investigation, but using *CPMP-Tools* enables students to *quickly* perform compositions in both orders and examine the resulting figures. The built-in measurement options make comparison of lengths, areas, and angles easy.

b. i. The triangles are congruent. The "Measurement" command will indicate that all three sets of corresponding sides are congruent. If students are using graph paper, they can compute the distances or use the calculator program they wrote in Lesson 1.

ii. Since $AB^2 + BC^2 = AC^2$, the converse of the Pythagorean Theorem ensures that $\angle B$ is a right angle. Alternatively, students could use the "Angles" command in the Measurements menu to obtain the angle measures. $m\angle B''$ is 90° also since angle measure is preserved under reflections and rotations. They might also show that the slope of $\overline{AB}$ and the slope of $\overline{CB}$ are opposite reciprocals.

iii. The vertices of $\triangle ABC$ are labeled clockwise while the vertices of $\triangle A''B''C''$ are labeled counterclockwise, so the orientation is reversed. Since the first transformation was a line reflection (flipping), the vertices of $\triangle A'B'C'$ were labeled counterclockwise. Since the second transformation was a rotation, the orientation did not change again. It remained a counterclockwise labeling.

c. Switching the order of applying the line reflection and the rotation does not produce the same image. The coordinates of this final image are $A''(15, 7)$, $B''(2, 7)$, and $C''(6, 13)$.

d. $\triangle A''B''C''$ is the image of $\triangle ABC$ under a reflection across the line $y = x$.

INSTRUCTIONAL NOTE If students have difficulty comparing the *orientation* of the triangles, ask them to use their finger to move from point *A* to point *B* to point *C* of the original triangle and consider whether the movement was counterclockwise or clockwise. Then do the same for points *A"* to *B"* to *C"*.

NOTE The solution to Problem 2 is on page T212.

Unit 3

e. Could you apply a *single* transformation to △ABC and obtain the same final image? If so, describe that transformation as completely as possible.

f. Repeat Parts a–e for a new figure and two new translations of your choice. Keep a record of the coordinates of the vertices of your figure and its final image. Also, record the components of your translations.

g. Look back at your work in Parts a–f. Suppose the following two translations are applied in succession.

$$(x, y) \rightarrow (x + a, y + b)$$
$$(x, y) \rightarrow (x + h, y + k)$$

Write a symbolic rule $(x, y) \rightarrow (\_\_, \_\_)$ which describes the new combined transformation. Compare your rule with that of others and resolve any differences.

③ Combining Two Size Transformations Next, investigate the effects of successively applying two size transformations with center at the origin.

a. Draw △ABC with vertex coordinates $A(-5, 1)$, $B(0, -4)$, $C(2, 5)$.

b. Apply a size transformation of magnitude 2 to △ABC. Then apply a size transformation of magnitude 1.5 to the image of △ABC.

c. Compare the size, shape, and orientation of △ABC to the final image.

d. Compare the coordinates of the vertices of the final image with those of △ABC. What pattern do you observe?

e. Make a conjecture about the effects of applying two size transformations in succession, both centered at the origin. Test your conjecture using a different figure and two new size transformations with center at the origin; one should have magnitude k, $0 < k < 1$. Keep a record of the coordinates of the vertices of your figure and its image. Also, record the magnitudes of your size transformations.

f. Look back at your work in Parts a–e. Suppose the following two size transformations with magnitudes $k > 0$ and $m > 0$ are applied in succession.

$$(x, y) \rightarrow (kx, ky)$$
$$(x, y) \rightarrow (mx, my)$$

Write a symbolic rule that describes the new combined transformation. Compare your rule with that of others and resolve any differences.

2 **a.** See the interactive geometry screen at the right.

b. The net horizontal distance moved is −2 and the net vertical distance is 8.

c. The size, shape, and orientation of $\triangle ABC$ and the final image are the same.

d. Final image $= \begin{bmatrix} -1 & 4 & 6 \\ -3 & -6 & 3 \end{bmatrix}$.

Each point of $\triangle ABC$ was translated horizontally and vertically the sum of the horizontal and vertical components of the two translations.

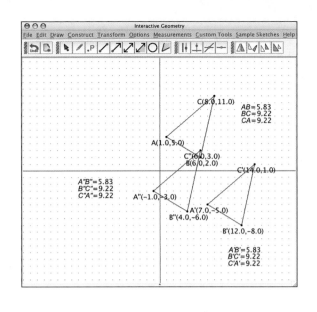

e. Yes. The single translation has horizontal component −2 and vertical component −8.

f. Student choices of figures and components will vary. Students should find that the x- and y-coordinates for the image can be obtained by adding both translation components at one time to the corresponding coordinates for the preimage for each pair of translations.

g. $(x, y) \rightarrow (x + a + h, y + b + k)$

3 **a–b.**

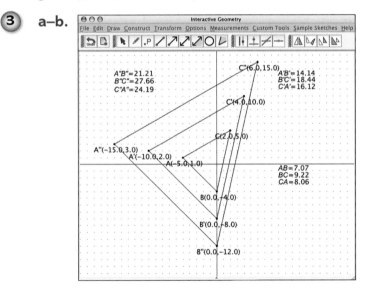

c. $\triangle ABC$ and the final image have the same shape and orientation but are different sizes. The final image is 3 times larger than $\triangle ABC$.

d. The x- and y-coordinates for the final image can be obtained by multiplying each pair of coordinates of the preimage by the product of the two magnitudes, $(2)(1.5) = 3$.

e. Student choices of figures and magnitudes will vary. Conjecture: The image of a figure that has undergone two size transformations will be the same shape and orientation as the original figure but may not be the same size. The length of a side will change by a factor equal to the product of the magnitudes of the two size transformations.

f. $(x, y) \rightarrow (kmx, kmy)$

> **POSSIBLE ERROR** Be sure students recognize that the magnitude of the composite size transformation is the product of the magnitudes of the original two size transformations. They may have the rule correct but be thinking of a sum.

The process of successively applying two transformations is called **composing** the transformations. The transformation that maps the *original* preimage to the *final* image is called the **composite transformation**.

(4) **Combining Two Rotations** Use methods similar to your work in Problems 2 and 3 to investigate the effects of composing two rotations about the origin.

   a. Draw $\triangle ABC$ with vertex coordinates $A(1, 4)$, $B(7, 1)$, $C(12, 8)$.

   b. Rotate $\triangle ABC$ 90° counterclockwise about the origin. Then rotate the image of $\triangle ABC$ 180° about the origin. Compare the coordinates, size, shape, and orientation of $\triangle ABC$ to the final image.

   c. Make a conjecture about the effects of composing two rotations about the origin. Test your conjecture using a different figure and two new counterclockwise rotations about the origin. Keep a record of the degree measures of your rotations.

   d. Look back at your work in Parts a–c. Write a statement summarizing your findings.

(5) **Combining Two Reflections** Examine the effects of composing two line reflections that you have studied.

   a. Draw a triangle or a quadrilateral of your choice.

   b. Reflect the figure across the *x*-axis. Then reflect the image across the line $y = x$.

   i. Compare the size, shape, and orientation of the preimage and image under the composite transformation.

   ii. What kind of transformation does the composition of the two line reflections appear to be? Be as specific as you can.

   iii. Write a symbolic rule $(x, y) \rightarrow (\_\_, \_\_)$ which describes the composite transformation.

   iv. Does the order in which you compose the two line reflections lead to the same final image?

   c. Now reflect the figure across the *x*-axis and then reflect the image across the *y*-axis.

   i. Compare the size, shape, and orientation of the preimage and image under the composite transformation.

   ii. What kind of transformation does the composition of the two line reflections appear to be?

   iii. Write a symbolic rule $(x, y) \rightarrow (\_\_, \_\_)$ which describes the composite transformation.

   d. What is the effect of reflecting across the same line twice?

4 **a–b.**

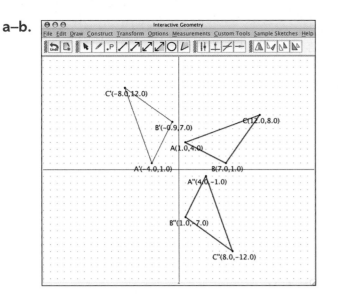

The size, shape, and orientation of △A″B″C″ are the same as △ABC. The coordinates of the image are A″(4, −1), B″(1, −7), and C″(8, −12).

c. Conjecture: The effect of composing two rotations about the origin has the same effect as doing one rotation through an angle with measure that is the sum of the measures of the two angles of rotation about the same point. Students should test their conjectures. Applying a 90° counterclockwise rotation and then a 180° counterclockwise rotation results in an image of the original triangle rotated 270° counterclockwise. The rule developed in Investigation 1 for a 270° counterclockwise rotation, $(x, y) \rightarrow (y, −x)$, matches the preimage to final image here.

d. When two rotations about the origin are successively applied, the transformations mapping the original preimage to the final image can be described as one transformation: a rotation about the origin that has magnitude of the sum of the measures of the angles of the two rotations.

Unit 3

5 a.

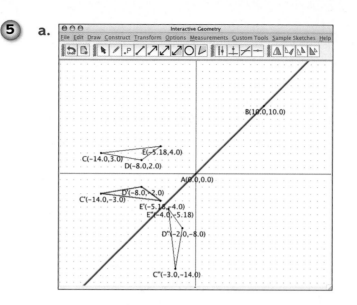

b. i. The size, shape, and orientation remain the same.

ii. The composite of the line reflections appears to be a counterclockwise rotation of 90°.

iii. Reflect across x-axis $\qquad (x, y) \rightarrow (x, -y)$
Reflect across $y = x$ $\qquad\qquad \rightarrow (-y, x)$
This confirms a counterclockwise rotation of 90° since the rule for the single transformation is $(x, y) \rightarrow (-y, x)$.

iv. Changing the order of the line reflections leads to a different final image. The composite transformation in the second case is a 270° counterclockwise rotation (or a 90° clockwise rotation).

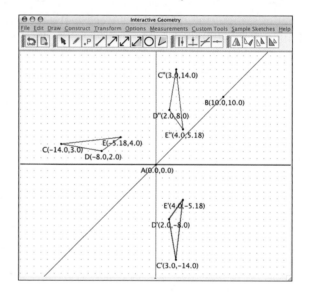

c. Reflecting across the *x*-axis and then the *y*-axis produces the display below.

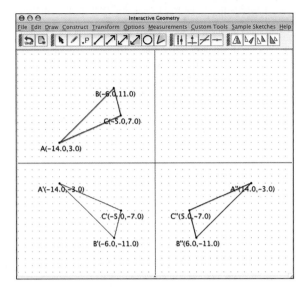

   i. The size, shape, and orientation remain the same.

   ii. It appears to be a 180° rotation about the origin.

   iii. Reflect across the *x*-axis $(x, y) \rightarrow (x, -y)$
   Reflect across the *y*-axis $\rightarrow (-x, -y)$
   This matches the coordinate rule for a 180° rotation about the origin, $(x, y) \rightarrow (-x, -y)$.

d. When you reflect across the same line twice, every point will be mapped back onto itself.

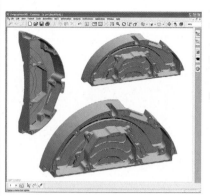

When composing transformations, the two transformations do not have to be two of the same kind. In the problems that follow, you will explore compositions of size transformations and rigid transformations (translations, rotations, and reflections). Such composite transformations allow shapes to be rotated and enlarged or reduced in computer graphics applications.

6 Combining a Rotation and a Size Transformation

Investigate the effects of composing a size transformation and a counterclockwise rotation with centers at the origin.

a. Suppose you rotate a triangle 90° counterclockwise about the origin and then apply a size transformation of magnitude 2 to the image triangle.

   i. Predict how the coordinates of the preimage will be related to those of the image.

   ii. Predict how the lengths of corresponding sides will be related.

   iii. Predict how the measures of corresponding angles will be related.

   iv. Predict how the areas of the preimage and image will be related.

b. Check your predictions by applying the composite transformation to △ABC with vertex coordinates A(1, 4), B(7, 1), and C(12, 8).

c. Reverse the order in which the transformations are applied—apply the size transformation first, then the rotation. How are the preimage and the image related this time?

d. On the basis of Parts a–c, what would you predict would happen if you used a different rotation with center at the origin but the same size transformation? The same rotation but a different size transformation? Would the order in which you applied the transformations lead to different final images? Test your conjectures.

7 Combining a Size Transformation and a Translation

Make a conjecture about the effects on shapes of composing a size transformation with center at the origin and a translation.

a. Test your conjecture by drawing △ABC with vertex coordinates A(2, 8), B(14, 4), and C(18, 10). Then find the image of △ABC under the composite transformation: size transformation of magnitude $\frac{1}{2}$ with center at the origin followed by a translation with components 3 and −10. What are the coordinates of the vertices of the image of △ABC under this composite transformation?

b. How are segment lengths affected by composing a size transformation with a translation?

c. How are angle measures affected by composing a size transformation with a translation?

6 a. For a 90° counterclockwise rotation about the origin and a size transformation of magnitude 2:

   i. $(x, y) \rightarrow (-y, x) \rightarrow (-2y, 2x)$ so the coordinate rule for the composition is $(x, y) \rightarrow (-2y, 2x)$.

   ii. The length of the image sides are changed by a factor of 2.

   iii. The angle sizes remain the same.

   iv. The area of the image triangle is changed by a factor of 4.

b.

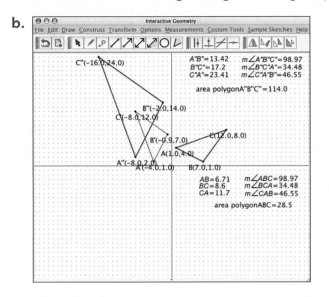

c. The relationship between the preimage and the image is the same regardless of the order in which the transformations are applied.

d. All answers to questions in Part a would be the same. It does not make a difference in which order the size transformation and rotation are applied.

7 a. Students will likely conjecture that an enlarged or reduced shape will occur at a new location. The vertices of the image of $\triangle ABC$ under this composite transformation are $A''(4, -6)$, $B''(10, -8)$, and $C''(12, -5)$.

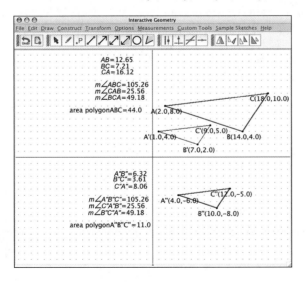

b. For a size transformation of magnitude $\frac{1}{2}$, the length of the image sides are changed by a factor of $\frac{1}{2}$.

c. Corresponding angle measures remain the same.

d. How are areas affected by composing a size transformation with a translation?

e. Does the order in which you apply the transformations lead to different final images? If it does, are the effects on segment lengths, angle measures, and areas different also? Give evidence supporting your claims.

Figures that are related by a size transformation, or by a composite of a size transformation with a rigid transformation, are called **similar**. The composite transformation is called a **similarity transformation**. In Problems 6 and 7, each of the preimage/image pairs of shapes are examples of similar shapes. The magnitude of the similarity transformation is the **scale factor**. It is the multiplier you use to convert lengths in the original figure to those in the similar image.

8 Examine the computer graphics screen to the right.

a. How would you check to see if the two dart shapes are similar?

b. Describe in words a similarity transformation that maps the smaller dart onto the larger dart.

c. Write a coordinate rule $(x, y) \rightarrow (\_\_, \_\_)$ that describes this similarity transformation.

d. Write a coordinate rule $(x, y) \rightarrow (\_\_, \_\_)$ that maps the larger dart onto the smaller dart. What is the scale factor?

9 Consider the similarity transformation that is the composition of these two transformations in the order given:

Transformation I $\qquad (x, y) \rightarrow \left(\frac{2}{3}x, \frac{2}{3}y\right)$

Transformation II $\qquad (x, y) \rightarrow (x, -y)$

a. Describe each of the transformations as completely as possible.

b. Suppose $\triangle PQR = \begin{bmatrix} 6 & 18 & 12 \\ 12 & 0 & -6 \end{bmatrix}$. What is the image of $\triangle PQR$ under the similarity transformation?

c. Write a rule $(x, y) \rightarrow (\_\_, \_\_)$ which describes the similarity transformation. Compare your rule to that of others and resolve any differences.

d. What is the scale factor of the similarity transformation?

e. How would your answers to Parts b–d change if Transformation II was applied first to $\triangle PQR$?

Unit 3

d. The area of the image triangle is changed by a factor of $\frac{1}{4}$.

e. With these two transformations, the order of application does produce a different image, but the two different images are congruent and so have the same length sides, angle measures, and areas. What is different is their positions in the coordinate plane. Students may justify this by looking at sketches and coordinates of a particular figure and images. The vertices of the composite transformation are $A''(2.5, -1)$, $B''(8.5, -3)$, and $C''(10.5, 0)$.

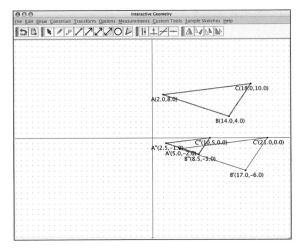

8　**a.** Find the lengths of the sides to see if corresponding sides are proportional. Then check to see if the angles formed by the sides of the dart are congruent.

　b. Rotate clockwise 90°, then use a size transformation centered at the origin with magnitude 2.

　c. $(x, y) \rightarrow (y, -x) \rightarrow (2y, -2x)$

　d. $(x, y) \rightarrow (-y, x) \rightarrow \left(-\frac{1}{2}y, \frac{1}{2}x\right)$. The scale factor is $\frac{1}{2}$.

9　**a.** Transformation I is a size transformation with scale factor $\frac{2}{3}$ and center at the origin. Transformation II is a reflection across the x-axis.

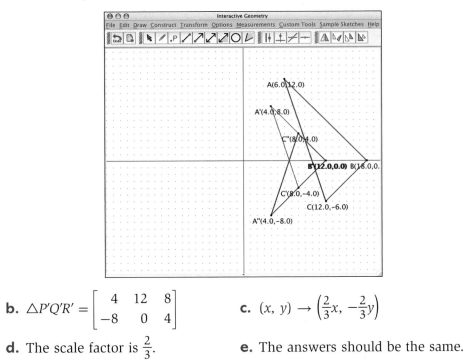

b. $\triangle P'Q'R' = \begin{bmatrix} 4 & 12 & 8 \\ -8 & 0 & 4 \end{bmatrix}$

c. $(x, y) \rightarrow \left(\frac{2}{3}x, -\frac{2}{3}y\right)$

d. The scale factor is $\frac{2}{3}$.

e. The answers should be the same.

In this investigation, you explored compositions of rigid transformations and size transformations.

a What kind of transformation is formed by composing the transformations given in each case below? Be as specific as you can.

   i. Two translations

   ii. Two counterclockwise rotations about the origin

   iii. Two line reflections involving lines intersecting at the origin

   iv. Two size transformations with center at the origin

b What kind of transformation is formed by composing a rigid transformation and a size transformation? Under such a transformation:

   i. how are corresponding segments of the preimage and image shapes related?

   ii. how are corresponding angles related?

   iii. how are corresponding areas related?

c Does the order in which you compose two transformations make a difference? Explain.

d If you are given symbolic rules for two transformations, how can you find a symbolic rule for the composite transformation?

Be prepared to share your ideas with the class.

✔Check Your Understanding

A figure is congruent to its image under the composition of two rigid transformations. The figure is similar to its image under the composition of a size transformation and a rigid transformation.

a. Refer to this coordinate grid. The scale on both axes is 1. For each pair of triangles given, determine if they are congruent or similar. In each case, describe in words a transformation or a composition of transformations that will map the first triangle onto the second.

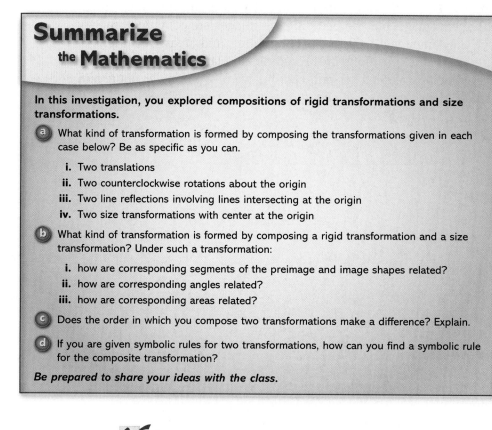

   i. △I and △IV

   ii. △II and △V

   iii. △III and △V

   iv. △V and △I

b. For each transformation you identified in Part a, write a symbolic rule that describes the transformation.

During your discussion of Part a, ask students, "Do you think your answer about rotations would be different if the center of the rotation was a point other than (0, 0)?" Follow this with similar questions for the center of a size transformation and the intersection point of two reflection lines.

Summarize
the Mathematics

Teaching Resources

Transparency Master 29.

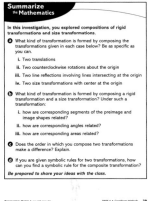

a   **i.** The resulting transformation will be a translation with components that are the sum of the components of the individual translations.

  ii. The composition of two rotations about the origin is a rotation about the origin with a magnitude that equals the sum of the magnitudes of the individual rotations.

  iii. The composition of two line reflections when lines intersect at the origin is a rotation about the origin.

  iv. The composition of two size transformations with center at the origin is a size transformation with center at the origin of magnitude equal to the product of the magnitudes of the individual size transformations.

b The composition of a rigid and a size transformation is called a similarity transformation.

  i. Corresponding segment lengths of the image are changed (magnified or reduced) by the scale factor.

  ii. Corresponding angle measures are the same for preimage and image shapes.

  iii. The area of the image is the scale factor squared times the preimage area.

c The order in which transformations are composed can make a difference.

    When a line reflection is composed with a different line reflection, the order matters (unless the lines of reflection are perpendicular).

    When a size transformation is composed with a translation, the order matters. (Problem 7)

    When two rotations (or size transformations) with center at the origin or two translations are composed, the order does *not* matter.

    When a size transformation is composed with a rotation both centered at the origin, the order does *not* matter. (Problem 6)

    When a size transformation is composed with a reflection across the x-axis, the order does *not* matter. (Problem 9)

    As a general rule of thumb, one should be careful when composing line reflections with any transformation and when composing translations with other transformations.

d Using the symbolic rule for the second transformation, substitute for x in the x-coordinate expression the x-coordinate expression in the symbolic rule for the first transformation. Similarly for the y-coordinate expression.

POSSIBLE MISCONCEPTION
Students may suggest that preimage and image segments are parallel under similarity transformations. This is not true in the case of a composition of a size transformation and a rotation (other than 180°).

COLLABORATION PROMPT
During this investigation, I practiced respectfully listening to others. An example is when I ... .

Unit 3

✔ Check Your Understanding

a. The transformations or composite of transformations that students give may differ. One possible response for each part is given here.

  i. Similar: a size transformation of magnitude 2 centered at the origin, then a translation with horizontal component -5 and vertical component 0

  ii. Similar: reflection across the x-axis, then a size transformation of magnitude $\frac{4}{3}$ centered at the origin

  iii. Congruent: 180° rotation about the origin, then a translation with horizontal component 0 and vertical component 1

  iv. A size transformation of magnitude $\frac{1}{2}$ centered at the origin, then a 90° counterclockwise rotation about the origin

b. **i.** $(x, y) \rightarrow (2x - 5, 2y)$

  ii. $(x, y) \rightarrow \left(\frac{4}{3}x, -\frac{4}{3}y\right)$

  iii. $(x, y) \rightarrow (-x, -y + 1)$

  iv. $(x, y) \rightarrow \left(-\frac{1}{2}y, \frac{1}{2}x\right)$

Teacher Notes

Applications

1 Copy each polygon below on a separate coordinate grid. Draw and label the transformed image according to the given rule. Identify as precisely as you can the type of transformation.

a. $(x, y) \rightarrow (x + 2, y - 3)$

b. $(x, y) \rightarrow (-y, x)$

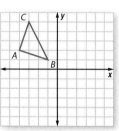

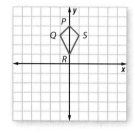

c. $(x, y) \rightarrow (-x, y)$

d. $(x, y) \rightarrow (-x, -y)$

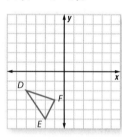

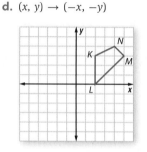

2 $\triangle ABC$ has vertices as follows: $A(1, 2)$, $B(4, 4)$, and $C(3, 6)$.

a. Draw $\triangle ABC$ on a coordinate grid. Then draw and label the image of $\triangle ABC$ under each of the following transformations.

   i. Translation with horizontal component 5 and vertical component -4

   ii. Horizontal translation 7 units to the left

   iii. Translation that maps the origin to the point $(-3, -6)$

b. Choose one of the image triangles in Part a and verify that it is congruent to $\triangle ABC$.

On Your Own

Applications

1 **a.**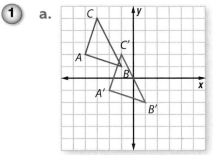

A translation with horizontal component 2 and vertical component −3

b.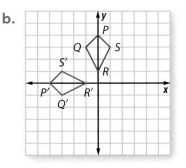

A 90° counterclockwise rotation about the origin

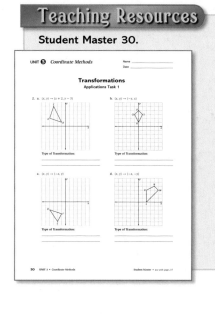
c.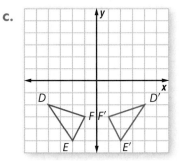

A reflection across the *y*-axis

d.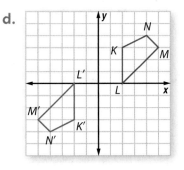

A 180° clockwise or counterclockwise rotation about the origin

2 The scale on these grids is 2.

a. **i.**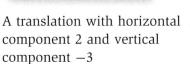

ii.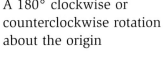

iii.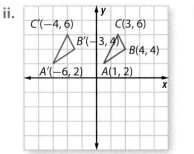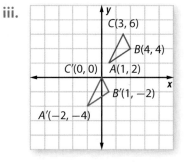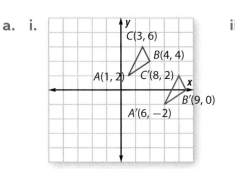

b. Students should verify that the triangles are congruent by the SSS congruence condition using the distance formula. $AB \approx 3.61$, $BC \approx 2.24$, and $AC \approx 4.47$.

Unit 3

3 △PQR has vertices as follows: P(3, −2), Q(6, −1), and R(4, 3).

a. On separate coordinate grids, draw △PQR and its image under each of the following transformations. Label the vertices of the images.

  i. Rotation of 180° about the origin

  ii. Rotation of 90° counterclockwise about the origin

  iii. Rotation of 90° clockwise about the origin

b. Choose one of the image triangles in Part a and verify that it is congruent to △PQR.

4 Consider ▱ABCD = $\begin{bmatrix} 1 & 2 & 6 & 5 \\ -1 & 2 & 2 & -1 \end{bmatrix}$.

a. On separate coordinate grids, draw ▱ABCD and its image under each of the following transformations. Label the vertices of the images.

  i. Reflection across the x-axis

  ii. Reflection across the line y = x

  iii. Reflection across the y-axis

b. Choose one of the image quadrilaterals in Part a and verify that it is a parallelogram.

c. What is the perimeter of ▱ABCD? How do you know that each of the image parallelograms in Part a will have the same perimeter?

5 Consider △PQR = $\begin{bmatrix} -2 & 2 & 0 \\ -1 & 1 & 5 \end{bmatrix}$.

a. What kind of triangle is △PQR? How do you know?

b. What is the area of △PQR?

c. On separate coordinate grids, draw △PQR and its image under each of the following transformations. Label the vertices of the images.

  i. Translation that maps the origin to the point (−2, −2)

  ii. Counterclockwise rotation of 270° about the origin

  iii. Reflection across the line y = −x

d. What kind of triangle is each of the three image triangles in Part c? How do you know?

e. Find and compare the areas of the three image triangles in Part c.

3 **a.** **i.**
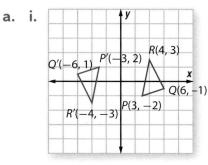

ii.
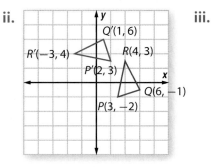

iii.
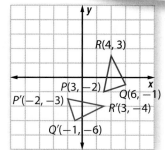

b. Students should verify that the triangles are congruent by the SSS congruence condition using the distance formula. $AB \approx 3.16$, $BC \approx 4.47$, and $AC \approx 5.1$.

4 **a.** **i.**
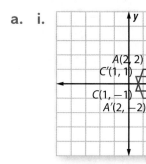

ii.
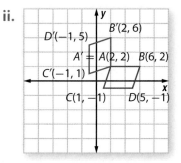

iii.
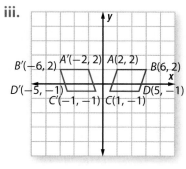

b. $A'B' = C'D' \approx 3.16$ and $B'C' = A'C' = 4$. Since opposite sides are congruent, $ABCD$ is a parallelogram. Alternatively, students might verify using slopes.

c. The perimeter of $\Box ABCD$ is approximately 14.32 units. Since lengths are congruent under line reflections, the image parallelogram will have the same perimeter.

5 **a.** Triangle PQR is an isosceles right triangle. The slope of $\overline{PQ}$ is 0.5 and the slope of $\overline{QR}$ is -2. Since the slope of $\overline{QR}$ is the opposite reciprocal of the slope of $\overline{PQ}$, the lines are perpendicular. Alternatively, students can use the converse of the Pythagorean Theorem to conclude that $\angle Q$ is a right angle. Since $PQ = QR = \sqrt{20}$, the triangle is isosceles.

b. The area of $\triangle PQR$ is 10 square units: $\dfrac{\sqrt{20}\ \sqrt{20}}{2} = \dfrac{20}{2} = 10$.

c. **i.**
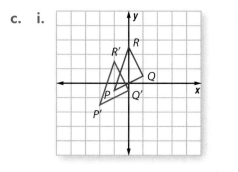

ii.
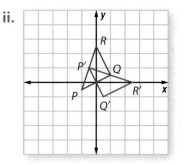

iii.
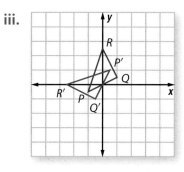

NOTE Solutions for Task 5 Parts d and e are on page T219.

Unit 3

(6) A triangle translation program that implements the translation planning algorithm in Investigation 1, Problem 5 (page 199) is given below.

a. Analyze this program and explain the purpose of each command line not already described.

b. Enter the program in your calculator and test the program with a sample triangle.

TRANSL Program

Program	Function in Program
ClrHome	1. Clears the home screen.
Input "X1 COORD-PRE",A	2. Requests input for x-coordinate of one vertex. Stores the value in variable named A.
Input "Y1 COORD-PRE",B	3. _____
Input "X2 COORD-PRE",C	4. _____
Input "Y2 COORD-PRE",D	5. _____
Input "X3 COORD-PRE",E	6. _____
Input "Y3 COORD-PRE",F	7. _____
Input "X COMP-TRANS",H	8. _____
Input "Y COMP-TRANS",K	9. Requests input for the vertical component of the translation. Stores the value in variable K.
ClrHome	10. _____
Disp "PREIMAGE"	11. _____
Pause	12. Pause stops a program from continuing until ENTER is pressed.
ClrDraw	13. Clears all drawings.
Line(A,B,C,D)	14. Draws a line segment from vertex (A, B) to vertex (C, D).
Line(C,D,E,F)	15. _____
Line(E,F,A,B)	16. _____
Pause	17. _____
ClrHome	18. _____
Disp "IMAGE"	19. _____
Pause	20. _____
Line(A+H,B+K,C+H,D+K)	21. _____
Line(C+H,D+K,E+H,F+K)	22. _____
Line(E+H,F+K,A+H,B+K)	23. _____

d. The images are all isosceles right triangles because for each of the transformations, the lengths of the image segments are congruent to the lengths of the original segments. All images are congruent to △*PQR*.

e. The area of each of the three image triangles is 10 square units. Areas are not changed by translations, rotations, or reflections.

6 **a–b.** **INSTRUCTIONAL NOTE** Some students may find the programming language intimidating and may need help to make sense of what the program instructions do.

Lines 3, 5, and 7 request input of the *y*-coordinate for three different points, then store the values in *B*, *D*, and *F*, respectively.

Lines 4 and 6 request input of the *x*-coordinate for two different points, then store the values in *C* and *E*, respectively.

Line 8 requests input of the horizontal component of the translation, then stores the value in variable *H*.

Lines 10 and 18 clear the home screen.

Line 11 displays the word "PREIMAGE" on the home screen.

Lines 15 and 16 draw the remaining two line segments that make up the triangle.

Lines 17 and 20 stop the program from continuing until **ENTER** is pressed.

Lines 21–23 draw the three line segments that make up the image triangle.

Teaching Resources

Student Master 31.

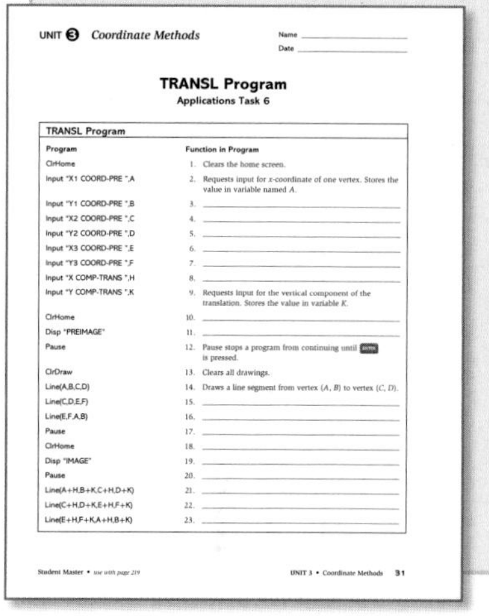

Unit 3

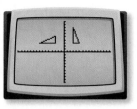

7 Look back at the TRANSL program in Applications Task 6.

   a. How would you modify the program to display a triangle and its image under a 90° counterclockwise rotation about the origin?

   b. Enter the modified program, name it ROT90 in your calculator, and test the program with a sample triangle.

8 Copy each polygon below on a separate coordinate grid. Draw and label the transformed image according to the given rule. Identify as precisely as you can the type of transformation.

   a. $(x, y) \rightarrow (3x, 3y)$

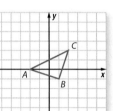

   b. $(x, y) \rightarrow (-x + 8, y)$

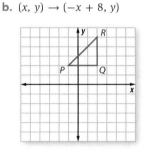

   c. $(x, y) \rightarrow \left(\frac{1}{2}x, \frac{1}{2}y\right)$

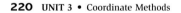

   d. $(x, y) \rightarrow (x, -y - 4)$

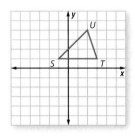

9 A picture is to be placed in a brochure, and the designer wants it positioned in a 2" × 3" frame. If the original picture is 6" × 9", what size transformation should be applied to the picture so it will fit the frame?

7 **a–b.** One modified program would delete lines 8 and 9 and revise the
image display (lines 21–23) to be

Line(−B,A,−D,C)
Line(−D,C,−F,E)
Line(−F,E,−B,A)

8 **a.**

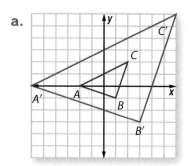

Size transformation centered
at the origin of magnitude 3

b.

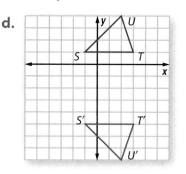

Reflection across the *y*-axis
followed by a horizontal
translation of 8 units to the right
(or reflection across the line
$x = 4$)

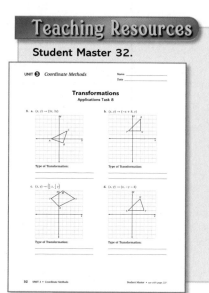
c.

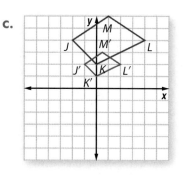

Size transformation centered
at the origin of magnitude $\frac{1}{2}$

d.

Reflection across the *x*-axis
followed by a vertical translation
down 4 units (or reflection across
the line $y = -2$)

9 A size transformation: $(x, y) \rightarrow \left(\frac{1}{3}x, \frac{1}{3}y\right)$

Unit 3

10 Consider quadrilateral $ABCD = \begin{bmatrix} 6 & -4 & -3 & 7 \\ 2 & 0 & -5 & -3 \end{bmatrix}$.

    a. Draw quadrilateral $ABCD$ on a coordinate grid.

    b. Draw the image quadrilateral, $A'B'C'D'$, resulting from transforming $ABCD$ with a size transformation of magnitude 2.5 and center at the origin.

    c. How do $\overleftrightarrow{AB}$ and $\overleftrightarrow{BC}$ appear to be related? How do $\overleftrightarrow{A'B'}$ and $\overleftrightarrow{B'C'}$ appear to be related? Verify your conjectures using coordinates.

    d. How do $\overleftrightarrow{AB}$ and $\overleftrightarrow{A'B'}$ appear to be related? How do $\overleftrightarrow{BC}$ and $\overleftrightarrow{B'C'}$ appear to be related? Verify your conjectures using coordinates.

    e. Find the area of quadrilateral $ABCD$.

        i. Predict the area of quadrilateral $A'B'C'D'$.

        ii. Check your prediction.

    f. Connect each preimage point and its image with a line. What is true about the lines?

11 Preimage and image pairs of a figure under certain transformations are shown below. The image figure is darker blue. In each case, identify as precisely as you can the type of transformation. Then write a coordinate rule for the transformation.

a.

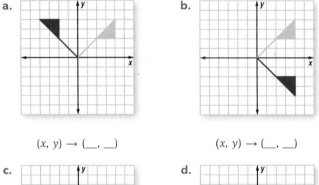

$(x, y) \rightarrow (\_\_, \_\_)$

b.

$(x, y) \rightarrow (\_\_, \_\_)$

c.

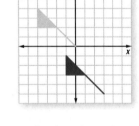

$(x, y) \rightarrow (\_\_, \_\_)$

d.

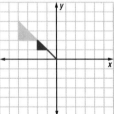

$(x, y) \rightarrow (\_\_, \_\_)$

10 a–b.

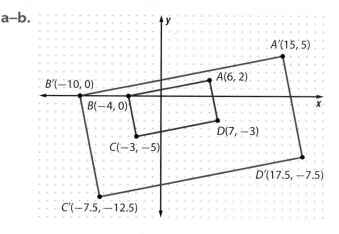

c. The slope of $\overleftrightarrow{AB}$ is $\frac{1}{5}$ and the slope of $\overleftrightarrow{BC}$ is -5; therefore $\overleftrightarrow{AB}$ is perpendicular to $\overleftrightarrow{BC}$. The same is true for $\overleftrightarrow{A'B'}$ and $\overleftrightarrow{B'C'}$.

d. $\overleftrightarrow{AB}$ and $\overleftrightarrow{A'B'}$ (and $\overleftrightarrow{BC}$ and $\overleftrightarrow{B'C'}$) appear to be parallel. Checking, the slope of $\overleftrightarrow{A'B'}$ is $\frac{1}{5}$ which is the same as the slope of $\overleftrightarrow{AB}$. The slopes of $\overleftrightarrow{BC}$ and $\overleftrightarrow{B'C'}$ are -5.

e. *Area of quadrilateral ABCD* $= \sqrt{104}\,\sqrt{26} \approx 52$ square units

   i. Students should predict the area to be $52 \cdot (2.5)^2$ square units.

   ii. *Area of quadrilateral A'B'C'D'* $\approx 52(2.5^2) = 325$ square units

f. The lines all intersect at the origin which is the center of the transformation.

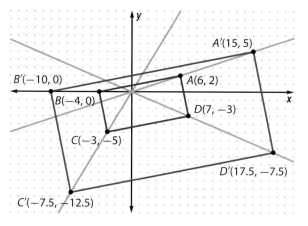

11 a. A 90° counterclockwise rotation about the origin: $(x, y) \rightarrow (-y, x)$

b. A reflection across the x-axis: $(x, y) \rightarrow (x, -y)$

c. A translation of $(3, -5)$: $(x, y) \rightarrow (x + 3, y - 5)$

d. A size transformation centered at $(0, 0)$ of magnitude $\frac{1}{2}$:

$$(x, y) \rightarrow \left(\tfrac{1}{2}x, \tfrac{1}{2}y\right)$$

12 Size transformations have their center at the origin. However, in producing graphics displays, it is sometimes useful to enlarge or reduce a figure using a center different from the origin.

a. Consider the following procedure for applying a size transformation to a figure when the center of the size transformation is $A(2, 1)$ and the magnitude is 3.

Draw $\triangle PQR$ on a coordinate grid. Plot point A.

$$\triangle PQR = \begin{bmatrix} 3 & 4 & 4 \\ 3 & 3 & 5 \end{bmatrix}$$

Step 1: Determine the horizontal and vertical components of the translation that will translate $A(2, 1)$ to the origin. Find the image of $\triangle PQR$ under that translation. Label as $\triangle 1$ the image of $\triangle PQR$.

Step 2: Apply a size transformation to $\triangle 1$ using the origin as center and 3 as the magnitude. Label the new image $\triangle 2$.

Step 3: Find the components of the translation that maps the origin back to $A(2, 1)$. Then find the image of $\triangle 2$ under that transformation. Label the final image $\triangle P'Q'R'$.

b. Examine $\triangle PQR$ and $\triangle P'Q'R'$. Does this procedure produce the desired result—that is, a size transformation of magnitude 3 with center $A(2, 1)$? Explain.

c. Write a symbolic rule $(x, y) \rightarrow (\_\_, \_\_)$ that describes this composite transformation.

13 Modify the "translate-transform-translate back" procedure outlined in Applications Task 12 to create a procedure for rotating $\triangle PQR$ 90° counterclockwise about the point $A(2, 1)$. Then write a symbolic rule $(x, y) \rightarrow (\_\_, \_\_)$ that describes this composite transformation.

14 For each of the following pairs of triangles, describe a composition of two or more transformations that will map the first triangle to the second triangle. Write a symbolic rule $(x, y) \rightarrow (\_\_, \_\_)$ that describes the composite transformation.

a. $\triangle$I onto $\triangle$II

b. $\triangle$I onto $\triangle$III

c. $\triangle$II onto $\triangle$IV

d. $\triangle$I onto $\triangle$IV

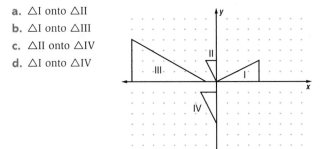

12 **a–b.** This method correctly performs the size transformation centered at $A(2, 1)$. The center A is moved to the origin by the initial translation $(x, y) \to (-2, -1)$; this also moves the position of $\triangle PQR$ to $\triangle 1$. Then the size transformation is applied using the center $(0, 0)$. Finally, the image $\triangle 2$ along with the center is translated back, using the opposite of the original translation. This triple composition sends the point $(2, 1)$ to its original position.

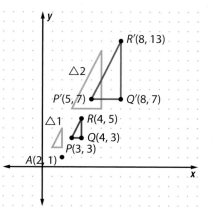

c. $(x, y) \to (3(x - 2) + 2, 3(y - 1) + 1) = (3x - 4, 3y - 2)$

13 The procedure should only be different in Step 3. At that point, a 90° counterclockwise rotation about the origin should be applied.
$(x, y) \to (-(y - 1) + 2, (x - 2) + 1) = (-y + 3, x - 1)$

14 Descriptions may vary, but simplified symbolic rules should be the same as those below.

a. A 90° counterclockwise rotation about the origin and a size transformation centered at $(0, 0)$ of magnitude $\frac{1}{2}$ (The order of the transformations is not important.) $(x, y) \to \left(-\frac{1}{2}y, \frac{1}{2}x\right)$

b. A reflection across the y-axis and a size transformation centered at $(0, 0)$ of magnitude 2 (The order of the transformations is not important.) $(x, y) \to (-2x, 2y)$

c. A size transformation centered at $(0, 0)$ of magnitude 1.5 and then a vertical translation down 4 units (Order is important here.)
$(x, y) \to (1.5x, 1.5y - 4)$

d. A 90° counterclockwise rotation and a size transformation both centered at the origin of magnitude $\frac{3}{4}$ (in either order), then a vertical translation down 4 units $(x, y) \to \left(-\frac{3}{4}y - 4, \frac{3}{4}x - 4\right)$

Unit 3

Connections

15 Suppose a size transformation with magnitude k and center at the origin maps points $A(x_1, y_1)$ and $B(x_2, y_2)$ onto points A' and B', respectively.

   a. What are the coordinates of points A' and B'?

   b. Ivan provided the following general argument to show that distance $A'B' = k \cdot$ (distance AB).

   Check the correctness of Ivan's work by giving a reason justifying each step. Correct any errors that you find.

$$\text{distance } A'B' = \sqrt{(kx_1 - kx_2)^2 + (ky_1 - ky_2)^2} \quad (1)$$

$$\text{distance } A'B' = \sqrt{k^2(x_1 - x_2)^2 + k^2(y_1 - y_2)^2} \quad (2)$$

$$\text{distance } A'B' = k\sqrt{(x_1 - x_2)^2 + (y_1 - y_2)^2} \quad (3)$$

$$\text{distance } A'B' = k \cdot (\text{distance } AB) \quad (4)$$

   c. Use the definition of slope and reasoning with the general coordinates of points A, B, A', and B' to show that $\overleftrightarrow{A'B'}$ is parallel to $\overleftrightarrow{AB}$.

   d. State in words the property of size transformations you justified in Part c.

16 In Investigation 1, you developed a rule for a reflection across the y-axis. You can use a "translate-transform-translate back" method (see Applications Tasks 12 and 13) to develop rules for reflections across other vertical lines.

   a. Draw the vertical line $x = 5$ on a coordinate grid. To find the coordinates of the reflected image of point $A(a, b)$ across this line:

   i. translate the line $x = 5$ so that it coincides with the y-axis. What are the horizontal and vertical components of that translation? What are the coordinates of A_1, the image of $A(a, b)$ under the translation?

   ii. What are the coordinates of the image of A_1 when reflected across the y-axis? Label the image point A_2.

   iii. What are the components of the translation that maps the y-axis (back) to the line $x = 5$? What are the coordinates of A', the image of A_2 under that translation?

   iv. Write a symbolic rule $(x, y) \rightarrow (\_\_, \_\_)$ that describes the composite transformation.

   b. The rule $(x, y) \rightarrow (-x + 2h, y)$ gives the coordinates of the reflected image of any point (x, y) across the vertical line $x = h$.

   i. Verify the rule for the point $P(2, -6)$ reflected across the line $x = -3$.

   ii. Use the translate-transform-translate back connection to show that the general rule is correct.

Connections

15 **a.** $A' = (kx_1, ky_1)$ and $B' = (kx_2, ky_2)$

b. Ivan is correct.

distance $A'B' = \sqrt{(kx_1 - kx_2)^2 + (ky_1 - ky_2)^2}$ (1) Distance formula

distance $A'B' = \sqrt{k^2(x_1 - x_2)^2 + k^2(y_1 - y_2)^2}$ (2) Distributive property and Power of a Product $(ab)^2 = a^2b^2$

distance $A'B' = k\sqrt{(x_1 - x_2)^2 + (y_1 - y_2)^2}$ (3) Distributive property and $\sqrt{a^2b} = a\sqrt{b}$

distance $A'B' = k \cdot$ (distance AB)   (4) Distance formula

c. The slope of $\overleftrightarrow{AB}$ is $\dfrac{y_1 - y_2}{x_1 - x_2}$.

The slope of $\overleftrightarrow{A'B'}$ is $\dfrac{ky_1 - ky_2}{kx_1 - kx_2} = \dfrac{k(y_1 - y_2)}{k(x_1 - x_2)} = \dfrac{y_1 - y_2}{x_1 - x_2}$.

d. Under a size transformation, an image line is parallel to the preimage line.

16 **a.** **i.** $(h, k) = (-5, 0)$
$A(a, b) \rightarrow A_1(a - 5, b)$

ii. $A_2(5 - a, b)$

iii. $(h, k) = (5, 0)$
$A'(10 - a, b)$

iv. $(x, y) \rightarrow (10 - x, y)$

b. **i.** $P(2, -6) \rightarrow P'(-8, -6)$

ii. Translate to y-axis $(x, y) \rightarrow (x - h, y)$
Reflect across y-axis $\rightarrow (-x + h, y)$
Translate to line $x = h$ $\rightarrow (-x + 2h, y)$

INSTRUCTIONAL NOTE
Task 15 provides an opportunity to discuss properties of powers, specifically in regard to squares and square roots.

Unit 3

17 In Investigation 1, you developed a rule for a reflection across the *x*-axis. Symbolic rules can also be developed for reflections across other horizontal lines. Use reasoning similar to that in Connections Task 16 to write a rule that gives the coordinates of the image of any point (*x*, *y*) when reflected across the horizontal line *y* = *k*.

18 Draw and label a triangle or quadrilateral of your choice. Reflect the figure across the *x*-axis and then reflect the image across the line *y* = −6.

   a. Compare the size, shape, and orientation of the preimage and image under the composite transformation.

   b. What kind of transformation does the composite transformation appear to be? Write a symbolic rule (*x*, *y*) → (__, __) that describes the composite transformation.

   c. Does the order in which you apply the two line reflections lead to the same final image?

19 Investigate the effects of composing a reflection across a line with a translation in a direction parallel to the line.

   a. On a coordinate grid, draw a triangle △*ABC* near the *x*-axis to represent a duck foot. Record the coordinates of its vertices.

   b. Reflect △*ABC* across the *x*-axis, then translate the image horizontally 8 units. Label the final image △*A'B'C'*.

   c. How are the coordinates of △*A'B'C'* related to those of △*ABC*? Write a coordinate rule for this composite transformation.

   d. Apply the same combination of the two transformations to △*ABC* but in the opposite order. Does the order in which you apply the translation and reflection matter?

   e. Now apply the coordinate rule you gave in Part c at least three more times to △*A'B'C'*. Describe how alternate images such as images one and three or two and four are related.

   f. The combination of a reflection across a line and a translation in a direction parallel to the line is called a **glide reflection**.

   i. Start with a new triangle. Then apply a glide reflection in which the reflection line is the *y*-axis.

   ii. Write a coordinate rule for this glide reflection.

17 $(x, y) \rightarrow (x, -y + 2k)$

18 **a.** The size, shape, and orientation are the same.

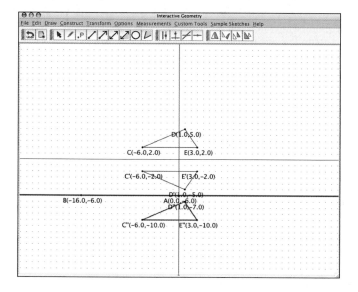

b. It is a translation. $(x, y) \rightarrow (x, y - 12)$

c. The order does make a difference. Students should check with an example.

19 **a–b.** Student choices of triangles will vary.

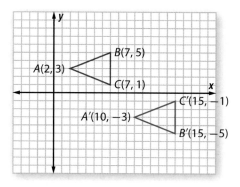

c. For the image triangle, the x-coordinate increases by 8 and the y-coordinate is the opposite value: $(x, y) \rightarrow (x + 8, -y)$.

d. The order in which you apply the transformations does not matter.

e. Alternate images are related by a translation with horizontal component 16.

f. **i.** Student choices of triangles and vertical component will vary.

ii. Student coordinate rules should match their choice for a glide reflection. In general, $(x, y) \rightarrow (-x, y + k)$.

20 The order in which two transformations are composed is often important.

    a. In Investigation 3, you found that the order in which you applied a size transformation and a rotation about the origin made no difference. Use the symbolic representations for a size transformation $(x, y) \rightarrow (kx, ky)$ and a 90° counterclockwise rotation about the origin $(x, y) \rightarrow (-y, x)$ to justify this observation.

    b. Order makes a difference in composing size transformations and translations. Use symbolic representations of these transformations to explain why and how the positions of the images differ.

    c. Order makes a difference in composing two different line reflections. Use symbolic representations of a reflection across the *x*-axis and a reflection across the line $y = x$ to explain why and how the positions of the images differ.

21 Refer to the table you completed for Connections Task 18 in Lesson 1 (page 188). Extend that table to include the coordinate models of rigid transformations you developed in this lesson.

Geometric Transformation	Coordinate Model	Example
Translation	$(x, y) \rightarrow (x + h, y + k)$	
Reflection across *y*-axis		
Reflection across line $x = h$	See Connections Task 16	
Reflection across *x*-axis		
Reflection across line $y = k$	See Connections Task 17	
Reflection across line $y = x$		
Reflection across line $y = -x$		
90° counterclockwise rotation about origin		
180° rotation about origin		
270° counterclockwise rotation about origin		
Size transformation magnitude *k* and center at the origin		
Similarity transformation		

20 **a.**

		Counterclockwise rotation of 90°		Size transformation
(x, y)	$\rightarrow$	$(-y, x)$	$\rightarrow$	$(-ky, kx)$

		Size transformation		Counterclockwise rotation of 90°
(x, y)	$\rightarrow$	(kx, ky)	$\rightarrow$	$(-ky, kx)$

b.

		Size transformation		Translation (a, b)
(x, y)	$\rightarrow$	(kx, ky)	$\rightarrow$	$(kx + a, ky + b)$

		Translation (a, b)		Size transformation
(x, y)	$\rightarrow$	$(x + a, y + b)$	$\rightarrow$	$(kx + ka, ky + kb)$

When the size transformation is applied first, the translation components are not multiplied by a factor of k, as they are when the translation is applied first. (The images differ by a translation with horizontal component $(k - 1)a$ and vertical component $(k - 1)b$, where a and b are the respective components of the translation.)

c.

Reflection across x-axis				Reflection across $y = x$
(x, y)	$\rightarrow$	$(x, -y)$	$\rightarrow$	$(-y, x)$

Reflection across $y = x$				Reflection across x-axis
(x, y)	$\rightarrow$	(y, x)	$\rightarrow$	$(y, -x)$

The images have opposite coordinates. Thus, they would be 180° rotations of each other.

21

Geometric Idea	Coordinate Model	Example
Translation	$(x, y) \rightarrow (x + h, y + k)$	$(3, 4) \rightarrow (8, 1)$ $(h = 5, k = -3)$
Reflection across y-axis	$(x, y) \rightarrow (-x, y)$	$(2, 5) \rightarrow (-2, 5)$
Reflection across line $x = h$	$(x, y) \rightarrow (2h - x, y)$	$(-2, 3) \rightarrow (10, 3)$, $(h = 3)$
Reflection across x-axis	$(x, y) \rightarrow (x, -y)$	$(1, -3) \rightarrow (1, 3)$
Reflection across line $y = k$	$(x, y) \rightarrow (x, 2k - y)$	$(-2, 3) \rightarrow (-2, 5)$, $(k = 4)$
Reflection across line $y = x$	$(x, y) \rightarrow (y, x)$	$(3, 6) \rightarrow (6, 3)$
Reflection across line $y = -x$	$(x, y) \rightarrow (-y, -x)$	$(-2, 5) \rightarrow (-5, 2)$
90° counterclockwise rotation about the origin	$(x, y) \rightarrow (-y, x)$	$(6, -1) \rightarrow (1, 6)$
180° rotation about the origin	$(x, y) \rightarrow (-x, -y)$	$(3, -2) \rightarrow (-3, 2)$
270° counterclockwise rotation about the origin	$(x, y) \rightarrow (y, -x)$	$(2, 5) \rightarrow (5, -2)$
Size transformation magnitude k and center at the origin	$(x, y) \rightarrow (kx, ky)$	$(3, 4) \rightarrow (6, 8)$ $(k = 2)$
Similarity transformation	The composition of a size transformation and any of the above rigid transformations	$(x, y) \rightarrow (8y, 8x)$

Unit 3

22 If you reflect a point $P(x, y)$ across the y-axis, its image is $P'(-x, y)$. If you then reflect the image point $P'(-x, y)$ across the y-axis, the final image is $P(x, y)$, your original point.

a. For each rigid transformation (translation, line reflection, rotation, and glide reflection (see Connections Task 19)), describe a transformation with which it can be composed so that for any point, the preimage and the final image are the same.

b. For a size transformation with magnitude k and center at the origin, describe a transformation with which it can be composed so that for any point, the preimage and the final image are the same.

c. How is your work in Parts a and b related to the concept of *multiplicative inverses* for real numbers and for matrices?

Reflections

23 What clockwise rotation will be the same as a 270° counterclockwise rotation? Why? What clockwise rotation will be the same as a 90° counterclockwise rotation? Why?

24 In Investigations 1 and 2, you and your classmates developed symbolic rules for describing various transformations of a coordinate plane. If you forget one of these rules, how would you go about reconstructing it? Illustrate with a rule for a specific transformation.

25 How is the **Zoom** feature on your graphing calculator or computer software like a size transformation?

a. What determines the center?

b. What determines the magnitude?

26 The coordinate models of size transformations that you investigated had their centers at the origin of a coordinate plane. Think about how you could enlarge a figure *without* using a coordinate grid. Draw a triangle PQR on a sheet of plain paper. Mark a point C on the paper. How could you use a ruler to find the image of $\triangle PQR$ under a size transformation with the given point as center and magnitude 3? Write an explanation of your method that could be used by a classmate.

27 For all the rigid transformations and size transformations you examined in Lesson 2, the image of a line is a line. For some of the transformations, the image of a line is *always* parallel to the preimage line. For which transformations is the image of a line parallel to the preimage? Verify your choices by showing that the image of the line containing points $(-1, 3)$ and $(2, 5)$ is parallel to the preimage line for each transformation.

22 **a.** Translation For a translation with components (h, k), use the
translation with components $(-h, -k)$:
$$(x, y) \rightarrow (x + h, y + k) \rightarrow (x + h - h, y + k - k) \rightarrow (x, y)$$

Reflection For a reflection across a line, use the reflection across the
same line. For example, across the line $y = -x$:
$$(x, y) \rightarrow (-y, -x) \rightarrow (-(-x), -(-y)) \rightarrow (x, y)$$

Rotation For a counterclockwise rotation of $n°$, use a
counterclockwise rotation of $(360 - n)°$. For example,
a counterclockwise rotation of 270° followed by a
counterclockwise rotation of 90°:
$$(x, y) \rightarrow (y, -x) \rightarrow (-(-x), y) \rightarrow (x, y)$$

Glide For a glide reflection, you would translate with the
Reflection opposite coordinates and then reflect across the same line.
For example, for a glide reflection across the x-axis with
horizontal translation h, use a horizontal translation of $-h$
followed by a reflection across the x-axis.

b. For a size transformation centered at the origin of magnitude k, use a
size transformation of magnitude $\frac{1}{k}$ centered at the origin.

c. In Parts a and b, we were finding a transformation that undoes the
original transformation, the same way that multiplying a by $\frac{1}{a}$ undoes
the effect of multiplying by a and multiplying a matrix A by A^{-1}
undoes the effect of multiplying by A.

Reflections

23 Assuming the same centers, clockwise rotation of 90° will be the same as
a 270° counterclockwise rotation. Likewise, a 270° clockwise rotation will
be the same as a counterclockwise rotation of 90°. This is because a circle
has 360°, and 270° + 90°= 360°. So, 90° in one direction brings you to
the same place as 270° in the opposite direction.

24 Most students probably will suggest choosing three or four points and
performing the indicated transformation, based upon what they know
about the transformation. Then, by examining the coordinates of the
preimage points and the image points, they should be able to reconstruct
the symbolic rule.

25 The **Zoom** feature scales the shape proportionally larger or smaller.

a. The location of the cursor determines the center.

b. Zoom factors define the magnification.

26 • Draw $\overleftrightarrow{CP}$, $\overleftrightarrow{CQ}$, and $\overleftrightarrow{CR}$. Extend the lines well beyond the endpoints
of $\triangle PQR$.

• Measure the distance CP.

• Multiply the measurement by 3 and mark off that length on $\overleftrightarrow{CP}$ from C
in the direction of P. Mark the length as $\overline{CP'}$.

• Repeat for Q and R.

• Draw $\triangle P'Q'R'$.

NOTE The solution to
Task 27 is on page T227.

Unit 3

28. In your earlier work in algebra, you learned how to recognize linear, exponential, and quadratic functions by the form of their symbolic rules. Geometric transformations also can be recognized by their symbolic rules. What transformation is defined by each of the following coordinate rules?

    a. $(x, y) \rightarrow (5y, 5x)$

    b. $(x, y) \rightarrow \left(-\frac{1}{2}x, -\frac{1}{2}y\right)$

    c. $(x, y) \rightarrow (4x - 12, 4y + 8)$

Extensions

29. A line ℓ contains points $A(a, b)$ and $B(c, d)$. Use these general coordinates to justify each of the following statements:

    a. Under a 180° rotation about the origin, the image of a line is a line parallel to the preimage line.

    b. Under a translation with components h and k, the image of a line is a line parallel to the preimage line.

30. In Investigation 3, Problem 5 (page 213), you found that the composition of reflections across two intersecting lines was a rotation about their point of intersection. In Connections Task 18 (page 224), you found that the composition of reflections across two parallel lines was a translation.

    a. Use interactive geometry software to explore the composition of reflections across any two intersecting lines. Is the composite transformation always a rotation? If so, what is the center of the rotation? How are the direction and amount of rotation related to the two intersecting lines?

    b. Use interactive geometry software to explore the composition of reflections across any two parallel lines. Is the composite transformation always a translation? If so, how are the direction and magnitude related to the two parallel lines?

31. This task will provide you additional experiences using the programming window of your interactive geometry software and in analyzing programs for the "Design by Robot" custom tool.

    a. Predict the shape created by the command:

       fd 3 rt 90 fd 4 rt 143 fd 5

       Check your prediction.

    b. The **fd** and **rt** instructions translate and rotate the position of the robot.

       i. For each translation instruction in Part a, describe the magnitude and direction of the translation.

       ii. For each rotation instruction in Part a, describe the center and angle of rotation (clockwise/counterclockwise).

LESSON 2 • Coordinate Models of Transformations **227**

27 Under any translation or size transformation centered at the origin, the image of a line is parallel to the preimage line.

28 **a.** A similarity transformation that is the composite of a size transformation centered at the origin of magnitude 5 and a reflection across the line $y = x$ (Order is not important.)

b. A similarity transformation that is the composite of a 180° rotation and a size transformation both centered at the origin of magnitude $\frac{1}{2}$ (Order is not important.)

c. A similarity transformation that can be described as one of the following composite transformations (order is important):

(1) a size transformation centered at the origin of magnitude 4 followed by a translation with horizontal component −12 and vertical component 8, or

(2) a translation with components (−3, 2) followed by a size transformation centered at the origin of magnitude 4.

Extensions

29 **a.** The slope of the line containing preimage points (a, b) and (c, d) is $\frac{d - b}{c - a}$. The coordinates of the image points under a 180° rotation about the origin are $(-a, -b)$ and $(-c, -d)$. The slope of the line containing the image points is $\frac{-d + b}{-c + a} = \frac{-1(d - b)}{-1(c - a)} = \frac{d - b}{c - a}$. The image and preimage lines have equal slopes and so they must be parallel.

b. The slope of the line containing preimage points (a, b) and (c, d) is $\frac{d - b}{c - a}$. The coordinates of the image points under a translation with components (h, k) are $(a + h, b + k)$ and $(c + h, d + k)$. The slope of the line containing the image points is $\frac{(d + k) - (b + k)}{(c + h) - (a + h)}$, or $\frac{d - b}{c - a}$. The image and preimage lines have equal slopes and so they must be parallel.

30 **a.**

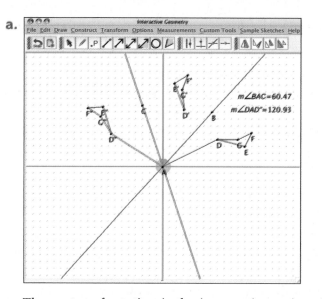

The center of rotation is the intersection point of the two lines of reflection. To find the direction of rotation (clockwise or counterclockwise), identify the nonobtuse angle formed by the intersecting lines. The direction is from the first line of reflection to the second line of reflection. The amount of rotation is twice the measure of this nonobtuse angle.

b.

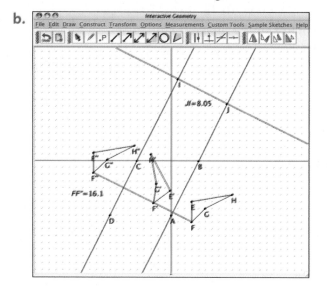

The composition of reflections across any two parallel lines is a translation. A figure is translated along a line perpendicular to the parallel lines through a distance twice the distance between the two parallel lines. The direction of the translation is from the first line of reflection to the second.

31

a. The shape is a 3-4-5 right triangle.

b. **i.** **fd 3** is 3 units directly up.

fd 4 is 4 units directly right.

fd 5 is 5 units 143° clockwise from the horizontal.

ii. **rt 90** has the center of the robot at (0, 3) and a clockwise rotation of 90°.

rt 143 has the center of the robot at (4, 3) and a clockwise rotation of 143°.

c. Transformations are performed on images of other transformations.

d. i–ii. The program "triangle" draws a 3-4-5 right triangle and various size transformations using magnitudes 1, 2, and 4.

e. **repeat 4 [fd 10 rt 90]** draws a square with sides of length 10 units. The robot is then rotated clockwise 72° and a congruent square is drawn in the same way as the first. This is repeated three more times to form the shape below.

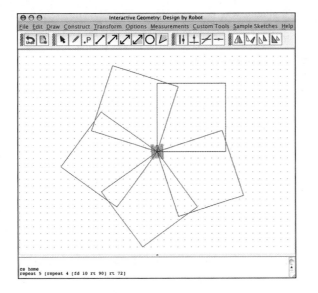

Unit 3

c. How is the idea of composition of transformations used in the command in Part a?

d. Enter the *procedure* below in your software programming window.

```
program triangle
parameter [k]
fd 3*k rt 90
fd 4*k rt 143
fd 5*k
home
end
```

i. Explore what happens when you type each of these commands in the command window (after closing the pop-up window).

- triangle 1
- triangle 2
- triangle 4

ii. How does the "triangle" procedure use the idea of transformation of shape?

e. Predict the figure created by the following program. Then check your prediction. Explain any differences between your prediction and the figure created.

```
cs home
repeat 5 [repeat 4 [fd 10 rt 90] rt 72]
```

32 The word **ATTENTION** is to be illustrated in a space that is 10" high by 30" wide. The letters are to take up the whole space. The font available produces a word 10" high by 24" wide. Find a transformation that will scale the letters in a horizontal direction to fill the space.

33 Investigate the effects of the transformation described by the following rule.

$$(x, y) \rightarrow (2x, 3y)$$

a. Describe the image of square *ABCD* with vertices $A(0, 0)$, $B(0, 2)$, $C(2, 2)$, $D(2, 0)$ under this transformation.

b. Are any points in the coordinate plane their own images?

c. Consider points on a line. Are their images also on a line?

d. Consider midpoints of segments. Are their images the midpoints of the image segments?

e. What is the effect of this transformation on the length of line segments?

f. What is the effect of this transformation on areas?

32 $(x, y) \rightarrow (1.25x, y)$

33 **DIFFERENTIATION NOTE** Students might investigate the collinearity, midpoints, lengths, and areas using specific coordinates such as $A(0, 0)$, $C(2, 2)$, and $M(1, 1)$. Since this is an Extensions task, you may wish to encourage some students to reason abstractly, as indicated in the solutions below.

NOTE The solutions to Task 31 Parts c–e are on page T227B.

a.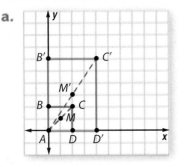

The image is a rectangle with double the length of the base and triple the height of the square.

b. Only the point $A(0, 0)$ is its own image.

c. Yes. If the collinear preimage points are (a, b), (c, d), and (e, f), the image points are $(2a, 3b)$, $(2c, 3d)$, and $(2e, 3f)$. The slopes of the line segments containing the image points can be represented by $\frac{3(b - d)}{2(a - c)}$, $\frac{3(d - f)}{2(c - e)}$, and $\frac{3(a - e)}{2(b - f)}$. Since the preimage points are collinear and $\frac{b - d}{a - c}$, $\frac{d - f}{c - e}$, and $\frac{a - e}{b - f}$ are therefore equal, the image points are collinear.

d. Yes. The midpoint of the preimage segment with endpoints (a, b) and (c, d) is $\left(\frac{a + c}{2}, \frac{b + d}{2}\right)$. The image segment has endpoints $(2a, 3b)$ and $(2c, 3d)$. The midpoint is $\left(\frac{2a + 2c}{2}, \frac{3b + 3d}{2}\right)$ which simplifies to $\left(a + c, \frac{3}{2}(b + d)\right)$. Using the transformation rule, the coordinates of the image of the preimage midpoint are $\left(a + c, \frac{3}{2}(b + d)\right)$. So, the image of the midpoint of the original segment is the same point as the midpoint of the image segment.

e. The size transformation on the length of a horizontal line segment is 2, but the size transformation on the length of a vertical line segment is 3. For oblique line segments, the length of the image segment will be between 2 and 3 times the length of the preimage segment.

f. The ratio of the area of the image to the area of the preimage will be 6. It is easy to show this for rectangles positioned with one side on the *x*-axis and one vertex at the origin. If b represents the length of the base and h represents the height, the area of the preimage is bh. The area of the image is $(2b)(3h) = 6bh$, or 6 times the area of the preimage. (Similar arguments hold for triangles, parallelograms, and trapezoids with a base on the *x*-axis.)

Unit 3

34 Investigate the effects of the transformation described below.

$$(x, y) \rightarrow (x + y, x)$$

a. Describe the image of square *ABCD* with vertices $A(0, 0)$, $B(0, 2)$, $C(2, 2)$, $D(2, 0)$ under this transformation.

b. Are any points in the coordinate plane their own images?

c. When you transform points on a line, are the images also on a line?

d. When you transform midpoints of segments, are the images also midpoints of the image segments?

e. What is the effect of this transformation on the length of line segments?

f. What is the effect of this transformation on areas?

35 Look back at your work in Applications Tasks 12 and 13 with an eye to generalizing the results. Use the translate-transform-translate back method to develop symbolic rules $(x, y) \rightarrow (\_\_, \_\_)$ for each of the following transformations:

a. Size transformation with center $C(a, b)$ and magnitude k

b. 90° counterclockwise rotation about the point $C(a, b)$

c. **Half-turn** (180° rotation) about the point $C(a, b)$

Review

36 Ava put $1,500 into a bank account that earns 5% interest compounded yearly. She does not take any money out of the account.

a. How much money will Ava have after 5 years?

b. How long will it take for the balance in the account to reach $3,000?

37 Find the values of x and y for each matrix equation.

a. $\begin{bmatrix} x & 3 \\ 4 & 5 \end{bmatrix} \begin{bmatrix} 6 & -2 \\ 0 & y \end{bmatrix} = \begin{bmatrix} -12 & 16 \\ 24 & 12 \end{bmatrix}$

b. $\begin{bmatrix} 4 & y \\ x & 1 \end{bmatrix} \begin{bmatrix} 3 & -2 \\ 10 & -5 \end{bmatrix} = \begin{bmatrix} 42 & -23 \\ 31 & -19 \end{bmatrix}$

38 Rewrite each equation so that y is expressed as a function of x.

a. $4x + 7y = 10$

b. $3(2x + y) = 2$

c. $\dfrac{12y - 6x}{4} = 20$

d. $\dfrac{x}{6} + 2y = 32$

34 **DIFFERENTIATION NOTE** This is an example of a *linear transformation* that is not a composite of any functions studied thus far. Encourage some students to reason abstractly, as done in the solutions below.

a.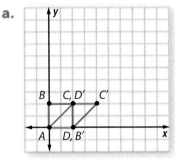

Preimage	Image
$B(0, 2)$	$B'(2, 0) = D$
$C(2, 2)$	$C'(4, 2)$
$D(2, 0)$	$D'(2, 2)$

The image is a parallelogram with the same base and height as the preimage. Visually, the parallelogram is formed by dragging $\overline{BC}$ of the square 2 units (the height) to the right.

b. The origin A is the only point that is its own image.

c. Yes. If three collinear preimage points have coordinates (x_1, y_1), (x_2, y_2), and (x_3, y_3), and the points are not on the same vertical line, the slope m equals $\frac{y_3 - y_2}{x_3 - x_2}$ which is equal to $\frac{y_2 - y_1}{x_2 - x_1}$. The equation for the line can be written as $y_3 - y_2 = m(x_3 - x_2)$ and as $y_2 - y_1 = m(x_2 - x_1)$. The coordinates of the image points are $(x_1 + y_1, x_1)$, $(x_2 + y_2, x_2)$, and $(x_3 + y_3, x_3)$. The slope of the line containing the first two image points is $\frac{(x_2 - x_1)}{(x_2 - x_1) + (y_2 - y_1)}$ which is equivalent to $\frac{(x_2 - x_1)}{(x_2 - x_1) + m(x_2 - x_1)}$ and simplifies to $\frac{1}{1 + m}$. Finding the slope of the line containing another pair of image points also yields a slope of $\frac{1}{1 + m}$. Thus, the image points are collinear.

If the preimage points are on the same vertical line, their x-coordinates are the same and thus slopes are undefined. The image points will have the original x-coordinates as their image y-coordinates, and so they will be collinear on the same horizontal line.

d. Yes. The midpoint of the preimage segment with endpoints (a, b) and (c, d) is the point $\left(\frac{a + c}{2}, \frac{b + d}{2}\right)$. The transformation of the preimage midpoint yields the point $\left(\frac{a + b + c + d}{2}, \frac{a + c}{2}\right)$. The image segment has endpoints $(a + b, a)$ and $(c + d, c)$. The midpoint is $\left(\frac{a + b + c + d}{2}, \frac{a + c}{2}\right)$. From this, we see that the image of the midpoint of a segment is the midpoint of the image segment.

e. If the preimage line is vertical ($a = c$), the length of the image segment will be the same as the length of the preimage. If $a \neq c$, the length of the image segment will be longer than the preimage if the line containing the preimage points has positive slope. The length of the image segment will be shorter if the line containing the preimage points has negative slope. To notice this, students could investigate the changes in the diagonals $\overline{AC}$ and $\overline{BD}$ under this transformation.

Reasoning symbolically, the length of the preimage segment with endpoints (a, b) and (c, d) is

$$D_p = \sqrt{(c - a)^2 + (d - b)^2}.$$

The length of the image segment with endpoints $(a + b, a)$ and $(c + d, c)$ is

$$
\begin{aligned}
D_i &= \sqrt{[(c + d) - (a + b)]^2 + (c - a)^2} \\
&= \sqrt{[(c - a) + (d - b)]^2 + (c - a)^2} \\
&= \sqrt{(c - a)^2 + [(c - a) + (d - b)]^2}
\end{aligned}
$$

Compare the expression for D_p to the last expression for D_i. From this, we can see that if $c - a$ and $d - b$ are both negative or both positive, the length of the image segment will be greater because then $|(c - a) + (d - b)| > |d - b|$. If $c - a$ and $d - b$ are opposite signs, the image length will be smaller because then $|(c - a) + (d - b)| < |d - b|$.

f. The area remains unchanged. Any triangle can be transformed under rigid motions so that its vertices are given by $(0, 0)$, (a, b), and $(c, 0)$. This triangle will be congruent (identical in size and shape) to the original triangle. The area of the preimage triangle is $\frac{1}{2}bc$.

The coordinates of the image vertices under the transformation given in this task are $(0, 0)$, $(a + b, a)$ and (c, c). Finding the area of this triangle is more difficult. Using the side with vertices $(0, 0)$ and (c, c) as the base, the base length is $c\sqrt{2}$. The altitude to this base is on the line perpendicular to the line $y = x$ and goes through $(a + b, a)$. This line is $y = -x + 2a + b$, and the intersection of these two lines is $\left(a + \frac{b}{2}, a + \frac{b}{2}\right)$. The height of the triangle is the distance from the intersection to $(a + b, a)$, which is $\frac{b}{\sqrt{2}}$. Therefore, the area of the image triangle is $\frac{1}{2}bc$.

35 **a.** Translate $C(a, b)$ to origin $(x, y) \rightarrow (x - a, y - b)$
Size transformation $\rightarrow (k(x - a), k(y - b))$
Translate back to $C(a, b)$ $\rightarrow (k(x - a) + a, k(y - b) + b)$
   $= (kx - (k - 1)a, ky - (k - 1)b)$

b. Translate $C(a, b)$ to origin $(x, y) \rightarrow (x - a, y - b)$
Rotate 90° counterclockwise $\rightarrow (-(y - b), x - a)$
Translate back to $C(a, b)$ $\rightarrow (-y + b + a, x - a + b)$

c. Translate $C(a, b)$ to origin $(x, y) \rightarrow (x - a, y - b)$
Half-turn $\rightarrow (-x + a, -y + b)$
Translate back to $C(a, b)$ $\rightarrow (-x + 2a, -y + 2b)$

Review

36 a. $1,914.42

b. 15 years

37 a. $x = -2; y = 4$

b. $x = 7; y = 3$

38 a. $y = \dfrac{10 - 4x}{7} = -\dfrac{4}{7}x + \dfrac{10}{7}$

b. $y = \dfrac{2}{3} - 2x = -2x + \dfrac{2}{3}$

c. $y = \dfrac{80 + 6x}{12} = \dfrac{1}{2}x + \dfrac{20}{3}$

d. $y = \dfrac{32 - \frac{x}{6}}{2} = 16 - \dfrac{1}{12}x = -\dfrac{1}{12}x + 16$

39 The measure of ∠ABC is 30°. Find the measures of each indicated angle.

a. ∠CBD

b. ∠DBA

c. ∠EBF

d. ∠CBE

e. ∠FBA

f. ∠FBD

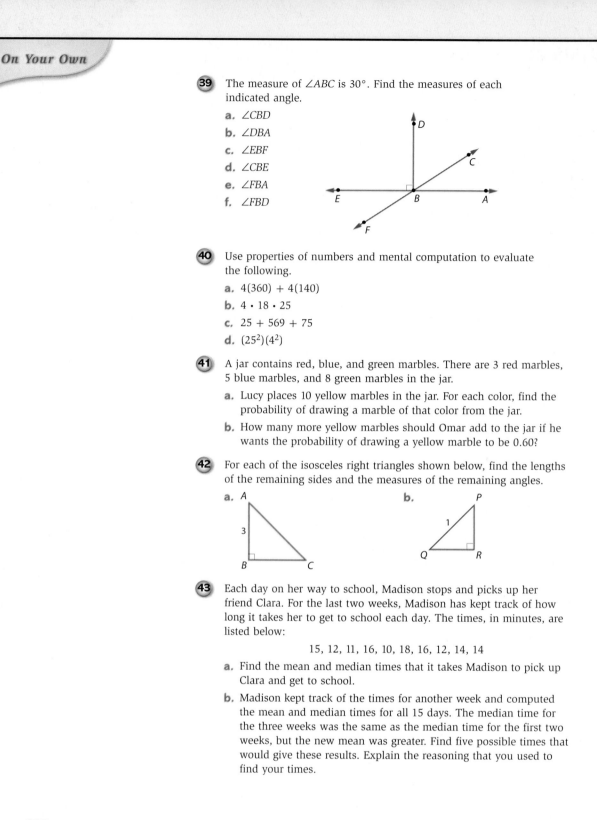

40 Use properties of numbers and mental computation to evaluate the following.

a. $4(360) + 4(140)$

b. $4 \cdot 18 \cdot 25$

c. $25 + 569 + 75$

d. $(25^2)(4^2)$

41 A jar contains red, blue, and green marbles. There are 3 red marbles, 5 blue marbles, and 8 green marbles in the jar.

a. Lucy places 10 yellow marbles in the jar. For each color, find the probability of drawing a marble of that color from the jar.

b. How many more yellow marbles should Omar add to the jar if he wants the probability of drawing a yellow marble to be 0.60?

42 For each of the isosceles right triangles shown below, find the lengths of the remaining sides and the measures of the remaining angles.

a.

b.

43 Each day on her way to school, Madison stops and picks up her friend Clara. For the last two weeks, Madison has kept track of how long it takes her to get to school each day. The times, in minutes, are listed below:

15, 12, 11, 16, 10, 18, 16, 12, 14, 14

a. Find the mean and median times that it takes Madison to pick up Clara and get to school.

b. Madison kept track of the times for another week and computed the mean and median times for all 15 days. The median time for the three weeks was the same as the median time for the first two weeks, but the new mean was greater. Find five possible times that would give these results. Explain the reasoning that you used to find your times.

39 a. 60°

b. 90°

c. 30°

d. 150°

e. 150°

f. 120°

40 a. $4 \cdot 500 = 2,000$

b. $4 \cdot 25 \cdot 18 = 100 \cdot 18 = 1,800$

c. $25 + 75 + 569 = 669$

d. $(25 \cdot 4)^2 = 100^2 = 10,000$

41 a. $P(R) = \frac{3}{26}$; $P(B) = \frac{5}{26}$; $P(G) = \frac{8}{26}$; $P(Y) = \frac{10}{26}$

b. Omar needs to find x so that $\frac{10 + x}{26 + x} = 0.60$. He needs to add 14 more

yellow marbles for $P(Y) = \frac{10 + 14}{26 + 14} = \frac{24}{40} = 0.60$.

42 a. $BC = 3$ units

$AC = \sqrt{3^2 + 3^2} = 3\sqrt{2}$ units

$m\angle A = m\angle C = 45°$

b. $PR = QR = \frac{\sqrt{2}}{2}$ units

$m\angle P = m\angle Q = 45°$

43 a. Mean time: 13.8 minutes

Median time: 14 minutes

b. One possible set of 5 times is 9, 9, 20, 21, and 22.

Mean time: 14.6 minutes

Median time: 14 minutes

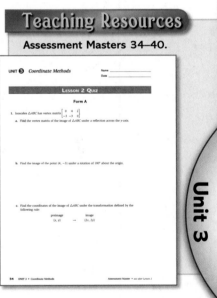

Transformations, Matrices, and Animation

In the first two lessons of this unit, you used coordinates to model geometric shapes such as polygons and circles, and to investigate geometric relationships such as perpendicularity. Coordinates provided ways to describe and reason about familiar and not-so-familiar ideas numerically and algebraically. You also explored how coordinate representations can be used to transform shapes in computer and calculator graphics displays. In this lesson, you will investigate how graphics displays can be linked to create animated effects.

Consider the following sequence of images in a mock animation of a space shuttle. These images were created using a two-dimensional photo image of the shuttle superimposed on an aerial photo of Earth.

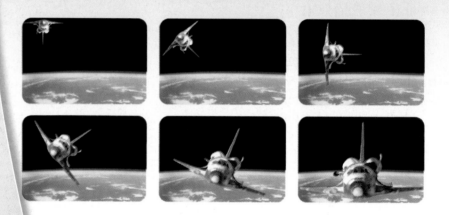

LESSON 3 • Transformations, Matrices, and Animation **231**

Transformations, Matrices, and Animation

In this lesson, students are able to pull together what they know about coordinate representations of geometric figures and transformations of them. Here, they consider how these ideas can be used to produce animation effects. A key idea is recognizing that certain transformations can be represented by matrices. A second important idea is that composition of two transformations corresponds to multiplication of the corresponding transformation matrices.

Lesson Objectives

- Use coordinate rules for rotations about the origin to develop the corresponding matrix representations
- Use coordinate rules for size transformations centered at the origin to develop the corresponding matrix representations
- Use matrix representations of shapes and matrix representations of transformations to create simple animations involving rotations and size transformations

Lesson Launch

You might wish to launch this lesson by discussing the apparent transformations used in the "Animate Shuttle" custom tool. Alternatively, you could use the video of a shuttle at www.cnn.com/TECH/specials/shuttle.100/shuttle.3d/. Then have students consider more carefully the sequence of images preceding the Think About This Situation.

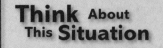

Think About This Situation

Examine how the sequence of images changes from frame to frame.

a Where do you think the origin of a coordinate system was placed in creating this animation?

b What point(s) on the shuttle image would you use in determining how each image was transformed?

c Describe the types of transformations that appear to have been used in creating the animation.

d Computer animations are frequently used in movies and video games. Are there other applications of computer animation with which you are familiar?

In the investigations of this lesson, you will learn how to use matrices to perform transformations of two-dimensional shapes and create simple animations. The tools that you develop have straightforward extensions to work in three dimensions and the methods that are typically used in computer animation.

Investigation 1 — Building and Using Rotation Matrices

For the purpose of this lesson, you can simplify the space shuttle animation by representing the space shuttle and sequence of images with two-dimensional figures similar to the ones shown below. Such simple representations are used when a "storyboard," or outline, of an animation is developed.

As a class, study the animation created by the interactive geometry custom tool "Animate Shuttle." In that animation, the space shuttle performs a rollover maneuver as if in preparation for re-entry.

As you work on the problems of this investigation, look for answers to the following questions:

How can a rotation with center at the origin be represented by a matrix?

How can rotation matrices be used to animate the rotation of two-dimensional shapes?

232 UNIT 3 • Coordinate Methods

Think About This Situation

a Suggestions may vary. Students are likely to choose the center of the frame as the origin (or at least a point along the vertical midline of the frame) since in the final frame of the animation, the shuttle is centered. Alternatively, students may choose the upper-left corner of the frame to be the origin, since the shuttle would get larger and move away from the origin under a size transformation with center at the upper-left corner, as takes place in the animation. Other suggestions are possible and should be supported by reasoning.

b The two wing tips and the top-most point of the shuttle image would help determine the transformations. Students might have other suggestions also.

c It appears that rotations and size transformations and perhaps translations are being used in the animation.

d Commercials, advertising signs, Web sites, and *PowerPoint* presentations sometimes use animation. Students may list others.

Investigation 1 — Building and Using Rotation Matrices

In this investigation, students begin by using coordinate rules for 180° and 90° counterclockwise rotations about the origin to find the matrix representation of such rotations. To allow for more interesting animations, students are next introduced to a more systematic method for finding rotation matrices—here in the case of the matrix for a 45° counterclockwise rotation about the origin.

Problem 7 introduces students to *CPMP-Tools* programming commands as they are used to implement a shuttle Roll Over Algorithm. Students may find this "figure-oriented" programming language more powerful and easier to use than the programming language built into their calculators. You may wish to give students the choice of language and platform they use to implement animations.

Unit 3

① One possible coordinate model of the shuttle is shown below.

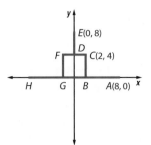

a. What are the coordinates for points *F* and *H*? For points *B* and *G*?

b. Find the coordinates of the image of the shuttle model when rotated 180° about the origin.

c. Write a symbolic rule $(x, y) \rightarrow (\_\_, \_\_)$ that gives the coordinates of the image of any point *P*(*x*, *y*) under a 180° rotation.

d. What is a symbolic rule that gives the coordinates of the image of any point *P*(*x*, *y*) under a 90° counterclockwise rotation about the origin?

e. How would you modify your rule in Part d so that it describes a 90° *clockwise* rotation about the origin?

② Matrix multiplication can be used to express each of the rotations in Problem 1. To do this, coordinates of points (*x*, *y*) need to be represented as one-column matrices, $\begin{bmatrix} x \\ y \end{bmatrix}$. For example, the one-column or **point matrix** for (−2, 4) is $\begin{bmatrix} -2 \\ 4 \end{bmatrix}$.

a. Look back at the symbolic rule for a 180° rotation that you found in Problem 1 Part c. To build a 2 × 2 matrix representation for the 180° rotation, find numbers *a*, *b*, *c*, and *d* that make this matrix equation true.

180° Rotation Matrix		General Point Matrix		Image Point Matrix
$\begin{bmatrix} a & b \\ c & d \end{bmatrix}$	×	$\begin{bmatrix} x \\ y \end{bmatrix}$	=	$\begin{bmatrix} -x \\ -y \end{bmatrix}$

i. Test your rotation matrix by using it to find the rotation images of points *A*(8, 0) and *C*(2, 4). Compare your image points with those found in Problem 1 Part b.

ii. Why is the general point matrix placed to the right of the rotation matrix?

ASSIGNMENT NOTE
Students should have reviewed matrix multiplication by completing just-in-time Review Task 37 on page 229.

You may wish to introduce this investigation by rerunning "Animate Shuttle." Student masters are provided to help students organize their work.

1 **a.** $F(-2, 4)$
$H(-8, 0)$
$B(2, 0)$
$G(-2, 0)$

b. $A'(-8, 0)$
$B'(-2, 0)$
$C'(-2, -4)$
$D'(0, -4)$
$E'(0, -8)$
$F'(2, -4)$
$G'(2, 0)$
$H'(8, 0)$

c. 180° rotation about the origin: $(x, y) \rightarrow (-x, -y)$

d. 90° counterclockwise rotation about the origin: $(x, y) \rightarrow (-y, x)$

e. 90° clockwise rotation about the origin: $(x, y) \rightarrow (y, -x)$

Teaching Resources

Student Masters 42–44.

2 **a.** $ax + by = -x$ implies $a = -1$ and $b = 0$.
$cx + dy = -y$ implies $c = 0$ and $d = -1$.

So, $\begin{bmatrix} -1 & 0 \\ 0 & -1 \end{bmatrix}$ is the rotation matrix.

i. $\begin{bmatrix} -1 & 0 \\ 0 & -1 \end{bmatrix} \begin{bmatrix} 8 \\ 0 \end{bmatrix} = \begin{bmatrix} -8 \\ 0 \end{bmatrix}$ and $\begin{bmatrix} -1 & 0 \\ 0 & -1 \end{bmatrix} \begin{bmatrix} 2 \\ 4 \end{bmatrix} = \begin{bmatrix} -2 \\ -4 \end{bmatrix}$

The coordinates of the image points are the opposite of the coordinates of the preimage points and should match image points found in Problem 1 Part b.

ii. The rotation matrix is a 2 × 2 matrix and the general point matrix is a 2 × 1 matrix. The only way to match the number of columns of the first matrix to the number of rows of the second matrix would be to place the general point matrix on the right.

Unit 3

b. Determine the matrix for a 90° counterclockwise rotation about the origin.

$$\begin{bmatrix} a & b \\ c & d \end{bmatrix} \begin{bmatrix} x \\ y \end{bmatrix} = \begin{bmatrix} -y \\ x \end{bmatrix}$$

   i. Check your rotation matrix by using it to find the images of points $B(2, 0)$ and $C(2, 4)$ in Problem 1.

   ii. Do these image points make sense?

c. Geometrically, you know that a 90° counterclockwise rotation followed by another 90° counterclockwise rotation gives a 180° rotation. See if multiplying the matrix for the 90° counterclockwise rotation by itself yields the matrix for the 180° rotation.

d. What do you notice about the entries of the matrices used to express these rotations?

3 One advantage of a matrix representation of a transformation is that you can use it quickly to transform an entire shape. Consider

$$\triangle AEH = \begin{bmatrix} 8 & 0 & -8 \\ 0 & 8 & 0 \end{bmatrix}$$ determined by the tips of the shuttle model.

a. Multiply the matrix representation of $\triangle AEH$ by the 90° counterclockwise rotation matrix. Using the coordinate rule for the 90° counterclockwise rotation, verify that the result of your calculation is the image triangle, $\triangle A'E'H'$.

b. When transforming an n-sided polygon using matrices, why should the coordinate matrix of the polygon be the factor on the right?

4 Designing animations often requires use of rotations through many different angles, in addition to those that are multiples of 90°. When building matrix representations for rotations and other transformations, it is very useful to know what happens to the points $(1, 0)$ and $(0, 1)$. Diagram I below shows the images of points $P(1, 0)$ and $Q(0, 1)$ under a 45° counterclockwise rotation about the origin.

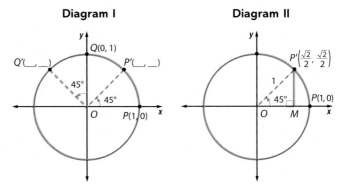

a. Explain why the image of point P and the image of point Q will be on a circle of radius 1 with center at the origin.

b. $\begin{bmatrix} 0 & -1 \\ 1 & 0 \end{bmatrix}$

i–ii. Students should use this matrix to find the images of $B(2, 0)$ and $C(2, 4)$ which are $B'(0, 2)$ and $C'(-4, 2)$. They can check that the images make sense for a 90° counterclockwise rotation about the origin by plotting the points and their images and joining each point to the origin. The segments that join image and preimage points to the origin should form a 90° angle.

c. Yes, multiplying the 90° counterclockwise rotation matrix by itself produces the 180° rotation matrix.

d. There are two zero entries along one of the diagonals. The other diagonal contains ±1s. (Students will extend this observation in Problem 5.)

3 **a.** The resulting matrix should be $\begin{bmatrix} 0 & -8 & 0 \\ 8 & 0 & -8 \end{bmatrix}$.

b. An n-sided polygon ($n \geq 3$) will be listed by its vertex coordinates and have at least 3 rows. So, it will be a $2 \times n$ matrix. Since the rotation matrices are 2×2 matrices, the rows of the polygon can match the columns of the rotation matrix. Matrix multiplication is not possible if the $2 \times n$ matrix is on the left of a 2×2 matrix.

4 **a.** $OP = 1$, so the image $OP' = 1$ since distance is preserved under rotations. A circle of radius 1 centered at the origin consists of all points 1 unit away from $(0, 0)$, so P' must be on the circle.

INSTRUCTIONAL NOTE

If a 2-point matrix representing a segment was used in matrix multiplication, the transformation matrix could be placed on the right. In this unit, we will use point matrices for $n \geq 3$.

INSTRUCTIONAL NOTE

Using $\pm\dfrac{\sqrt{2}}{2}$ for the $R_{45°}$ matrix results in exact entries for powers of matrices. If students' $R_{45°}$ matrices do not work in Part e, ask them to check the ± signs by rotating $(1, 0)$ and $(0, 1)$ 45° counterclockwise about the origin.

Unit 3

b. Using Diagram II, explain as precisely as you can why the image of point P under the 45° rotation has coordinates $\left(\frac{\sqrt{2}}{2}, \frac{\sqrt{2}}{2}\right)$.

c. Find the coordinates of point Q'.

d. Now find the entries of the 45° counterclockwise rotation matrix

$R_{45°} = \begin{bmatrix} a & b \\ c & d \end{bmatrix}$ by solving the two matrix equations below. Begin

by entering the coordinates of point P' and point Q' in the appropriate column matrices.

i. $\begin{bmatrix} a & b \\ c & d \end{bmatrix} \begin{bmatrix} 1 \\ 0 \end{bmatrix} = \begin{bmatrix} \underline{\quad} \\ \underline{\quad} \end{bmatrix}$

ii. $\begin{bmatrix} a & b \\ c & d \end{bmatrix} \begin{bmatrix} 0 \\ 1 \end{bmatrix} = \begin{bmatrix} \underline{\quad} \\ \underline{\quad} \end{bmatrix}$

iii. So, $R_{45°} = \begin{bmatrix} \underline{\quad} & \underline{\quad} \\ \underline{\quad} & \underline{\quad} \end{bmatrix}$.

e. Check that multiplying the 45° counterclockwise rotation matrix by itself (with entries expressed in radical form) gives the matrix for a 90° counterclockwise rotation about the origin that you found in Problem 2 Part b.

5 Look back at the entries for the 45° counterclockwise rotation matrix $R_{45°}$ and how they were calculated.

a. How are the entries of matrix $R_{45°}$ related to the rotation images of $P(1, 0)$ and $Q(0, 1)$?

b. Does the pattern hold for the 180° and 90° rotation matrices you found in Problem 2? Explain.

6 A computer or calculator program can be written that will rotate the space shuttle model counterclockwise about the origin using steps of 45°. Study the Roll Over Algorithm given below.

Roll Over Algorithm

Step 1. Set up the coordinate matrix representing the space shuttle.

Step 2. Set up the 45° counterclockwise rotation matrix.

Step 3. Draw the shuttle.

Step 4. Compute and store the coordinates of the shuttle rotated 45°.

Step 5. Clear the old shuttle and draw the rotated image.

Step 6. Pause.

Step 7. Repeat Steps 4–6 as needed.

---

a. Identify the input, processing, and output parts of the Roll Over Algorithm.

b. Step 7 is a *control* command. It controls the action of the algorithm. To make the shuttle rotate all the way around once, how many times should Steps 4–6 be performed?

b. $\triangle OP'M$ is an isosceles right triangle since $m\angle OP'M = 45°$. $OM = MP'$ since these are the lengths of the legs of the isosceles $45°$-$45°$-$90°$ triangle. This means that the horizontal and vertical coordinates of P' are the same, $\frac{1}{\sqrt{2}} = \frac{\sqrt{2}}{2}$. Some students may use the Pythagorean Theorem by letting one side length be x, then solving the equation $x^2 + x^2 = 1$ to find the coordinates. Another solution is to note that P' is on the line $y = x$ and the circle $x^2 + y^2 = 1$; substitution of $y = x$ into the circle equation gives $2x^2 = 1$ and $x = y = \frac{\sqrt{2}}{2}$.

c. Since $\triangle OQ'N$ is an isosceles right triangle with hypotenuse of length 1 unit, the lengths of the legs are $\frac{1}{\sqrt{2}} = \frac{\sqrt{2}}{2}$. Since Q' is in the second quadrant, $Q'\left(-\frac{\sqrt{2}}{2}, \frac{\sqrt{2}}{2}\right)$. The coordinates of Q' can also be found by noting that Q' is the image of P' under reflection across the y-axis.

d. **i.** $a(1) + b(0) = \frac{\sqrt{2}}{2}; a = \frac{\sqrt{2}}{2}$

$c(1) + d(0) = \frac{\sqrt{2}}{2}; c = \frac{\sqrt{2}}{2}$

ii. $a(0) + b(1) = -\frac{\sqrt{2}}{2}; b = -\frac{\sqrt{2}}{2}$

$c(0) + d(1) = \frac{\sqrt{2}}{2}; d = \frac{\sqrt{2}}{2}$

iii. $R_{45°} = \begin{bmatrix} \dfrac{\sqrt{2}}{2} & -\dfrac{\sqrt{2}}{2} \\ \dfrac{\sqrt{2}}{2} & \dfrac{\sqrt{2}}{2} \end{bmatrix}$

e. Multiplying the $45°$ counterclockwise rotation matrix by itself results in the $90°$ counterclockwise rotation matrix.

ASSIGNMENT NOTE
Connections Task 8 (page 245) develops the matrix for a $30°$ counterclockwise rotation.

5 **a.** The first column of the $45°$ counterclockwise rotation matrix is the coordinates of the image of P and the second column is the coordinates of the image of Q; $P'\left(\frac{\sqrt{2}}{2}, \frac{\sqrt{2}}{2}\right)$ and $Q'\left(-\frac{\sqrt{2}}{2}, \frac{\sqrt{2}}{2}\right)$.

b. The same pattern holds. The image of $P(1, 0)$ is the first column of the rotation matrix and the image of $Q(0, 1)$ is the second column.

6 **a.** Steps 1 and 2 are input. Steps 3 and 5 are output. Step 4 is process. Step 6 can be thought of as process also.

b. 8 times

Unit 3

The roll over portion of the animation can be created using commands such as those below. Note how assigning names to the shuttle coordinate matrix and the rotation matrix simplifies the programming.

Roll Over Program

let shuttle = [[8,0][2,0][2,4][0,4][0,8][0,4][–2,4][–2,0][–8,0][8,0]]
let rotmatrix = [[0.7071,0.7071][–0.7071,0.7071]]
draw shuttle
repeat 8 [draw [let shuttle = [rotmatrix*shuttle]] pause 500]

a. Discuss with your classmates how the commands in this program match corresponding steps in the Roll Over Algorithm.

b. Test the program by entering it in the Command window of your interactive geometry software.

c. Predict the animation that will be produced by replacing the last *three* lines of the program by these *two* lines:

draw shuttle
repeat 8 [draw [let shuttle = [rotate shuttle 45]] pause 500]

Run the program to test your prediction. Make notes of any misunderstandings of programming commands.

Summarize
the Mathematics

In this investigation, you explored how to find matrix representations for certain rotations and how matrices can be used to create an animation.

a Explain how to use the coordinate rule for a 270° counterclockwise rotation about the origin to find the matrix representation for that rotation. Find the matrix.

b How would you modify the Roll Over program so that it will rotate the space shuttle *clockwise* about the origin in steps of 45°?

c Describe a systematic way of determining the entries of a rotation matrix.

d The matrix $\begin{bmatrix} 0.5 & 0.866 \\ -0.866 & 0.5 \end{bmatrix}$ is the matrix for a 60° clockwise rotation about the origin. Explain how to use the matrix to find a coordinate rule for the image of a point (x, y) under this rotation.

Be prepared to share your ideas and reasoning with the class.

7 **TECHNOLOGY NOTE** The program in Problem 7 works in *CPMP-Tools* interactive geometry software. Encourage students to pay attention to the syntax in the Roll Over Program. The Command window can be opened from the Options menu. Note that this programming language redefines the shuttle matrix and does not require a separate clear screen command to erase the preimage. If you are using geometry software other than *CPMP-Tools*, program commands may need to be modified.

a. Line 1 matches Step 1.
Line 2 matches Step 2.
Line 3 matches Step 3.
Line 4 matches Steps 4–7.

b. Students should test the program. (Press the Return key at the end of each line to activate the program properly.)

c. The new commands rotate the shuttle 45° counterclockwise about the origin without defining a rotation matrix and thus produce the same result.

Summarize
the Mathematics

a The rule for a 270° counterclockwise rotation about the origin is $(x, y) \rightarrow (y, -x)$. To find the rotation matrix $\begin{bmatrix} a & b \\ c & d \end{bmatrix}$, you could set up two equations based on the points (1, 0) and (0, 1),

$$\begin{bmatrix} a & b \\ c & d \end{bmatrix}\begin{bmatrix} 1 \\ 0 \end{bmatrix} = \begin{bmatrix} 0 \\ -1 \end{bmatrix} \text{ and } \begin{bmatrix} a & b \\ c & d \end{bmatrix}\begin{bmatrix} 0 \\ 1 \end{bmatrix} = \begin{bmatrix} 1 \\ 0 \end{bmatrix}.$$

Multiplying these matrices gives equations that identify the values of a, b, c, and d, $\begin{bmatrix} 0 & 1 \\ -1 & 0 \end{bmatrix}$.

b Modify the rotation matrix in Line 2 to represent a 45° clockwise rotation about the origin. Using the symmetry of the unit circle, the images of (1, 0) and (0, 1) are $\left(\dfrac{\sqrt{2}}{2}, -\dfrac{\sqrt{2}}{2}\right)$ and $\left(\dfrac{\sqrt{2}}{2}, \dfrac{\sqrt{2}}{2}\right)$, respectively. The 45° clockwise rotation matrix is $\begin{bmatrix} \dfrac{\sqrt{2}}{2} & \dfrac{\sqrt{2}}{2} \\ -\dfrac{\sqrt{2}}{2} & \dfrac{\sqrt{2}}{2} \end{bmatrix}$.

c Find the image of (1, 0) and (0, 1). Then place the image of (1, 0) in the first column and the image of (0, 1) in the second column to form the rotation matrix.

d Multiply the rotation matrix times a general point matrix to obtain rules for each coordinate of the image point.

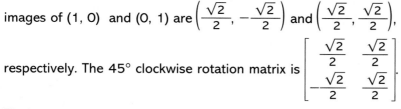

$$\begin{bmatrix} 0.5 & 0.866 \\ -0.866 & 0.5 \end{bmatrix}\begin{bmatrix} x \\ y \end{bmatrix} = \begin{bmatrix} 0.5x + 0.866y \\ -0.866x + 0.5y \end{bmatrix}$$

$(x, y) \rightarrow (0.5x + 0.866y, -0.866x + 0.5y)$
This is the rule for a 60° clockwise rotation about the origin.

Unit 3

MATH TOOLKIT Provide an example of how to use the coordinate rule for a rotation about the origin to find the rotation matrix and vice versa (Parts a and d of the STM). What key role can the points (1, 0) and (0, 1) play in finding rotation matrices? Give an example.

✓ Check Your Understanding

Build a matrix that represents a 135° counterclockwise rotation about the origin.

a. Use the matrix to find the rotation image of the point (−1, 5).

b. Use the matrix to find the rotation image of $\triangle HJK = \begin{bmatrix} -1 & 4 & 3 \\ 2 & -3 & 5 \end{bmatrix}$.

c. Sketch $\triangle HJK$ and its rotation image on a coordinate grid.

Investigation 2 · Building and Using Size Transformation Matrices

Consider again the sequence of images in the mock animation of a space shuttle.

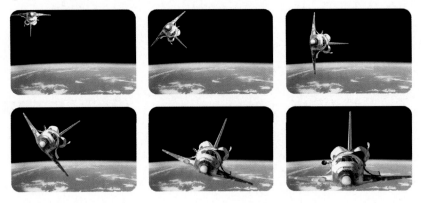

Note how the shuttle image increases in size from frame to frame as it rolls over and moves forward. This simulation was accomplished by using size transformations, translations, and rotations. In this investigation, all size transformations will be centered at the origin.

As you work on problems in this investigation, look for answers to the following questions:

> *How can size transformations be represented using matrices?*
>
> *How can you animate size change and translation of two-dimensional shapes?*
>
> *How can size transformations and translations be combined with rotations to create more complex animations?*

✔ Check Your Understanding

Rotating points $A(1, 0)$ and $B(0, 1)$ counterclockwise 135° about the origin and using previous work and symmetry, A' and B' can be found. The 135° counterclockwise rotation

matrix is $\begin{bmatrix} -\dfrac{\sqrt{2}}{2} & -\dfrac{\sqrt{2}}{2} \\ \dfrac{\sqrt{2}}{2} & -\dfrac{\sqrt{2}}{2} \end{bmatrix}$.

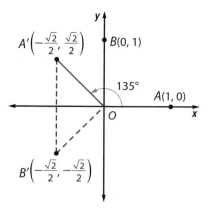

a. $(-2.8284, -4.2426)$

b. $\begin{bmatrix} -0.7071 & -0.7071 & -5.6569 \\ -2.1213 & 4.9497 & -1.4142 \end{bmatrix}$

c.

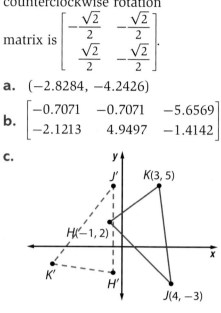

INSTRUCTIONAL NOTE

Some students may use equations to find the 135° counterclockwise rotation matrix. The following solutions use the image of points (1, 0) and (0, 1). Alternatively, students may use $R^3_{45°}$, although the intent of the task is to practice the methods learned in this investigation.

Investigation 2 — Building and Using Size Transformation Matrices

In this investigation, students will use the coordinate rule for a size transformation centered at the origin to build the matrix representation. They will also explore issues involved with representing translations with matrices.

Launch

A short and motivating introduction to this investigation can be achieved by showing "Animate Shuttle" again. You might have students call out (this is noisy, but fun) whenever they observe a particular transformation being used. Then tell them they are going to learn how to use matrix multiplication to model size transformations.

If your students have exhibited previous exposure to geometric transformations and coordinate rules or the ability to quickly pick up these ideas, have them complete Problem 1 by *individually thinking* about responses and then checking with each other as follows. Ask each student to write down a coordinate matrix for the shuttle in the diagram (these may vary). Then ask them to *think about* the answer to Problem 1 Part a without writing the two matrices requested. This could be done by reformulating the question as: "How would you find the coordinate matrix ... ?" Most students will likely be able to write the rule requested in Part b without writing the full matrix for a shuttle with sides twice and half the lengths of those in the diagram. A similar approach can be taken for Parts c and d.

1. Begin by examining the space shuttle model shown below.

   a. What is the coordinate matrix for a similar shuttle model (in the same position) whose sides are twice the length of those in the given model? Half the length?

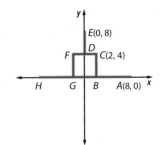

   b. Write two coordinate rules $(x, y) \rightarrow (\underline{}, \underline{})$ that would resize the shuttle model as described in Part a.

   c. What is the coordinate matrix for the image of the given shuttle model when translated:

      i. 5 units to the right?

      ii. 3 units down?

      iii. 5 units to the right and 3 units down?

   d. Write coordinate rules for these three transformations in the form $(x, y) \rightarrow (\underline{}, \underline{})$.

2. Matrix representations for size transformations with center at the origin can be found using the same method you used to find rotation matrices.

   a. Determine the entries a, b, c, and d of the matrix for a size transformation with magnitude 2.

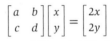

   b. What should be the image of the point $F(-2, 4)$ under this transformation? Multiply the transformation matrix by the one-column matrix for point F and check to see if you get the correct image point.

   c. Multiply the size transformation matrix you found in Part a by the matrix for $\triangle AEH$, where A, E, and H are the wing tips of the shuttle model.

      i. Compare the coordinates of the image $\triangle A'E'H'$ with those found using the appropriate coordinate rule for a size transformation with magnitude 2.

      ii. Compare the lengths of $\overline{EH}$ and $\overline{E'H'}$. Why does that relationship make sense?

   d. Find the matrix for a size transformation with magnitude $\frac{1}{2}$. With magnitude 5.

3. How could you use the idea of multiplying a matrix by a real number to find the image of a point or a polygon under a size transformation of magnitude 3 with center at the origin? Of magnitude $\frac{1}{4}$? Compare methods with others and resolve any differences.

Then have students check with each other before their group tackles Problem 2. Students need not necessarily write the full matrices requested in Parts a and c. Problem 8 provides a useful summary of key ideas in creating animation effects.

1 **INSTRUCTIONAL NOTE** This problem uses the shuttle matrix of

$$\begin{bmatrix} 8 & 2 & 2 & 0 & 0 & 0 & -2 & -2 & -8 & 8 \\ 0 & 0 & 4 & 4 & 8 & 4 & 4 & 0 & 0 & 0 \end{bmatrix}$$ given in the Roll Over Program in

Problem 7 of Investigation 1. Other matrices could be used.

a. Twice the length: $\begin{bmatrix} 16 & 4 & 4 & 0 & 0 & 0 & -4 & -4 & -16 & 16 \\ 0 & 0 & 8 & 8 & 16 & 8 & 8 & 0 & 0 & 0 \end{bmatrix}$

Half the length: $\begin{bmatrix} 4 & 1 & 1 & 0 & 0 & 0 & -1 & -1 & -4 & 4 \\ 0 & 0 & 2 & 2 & 4 & 2 & 2 & 0 & 0 & 0 \end{bmatrix}$

b. $(x, y) \rightarrow (2x, 2y)$

$(x, y) \rightarrow \left(\frac{1}{2}x, \frac{1}{2}y\right)$

c. **i.** $\begin{bmatrix} 13 & 7 & 7 & 5 & 5 & 5 & 3 & 3 & -3 & 13 \\ 0 & 0 & 4 & 4 & 8 & 4 & 4 & 0 & 0 & 0 \end{bmatrix}$

ii. $\begin{bmatrix} 8 & 2 & 2 & 0 & 0 & 0 & -2 & -2 & -8 & 8 \\ -3 & -3 & 1 & 1 & 5 & 1 & 1 & -3 & -3 & -3 \end{bmatrix}$

iii. $\begin{bmatrix} 13 & 7 & 7 & 5 & 5 & 5 & 3 & 3 & -3 & 13 \\ -3 & -3 & 1 & 1 & 5 & 1 & 1 & -3 & -3 & -3 \end{bmatrix}$

d. **i.** $(x, y) \rightarrow (x + 5, y)$

ii. $(x, y) \rightarrow (x, y - 3)$

iii. $(x, y) \rightarrow (x + 5, y - 3)$

2 **a.** $\begin{bmatrix} 2 & 0 \\ 0 & 2 \end{bmatrix}$

b. $F' = (-4, 8);$ $\begin{bmatrix} 2 & 0 \\ 0 & 2 \end{bmatrix}\begin{bmatrix} -2 \\ 4 \end{bmatrix} = \begin{bmatrix} -4 \\ 8 \end{bmatrix}$

c. $\begin{bmatrix} 2 & 0 \\ 0 & 2 \end{bmatrix}\begin{bmatrix} 8 & 0 & -8 \\ 0 & 8 & 0 \end{bmatrix} = \begin{bmatrix} 16 & 0 & -16 \\ 0 & 16 & 0 \end{bmatrix}$

i. The coordinate matrix should match coordinates found using the rule.

ii. $EH = \sqrt{128} = 8\sqrt{2};\ E'H' = \sqrt{512} = 16\sqrt{2}$

$E'H'$ is twice EH. The image lengths should be twice the length of preimage lengths under a size transformation with magnitude 2.

d. $\begin{bmatrix} 0.5 & 0 \\ 0 & 0.5 \end{bmatrix};\begin{bmatrix} 5 & 0 \\ 0 & 5 \end{bmatrix}$

3 $3\begin{bmatrix} x \\ y \end{bmatrix} = \begin{bmatrix} 3x \\ 3y \end{bmatrix}$ (image of a point)

$\frac{1}{4}\begin{bmatrix} a & b & c \\ d & e & f \end{bmatrix} = \begin{bmatrix} \frac{1}{4}a & \frac{1}{4}b & \frac{1}{4}c \\ \frac{1}{4}d & \frac{1}{4}e & \frac{1}{4}f \end{bmatrix}$ (image of a polygon)

INSTRUCTIONAL NOTE
If students write the answers to Problem 2 Part cii in radical form, you can use the opportunity to reinforce the 45°-45° right triangle side length relationship.

INSTRUCTIONAL NOTE
Problem 3 provides an opportunity for students to recall and use *scalar multiplication*.

Unit 3

4 Use the Roll Over Algorithm on page 235 and the following questions to help you develop an algorithm for a program that will repeatedly scale the space shuttle model by a factor of 1.5 using a size transformation with center at the origin.

* What information would you need to input?

* What processing would the program need to complete?

* What information should the calculator or computer output?

Resizing Algorithm

Step 1. Set up the coordinate matrix representing the shuttle. (input)

Step 2. _____ (_____)

Step 3. _____ (_____)
⋮

---

5 The animation described in Problem 4 can be created using commands such as:

Resizing Program
let shuttle = [[8,0][2,0][2,4][0,4][0,8][0,4][–2,4][–2,0][–8,0][8,0]]
let sizematrix = [[1.5,0][0,1.5]]
draw shuttle
repeat 4 [draw [let shuttle = [sizematrix*shuttle]] pause 500]

a. Test the program by entering it in the Command window of your software.

b. Suppose the last *three* lines of the program were replaced by these *two* lines:

draw shuttle
repeat 4 [draw [let shuttle = [scale shuttle 1.5]] pause 500]

What animation do you think will be produced by the modified program? Check your conjecture by running the modified program.

c. Write a series of commands that could be used to create an animation that repeatedly scales the shuttle by a factor of 4 with center at the origin.

d. Test your program by entering it in the Command window. Revise commands as necessary.

6 Unlike in the cases of rotations and size transformations, translations cannot be represented with 2 × 2 matrices. (See Extensions Task 18.) Instead of using matrix multiplication, the coordinate rule form is frequently used to describe translations. For example, you can translate the shuttle and display the image with the commands shown below.

let shuttle = [[8,0][2,0][2,4][0,4][0,8][0,4][–2,4][–2,0][–8,0][8,0]]
let shuttle = [translate shuttle [5,–3]]
draw shuttle

④

┌───┐
│ **Resizing Algorithm**   │
│   │
│ **Step 1.** Set up the coordinate matrix representing the shuttle. (input) │
│ **Step 2.** Set up the 1.5 size transformation matrix. (input)   │
│ **Step 3.** Draw original figure. (output)   │
│ **Step 4.** Compute the new coordinates of the scaled shape. (processing) │
│ **Step 5.** Clear the old shape and draw the scaled shape. (output) │
│ **Step 6.** Pause. (processing)   │
│ **Step 7.** Repeat Steps 4–6 as needed.   │
└───┘

⑤
  a. Students should test the program. (Press the Return key at the end of each line to activate the program properly.)

  b. The new commands scale the shuttle by a factor of 1.5 without defining a size transformation matrix and thus produce the same result.

  c. **let shuttle = [[8,0][2,0][2,4][0,4][0,8][0,4][−2,4][−2,0][−8,0][8,0]]**
  draw shuttle
  repeat 4 [draw [let shuttle = [scale shuttle 4]] pause 500]

  d. Students should test their programs.

TECHNOLOGY NOTE In *CPMP-Tools*, the Command window is located under the Options menu. The use of spaces is not arbitrary in all commands. If students obtain "syntax errors," it may be due to missing space characters.

Unit 3

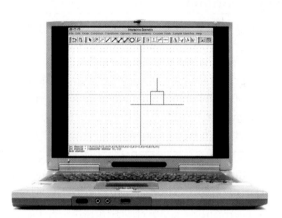

a. Write a series of commands that could be used to create an animation that repeatedly translates the shuttle 2 units to the right and 3 units up.

b. Test your program. Revise it as necessary.

In the following problems, you will explore ways in which transformations can be combined to create more complex animations.

7 Suppose you want to create an animation that starts with the shuttle wingspan repositioned so that its center is at $(-4, 5)$ and is rescaled to 75% the original size.

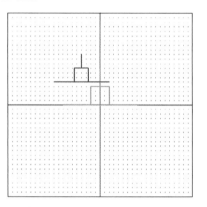

a. Describe the horizontal and vertical components of the translation and scale factor of the size transformation that will produce this image when drawn.

b. Will the order in which you choose to apply the translation and size transformation matter? Explain.

c. Write a series of programming commands that could be used to create this initial image of the shuttle.

d. Test your program and revise it as necessary.

6 **a.** **let shuttle = [[8,0][2,0][2,4][0,4][0,8][0,4][−2,4][−2,0][−8,0][8,0]]**
draw shuttle
repeat 5 [draw [let shuttle = [translate shuttle [2, 3]]] pause 500]

b. Students should test their program.

7 **a.** The shuttle wingspan is currently centered at $(0, 0)$; so to translate the center to $(−4, 5)$, you would need to apply a translation with horizontal component −4 and vertical component 5. To resize the shuttle to 75% the size, you would need to apply a size transformation with magnitude 0.75.

b. The order you choose to apply the transformations matters. You need to apply the size transformation then the translation. If you translate first, the size transformation will draw the shape back towards the origin, thus moving the center of the wingspan away from $(−4, 5)$.

c. One possible set of commands:
let shuttle = [[8,0][2,0][2,4][0,4][0,8][0,4][−2,4][−2,0][−8,0][8,0]]
let shuttle = [scale shuttle 0.75]
draw [let shuttle = [translate shuttle [−4, 5]]]

d. Students should test their program.

(8) By repeatedly combining a size transformation, rotation, and a translation, you can create an animation where the shuttle model appears to move from being far away to flying by the observer.

a. Study the two algorithms for gradually growing the size of the shuttle model.

Grow Algorithm 1
Step 1. Set up the coordinate matrix representing the shuttle.
Step 2. Set up a 0.25 scale factor.
Step 3. Compute the image of the original shuttle under the size transformation.
Step 4. Draw the image.
Step 5. Increase the scale factor by 0.05.
Step 6. Pause.
Step 7. Repeat Steps 3–6 as needed.

Grow Algorithm 2
Step 1. Set up the coordinate matrix representing the shuttle.
Step 2. Set up a 0.25 scale factor.
Step 3. Compute the image of the original shuttle under the size transformation.
Step 4. Draw the image.
Step 5. Multiply the scale factor by 1.2.
Step 6. Pause.
Step 7. Repeat Steps 3–6 as needed.

    i. How does the size of the shuttle grow for each algorithm?

    ii. For each algorithm, how many times must the steps be repeated before the shuttle image reaches its original size?

b. Suppose to start an animation sequence, the center of the shuttle wingspan needs to be translated to $(-20, 20)$ and the shuttle scaled to 25%. In which order should you perform the translation and size transformation?

c. Study the program below that creates an animation of the space shuttle similar to that produced by the "Animate Shuttle" custom tool. Describe as precisely as you can the effect of each line.

Shuttle Animation Program

```
 1. pgm animateShuttle
 2. gridstyle grid off axes off
 3. let shuttle=[shape [[10,0][2.5,0][2.5,5][0,5][0,10][0,5][-2.5,5][-2.5,0][-10,0][10,0]]]
 4. style shuttle filled on fillcolor 0 255 0 visible off label off
 5. let currentCenter=[-18,18]
 6. let currentAngle=180
 7. let currentScale=0.2
 8. let shuttleImage=[translate [scale [rotate shuttle currentAngle] currentScale] currentCenter]
 9. style shuttleImage filled on fillcolor 200 0 200 label off visible on
10. pause 500
11. repeat 18 [let currentAngle=currentAngle+10 let currentScale=currentScale+0.05
    let currentCenter=currentCenter+[1,-1] let shuttleImage=[translate [scale [rotate shuttle currentAngle]
    currentScale] currentCenter] draw shuttleImage pause 100]
12. clear currentCenter currentAngle currentScale shuttleImage
13. gridstyle grid on axes on
14. draw shuttle
15. end
```

---

d. Compare your description of the program with the execution of the "Animate Shuttle" custom tool.

8 **a.** **i.** **Grow Algorithm 1:** The shuttle is first reduced to 25% of its original size. Subsequent size transformations of the original shuttle are by factors of $0.25 + 0.05n$ (0.30, 0.35, 0.40, etc.), where n is the number of size transformations after the first one. This represents constant or linear growth.

Grow Algorithm 2: The shuttle is first reduced to 25% of its original size. Subsequent size transformations of the original shuttle are by factors of $0.25(1.2^n)$ (0.30, 0.36, 0.432, etc.), where n is the number of size transformations after the first one. This represents exponential growth.

ii. **Grow Algorithm 1:** 15 times
Grow Algorithm 2: 8 times

b. In order for the center of the wingspan of the reduced shuttle to remain at $(-20, 20)$, the size transformation should be applied first while the shuttle is still at the origin. Scaling to 25% using the origin as a center draws the shape back towards the origin. So, translating to $(-20, 20)$ first and then scaling will draw the object away from $(-20, 20)$.

c. **Line 1:** Titles the program "animateShuttle".
Line 2: Turns off grid and axes.
Line 3: Defines "shuttle" as a shape by connecting the points listed.
Line 4: Fills the shuttle with color.
Line 5: Defines the current center as point $(-18, 18)$.
Line 6: Defines the current angle as 180°.
Line 7: Defines the current scale change factor as 0.2.
Line 8: Defines "shuttleImage" as the image of rotation, then scale change, then translation, all using current magnitudes and center.
Line 9: Colors the image shuttle.
Line 10: Pauses.
Line 11: Increases the angle of rotation by 10°, the scale factor by 0.05, and the center by translating 1 unit right and 1 unit down from the current center. This is done 18 times.
Line 12: Clears the current center, angle, scale, and shuttle image.
Line 13: Turns the grid and axes on.
Line 14: Draws the shuttle.
Line 15: Ends the program.

d. Students' descriptions should match the "Animate Shuttle" custom tool. If not, they can adjust their response to Part c.

Summarize
the Mathematics

In this investigation, you extended your work with matrices and animation to include size transformations with center at the origin which were then combined with translations.

a What are two different ways of representing a size transformation with magnitude k using matrices? Why would you choose one form over the other?

b Explain how each form in Part a can be used to find the image of a point and the image of a polygon under a size transformation.

c How could you use general coordinate rules, matrices, or drawing on a coordinate grid to show that order is important when combining size transformations and translations?

Be prepared to share your ideas and reasoning with the entire class.

✔ Check Your Understanding

Build a coordinate matrix for flag *PQRS* shown below. Then do the following:

a. Write the matrix for a size transformation of magnitude 3 centered at the origin.

b. Use the matrix to find the image of flag *PQRS* under the transformation.

c. Sketch the original flag and its image on a coordinate grid.

d. Write a series of commands for an animation program that:

- begins with the flag as shown above.
- uses composition of size transformations of magnitude 1.1 to show the flag growing and moving away from the origin until its pole is beyond (20, 0).

e. Test your program and revise it as necessary.

For Part c, you may wish to have three different groups present the methods for checking if the order of combining size transformations and translations is important.

Summarize
the Mathematics

Teaching Resources

Student Master 46.

UNIT ❸ Coordinate Methods

Summarize
the Mathematics

In this investigation, you extended your work with matrices and animation to include size transformations with center at the origin which were then combined with translations.

ⓐ What are two different ways of representing a size transformation with magnitude k using matrices? Why would you choose one form over the other?

ⓑ Explain how each form in Part a can be used to find the image of a point and the image of a polygon under a size transformation.

ⓒ How could you use general coordinate rules, matrices, or drawing on a coordinate grid to show that order is important when combining size transformations and translations?

Be prepared to share your ideas and reasoning with the entire class.

46   UNIT 3 • Coordinate Methods   Student Master • use with page 242

ⓐ You could scalar multiply the point matrix by the number k, or by the matrix $\begin{bmatrix} k & 0 \\ 0 & k \end{bmatrix}$. When computing by hand, it is easier to multiply the matrix by a number. In programming, it is easier to cast everything in terms of matrices.

ⓑ To find the image of a point or polygon, represent the coordinates of the point or vertices of the polygon as a matrix as shown below. Then multiply the point matrix on the left by either the scalar k or the size transformation $\begin{bmatrix} k & 0 \\ 0 & k \end{bmatrix}$. The resulting matrix represents the coordinates of the image point or vertices of the polygon.

$$
\text{(1)} \quad \underset{\text{Scalar}}{k} \quad \times \quad \underset{\text{Point Matrix}}{\begin{bmatrix} x_1 & x_2 & \cdots & x_n \\ y_1 & y_2 & & y_n \end{bmatrix}} = \underset{\text{Image Point Matrix}}{\begin{bmatrix} kx_1 & kx_2 & \cdots & kx_n \\ ky_1 & ky_2 & & ky_n \end{bmatrix}}
$$

$$
\text{(2)} \quad \underset{\text{Size Trans. Matrix}}{\begin{bmatrix} k & 0 \\ 0 & k \end{bmatrix}} \times \underset{\text{Point Matrix}}{\begin{bmatrix} x_1 & x_2 & \cdots & x_n \\ y_1 & y_2 & & y_n \end{bmatrix}} = \underset{\text{Image Point Matrix}}{\begin{bmatrix} kx_1 & kx_2 & \cdots & kx_n \\ ky_1 & ky_2 & & ky_n \end{bmatrix}}
$$

ⓒ You could apply a size transformation and translation on general coordinates (x, y) in both orders to see if the same coordinates result. For example, apply a size transformation of magnitude 2 and a translation with components $(3, -4)$ to (x, y).

Using coordinate rules: $(x, y) \rightarrow (2x, 2y) \rightarrow (2x + 3, 2y - 4)$.
Reversing order, $(x, y) \rightarrow (x + 3, y - 4) \rightarrow (2x + 6, 2y - 8)$; results are not the same.

Using matrices: $\begin{bmatrix} 2 & 0 \\ 0 & 2 \end{bmatrix}\begin{bmatrix} x \\ y \end{bmatrix} = \begin{bmatrix} 2x \\ 2y \end{bmatrix}$, $\begin{bmatrix} 2x \\ 2y \end{bmatrix} + \begin{bmatrix} 3 \\ -4 \end{bmatrix} = \begin{bmatrix} 2x + 3 \\ 2y - 4 \end{bmatrix}$, while

$\begin{bmatrix} x \\ y \end{bmatrix} + \begin{bmatrix} 3 \\ -4 \end{bmatrix} = \begin{bmatrix} x + 3 \\ y - 4 \end{bmatrix}$, $\begin{bmatrix} 2 & 0 \\ 0 & 2 \end{bmatrix}\begin{bmatrix} x + 3 \\ y - 4 \end{bmatrix} = \begin{bmatrix} 2x + 6 \\ 2y - 8 \end{bmatrix}$; results are not the same. You could test the importance of order on a coordinate grid by drawing a specific polygon and applying the two transformations in both orders. Then check whether or not the resulting images are in the same position.

MATH TOOLKIT Provide examples of the two ways to find an image of a figure under a size transformation. Record a specific example of a composite of two transformations using their coordinate rules where the order of applying the two transformations is important.

Unit 3

$$PQRS = \begin{bmatrix} 5 & 5 & 3 & 5 \\ 0 & 4 & 3 & 2 \end{bmatrix}$$

a. $\begin{bmatrix} 3 & 0 \\ 0 & 3 \end{bmatrix}$

b. $P'Q'R'S' = \begin{bmatrix} 15 & 15 & 9 & 15 \\ 0 & 12 & 9 & 6 \end{bmatrix}$

c.

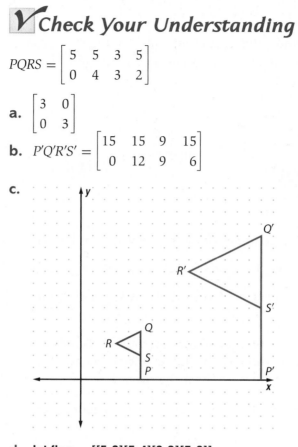

d. **let flag = [[5,0][5,4][3,3][5,2]]**
   draw flag
   repeat 18 [draw [let flag = [scale flag 1.1]] pause 500]

e. Students refine their programs here.

Unit 3

Applications

(1) **a.** 90° clockwise rotation matrix: $\begin{bmatrix} 0 & 1 \\ -1 & 0 \end{bmatrix}$

b. As can be seen by the diagram, the image of P is Q and the image of R is P'. The coordinate of Q can be found by symmetry.

Thus, the 45° clockwise rotation

matrix is $\begin{bmatrix} \dfrac{\sqrt{2}}{2} & \dfrac{\sqrt{2}}{2} \\ -\dfrac{\sqrt{2}}{2} & \dfrac{\sqrt{2}}{2} \end{bmatrix}$.

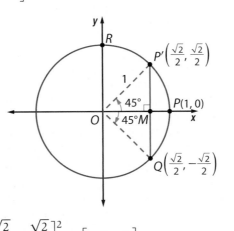

c. 90° clockwise rotation matrix: $\begin{bmatrix} \dfrac{\sqrt{2}}{2} & \dfrac{\sqrt{2}}{2} \\ -\dfrac{\sqrt{2}}{2} & \dfrac{\sqrt{2}}{2} \end{bmatrix}^2 = \begin{bmatrix} 0 & 1 \\ -1 & 0 \end{bmatrix}$

d. One way is to use the one diagram in Part b above. The image of $P(1, 0)$ is the opposite of P', namely $\left(-\dfrac{\sqrt{2}}{2}, -\dfrac{\sqrt{2}}{2}\right)$, and the image of R is the point $Q\left(\dfrac{\sqrt{2}}{2}, -\dfrac{\sqrt{2}}{2}\right)$. Another way is to multiply the 90° clockwise rotation matrix by the 45° clockwise rotation matrix.

So, the matrix for a 135° clockwise rotation is $\begin{bmatrix} -\dfrac{\sqrt{2}}{2} & \dfrac{\sqrt{2}}{2} \\ -\dfrac{\sqrt{2}}{2} & -\dfrac{\sqrt{2}}{2} \end{bmatrix}$.

Applications

1. In Investigation 1, you determined the matrix representations for counterclockwise rotations of 90° and 45° about the origin. You also determined the matrix for a 180° rotation about the origin.

   a. Find the entries of the matrix for a 90° *clockwise* rotation about the origin.

   b. Write the matrix for a 45° *clockwise* rotation about the origin. Explain how its entries can be found by using Diagram II on page 234 and symmetry of the circle.

   c. What matrix should you get if you multiply the matrix in Part b by itself? Verify that is the case.

   d. Describe two ways to find the entries of the matrix for a 135° *clockwise* rotation about the origin. Use one of the ways to find the matrix.

2. Computer animations are used to design and test choreographing movements such as the motions of a flag typically used by Color Guards or the motion of the people themselves. Consider the two basic flag motions of a twirl and a flip. In a twirl, the entire flag is rotated 360°. In a flip, the handle of the flag is turned so that a flag pointing left then points right and vice-versa.

   a. What type of transformation can be used to create the flip effect in a coordinate plane?

   b. Consider a reflection across the *y*-axis. What is the image of $A(2, 3)$ under this reflection? The image of $B(3, -4)$?

   c. Write a coordinate rule for reflection across the *y*-axis.

   d. Use the coordinate rule to find the matrix representation of a reflection across the *y*-axis.

   e. Write a Flag Animation Algorithm that meets the following specifications.

   - Begin with the vertical flag *PQRS* with coordinate matrix $\begin{bmatrix} 0 & 0 & -3 & 0 \\ 0 & 8 & 6 & 4 \end{bmatrix}$.

   - Using matrix multiplication, twirl the banner counterclockwise twice about the origin, showing progressive images rotated 45°.

   - Flip the flag using matrix multiplication and then twirl the banner *clockwise* twice, again showing progressive images rotated 45°.

   f. What are the coordinates of the final flag image after completion of the animation outlined in Part e?

2 **a.** A reflection across a vertical line

    b. $A(2, 3) \rightarrow A'(-2, 3)$
       $B(3, -4) \rightarrow B'(-3, -4)$

NOTE The solutions to Applications Task 1 are on page T242B.

    c. $(x, y) \rightarrow (-x, y)$

    d. Since the image of $P(1, 0)$ is $(-1, 0)$ and the image of $Q(0, 1)$ is $(0, 1)$, the matrix representation of a reflection across the y-axis is $\begin{bmatrix} -1 & 0 \\ 0 & 1 \end{bmatrix}$.

    e.

> **Flag Animation Algorithm**
>
> **Step 1.** Set up the coordinate matrix representing the flag.
> **Step 2.** Set up the 45° counterclockwise rotation matrix.
> **Step 3.** Draw flag.
> **Step 4.** Compute and store the new coordinates of the flag rotated 45°.
> **Step 5.** Clear the old flag and draw the rotated image.
> **Step 6.** Pause.
> **Step 7.** Repeat Steps 4–6 fifteen more times (16 total).
> **Step 8.** Set up the reflection across the y-axis matrix.
> **Step 9.** Compute and store the new coordinates of the reflected image.
> **Step 10.** Set up the 45° clockwise rotation matrix.
> **Step 11.** Compute the new coordinates of the rotated image.
> **Step 12.** Clear the old flag and draw the rotated image.
> **Step 13.** Pause.
> **Step 14.** Repeat Steps 11–13 fifteen more times (16 total).

    f. The final flag image is represented by the matrix $\begin{bmatrix} 0 & 0 & 3 & 0 \\ 0 & 8 & 6 & 4 \end{bmatrix}$. The final image is the original flag reflected across the y-axis.

3 In addition to reflection across the y-axis as investigated in Applications Task 2, two other important line reflections are reflection across the x-axis and reflection across the line $y = x$.

a. Find the matrix representation of a reflection across the x-axis.

b. Find the matrix representation of a reflection across the line $y = x$.

c. Use these two matrix representations to model composition of the two line reflections, first reflecting over the x-axis. Write a matrix representation for the composite transformation.

d. What special transformation is represented by the matrix in Part c? Explain your reasoning.

4 Transformations are used by graphic design artists to produce letters of different sizes and orientation and to position them in a layout.

a. For each of your first and last initials, identify key points on a coordinate grid that define the shape and size of the letters. Then give a matrix that could be used to draw each letter.

b. Placement of shapes in relation to the origin is a very useful starting point when creating graphics.

   i. Describe how you used the origin to determine the coordinates of your initials.

   ii. Imagining both letters anchored at the origin or both appearing next to each other would lead to different coordinate representations. Why might a graphic designer prefer one placement over the other?

c. Determine the matrices for your initials rotated clockwise 90° about the origin.

d. *Optional:* Design and test a program that will animate your initials across the screen.

5 Consider rectangle $PQRS = \begin{bmatrix} 1 & 1 & 6 & 6 \\ 2 & 5 & 5 & 2 \end{bmatrix}$.

a. Illustrate two ways of using matrices to find the image of the rectangle under a size transformation with center at the origin and magnitude 5.

b. Find the coordinate matrix for the image of rectangle $PQRS$ under the composition of first a rotation of 180° about the origin and then a size transformation of magnitude 3.

3 **a.** The matrix representation for a reflection across the x-axis is $\begin{bmatrix} 1 & 0 \\ 0 & -1 \end{bmatrix}$.

b. The matrix representation for a reflection across the line $y = x$
is $\begin{bmatrix} 0 & 1 \\ 1 & 0 \end{bmatrix}$.

c. The composite transformation can be found by multiplying the
matrices from Parts a and b.

$$\begin{bmatrix} 0 & 1 \\ 1 & 0 \end{bmatrix}\begin{bmatrix} 1 & 0 \\ 0 & -1 \end{bmatrix} = \begin{bmatrix} 0 & -1 \\ 1 & 0 \end{bmatrix}$$

The matrix representing the composite transformation is $\begin{bmatrix} 0 & -1 \\ 1 & 0 \end{bmatrix}$.

> **INSTRUCTIONAL NOTE**
> For Part c, since the reflection across the x-axis is done first, the matrix representing it must be on the right.

d. The matrix $\begin{bmatrix} 0 & -1 \\ 1 & 0 \end{bmatrix}$ is the matrix representing a 90° counterclockwise
rotation with center at the origin. One efficient way to recognize this is
to use the relationship that under this transformation, $P(1, 0) \rightarrow P'(0, 1)$
(first column of matrix in Part c) and $Q(0, 1) \rightarrow Q'(-1, 0)$ (second
column of matrix). These images represent a 90° counterclockwise
rotation about the origin.

4 **a–d.** See student layout, matrices, and algorithms. (In Part b, students
should note that the choice of the origin on this coordinate grid
determined the coordinates that specify their initials.)

5 **a.** (1) $5\begin{bmatrix} 1 & 1 & 6 & 6 \\ 2 & 5 & 5 & 2 \end{bmatrix}$

(2) $\begin{bmatrix} 5 & 0 \\ 0 & 5 \end{bmatrix}\begin{bmatrix} 1 & 1 & 6 & 6 \\ 2 & 5 & 5 & 2 \end{bmatrix}$

Both ways result in $\begin{bmatrix} 5 & 5 & 30 & 30 \\ 10 & 25 & 25 & 10 \end{bmatrix}$.

b. $PQRS$ rotated 180° $= \begin{bmatrix} -1 & -1 & -6 & -6 \\ -2 & -5 & -5 & -2 \end{bmatrix}$.

So, $\begin{bmatrix} 3 & 0 \\ 0 & 3 \end{bmatrix}\begin{bmatrix} -1 & -1 & -6 & -6 \\ -2 & -5 & -5 & -2 \end{bmatrix} = \begin{bmatrix} -3 & -3 & -18 & -18 \\ -6 & -15 & -15 & -6 \end{bmatrix}$ is the
matrix of the image rectangle under the composite transformation.

Unit 3

6 Build a coordinate matrix for a model of a rocket similar to the one shown at the right. Then do the following:

  a. Write an algorithm for animating the launch of the rocket.

  b. Explain your methods for performing translations and size transformations on the rocket in your algorithm.

  c. Give the coordinate matrix for the rocket half way through the animation.

Connections

7 In Investigation 1, you developed matrix representations for counterclockwise rotations about the origin through angles of 45°, 90°, 180°, and 270°. In this task, you will build the matrix for a 60° counterclockwise rotation about the origin.

  a. Use the diagram below of an equilateral triangle to help you determine the coordinates of points $P(1, 0)$ and $Q(0, 1)$ under a 60° counterclockwise rotation about the origin.

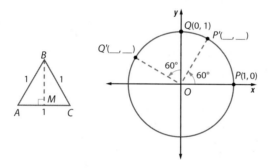

  b. Use your results in Part a to help determine the entries for the

  60° counterclockwise rotation matrix $R_{60°} = \begin{bmatrix} a & b \\ c & d \end{bmatrix}$. Express

  matrix entries in radical form, not as decimal approximations.

  c. Write a coordinate rule $(x, y) \rightarrow (\_\_, \_\_)$ for the 60° counterclockwise rotation about the origin.

8 Use reasoning similar to that in Connections Task 7 to help determine the entries of the matrix $R_{30°}$ for a 30° counterclockwise rotation about the origin.

  a. Verify that the product of the matrices $R_{60°}$ and $R_{30°}$ is the matrix for a 90° counterclockwise rotation about the origin.

  b. Write a coordinate rule $(x, y) \rightarrow (\_\_, \_\_)$ for the 30° counterclockwise rotation about the origin.

6 Students' coordinate matrices for their rockets will vary. An example of a triangular rocket is $\begin{bmatrix} 4 & 0 & -4 \\ 0 & 10 & 0 \end{bmatrix}$.

a. Student algorithms will vary. The following sample algorithm uses the coordinate matrix above along with initial scale factor of 0.9, initial translation of 4 units up, incremental decrease of scale factor 0.1, incremental increase of vertical translation by 4 units, and number of times to repeat. All these choices are arbitrary, and students may vary the algorithm to include some rotation of the rocket as well.

Step 1. Set up the coordinate matrix representing the rocket.
Step 2. Set up a 0.9 scale factor.
Step 3. Set up a vertical translation of 4 units.
Step 4. Draw the rocket.
Step 5. Compute the new coordinates of the original rocket scaled and then translated.
Step 6. Clear the old rocket and draw the new rocket.
Step 7. Pause.
Step 8. Decrease the scale factor by 0.1.
Step 9. Increase the vertical translation by 4 units.
Step 10. Repeat Steps 5–9 six times.

b. Responses may vary. The sample algorithm in Part a repeatedly performs a size transformation of the original rocket and translates the image rocket vertically. To create the appearance of launching, at each iteration the scale factor is reduced to make the original rocket appear smaller while at the same time, the translation is increased to make the image rocket move farther along the positive y-axis.

c. For this sample algorithm, the coordinates of the rocket half way through the animation are the coordinates of the image rocket after the third repetition of Steps 5–9, $\begin{bmatrix} 2.8 & 0 & -2.8 \\ 12 & 19 & 12 \end{bmatrix}$.

Connections

7 a. $P'\left(\dfrac{1}{2}, \dfrac{\sqrt{3}}{2}\right)$ and $Q'\left(-\dfrac{\sqrt{3}}{2}, \dfrac{1}{2}\right)$

b. $\begin{bmatrix} a & b \\ c & d \end{bmatrix}\begin{bmatrix} 1 \\ 0 \end{bmatrix} = \begin{bmatrix} \frac{1}{2} \\ \frac{\sqrt{3}}{2} \end{bmatrix}$, so $a = \dfrac{1}{2}$ and $c = \dfrac{\sqrt{3}}{2}$.

$\begin{bmatrix} a & b \\ c & d \end{bmatrix}\begin{bmatrix} 0 \\ 1 \end{bmatrix} = \begin{bmatrix} -\frac{\sqrt{3}}{2} \\ \frac{1}{2} \end{bmatrix}$, so $b = -\dfrac{\sqrt{3}}{2}$ and $d = \dfrac{1}{2}$.

$R_{60°} = \begin{bmatrix} \frac{1}{2} & -\frac{\sqrt{3}}{2} \\ \frac{\sqrt{3}}{2} & \frac{1}{2} \end{bmatrix}$

c. $R_{60°}: (x, y) \rightarrow \left(\dfrac{1}{2}x - \dfrac{\sqrt{3}}{2}y, \dfrac{\sqrt{3}}{2}x + \dfrac{1}{2}y\right)$

8 $R_{30°} = \begin{bmatrix} \frac{\sqrt{3}}{2} & -\frac{1}{2} \\ \frac{1}{2} & \frac{\sqrt{3}}{2} \end{bmatrix}$

a. $R_{60°} \circ R_{30°}$ $\begin{bmatrix} \frac{1}{2} & -\frac{\sqrt{3}}{2} \\ \frac{\sqrt{3}}{2} & \frac{1}{2} \end{bmatrix}\begin{bmatrix} \frac{\sqrt{3}}{2} & -\frac{1}{2} \\ \frac{1}{2} & \frac{\sqrt{3}}{2} \end{bmatrix} = \begin{bmatrix} 0 & -1 \\ 1 & 0 \end{bmatrix} =$

$\begin{bmatrix} \frac{\sqrt{3}}{2} & -\frac{1}{2} \\ \frac{1}{2} & \frac{\sqrt{3}}{2} \end{bmatrix}\begin{bmatrix} \frac{1}{2} & -\frac{\sqrt{3}}{2} \\ \frac{\sqrt{3}}{2} & \frac{1}{2} \end{bmatrix} = R_{30°} \circ R_{60°}$

b. $R_{30°}: (x, y) \rightarrow \left(\dfrac{\sqrt{3}}{2}x + \dfrac{1}{2}y, -\dfrac{1}{2}x + \dfrac{\sqrt{3}}{2}y\right)$

9 In the *Patterns in Shape* unit of Course 1, you analyzed tessellations and frieze patterns in terms of their symmetries. Those symmetries were described in terms of transformations—reflections, rotations, and translations. Those same transformations can be used to create repeating patterns such as the one shown below.

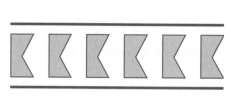

Write an algorithm that inputs the coordinates of the figure at the right and produces the frieze pattern shown at the left.

10 In Unit 2, *Matrix Methods*, you found many useful interpretations of powers of matrices. When matrices are used to represent transformations, their powers have a special interpretation. Recall that the matrix

$$R_{45°} = \begin{bmatrix} \frac{\sqrt{2}}{2} & -\frac{\sqrt{2}}{2} \\ \frac{\sqrt{2}}{2} & \frac{\sqrt{2}}{2} \end{bmatrix}$$

is the matrix representation for a 45° counterclockwise rotation about the origin.

   a. Compute $R_{45°}^2$ and $R_{45°}^4$, and compare your results to the other matrices you constructed in Investigation 1.

   b. What rotation do you think $R_{45°}^6$ represents? $R_{45°}^3$? Explain your reasoning.

   c. Represent a 270° counterclockwise rotation about the origin as a power of the matrix for a 90° counterclockwise rotation.

11 In the *Matrix Methods* unit, you compared operations on matrices with operations on real numbers. Consider the case of square roots. The real number 1, which is the multiplicative identity, has two square roots, 1 and −1. The multiplicative identity for 2 × 2 matrices is $I = \begin{bmatrix} 1 & 0 \\ 0 & 1 \end{bmatrix}$.

   a. Verify that the matrix for a line reflection across the *x*-axis is a "square root" of *I*.

   b. Find two other "square roots" of *I*.

   c. How many "square roots" do you think *I* has? Explain.

⑨

Frieze Pattern

Step 1. Set up the coordinate matrix representing the figure.

Step 2. Set up the coordinate matrix for a reflection across the *x*-axis.

Step 3. Set up a horizontal translation of 6 units.

Step 4. Compute the image of the figure under a reflection across the *x*-axis.

Step 5. Draw the figure and its reflected image.

Step 6. Compute the image of the figure and its image under the translation.

Step 7. Draw the translated image. (Do not clear the previous drawn images.)

Step 8. Replace the previous figure and image with the ones computed in Step 6.

Step 9. Repeat Steps 6 to 8 as needed.

⑩ **a.** $R_{45°}^2 = \begin{bmatrix} 0 & -1 \\ 1 & 0 \end{bmatrix}$; $R_{45°}^4 = \begin{bmatrix} -1 & 0 \\ 0 & -1 \end{bmatrix}$

They are the same matrices as those previously identified with 90° counterclockwise and 180° rotations with center at the origin.

b. $R_{45°}^6$ represents a counterclockwise rotation of 270°. $R_{45°}^3$ represents a counterclockwise rotation of 135°. The power of the matrix represents the number of successive 45° counterclockwise rotations.

c. $R_{90°} = \begin{bmatrix} 0 & -1 \\ 1 & 0 \end{bmatrix}$

$R_{270°} = (R_{90°})^3 = \begin{bmatrix} 0 & -1 \\ 1 & 0 \end{bmatrix}^3 = \begin{bmatrix} 0 & 1 \\ -1 & 0 \end{bmatrix}$

⑪ **a.** The transformation matrix for a reflection across the *x*-axis is $\begin{bmatrix} 1 & 0 \\ 0 & -1 \end{bmatrix}$.

Since $\begin{bmatrix} 1 & 0 \\ 0 & -1 \end{bmatrix}^2 = \begin{bmatrix} 1 & 0 \\ 0 & 1 \end{bmatrix} = I$, the transformation matrix for a reflection across the *x*-axis is a "square root" of *I*.

b. Students will likely suggest matrices for any transformation that when composed with itself maps each point onto itself.

Reflection across the *y*-axis: $\begin{bmatrix} -1 & 0 \\ 0 & 1 \end{bmatrix}$

Reflection across *y* = *x*: $\begin{bmatrix} 0 & 1 \\ 1 & 0 \end{bmatrix}$

Reflection across *y* = −*x*: $\begin{bmatrix} 0 & -1 \\ -1 & 0 \end{bmatrix}$

180° rotation: $\begin{bmatrix} -1 & 0 \\ 0 & -1 \end{bmatrix}$

c. Since the image of each point under the composition of a line reflection (half-turn) with itself is the original point, any matrix that represents a line reflection would be a "square root" of *I*. Thus, there are an infinite number of "square roots" of *I*.

Reflections

12 Suppose $R = \begin{bmatrix} a & b \\ c & d \end{bmatrix}$ is the matrix for a rotation about the origin, and $I = \begin{bmatrix} 1 & 0 \\ 0 & 1 \end{bmatrix}$ is the identity matrix.

   a. What must be true about $R \times I$?

   b. How are the entries of any rotation matrix related to the entries of the identity matrix?

13 Look back at the Roll Over Algorithm in Investigation 1 (page 235). If *NOW* represents the matrix of the current shuttle image and *NEXT* represents the matrix of the next image in the animation sequence, write a rule relating *NOW* and *NEXT*.

14 Look back at your work on Connections Tasks 7 and 8.

   a. How could you use the matrix $R_{60°}$ to find the matrix for a 120° counterclockwise rotation about the origin?

   b. How could you use the matrix $R_{30°}$ to find the matrix for a 120° counterclockwise rotation about the origin?

   c. How could you use the symmetry of a circle to help write the matrix for each of the following transformations?

   i. 30° clockwise rotation about the origin

   ii. 60° clockwise rotation about the origin

   d. How could you find the matrix for a 150° clockwise rotation about the origin?

15 You have been able to use geometric reasoning to find rotation matrices for special angles. In the *Trigonometric Methods* unit, you will learn how to find rotation matrices for any angle. Investigate how you could use the reporting capabilities of interactive geometry software to find rotation matrices for other angles. Find the matrix representation for each of the following transformations.

   a. 15° counterclockwise rotation about the origin

   b. 75° clockwise rotation about the origin

Extensions

16 View the "Animate Person" and "Animate Humanoid" Sample Sketches in your interactive geometry software. Select one of the animations.

   a. Describe the transformations involved in creating that animation.

   b. Describe a possible algorithm for producing the animation.

Reflections

12 **a.** $R \times I = R$

b. For any rotation matrix R, the first column of R is the image under that rotation of the first column of the identity matrix; that is, the first column of R is $R \times \begin{bmatrix} 1 \\ 0 \end{bmatrix}$. Similarly, the second column is $R \times \begin{bmatrix} 0 \\ 1 \end{bmatrix}$.

13 $NEXT = [TRANSFORMATION] \times NOW$
(Note that the transformation matrix must be to the left of *NOW*.)

14 **a.** $(R_{60°})^2 = R_{120°}$

b. $(R_{30°})^4 = R_{120°}$

c. The symmetry of the circle allows you to write the coordinates of the points shown below. Then you can find the images of (1, 0) and (0, 1) for the first and second columns of the rotation matrix.

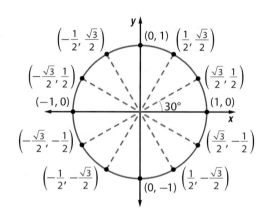

    i. 30° clockwise rotation matrix: $\begin{bmatrix} \dfrac{\sqrt{3}}{2} & \dfrac{1}{2} \\ -\dfrac{1}{2} & \dfrac{\sqrt{3}}{2} \end{bmatrix}$

    ii. 60° clockwise rotation matrix: $\begin{bmatrix} \dfrac{1}{2} & \dfrac{\sqrt{3}}{2} \\ -\dfrac{\sqrt{3}}{2} & \dfrac{1}{2} \end{bmatrix}$

d. Two possible responses are: raise the 30° clockwise rotation to the fifth power or find $R_{180°} \times R_{30°}$ which is a rotation of 210°, counterclockwise, rather than a 150° clockwise rotation about the origin.

15 **a.** Using *CPMP-Tools* interactive geometry, one strategy might be to do the following:

Step 1. Draw an arbitrary segment along the positive *x*-axis.

Step 2. Turn off "Snap to Grid" and turn on "Show Matrix Computations" from the Options menu.

Step 3. Select the segment and choose the Rotate toolbar button. Drag the segment counterclockwise until the angle in the commands window is 15°.

The Commands window will dynamically update as you drag the segment. It shows the command for drawing the rotated segment counterclockwise by an angle and will also show the rotation matrix used to transform the segment. The 15° counterclockwise rotation matrix given is $\begin{bmatrix} 0.96 & -0.258 \\ 0.258 & 0.96 \end{bmatrix}$.

A second approach using *CPMP-Tools*, or other software, would be to use the unit circle. Rotate (1, 0) and (0, 1) counterclockwise 15° by choosing "Rotate By" from the Transform menu. Then read the coordinates for the rotation matrix $\begin{bmatrix} 0.96 & -0.258 \\ 0.258 & 0.96 \end{bmatrix}$, by noting the coordinates of the images of $P(1, 0)$ and $Q(0, 1)$.

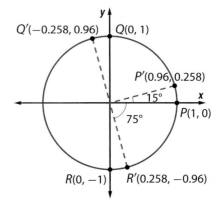

b. For the 75° clockwise rotation, use the symmetry of the circle as shown above. Alternatively, use either strategy in Part a for a 75° clockwise rotation, or a $360° - 75° = 285°$ counterclockwise rotation. The 75° clockwise rotation matrix given is $\begin{bmatrix} 0.258 & 0.96 \\ -0.9 & 0.258 \end{bmatrix}$.

Extensions

16 **a–b.** Students' descriptions may be more or less complete based on your guidelines.

Teacher Notes

17 All of the rotations and size transformations that you have worked with in this lesson have been centered at the origin. To spin a flag around a point P other than the origin, you can use the translate-transform-translate back method (see Applications Task 13 page 222). Use this method to write a program, using matrices, that will rotate a flag about the point $P(5, 0)$ in steps of $45°$.

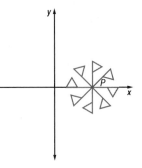

18 By combining creativity with an understanding of matrix representations of transformations, many other interesting animations are possible. For example, consider the image shown below created by successive applications of a size transformation followed by a rotation of a square:

a. Estimate the scale factor of the size transformation and the angle of rotation.

b. Write a calculator program that produces a spiral-type animation, according to these specifications:

- Start with the $\triangle ABC = \begin{bmatrix} 0 & 2 & 2 \\ 0 & 0.5 & -0.5 \end{bmatrix}$.

- Successively transform $\triangle ABC$ using the composition of a size transformation of magnitude 1.1, followed by a $45°$ counterclockwise rotation. Both transformations should be centered at the origin.

- Set up the viewing window so that you can see at least 30 steps.

17 One possible matrix to represent the flag is $B = \begin{bmatrix} 5 & 13 & 11 & 9 \\ 0 & 0 & -3 & 0 \end{bmatrix}$.

This may help students see that the flag is rotating about $(5, 0)$, since the end of the flagpole is the point $(5, 0)$, as shown on page 248.

Using the flag given by the matrix above, a reasonable viewing window is $-15 \le x \le 15$ and $-15 \le y \le 15$.

The program will use matrices A and C where $A = R_{45°}$, and $-C$ and C will be added to the flag to translate it back and forth from the origin.

$$A = \begin{bmatrix} \dfrac{\sqrt{2}}{2} & -\dfrac{\sqrt{2}}{2} \\ \dfrac{\sqrt{2}}{2} & \dfrac{\sqrt{2}}{2} \end{bmatrix} \qquad C = \begin{bmatrix} 5 & 5 & 5 & 5 \\ 0 & 0 & 0 & 0 \end{bmatrix}$$

The following program will run on a TI-82 or TI-83 series calculator.

```
PROGRAM: FLAGSPIN
For(N,1,8)
[B]−[C]→[B]
[A]*[B]→[B]
[B]+[C]→[B]
Line([B](1,1),[B](2,1),[B](1,2),[B](2,2))
Line([B](1,2),[B](2,2),[B](1,3),[B](2,3))
Line([B](1,3),[B](2,3),[B](1,4),[B](2,4))
For(K,1,50)
End
ClrDraw
End
Stop
```

The following program will run in *CPMP-Tools*.

```
program flagspin
let A=[[0.7071,0.7071][−0.7071,0.7071]]
let B=[[5,0][13,0][11,−3][9,0]]
let C=[[5,0][5,0][5,0][5,0]]
repeat 8 [let B=[B−C] let B=[A*B] let
B=[B+C] style B label off draw B pause 500]
end
```

18 a. Using the largest square as the preimage, a reasonable scale factor is 0.8. The rotation could be clockwise or counterclockwise 45°.

b. This is a program which defines the matrices within the program. It will run on a TI-82 or TI-83 series calculator. A window of $-90 \le x \le 90$ and $-60 \le y \le 60$ should suffice.

```
[[1.1,0][0,1.1]→[A]
[[0,2,2][0,0.5,−0.5]→[B]
[[√(2)/2,−√(2)/2][√(2)/2,√(2)/2]]→[C]
[A]*[C]→[D]
For(N,1,35,1)
ClrDraw
Line([B](1,1),[B](2,1),[B](1,2),[B](2,2))
Line([B](1,2),[B](2,2),[B](1,3),[B](2,3))
Line([B](1,3),[B](2,3),[B](1,1),[B](2,1))
[D]*[B]→[B]
For(K,1,10,1)
End
End
Stop
```

19 The **homogeneous coordinates** of a point (x, y) are $(x, y, 1)$; this represents the point in three-dimensional space, in a plane parallel to the x-y plane, and 1 unit above it. When plotting the point $(x, y, 1)$ in the x-y plane, the "1" is ignored. But representing points with homogeneous coordinates allows matrix multiplication to be used to translate points.

   a. Let $A = \begin{bmatrix} 1 & 0 & 2 \\ 0 & 1 & 3 \\ 0 & 0 & 1 \end{bmatrix}$. What is the effect of multiplying $\begin{bmatrix} x \\ y \\ 1 \end{bmatrix}$ on the left by A?

   b. Build a matrix that will translate a point 5 units to the right and 3 units down.

   c. Use homogeneous coordinates to build the matrix for a translation that has horizontal component h and vertical component k.

   d. How could you represent a 90° counterclockwise rotation about the origin with a 3×3 matrix?

   e. Write an algorithm for a flag animation using homogeneous coordinates and 3×3 matrices to represent a rotation and a translation.

20 Consider the transformation of the plane represented by this matrix:

   $$S = \begin{bmatrix} 1 & 0 \\ 0 & 1 \end{bmatrix}$$

   a. Represent the rectangle shown as a matrix. Then find the image of the rectangle under the transformation represented by S.

   b. Sketch the rectangle and its image on a coordinate grid.

   c. Describe as precisely as you can the transformation that S represents. This transformation is called a **horizontal shear**.

   d. Find the coordinate rule for the transformation.

   e. How does the transformation affect the perimeter of the rectangle? The area? Explain your answers.

   f. Compare S to the shear transformation $T = \begin{bmatrix} 1 & 0.5 \\ 0 & 1 \end{bmatrix}$.

   g. Use S or T to transform your initials in Applications Task 4 to italic font.

LESSON 3 • Transformations, Matrices, and Animation **249**

19 **a.** The product is $\begin{bmatrix} x + 2 \\ y + 3 \\ 1 \end{bmatrix}$. This is the homogeneous coordinate representation of the image of (x, y) under a translation with horizontal component 2 and vertical component 3.

b. $\begin{bmatrix} 1 & 0 & 5 \\ 0 & 1 & -3 \\ 0 & 0 & 1 \end{bmatrix}$ **c.** $\begin{bmatrix} 1 & 0 & h \\ 0 & 1 & k \\ 0 & 0 & 1 \end{bmatrix}$ **d.** $\begin{bmatrix} 0 & -1 & 0 \\ 1 & 0 & 0 \\ 0 & 0 & 1 \end{bmatrix}$

e. One possible planning algorithm:

> **Flag Rotation and Translation**
>
> **Step 1.** Define a 3 × 3 90° counterclockwise rotation about the origin matrix, $A = \begin{bmatrix} 0 & -1 & 0 \\ 1 & 0 & 0 \\ 0 & 0 & 1 \end{bmatrix}$.
>
> **Step 2.** Define a 3 × 3 translation matrix, $B = \begin{bmatrix} 1 & 0 & 5 \\ 0 & 1 & -3 \\ 0 & 0 & 1 \end{bmatrix}$.
>
> **Step 3.** Compute the matrix that first applies a rotation and then a translation, $B \cdot A = T$.
>
> **Step 4.** Define a 3 × 4 point matrix for the flag, $C = \begin{bmatrix} 5 & 13 & 11 & 9 \\ 0 & 0 & -3 & 0 \\ 1 & 1 & 1 & 1 \end{bmatrix}$.
>
> **Step 5.** Draw C.
> **Step 6.** Pause.
> **Step 7.** Define $C = T \cdot C$ and draw the image. (To draw the image, you have to use only the first three columns and first two rows of the product matrix.)
> **Step 8.** Repeat 4 times.

20

a. $\begin{bmatrix} 0 & 0 & 8 & 8 \\ 0 & 5 & 5 & 0 \end{bmatrix} \rightarrow \begin{bmatrix} 1 & 1 \\ 0 & 1 \end{bmatrix}\begin{bmatrix} 0 & 0 & 8 & 8 \\ 0 & 5 & 5 & 0 \end{bmatrix} = \begin{bmatrix} 0 & 5 & 13 & 8 \\ 0 & 5 & 5 & 0 \end{bmatrix}$

b.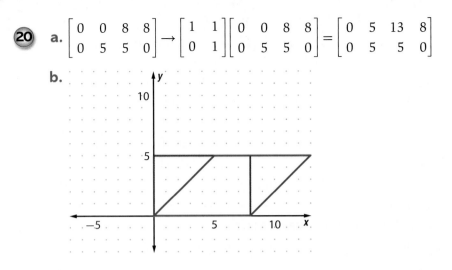

c. Descriptions will vary. The points on the *x*-axis remain the same while all other points shift 5 units to the right. This is the *y*-coordinate of the preimage point.

d. $(x, y) \rightarrow (x + y, y)$

To find the coordinate rule from the matrix, multiply the transformation matrix by the matrix for the point (x, y).

$$\begin{bmatrix} 1 & 1 \\ 0 & 1 \end{bmatrix}\begin{bmatrix} x \\ y \end{bmatrix} = \begin{bmatrix} x + y \\ y \end{bmatrix}$$

So, the transformation sends the point (x, y) to the point $(x + y, y)$.

e. The perimeter increases from 26 units to $16 + 10\sqrt{2}$ units. The area remains the same since the base and height do not change.

f. $\begin{bmatrix} 1 & 0.5 \\ 0 & 1 \end{bmatrix}\begin{bmatrix} x \\ y \end{bmatrix} = \begin{bmatrix} x + 0.5y \\ y \end{bmatrix}$; *T* transforms each point horizontally by adding half the *y*-coordinate value.

g. Applications Task 4 assumes that the initials are on a horizontal line in normal alignment. The final transformation applied should be a shear.

Teacher Notes

21 In addition to rigid transformations, size transformations, and shear transformations (Extensions Task 20), there are many other **linear transformations** of the plane. These are transformations whose coordinate rules $(x, y) \rightarrow (x', y')$ give x' and y' as linear expressions in x and y. Consider the transformation that has this coordinate rule:

$$(x, y) \rightarrow (2x + y, x + 2y)$$

a. Find the matrix representation of this transformation.

b. Write a 2×4 matrix that represents the rectangle shown below.

c. Multiply your matrix in Part b by the matrix for the transformation to find the transformed image of the rectangle.

d. Sketch the rectangle and its image on a coordinate grid.

e. Which of the following statements are true about the rectangle and its transformed image?

  i. Lengths do not change.

  ii. Angle sizes do not change.

  iii. Pairs of parallel sides are transformed into pairs of parallel sides.

  iv. Area does not change.

Review

22 Ten students in Mr. Malone's class measured the circumference of their wrists and their necks. Their measurements, in centimeters, are provided in the table below.

Wrist	14	16.5	15.3	18.1	20.5	23.1	21.2	17.1	19.3	17.8
Neck	27.1	32	31.5	37.3	42.1	45.2	41.6	33.8	37.5	35.2

a. Find the mean, median, and standard deviation of the wrist circumferences.

b. There are 2.54 centimeters in an inch. What would the mean, median, and standard deviation be if the students had measured their wrist circumferences using inches instead of centimeters?

21 **a.** $A = \begin{bmatrix} 2 & 1 \\ 1 & 2 \end{bmatrix}$. This is found by multiplying $A \times \begin{bmatrix} 1 \\ 0 \end{bmatrix}$ (first column) and

$A \times \begin{bmatrix} 0 \\ 1 \end{bmatrix}$ (second column).

b. $B = \begin{bmatrix} 0 & 0 & 8 & 8 \\ 0 & 5 & 5 & 0 \end{bmatrix}$

c. $A \times B = \begin{bmatrix} 0 & 5 & 21 & 16 \\ 0 & 10 & 18 & 8 \end{bmatrix}$

d.

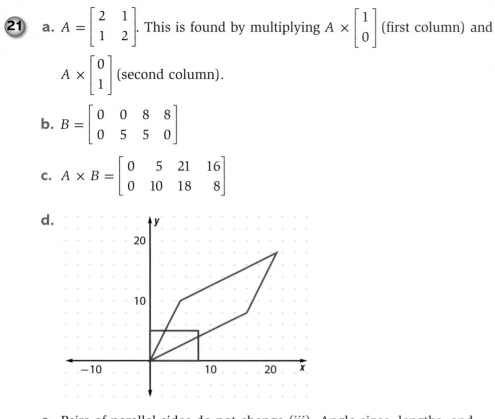

e. Pairs of parallel sides do not change (iii). Angle sizes, lengths, and areas do change.

Review

22 **a.** Mean: 18.29 cm
Median: 17.95 cm
Standard deviation: 2.64 cm

b. Mean: 7.2 in.
Median: 7.07 in.
Standard deviation: 1.04 in.

Unit 3

c. Madison wants a rule for predicting someone's neck circumference if she knows his or her wrist circumference. Find such a rule for Madison. Explain how you found your rule.

d. Sam, a sixth-grader, has a wrist circumference of 12.3 cm. Use your rule to predict the circumference of Sam's neck.

23 Consider the line segment with endpoints $A(0, 12)$ and $B(6, 8)$.

a. Find the length of $\overline{AB}$.

b. Find the midpoint of $\overline{AB}$.

c. Find an equation of the line containing $\overline{AB}$.

d. Find an equation of the line that contains the point $A(0, 12)$ and is perpendicular to $\overline{AB}$.

e. Find an equation of a line that would be parallel to $\overleftrightarrow{AB}$.

24 Determine the equations of the lines with the indicated characteristics.

a. Has slope of $-\frac{3}{2}$ and contains the point $(0, 9)$

b. Has slope of $\frac{4}{3}$ and contains the point $(-6, -10)$

c. Has graph as shown below   **d.** Has graph as shown below

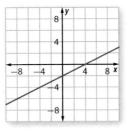 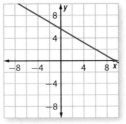

25 Raul's take-home pay for each week in the last month is represented by x_i where $x_1 = \$112.32$, $x_2 = \$89.17$, $x_3 = \$95.91$, and $x_4 = \$78.64$.

a. Compute Σx and then indicate what that number tells you about Raul's earnings.

b. Compute $\frac{\Sigma x}{4}$. What is this number called?

c. Each week, Raul has to give \$25 to his parents to help pay for his car insurance. Which of the following expressions correctly represents the total amount of money Raul had left to spend during this four-week period?

    I $(\Sigma x) - 25$ **II** $\Sigma 25x$ **III** $\Sigma(x - 25)$

d. Recall that $\bar{x}$ is the symbol for the mean of a set of values. Compute $\Sigma(x - \bar{x})$ for these values.

c. $y = 1.97x + 0.38$

Students will probably use the linear regression feature on their calculator with the provided centimeter measurements. (If students use the data transformed to inches, they will have approximately the same regression equation.)

d. $y = 1.97(12.3) + 0.38 = 24.611$; Sam's neck is approximately 24.6 cm in circumference.

23
  a. $AB = \sqrt{52} = 2\sqrt{13}$ **b.** (3, 10)

  c. $y = -\frac{2}{3}x + 12$ **d.** $y = \frac{3}{2}x + 12$

  e. Answers will vary but should all have a slope of $-\frac{2}{3}$.

Just in Time

24
  a. $y = -\frac{3}{2} + 9$

  b. $y = \frac{4}{3}x - 2$

  c. $y = \frac{1}{2}x - 2$

  d. $y = -\frac{3}{5}x + \frac{28}{5}$

Just in Time

25
  a. $\Sigma x = \$376.04$. This tells us that during this four-week period Raul's total take-home pay was $376.04.

  b. $\frac{\Sigma x}{4} = \$94.01$. This number is the mean of the take-home pay, or average weekly pay.

  c. The correct expression is III, $\Sigma(x - 25)$.

  d. $\Sigma(x - \bar{x}) = 0$

Teaching Resources

Assessment Masters 47–51.

Looking Back

In this unit, you learned how to use coordinates and matrices to represent figures in a coordinate plane and on a computer or calculator screen. Coordinate representations of slope and distance were helpful in creating and analyzing figures, particularly those with parallel or perpendicular sides. You developed methods to reposition and resize shapes using transformations represented by coordinate rules and by matrices.

You learned how the key ideas of congruence and similarity are related to transformations. The image of any figure under a rigid transformation—a translation, rotation, line reflection, or glide reflection—is congruent to the original figure, or preimage. The image of a figure under a size transformation or a similarity transformation—the composite of a size transformation and a rigid transformation—is always similar to the original figure. The connection between composition of transformations and matrix multiplication was seen to be particularly useful in creating animations of shapes.

The tasks in this final lesson will help you review and organize your thinking about coordinate methods and their connections with matrices.

1 **Designing Shapes** Examine this simplified image of an insect created by a graphic artist for a cell phone screen saver.

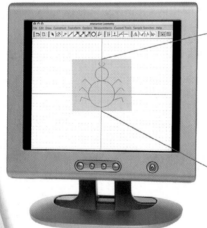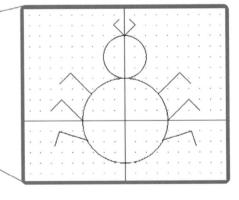

Looking Back

Assessment Differentiation If your students have demonstrated a firm understanding of the mathematics content that would be assessed using either Form A or Form B of the unit test, you may wish to have students create an animation rather that use a written test. The first project, "Animating Rides," outlines one such project. Alternatively, you could offer each student the option of creating an animation or completing the Take-Home Assessment tasks.

The second project in the assessment, "Street Distances," asks students to think about several situations in which taxi-distance makes sense. In the process, they think about what a "perpendicular bisector" looks like when using taxi-distance rather than Euclidean distance between two points.

Unit 3

a. What equation could be used to represent the main body (not including the legs)? The head (not including the antennae)?

b. Identify the coordinates of 5 points on the main body. Identify the coordinates of 2 other points without doing any calculations.

c. Use coordinates of key points on the middle leg and foot to verify that the foot is positioned at a right angle to the leg.

d. In creating the image, the artist drew the legs and antenna on the right side of the insect and then used a transformation to complete the image. What transformation was used and how could that transformation be described using coordinates?

e. Suppose the artist wanted to reposition the insect image using a translation with horizontal and vertical components 10 and −6, respectively.

  i. Write equations that could be used to represent the main body and head of the new figure.

  ii. What would be the perimeter of the main body of the new figure?

  iii. What would be the area of the main body of the new figure?

f. Describe a single transformation that the artist could use to reposition the insect image so that it is pointing downward. Describe a different single transformation that could be used. Write a coordinate rule for each of those transformations.

g. Suppose the artist wanted to resize the insect image using a size transformation of magnitude 2 with center at the origin.

  i. Write equations that could be used to represent the main body and head of the new figure.

  ii. What would be the perimeter of the main body of the new figure?

  iii. What would be the area of the main body of the new figure?

(2) **Analyzing Shapes** A quadrilateral $ABCD$ has vertices with coordinates $A(4, 9)$, $B(7, 5)$, $C(-2, -3)$, and $D(-1, 9)$.

a. Sketch this quadrilateral on a coordinate grid or display it on your calculator or computer.

b. Use coordinate methods to justify that quadrilateral $ABCD$ is a kite.

c. How are the diagonals of kite $ABCD$ related? Use coordinate methods to justify your answer.

d. Find the midpoints of each side and connect them in order with line segments. What kind of polygon is formed? (Be as specific as possible.) Justify your answer.

1　**a.** Body: $x^2 + y^2 = 16$
Head: $x^2 + (y - 6)^2 = 4$

b. Students should identify five points on the circle $x^2 + y^2 = 16$ and use symmetry to find two additional points.

c. The coordinates of key points on the right middle leg and foot are $(4, 0)$, $(6, 2)$, and $(7, 1)$. The slopes of the leg segments are 1 and -1, so they are perpendicular. Alternatively, the distance from $(4, 0)$ to $(6, 2)$ is $\sqrt{8}$, from $(6, 2)$ to $(7, 1)$ is $\sqrt{2}$, and from $(4, 0)$ to $(7, 1)$ is $\sqrt{10}$. So, since $(\sqrt{8})^2 + (\sqrt{2})^2 = (\sqrt{10})^2$, the three vertices of the insect leg form a right triangle by the converse of the Pythagorean Theorem.

d. The transformation was a reflection across the y-axis:
$(x, y) \rightarrow (-x, y)$

e. **i.** Body: $(x - 10)^2 + (y + 6)^2 = 16$
　　　Head: $(x - 10)^2 + y^2 = 4$

　　ii. *Perimeter body* $= 2\pi(4) = 8\pi$ units, the same as the original figure.

　　iii. *Area body* $= \pi(4)^2 = 16\pi$ square units, the same as the original figure.

f. One single transformation is a 180° rotation with center at the origin: $(x, y) \rightarrow (-x, -y)$. Another single transformation is a reflection across the x-axis: $(x, y) \rightarrow (x, -y)$.

g. **i.** Body: $x^2 + y^2 = 64$
　　　Head: $x^2 + (y - 12)^2 = 16$

　　ii. *Perimeter body* $= 2\pi(8) = 16\pi$ units, twice the perimeter of the original.

　　iii. *Area body* $= \pi(8)^2 = 64\pi$ square units, four times the area of the original.

2　**a.**

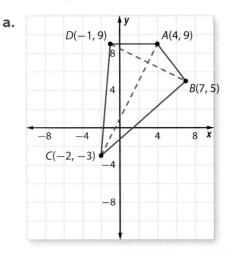

b. $AB = 5$, $BC = \sqrt{64 + 81} = \sqrt{145} \approx 12.04$,
$CD = \sqrt{12^2 + 1^2} = \sqrt{145} \approx 12.04$, $AD = 5$

The quadrilateral is a kite because it has two distinct pairs of consecutive sides the same length.

c. The diagonals are perpendicular because the slopes of those segments are negative reciprocals of each other. (See the diagram in Part a.) The slope of $\overline{AC}$ is 2, and the slope of $\overline{BD}$ is $-\frac{1}{2}$. The midpoint of $\overline{BD}$ is $\left(\frac{-1 + 7}{2}, \frac{9 + 5}{2}\right) = (3, 7)$. To show that $\overline{AC}$ bisects $\overline{BD}$, we need to show that $(3, 7)$ lies on $\overline{AC}$. Since the slope of $\overline{AC}$ is 2, the y-intercept of $\overline{AC}$ is 1 (up 4, over 2). The equation for $\overleftrightarrow{AC}$ is $y = 2x + 1$. The midpoint $(3, 7)$ lies on this line since $7 = 2(3) + 1$. Thus, $\overline{AC}$ is the perpendicular bisector of $\overline{BD}$.

d. The coordinates of the midpoints (as labeled in the diagram) are $X(5.5, 7)$, $Y(2.5, 1)$, $Z(-1.5, 3)$, and $W(1.5, 9)$. The slopes of opposite sides of $WXYZ$ are $-\frac{1}{2}$ and 2; therefore, opposite sides are parallel and right angles are formed at the vertices so, the quadrilateral is a rectangle.

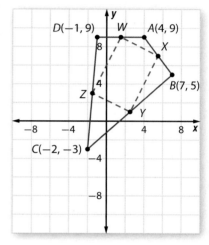

Teacher Notes

3 Relating Shapes Examine the screen below. The scale on each axis is 1.

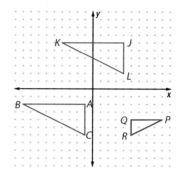

a. Explain why $\triangle ABC \cong \triangle JKL$.

b. Describe a transformation or sequence of transformations that maps $\triangle ABC$ onto $\triangle JKL$. Write a coordinate rule $(x, y) \rightarrow (\_\_, \_\_)$ that relates preimage and image points.

c. Explain why $\triangle ABC$ is similar to $\triangle QPR$.

d. Describe a transformation or sequence of transformations that maps $\triangle ABC$ onto $\triangle QPR$. Write a coordinate rule $(x, y) \rightarrow (\_\_, \_\_)$ that relates preimage and image points.

e. Describe a transformation or sequence of transformations that maps $\triangle JKL$ onto $\triangle QPR$. Write a coordinate rule $(x, y) \rightarrow (\_\_, \_\_)$ for the transformation.

f. Describe a sequence of transformations that repositions $\triangle ABC$ so that it meets both of the following specifications.

- The image is a right triangle of the same size.

- The longest leg of the image triangle lies along the positive y-axis with point A at the origin.

g. Write a coordinate rule for the composite transformation in Part f.

4 Repositioning and Resizing a Shape Use grid paper to display $\triangle ABC$, where

$$\triangle ABC = \begin{bmatrix} 1 & 9 & 1 \\ 7 & 2 & 2 \end{bmatrix}.$$

Use matrices to find the image of $\triangle ABC$ under each transformation below. Draw and label the vertices of the image and record the matrix representation.

a. 90° counterclockwise rotation about the origin

b. Reflection across the line $y = x$

c. Size transformation of magnitude 3 with center at the origin

3

a. Since $\overline{AB} \cong \overline{JK}$ and $\overline{AC} \cong \overline{JL}$ and the included angles at A and J are right angles, $\triangle ABC \cong \triangle JKL$ by the SAS or Hypotenuse-Leg congruence relationships.

b. $\triangle ABC$ can be mapped to $\triangle JKL$ by a translation with horizontal component 5 and vertical component 8. $(x, y) \rightarrow (x + 5, y + 8)$

c. Students should find the lengths of the corresponding sides and note that the lengths of the sides of $\triangle QPR$ are $\frac{1}{2}$ the lengths of the sides of $\triangle ABC$. This means that there was an underlying similarity transformation of magnitude 2.

d. One possible sequence is: Move A to the origin, apply a size transformation of magnitude $\frac{1}{2}$ centered at the origin, reflect across the y-axis, then translate $(5, -4)$.

$$(x, y) \rightarrow (x + 1, y + 2) \rightarrow \left(\frac{1}{2}x + \frac{1}{2}, \frac{1}{2}y + 1\right) \rightarrow$$
$$\left(-\frac{1}{2}x - \frac{1}{2}, \frac{1}{2}y + 1\right) \rightarrow \left(-\frac{1}{2}x + \frac{9}{2}, \frac{1}{2}y - 3\right)$$

e. One sequence of transformations that would map $\triangle KJL$ onto $\triangle PQR$ would include a size transformation of magnitude 0.5, followed by a reflection across the y-axis, followed by a translation with horizontal component 7 and vertical component -7. $(x, y) \rightarrow (-0.5x + 7, 0.5y - 7)$

f. Translate using horizontal component 1 and vertical component 2, then rotate 90° clockwise about the origin. (Students could also reflect across the y-axis after this transformation.)

g. For the transformation described in Part f above:
$(x, y) \rightarrow (x + 1, y + 2) \rightarrow (y + 2, -(x + 1))$.

④ $\triangle ABC = \begin{bmatrix} 1 & 9 & 1 \\ 7 & 2 & 2 \end{bmatrix}$

a. 90° counterclockwise rotation about the origin: $\begin{bmatrix} -7 & -2 & -2 \\ 1 & 9 & 1 \end{bmatrix}$

b. Reflection across the line $y = x$: $\begin{bmatrix} 7 & 2 & 2 \\ 1 & 9 & 1 \end{bmatrix}$

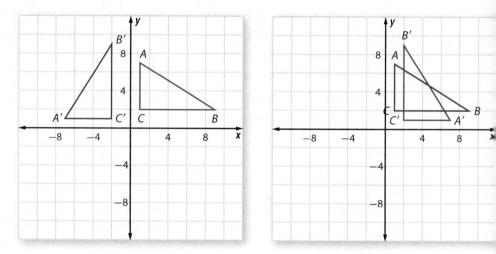

c. Size transformation of magnitude 3 with center at the origin: $\begin{bmatrix} 3 & 27 & 3 \\ 21 & 6 & 6 \end{bmatrix}$

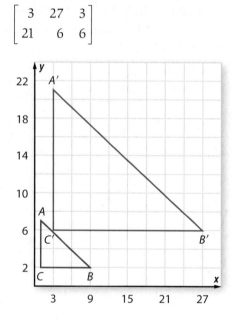

Teacher Notes

5 Reshaping a Shape Consider the transformation that stretches figures vertically by a factor of 3 but does not change them in any other way.

a. Investigate how this transformation affects shapes.

i. Begin by sketching the rectangle below and its image under the transformation.

ii. Write 2×4 matrices that represent the rectangle and its image.

b. Write a symbolic rule that relates the coordinates of any point (x, y) and its image under this transformation.

c. Construct a matrix representation of the transformation. Call the matrix T.

d. When you multiply a matrix of points that represents a polygon and a transformation matrix, on which side should the transformation matrix appear? Why?

i. Multiply the coordinate matrix for the rectangle in Part a by the matrix T.

ii. Compare the image points to those you found in Part a.

e. Consider powers of the matrix T.

i. Using matrix multiplication, find the image of the rectangle in Part a under the transformation represented by T^2. Sketch the rectangle and its image under this composite transformation.

ii. Describe the transformation represented by T^2.

iii. Without computing, describe the transformation represented by T^3.

f. Consider the matrix $S = \begin{bmatrix} 2 & 0 \\ 0 & 1 \end{bmatrix}$.

i. Make a conjecture about the effect on shapes of the transformation represented by S. Defend your conjecture.

ii. Make a conjecture about the effect of the transformation represented by $T \times S$. Defend your conjecture.

5 **a.** **i.**

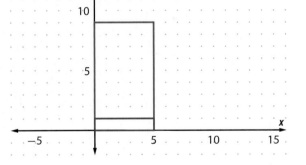

ii. Rectangle: $\begin{bmatrix} 0 & 0 & 5 & 5 \\ 0 & 1 & 1 & 0 \end{bmatrix}$

Image: $\begin{bmatrix} 0 & 0 & 5 & 5 \\ 0 & 3 & 3 & 0 \end{bmatrix}$

b. $(x, y) \rightarrow (x, 3y)$

c. $T = \begin{bmatrix} 1 & 0 \\ 0 & 3 \end{bmatrix}$

d. The transformation matrix should be on the left. If it was on the right, the dimensions would not match and multiplication would not be possible.

i. $\begin{bmatrix} 1 & 0 \\ 0 & 3 \end{bmatrix}\begin{bmatrix} 0 & 0 & 5 & 5 \\ 0 & 1 & 1 & 0 \end{bmatrix} = \begin{bmatrix} 0 & 0 & 5 & 5 \\ 0 & 3 & 3 & 0 \end{bmatrix}$

ii. Image points should be the same as Part a.

e. Students should see that powers of the matrix represent repeating the transformation.

i. $T^2 = \begin{bmatrix} 1 & 0 \\ 0 & 9 \end{bmatrix}$

$\begin{bmatrix} 1 & 0 \\ 0 & 9 \end{bmatrix}\begin{bmatrix} 0 & 0 & 5 & 5 \\ 0 & 1 & 1 & 0 \end{bmatrix} = \begin{bmatrix} 0 & 0 & 5 & 5 \\ 0 & 9 & 9 & 0 \end{bmatrix}$

ii. T^2 stretches the figure vertically by a factor of 3^2, or 9.

iii. T^3 stretches the figure vertically by a factor of 3^3, or 27.

f. **i.** S stretches figures horizontally by a factor of 2. Students should defend their conjectures. They might do this by relating it to previous situations or by showing examples.

ii. $T \times S = \begin{bmatrix} 2 & 0 \\ 0 & 3 \end{bmatrix}$

$T \times S$ stretches figures both vertically and horizontally—vertically by a factor of 3 and horizontally by a factor of 2. Students should defend their conjectures.

Unit 3

6 **Animating a Shape** Design and test an animation program that launches the rocket model shown into a circular orbit of radius 15, displays 20 orbits of the rocket, and returns the rocket to its base. Use steps of 45°.

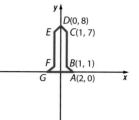

Summarize
the Mathematics

In this unit, you investigated how coordinates and matrices can be used to model geometric shapes, represent transformations, and create animations.

a How can polygons and circles be represented using coordinates? Illustrate with examples.

b How can coordinates be used to analyze properties of a polygon or to draw a polygon with special properties? Illustrate with examples.

c What transformations can be used to reposition a shape in a coordinate plane without changing its size? Illustrate with examples.

d How can you resize a shape in a coordinate plane? Illustrate with an example.

e What strategies are helpful in creating a symbolic rule for a transformation described in words? In creating a matrix representation of the transformation? Illustrate with an example.

f Describe how two transformations can be composed.

  i. How can you find a coordinate rule for a composite transformation?

  ii. How can you find a matrix representation for a transformation that is the composition of two transformations represented as matrices?

g What is a similarity transformation and how does it affect shapes? Give an example of a similarity transformation that is not a size transformation or a rigid transformation.

h How can animation effects be produced using coordinate methods?

Be prepared to share your descriptions, illustrations, and summaries with the class.

✓ Check Your Understanding

Write, in outline form, a summary of the important mathematical concepts and methods developed in this unit. Organize your summary so that it can be used as a quick reference in future units and courses.

6 The algorithm below uses transformation matrices and is written based on programming a TI-calculator.

Launch Algorithm

Step 1. Input matrix representing the rocket.

Step 2. Input size transformation matrices.

Step 3. Input matrices for counterclockwise rotations of 45° and of 90°.

Step 4. Draw rocket.

Step 5. Compute the new coordinates of the rocket translated 12 units up and resized by some arbitrary value a.

Step 6. Store coordinates in rocket matrix.

Step 7. Clear old rocket and draw image.

Step 8. Rotate rocket 90° counterclockwise about its center.

Step 9. Clear old rocket and draw image.

Step 10. Compute and store new coordinates of the rocket rotated counterclockwise 45°.

Step 11. Clear old rocket and draw image.

Step 12. Repeat Steps 10–11 159 times.

Step 13. Compute coordinates, then draw rocket properly reoriented and transformed back to its original size and position.

Other students may choose to write a program such as the following simple example.

```
pgm rotateRocket
cs
let rocket=[[2,0][1,1][1,6][0,8][−1,6][−1,1][−2,0][2,0]]
style rocket label off
draw rocket
pause 300
let rocket=[translate [scale rocket 0.75] [0,12]]
draw rocket
pause 500
let rocket=[translate [rotate [translate rocket [0,−15]] 90] [0,15]]
draw rocket
pause 500
repeat 160 [draw [let rocket=[rotate rocket 45]] pause 200]
let rocket=[translate [rotate [translate rocket [0,−15]] −90] [0,15]]
draw rocket
pause 500
let rocket=[scale [translate rocket [0,−12]] 4/3]
draw rocket
pause 500
end
```

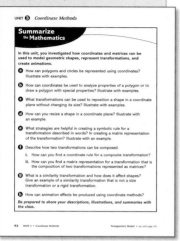

Summarize
the Mathematics

(a) Polygons can be represented by specifying the coordinates of the vertices in a coordinate plane or by listing the coordinates of vertices as column entries in a matrix. If the matrix will be used to draw the polygon, the first column (vertex) will be repeated as the last column (vertex) in the matrix to close the polygon. A circle can be represented with a coordinate rule based on the center and radius of the circle. Student examples will vary.

(b) Coordinates of the vertices of a polygon can be used to find lengths and slopes of segments. This allows you to determine if sides are the same length and are parallel or perpendicular. When you are drawing a polygon with special properties, such as a rectangle, you can use the coordinates to be sure that the opposite sides of your drawing are the same length and that the consecutive sides are perpendicular. Student examples will vary.

(c) To reposition a shape in the coordinate plane without changing its shape, use rigid transformations: rotations, translations, line reflections, and glide reflections. Students should provide at least one example of each type of transformation.

(d) You can resize a shape by using coordinate rules for transformations or transformation matrices to compute the coordinates of the image of the shape under a size transformation. The composite of a size transformation with a rigid transformation also resizes a shape. Students should provide examples. You may wish to have *CPMP-Tools* interactive geometry software available for quick demonstrations.

(e) To create a symbolic rule, it is helpful to take some specific points and find their images under the transformation. Then, you can use patterns in the coordinates of preimage–image points to generalize to the rule. To create a matrix representation, it is helpful to find the images of the points $(1, 0)$ and $(0, 1)$ under the transformation. The images of these points are the first and second columns, respectively, of the transformation matrix. Student examples will vary.

(f) To compose two transformations, you apply the first transformation and then apply the second transformation to the image points of the first transformation.

   i. To find a coordinate rule for a composite transformation, you would apply the first transformation to the general point (x, y) and then apply the second transformation to the image point. For example, a size transformation of magnitude 5 centered at the origin followed by a translation with horizontal component -2 and vertical component 4 would be found by $(x, y) \rightarrow (5x, 5y) \rightarrow (5x - 2, 5y + 4)$, so the rule is $(x, y) \rightarrow (5x - 2, 5y + 4)$.

Unit 3

ii. Assuming that you have the matrix representations for the individual transformations, you would find the matrix for the composite transformation by multiplying the individual matrices from left to right in the opposite order that they are applied to the shape matrix. For example, the matrix of the composite of a counterclockwise rotation of 90° about the origin followed by a reflection across the *y*-axis can be found by:

$$
\begin{matrix}
\text{Reflection} & & \text{90° Counterclockwise} \\
\text{Across } y\text{-axis} & & \text{Rotation}
\end{matrix}
$$

$$
\begin{bmatrix} -1 & 0 \\ 0 & 1 \end{bmatrix} \times \begin{bmatrix} 0 & -1 \\ 1 & 0 \end{bmatrix} = \begin{bmatrix} 0 & 1 \\ 1 & 0 \end{bmatrix}
$$

g A similarity transformation is a size transformation or a size transformation composed with a rigid transformation. Images of figures under similarity transformations are similar to the original figures; their scale changes but not their shape. An example of a similarity transformation that is not a size transformation or a rigid transformation is the composite of a 90° counterclockwise rotation about the origin with a size transformation of magnitude 1.5 centered at the origin. The matrix of this transformation is $\begin{bmatrix} 0 & -1.5 \\ 1.5 & 0 \end{bmatrix}$. (This is a *spiral transformation*.)

h Animation effects are produced by assigning coordinates to the vertices of figures. Then the coordinates are placed in columns in matrices. Transformation matrices are then applied to these matrices to produce vertex coordinates for the repositioned and/or resized figure. Transformations are repeatedly applied to the previous images to give the impression of motion. Commands such as Store, Draw, Clear, and Pause, and repetition (loops) help the animation proceed effectively.

✔ Check Your Understanding

You may wish to have students use the Teaching Master, *Coordinate Methods Unit Summary*, to help them organize the information. Above all, this should be something that is useful to the individual student.

Practicing for Standardized Tests

Each Practicing for Standardized Tests master presents 10 questions in the multiple-choice format of test items similar to how they often appear in standardized tests. Answers are provided below.

Answers to Practice Set 3

1. (c)	**2.** (e)	**3.** (a)	**4.** (b)	**5.** (c)
6. (c)	**7.** (d)	**8.** (b)	**9.** (d)	**10.** (b)

UNIT 4

REGRESSION AND CORRELATION

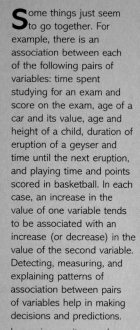

Some things just seem to go together. For example, there is an association between each of the following pairs of variables: time spent studying for an exam and score on the exam, age of a car and its value, age and height of a child, duration of eruption of a geyser and time until the next eruption, and playing time and points scored in basketball. In each case, an increase in the value of one variable tends to be associated with an increase (or decrease) in the value of the second variable. Detecting, measuring, and explaining patterns of association between pairs of variables help in making decisions and predictions.

In previous units, you have learned to make scatterplots and find the least squares regression line using technology. In this unit, you will learn more about this line and how to compute a correlation, which indicates how closely the points cluster about the regression line. Key ideas will be developed through your work on two lessons.

Lessons

1 Bivariate Relationships

Compute and interpret rank correlation, describe shapes and characteristics of scatterplots, and identify types of association.

2 Least Squares Regression and Correlation

Use a regression line to make predictions, interpret the coefficients of a regression equation, and predict the effect of influential points. Compute and interpret the correlation, predict the effect of influential points, and distinguish between correlation and cause-and-effect.

Unit 4

REGRESSION AND CORRELATION

Unit Overview

The Course 1 unit *Patterns in Data* presented the fundamental techniques of organizing, displaying, and summarizing distributions of univariate (one variable) data. *Regression and Correlation* presents parallel techniques for distributions of bivariate data as described in the table below.

	Univariate Data	Bivariate Data
Fundamental Graphic	histogram	scatterplot
Ideal Shape	normal	elliptical cluster
Usual Measure of Center	mean	least squares regression line
Usual Measure of Spread or Strength	standard deviation	correlation

Overview of the Lessons and Investigations

The following is an overview of the three lessons in *Regression and Correlation*.

Lesson 1 *Bivariate Relationships*

In this lesson, students learn to describe the shape of a scatterplot and are introduced to the vocabulary of correlation.

Investigation 1 *Rank Correlation*
Each student compares his or her ranking of different types of music with the ranking of another student by making a scatterplot of the ordered pairs:
(*first student's rank for rock, second student's rank for rock*),
(*first student's rank for Latin, second student's rank for Latin*), etc. From describing these scatterplots displayed in the classroom, students learn the basic vocabulary of association: direction (positive, negative) and strength (weak, moderate, strong). They use Spearman's rank correlation to compute a measure of the association, noting that again they have a statistic that is a sum of squared differences.

Investigation 2 *Shapes of Clouds of Points*
Students learn that, in statistics, a pattern on a scatterplot is called linear when the points form an elliptical cloud. They also learn to identify patterns that are curved, vary in strength, and when the points fall into clusters or include outliers. Outliers can be of four types: with respect to x only, with respect to y only, with respect to both x and y, and only when x and y are considered together. Finally, students learn to read a scatterplot matrix.

Lesson 2 *Least Squares Regression and Correlation*

In this lesson, students learn that if the points form an elliptical cloud—no matter how fat—a regression line is an appropriate way to summarize the bivariate relationship. Students investigate some properties of the regression line and see how it is computed. Finally, students learn to use Pearson's correlation coefficient to measure the strength of a linear relationship and that a strong correlation should not be interpreted as implying a cause-and-effect relationship.

Investigation 1 *How Good Is the Fit?*

Using data on compact car curb weights and highway mileage, students learn the difference between a residual (computed from a point used to determine the regression line) and an error in prediction (computed, when possible, from a point not used to determine the regression line). Students learn to compute errors in prediction and residuals and identify them geometrically as the vertical distance from the point to the regression line. Students learn that the sum of the residuals is 0 and that the regression equation minimizes the sum of the squared residuals (SSE).

Investigation 2 *Behavior of the Regression Line*

Students learn that the regression line always goes through the centroid $(\bar{x}, \bar{y})$ and that an influential point is one that changes the equation of the regression line quite a bit if it is removed from the data set.

Investigation 3 *How Strong is the Association?*

Students estimate and compute Pearson's correlation and examine why it works using the four quadrants when a scatterplot is centered at $(\bar{x}, \bar{y})$. They also explore the effect of influential points on the correlation and learn that the correlation may be 0 even if the points are very strongly associated (as with a quadratic relationship).

Investigation 4 *Association and Causation*

Data on ice cream consumption and recorded crimes in 12 countries of the world is used as an example to show that two variables may have a strong correlation without there being any reason to suspect that when one variable changes, it "causes" a change in the other variable. Students practice hypothesizing lurking variables that might, instead, explain the association.

Lesson 3 *Looking Back*

In this lesson, students review the major topics of the unit using data on the temperature when a baby is six months old and the age at which he or she learns to crawl.

Unit Objectives

- Describe the shape of a cloud of points on a scatterplot and describe the association between the two variables
- Interpret the coefficients of the regression equation, learn some properties of the regression line, and understand that a regression line is an appropriate way to summarize the bivariate relationship only if the points form an elliptical cloud
- Compute and interpret Pearson's correlation and understand that a strong correlation does not imply that one variable causes the other
- Determine whether a point is influential on the correlation and on the equation of the least squares regression line

CPMP-Tools

The *CPMP-Tools* data analysis software is particularly helpful for this unit. Students can enter data, fit their own line to a scatterplot, and compare their line to the regression line. Comparisons of slopes, *x*-intercepts, and the sum of squared residuals can be found using the information icon. In addition, the residuals and the squares formed by these residuals can be displayed graphically. The software includes a feature to allow investigation of outliers by selecting points to delete from the analysis.

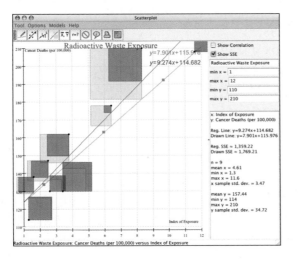

Entering your class data for (*arm span, kneeling height*) during the launch of Lesson 2 will provide students an opportunity to review or learn how to use the spreadsheet. You should save the data from each class as a text file for later use in the unit.

Data sets included in the software are listed below. If your students do not have ready access to graphing calculators with statistical capabilities at home, they can use the built-in data sets and *CPMP-Tools* from their *StudentWorks* CD or access *CPMP-Tools* from the Internet (www.wmich.edu/cpmp/CPMP-Tools/).

Hamburger Nutrition pp. 277–279
Compact Cars pp. 282–283
Radioactive Waste Exposure pp. 285–286
Horse Stride p. 288
Chicago White Sox p. 289
Batting Averages p. 290
Marriage/Divorce Rates p. 298
Hippos p. 305
Tree Age p. 306
Mammals p. 307
Federal Minimum Wage p. 308
Seal Sizes p. 310
Cherry Tree Blooming p. 317
Crawling Age pp. 322–324

Also included in *CPMP-Tools* is a data set for a midterm project titled "Land Use Change in the United States".

Unit 4 Planning Guide

Lesson Objectives	On Your Own Assignments*	Suggested Pacing	Materials
Lesson 1 *Bivariate Relationships* • Construct scatterplots with appropriate labels and scales • Describe shapes of clouds of points on scatterplots (linear, curved, vary in strength) • Identify types of association (positive and negative, strong and weak, perfect and none, linear and nonlinear) • Identify clusters and different types of outliers • Read and interpret a scatterplot matrix	**After Investigation 1:** Choose two of A1–A3, C6–C8, R10, R11, E14 or E15, E16, Rv18–Rv21 **After Investigation 2:** A4, A5, C9, R12, R13, E17, Rv22–Rv26	5 days (including assessment)	• Spaghetti • Paper for scatterplots of student rankings of music and method of displaying them in the classroom • Unit Resources
Lesson 2 *Least Squares Regression and Correlation* • Understand that a linear model is appropriate when the points form an elliptical cloud • Compute errors in prediction and residuals and locate them on the plot • Understand that for the regression equation, the sum of the residuals is 0 • Understand the regression line as the line that minimizes the sum of the squared residuals • Explore the effect of outliers and influential points on the regression equation • Distinguish between influential points and outliers • Compute and interpret Pearson's r as a measure of how closely the points cluster about the regression line • Interpret Pearson's r as the rescaled sum of products of $(x - \bar{x})$ and $(y - \bar{y})$ • Know that adding a constant to each value or multiplying by a positive constant does not change the correlation • Understand that association does not mean that one of the variables causes the other • Identify possible explanations (cause-and-effect, lurking variable) for an association and illustrate with a directed graph • Identify the explanatory variable and the response variable	**After Investigation 1:** A1 or A2, C10, C11, R18, Rv28, Rv29 **After Investigation 2:** A3 or A4, C12, R17, choose one of E22–E24 **After Investigation 3:** A5, A6, C13, C14 or C15, C16, choose two of R19–R21, E25 or E26 **After Investigation 4:** A7, A8 or A9, E27, Rv30–Rv33	8 days (including assessment)	• Yardsticks or metersticks for measuring each student's arm span and kneeling height • *CPMP-Tools*, data analysis software • Unit Resources
Lesson 3 *Looking Back* • Review and synthesize the major objectives of the unit		2 days (including assessment)	• *CPMP-Tools*, data analysis software • Unit Resources

* When choice is indicated, it is important to leave the choice to the student.

Note: It is best if Connections tasks are discussed as a whole class after they have been assigned as homework.

Bivariate Relationships

In your previous work in *Core-Plus Mathematics,* you have used scatterplots to examine possible relationships between two quantitative (numerical) variables. In this unit, you will develop further methods for detecting and describing patterns in bivariate data.

The points on the scatterplot below show (*height of husband, height of wife*) data for a randomly selected sample of two hundred married couples.

Husbands' and Wives' Heights

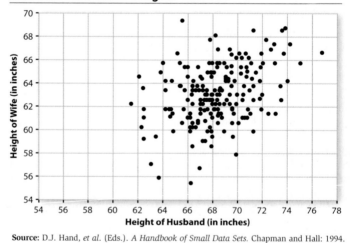

Source: D.J. Hand, *et al.* (Eds.). *A Handbook of Small Data Sets.* Chapman and Hall: 1994.

Bivariate Relationships

Prior to this unit, students have graphed paired variables on a scatterplot and modeled a linear relationship with a regression line. In this lesson, students explore the concept of association between pairs of variables. They learn to describe the shape of a scatterplot and are introduced to the vocabulary of correlation. In Lesson 2, students learn that if the points form an elliptical cloud—no matter how fat (as long as it is not circular)—a regression line is an appropriate way to summarize the bivariate relationship.

Association versus Correlation Your students may ask why this unit sometimes uses the word "association" (or "relationship") and sometimes uses the word "correlation." The distinction is that the word correlation is reserved by statisticians for the case of a linear relationship between two variables. When the ordered pairs appear to cluster about a line, even if the cluster is not tight, we can say the variables are correlated. Association and relationship are much more general terms. For example, two variables might follow a relationship that is quadratic or exponential. In those cases, we would say the variables are associated, and we would not use the word correlated. (It is also okay to say two variables are associated when they have a linear relationship. In fact, correlation is linear association.)

Lesson Objectves

- Construct scatterplots with appropriate labels and scales
- Describe shapes of clouds of points on scatterplots (linear, curved, vary in strength)
- Identify types of association (positive and negative, strong and weak, perfect and none, linear and nonlinear)
- Identify clusters and different types of outliers
- Read and interpret a scatterplot matrix

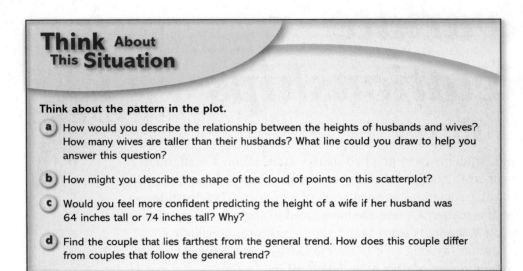

Think About This Situation

Think about the pattern in the plot.

a How would you describe the relationship between the heights of husbands and wives? How many wives are taller than their husbands? What line could you draw to help you answer this question?

b How might you describe the shape of the cloud of points on this scatterplot?

c Would you feel more confident predicting the height of a wife if her husband was 64 inches tall or 74 inches tall? Why?

d Find the couple that lies farthest from the general trend. How does this couple differ from couples that follow the general trend?

In this lesson, you will learn to describe and summarize the pattern in a scatterplot.

Investigation 1 • Rank Correlation

In the United States, we seem to be "rank happy." Sports teams are ranked on games won; motion pictures are ranked by viewer preference or gross revenue; DVDs are ranked on the number of rentals; automobiles are ranked by safety; and colleges are ranked on quality. As you work on the problems in this investigation, look for answers to this question:

How can you measure how closely the rankings of two people agree?

1 Consider the following music categories:

| Rock | Hip-Hop/Rap | Classical | Pop |
| Latin | Dance/Electronic | R&B/Soul | Country |

a. Rank your favorite type of music from the above choices with a 1. Continue ranking with a 2 for your second favorite and an 8 for your least favorite. Ties are not allowed!

b. Working with a partner, display your rankings on a scatterplot that has scales and labels on the axes. Plot one point (*one partner's rank, other partner's rank*) for each of the eight types of music. For example, in the figure at the right, Doris ranked Hip-Hop/Rap music seventh and Kuong ranked it second. Using a full sheet of paper, make your scatterplot as large as possible, with big dots, and then display it on the wall of your classroom.

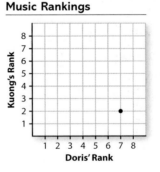

Music Rankings

Unit 4

By discussing the Think About This Situation questions with your students, you should be able to assess how well they remember how to interpret a scatterplot.

To help *all* students see the line $y = x$ in Part a and the variability in Part c, have some spaghetti available. For the second question in Part a, ask a student to place a piece of spaghetti on the transparency scatterplot that would identify the points where the husband's and wife's heights are the same. For Part c, spaghetti could be used to help *all* students recognize the variability in men's heights for 64 inches and 74 inches tall husbands. Ask students to break a piece of spaghetti to represent the variability in the heights of women married to men of height 64 inches. The piece should run vertically from about 56 inches to 66 inches. Then, place this spaghetti piece vertically at men's height of 74 inches to see the smaller variability.

Think About This Situation

PROMOTING MATHEMATICAL DISCOURSE

Teaching Resources

Transparency Master 1.

(a) Generally, taller husbands have taller wives and shorter husbands have shorter wives, but there is a lot of variability to this pattern. Further, husbands tend to be taller than their wives. Only eight wives out of two hundred are taller than their husbands. The line $y = x$ would help identify pairs where a wife is taller than her husband. (See the sample TATS discussion on page T259A.)

(b) The points form a single cluster that is roughly oval in shape but with a bit more variability in the heights of the wives for shorter husbands than for taller husbands. No points lie very far away from the main cluster.

(c) You would be less confident in predicting the height of the wife whose husband is 64 inches tall because the wives vary in height more for the shorter husbands than for the taller husbands.

(d) The couple farthest from the general trend has a husband 65.5 inches tall and a wife 69.5 inches tall. This couple is different from the others because the wife is much taller than expected, given the husband's height. (She is 4 inches taller.) Note that the couple where the husband is 77 inches and the wife is about 67 inches is unusual in that the husband is so tall, but they follow the general trend (and, in fact, this point is almost on the regression line).

COLLABORATION SKILL
Keep the group conversation focused on the mathematics of the lesson. You may wish to assign one group member to monitor your interactions.

Unit 4

Teacher: *(Teacher selects a student to read the opening paragraphs on the top of page 259.)* How does the first paragraph define bivariate data?

Toby: Bivariate means comparing two different things.

Teacher: Does anyone want to add anything to Toby's definition?

Natasha: I agree with Toby because "bi" always means two of something. The "variate" part could be a short way to talk about the two variables—"bivariate."

Teacher: *(The teacher places an overhead of the graph and TATS on the overhead.)* By looking at the scatterplot, who would like to tell me which two variables are being paired?

Mikala: The heights of a husband and wife. Each dot must be a husband-wife pair.

Teacher: How would you describe the relationship between the heights of husbands and wives?

Tilman: The points are quite spread out. But I guess you could say that taller husbands seem to be married to taller women.

Teacher: What exactly in the plot has lead you to that description?

Tilman: Well, I noticed that for the husbands taller than 72 inches, there are no wives under about 61 inches.

Kari: Yeah, and you see that for the shorter men, like 62 inches to 65 inches, there are more shorter wives and not as many tall wives.

Teacher: How many wives are taller than their husbands?

Josiah: You could tell by finding all the points above the regression line on the graph.

Alonso: I am not sure that is correct. Where would the regression line be Josiah?

Teacher: Josiah, would you place this piece of spaghetti where you think a regression line would lie? *(Josiah places the spaghetti through the points (60, 58) and (72, 66).)*

Josiah: Oh, this line doesn't help. There are a bunch of points where the husband is about 70 inches and their wives are under 68 inches tall—not taller.

Teacher: What is it about the regression line that makes it not helpful for this question? Alonso, since you questioned this a moment ago, what do you think?

Alonso: Well, the regression line runs through, kinda, the center of the data. The center of the data is not where husbands and wives are about the same height. Husbands are taller than wives there, so it does not help us find where wives are taller.

Teacher: Is there a different line that could help us identify the points representing wives who are taller than their husbands? Think about that individually a minute so that you would be able to give Josiah directions on where to place the line on this plot. *(Pause)* Heather, what line do you propose? And why do you propose that line?

Heather: I think Josiah should move the line up and check points near the line until he has only points above the line with wives taller than husbands. *(Josiah spends some time trying to do this and checking points as he goes.)*

Angelo: This could take awhile. Can I make a suggestion?

Teacher: Class, shall we allow Angelo to make a suggestion here or continue on this path. *(Students indicate willingness to hear another suggestion.)*

Angelo: I was thinking that if we find the points where the husbands and wives heights are the same and draw that line that would help. Place the line through those points Josiah. *(Josiah moves the line.)* The points above this line would be when wives heights are more than husbands heights.

Teacher: What is the equation for that line?

Corin: $y = x$

Teacher: Looking at the scatterplot of the 200 couples, how many wives are taller than their husbands?

Juliet: There are only 8 wives taller than their husbands because that is how many points there are above the line $y = x$.

Teacher: Thank you, Juliet. Now, let's look at the cloud of all the points on this scatterplot. What geometric shape could you use to describe the shape of this cloud?

Iris: It looks like a trapezoid.

Teacher: Any other ideas?

Tasha: If you squint your eyes and look at it, it looks like an egg shape.

Teacher: We are going to look at this idea of shapes formed by points, so watch for that while you do the next investigations. Now, let's focus on Part c. "Would you feel more confident predicting the height of the wife if the husband were 64 inches tall or 73 inches tall? Think about that a minute, and talk about it with your group. *(Teacher allows a minute or two for discussion.)* Olivia, what did your group decide?

Olivia: We decided that we would not be very confident predicting the wife's height for either husband's height—64 or 74 inches tall.

But if we had to choose, we would say the 74-inch tall husband. This is because, like Tilman said at the beginning, there are not many short wives out where the tall husbands are.

Teacher: But, isn't it also true that there are not as many tall wives where the shorter husbands are located on the graph? Maria?

Maria: Well, yeah, but it is more spread out on that side of the scatterplot.

Teacher: What do you mean by "it" and "spread out"? Maria, would you please come up to the overhead and explain what you mean?

Maria: *(Points along vertical line above 64 inches and 74 inches.)* See above 64 inches for husbands' heights, you have a wide range of points. Above 74 inches, the wives' heights only go from about 64 to 69 inches.

Teacher: Here would you use this spaghetti to make a piece showing the range of wives' heights at 74 inches? Then, show us how that compares to the range of wives' heights at 64 inches.

Maria: *(Breaks spaghetti to fit between 64 and 69 inches.)* Look, over at the 64 inch husband heights, I can fit a longer piece. That is what I meant by more spread out here. So, like Olivia said, we would be more confident of predicting the wife's height when the husband is 74 inches tall.

Teacher: What statistics term might we use that has a similar meaning to more or less "spread out?"

Brian: "More or less variable" or has "more or less variability."

Teacher: Okay. Now, look again at the plot and find the couple that lies farthest from the general trend. How does this couple differ from couples that follow the general trend?

Jamie: The couple with husband's height almost 66 and wife's height of almost 70 seems different to me because the wife is the tallest woman of the group and married to a man who is about average height.

Tricia: I think the couple way out to the right is different than others because the man is so tall.

Sam: Well, that is true, but that point is still somewhat in the pattern of the other points.

Teacher: That is good thinking. In this lesson, we will learn more about different types of points that seem to not follow the general trend of the data. For now, let's do some comparisons of our music preferences by beginning Investigation 1.

Investigation 1 introduces association from an intuitive standpoint with a problem that has students rank their music preferences and then compare their own ranking with that of a classmate. Students:

- develop an understanding of strong versus weak correlation and positive versus negative correlation for ranked data, describing the association that can be observed from the scatterplot.
- explore their own methods of finding a numerical measure of the direction and strength of the association.
- learn to use a numerical measurement of association, Spearman's rank correlation r_s.

Spearman's rank correlation can be used on ranked data when there are no or very few ties in each person's ranks.

Sums of Squared Differences Students may ask why the formula uses the sum of the squared differences rather than the sum of the absolute value of the differences. Remind them that the sum of the squared differences is commonly used in statistics, as they saw with the standard deviation, because it leads to easier and more powerful mathematical theory. The Euclidean distance formula is also a sum of squared differences; and similarly, we are computing a type of distance between the ranks. The sum of squared differences comes up again in the development of the least squares regression line. See the note with Lesson 2, Investigation 1, Problem 4 of this teacher's guide.

Interpreting Strength There is no widely established rule about when a correlation is called weak, moderate, or strong, but the following interpretations are often used as a guideline. At this stage, however, students should not memorize a table such as this one but should use their own judgment.

r	Interpretation
Less than 0.20	Very weak
0.20–0.40	Weak
0.40–0.70	Moderate
0.70–0.90	Strong
0.90–1.00	Very strong

Ranks versus Ranking A "ranking" is made up of a set of ranks. For example, in Problem 1 Part b, we would say that, "In Doris' ranking, Hip-Hop/Rap music had a rank of 7."

① **INSTRUCTIONAL NOTE** You can substitute other types of music for any of the eight types listed in the text, if they do not include the kind of music listened to by your students. Alternatively, you could have students rank favorite movies, animals, or another category that generates substantial enthusiasm.

Students should rank the music independently without any discussion. You might put your own ranking on the board or overhead after the students have finished ranking. If someone does not have a partner, then he or she can use your ranking for the plot (and possibly display a negative association).

Each pair of students should display their plot on a wall of the classroom, so everyone can see all of the plots. If you give students a large piece of paper and marking pen to use, the plots will be large enough so students see them easily from their seats. Alternatively, a student master is provided.

a–b. Each pair of students probably will have a unique scatterplot.

Teaching Resources

Student Master 2.

UNIT ❹ *Regression and Correlation* Name ___

Music Rankings
Problem 1

Unit 4

c. Does there seem to be an association between your ranking and your partner's ranking? Explain your reasoning.

d. Examine the various scatterplots from pairs of students posted around the classroom. Identify the plots that show **strong positive association**, that is, the ranks tend to be similar. Describe these plots.

e. Identify the plots that show **strong negative association**, that is, the ranks tend to be opposite. Describe these plots.

f. Which plots show **weak association** or **no association**?

g. From which plots would you feel confident in predicting a person's rank of a new type of music if you know the rank of their partner?

2 By looking at the scatterplots, it is fairly easy to make a decision about the *direction* (positive, negative, or none) of the association of two variables. But, as is often the case, it is helpful to have a numerical measure to aid your visual perception of the *strength* of the association.

a. Use the music rankings to brainstorm about ways to assign a number to each scatterplot that indicates the direction and the strength of the association.

> **i.** Use the method you prefer to assign a number to three of the scatterplots. Do the results make sense? If not, revise your method.
>
> **ii.** Describe your method to the rest of the class.
>
> **iii.** Where everyone can see it, post a list of the methods your class has suggested.

b. One way to test a method is to use it on extreme cases. What number does each method give for a **perfect positive association**—two rankings that are identical? For a **perfect negative association**—two rankings that are opposite of each other? As a class, decide on a method that seems to make the most sense.

c. Use the following pairs of ranks prepared by Tmeka and Aida to test the method your class selected.

$(1, 4), (2, 5), (3, 3), (4, 7), (5, 2), (6, 6), (7, 8), (8, 1)$

Music Rankings

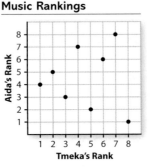

> **i.** Is there an obvious positive or negative association between the two rankings?

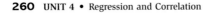

c. Students should look for similar rankings or opposite rankings.

d. Graphs that show strong positive association have points that cluster closely about the line $y = x$. Generally, the points move upward and to the right.

e. Negative association means a high rank by one partner tends to be paired with a low rank by the other and vice versa. The points generally fall from the upper-left corner to the lower-right corner of the scatterplot. The plots with the strongest negative association will have points that are clustered close to a line with negative slope.

f. In plots that show weak or no association, you would not be able to say that types of music ranked higher by one person tend to be ranked higher (or lower) by the other.

g. Those plots that show strong positive or strong negative association can help in predicting the rank of a new type of music of one person from that of the other. For other plots, there is no way to tell where the second person's rank will be because the points are too scattered.

> **COMMON MISCONCEPTION**
> Students often think that if two people have opposite rankings, there is no association. However, when the rankings are opposite, it is just as easy to predict one partner's rank from the other partner's rank as if the association were positive.

2 **INSTRUCTIONAL NOTE** This problem works best when students work in groups or when the teacher leads a class discussion. If you do this as a class discussion, give students some individual or partner brainstorming time to encourage a wide variety of methods of measuring association to surface. List the methods on the board, evaluating them after listing. Remind students that their method should result in a number that shows both direction (positive, negative, or none) and strength and that they should have an unambiguous way to calculate the number for any two rankings.

a. i–iii. Responses will vary depending on the method. Methods often suggested by students include finding the sum of the differences between the ranks (not a good method as the sum is always 0), finding the sum of the absolute differences, and finding the average absolute difference. One method almost invariably suggested is to find the number of exact matches. You can help students understand why this method is inadequate by giving them the examples below. Alternatively, good examples may have been generated by your class.

Music Rankings

Mary	1	2	3	4	5	6	7	8
Steve	2	1	4	3	6	5	8	7

Jason	1	2	3	4	5	6	7	8
Alka	8	7	6	4	5	3	2	1

Mary and Steve agree very closely, but they have no exact matches. Jason and Alka disagree almost totally, yet they have only two exact matches.

b. Responses will vary depending on the method.

c. **i.** No, there is almost no association between the two rankings and thus, it is difficult to choose between a positive or negative association.

ii. Use your class' method from Part b to assign a number to this association.

iii. How does your number indicate the direction and strength of this association?

British statistician Charles Spearman (1863–1945) invented a simple measure for the strength of the association between two rankings. The measure is called a rank correlation. **Spearman's rank correlation**, r_s, is given by the formula:

$$r_s = 1 - \frac{6\Sigma d^2}{n(n^2 - 1)}$$

Here, n represents the number of items ranked, and Σd^2 represents the sum of the squared differences between the ranks.

Charles Spearman

3 Working with your partner, make a table, like the one below, to help you compute Spearman's rank correlation for your music rankings from Problem 1.

Type of Music	Your Rank	Partner's Rank	Difference of Ranks (d)	Squared Difference (d²)
Rock				
Hip-Hop/Rap				
Classical				
Pop				
Latin				
Dance/Electronic				
R&B/Soul				
Country				

$$\Sigma d^2 =$$

a. Compute r_s for your ranking and your partner's ranking. Round your rank correlation to the nearest thousandth. Write this value on your scatterplot.

b. How could you use the lists on your calculator to help you compute r_s?

c. Exchange rankings with another pair of students. Check their work by computing r_s for their rankings.

ii. Answers will depend on the students' methods. Standard methods give a correlation of about 0.

iii. Students' methods should give a number that indicates that there is little or no association.

3 **INSTRUCTIONAL NOTE** Each table will probably be different for different pairs of students. In fact, if each student in a pair completes the table, only the squared difference column and Σd^2 will be the same. If Σd^2 is not the same for a pair of students, they should check that they recorded their ranks correctly as well as correctly computed differences and squares. In Problem 6, students will be asked to compute Σd.

a. Students should write the value of r_s on their scatterplot.

b. You can use lists as follows:

Type of Music	L1 Your Rank	L2 Partner's Rank	L3 = L1 − L2 Difference of Ranks (d)	L4 = L3² Squared Difference (d²)

Then Σd^2 can be found by calculating the sum of L4.

c. Students should check each others' work.

UNIT ④ *Regression and Correlation* Name _____
Date _____

Computing Spearman's Rank Correlation
Problem 3

$r = 1 - \frac{6 \Sigma d^2}{n(n^2 - 1)}$

Type of Music	Your Rank	Partner's Rank	Difference of Ranks (d)	Squared Difference (d²)
				$\Sigma d^2 =$

Student Master • *use with page 261*   UNIT 4 • *Regression and Correlation*   3

FORMULA NOTE We do not expect students to memorize Spearman's formula. You may wish to have them record it in their Math Toolkits. It will be provided on the Lesson 1 quiz.

DIFFERENTIATION Part c is optional, and you may wish to skip it if you are short on time, but it gives students another opportunity to practice finding r_s.

4   Study the scatterplots and rank correlations displayed in your classroom.

a. Which scatterplot has a rank correlation closest to 1? What can you say about the taste in music of those two classmates?

b. Which scatterplot has a rank correlation closest to −1? What can you say about the taste in music of those two classmates?

c. Which scatterplot has a rank correlation closest to 0? What can you say about the taste in music of those two classmates?

d. Suppose you had ranked the types of music in exactly the same way as your partner did.

   i. Describe the scatterplot of identical rankings.

   ii. What would the rank correlation be? Explain your response based on the formula for r_s.

e. Suppose you had ranked the types of music exactly opposite of the way your partner ranked the music.

   i. Describe the scatterplot of opposite rankings.

   ii. What would the rank correlation be? Verify by computing r_s.

5   Examine the plots below, showing paired rankings of favorite movies. Match each rank correlation below with the appropriate scatterplot. The scales on each scatterplot are the same.

a. $r_s = 0.1$ b. $r_s = 0.8$ c. $r_s = -0.9$ d. $r_s = 0.5$

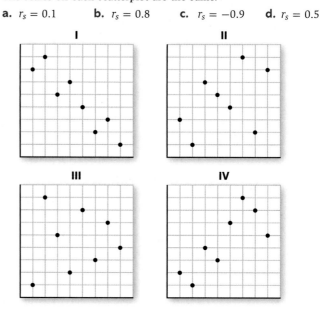

4 **a.** This scatterplot will have points that cluster around the line $y = x$. The students have similar taste in types of music. What one likes, the other tends to like. What one dislikes, the other tends to dislike.

b. This scatterplot will have points that tend downhill in an almost linear fashion. The students have dissimilar taste in types of music. What one likes, the other tends to dislike.

c. This scatterplot will have points that look like random scatter. There is no relationship between the tastes of the two students, and so it is impossible to predict one partner's rank by knowing the other's rank.

d. **i.** All points would lie on the line $y = x$.

  ii. With $\Sigma d^2 = 0$ and $n = 8$, the rank correlation is 1.

e. **i.** All points would lie on the line between $(1, 8)$ and $(8, 1)$.

  ii. With $\Sigma d^2 = 168$ and $n = 8$, the rank correlation is -1.

5 **a.** $r_s = 0.1 \rightarrow$ Plot III
 b. $r_s = 0.8 \rightarrow$ Plot IV
 c. $r_s = -0.9 \rightarrow$ Plot I
 d. $r_s = 0.5 \rightarrow$ Plot II

6 The formula for Spearman's rank correlation,

$$r_s = 1 - \frac{6\Sigma d^2}{n(n^2 - 1)},$$

includes a sum of squared differences, Σd^2. Such a sum is used in statistics to measure how much *variability* exists. In this problem, you will investigate one reason why the differences d are squared before they are summed.

a. What formulas have you seen before that involve a sum of squared differences?

b. Compute Σd using your table from Problem 3. Compare your results with those of other students.

c. Compute Σd again for a different pair of rankings. Again, compare your results with those of other students.

d. What does squaring the values of d in Spearman's formula accomplish?

Summarize
the Mathematics

In this investigation, you learned to describe association between two rankings by giving direction and strength and by computing Spearman's rank correlation.

a Sketch a scatterplot showing a strong positive association. A weak negative association. No association. A perfect negative association.

b Compare Spearman's rank correlation formula with the one invented and agreed on by your class in Problem 2. What are the advantages and disadvantages of each?

c How can positive rank correlation be seen in a list of paired ranks? In a scatterplot? In the value of r_s?

d How can negative rank correlation be seen in a list of paired ranks? In a scatterplot? In the value of r_s?

e Why are differences sometimes squared in statistics formulas that include a sum?

Be prepared to explain your ideas and examples to the class.

Unit 4

6 **a.** The formulas for the standard deviation and the Euclidian distance formula both involve a sum of squared differences. (In Connections Task 7 on page 275, students will compare Spearman's formula to the formula for Euclidean distance. The method of producing the regression equation also uses the idea of a sum of squared differences, as students will see in the next lesson.)

b. Students' computations should result in $\Sigma d = 0$. If $\Sigma d \neq 0$, students may not have consistently subtracted in the order *your rank − partner's rank*.

c. Again, Σd will be 0. (Students will prove that the sum of the differences always is 0 in Extensions Task 16 on page 276.)

d. One thing squaring does is eliminate negative signs so the resulting sum is always positive. Squaring does other things, as well. For example, a big difference, say 8, between two ranks is weighed more heavily than two smaller differences, say 4 and 4: $8^2 = 64$, but $4^2 + 4^2 = 32$.

DIFFERENTIATION Some students may be interested in an outline of the derivation of Spearman's formula. Suppose that you want to base a measure of association on the difference in ranks. As students saw in Problem 6 for their rankings and as shown in general in Extensions Task 16, you cannot just add the differences because it is always the case that $\Sigma d = 0$. So, we will use the usual procedure of squaring each difference before adding to get Σd^2. Because we want a value of 1 for a perfect correlation (when Σd^2 is 0), we subtract from 1: $1 - \Sigma d^2$. But now, when we have perfect negative correlation, $1 - \Sigma d^2$ gives us a number smaller than -1. Thus, we need to rescale this sum of squared differences so that it is always between -1 (perfect negative correlation) and $+1$ (perfect positive correlation). Let M be the value used to rescale. Then, for perfect negative correlation, we want

$$-1 = 1 - M \Sigma d^2$$
$$= 1 - M[(1 - n)^2 + (2 - (n - 1))^2 + \cdots + ((n - 1) - 2)^2 + (n - 1)^2].$$

Using some algebra and the formula for the sum of consecutive squares to simplify the expression in brackets and then solving for M, we get

$$M = \frac{6}{n(n^2 - 1)}.$$

You may also want to assign Extensions Task 15 on page 276 to these students.

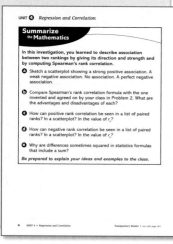

Summarize the Mathematics

a The first scatterplot should show points that cluster closely about a line with positive slope. The second scatterplot should show points that cluster loosely about a line with negative slope. The third scatterplot should show what looks like random scatter. The final scatterplot should show points that lie on a line with negative slope.

b Advantages of Spearman's correlation are that it is fairly simple to compute, it gives a positive number for positive correlation and a negative number for negative correlation, it always lies between -1 and 1, giving -1 and 1 for perfect correlation and 0 for no correlation, and scatterplots that are reflections over a vertical line down the center have correlations $-r_s$ and $+r_s$. A disadvantage is that it is not easy to understand why the differences are squared, where the 6 came from, and why the denominator is what it is.

Students should give a similar analysis for their formulas from Problem 2.

c Positive correlation shows up in the list of ranks as small differences between the ranks, in the scatterplot as points that cluster about a line with positive slope, and as a positive value of r_s.

d Negative correlation shows up in the list of ranks as large differences between the ranks, in the scatterplot as points that cluster about a line with negative slope, and as a negative value of r_s.

e Differences may be squared to eliminate negative signs, so the resulting sum is positive. Squared differences may also be used to make larger differences weigh more heavily than smaller differences in the sum.

✓ Check Your Understanding

a.

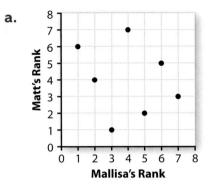

b. Closer to 0. The scatterplot does not show any strong positive (uphill) or negative (downhill) trend.

c.

Mallisa's Rank	Matt's Rank	Difference	Difference Squared
4	7	−3	9
5	2	3	9
2	4	−2	4
7	3	4	16
6	5	1	1
1	6	−5	25
3	1	2	4
	Sum	0	68

$$r_s = 1 - \frac{6\Sigma d^2}{n(n^2 - 1)} = 1 - \frac{6(68)}{7(48)} \approx -0.21$$

d. This couple is neither especially compatible nor incompatible. There is a weak negative relationship between their rankings.

✓Check Your Understanding

A couple decides to measure their compatibility by ranking their favorite leisure activities. The rankings are given below in the table.

	Mallisa	Matt
Watch TV	4	7
Read	5	2
Exercise	2	4
Talk to friends	7	3
Go to a movie	6	5
Go to dinner	1	6
Go to the mall	3	1

a. Make a scatterplot for the two rankings with appropriate scales and labels on the two axes.

b. Predict whether the value of r_s will be closer to -1, 0, or 1. Use the scatterplot to help explain your answer.

c. Calculate the value of r_s. Show your work.

d. What would you conclude about this couple's compatibility?

Investigation 2 • Shapes of Clouds of Points

In Investigation 1, you learned to describe the association between two rankings as shown in a scatterplot by giving its *direction* (positive, negative, or none) and its *strength* (strong, moderate, weak, none) or by reporting the correlation. In this investigation, you will examine more closely patterns in a scatterplot. As you complete the following problems, make notes of answers to this question:

What are the common shapes of bivariate data displayed on a scatterplot?

1 Bivariate data are **linear** if they form an *oval* or *elliptical cloud*. Two examples of linear relationships are shown below.

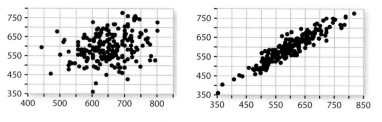

a. Place a sheet of paper over each plot. Sketch the axes and an oval that contains the points.

b. Describe the direction and strength of the relationship in the first plot. In the second plot.

NOTE The solution to the Check Your Understanding is on page T263B.

Investigation 2 teaches students:

- that a cloud of points is called linear when the points form an elliptical cloud.
- to identify patterns that are curved, vary in strength, and that have clusters or outliers.
- to identify various types of outliers.
- to read and interpret a scatterplot matrix.

Types of Outliers Outliers can be of four types: with respect to x only, with respect to y only, with respect to both x and y, and only when x and y are considered jointly. There is no agreed-upon rule for identifying them. Students may suggest using the rule from *Patterns in Data* that an outlier is a value that lies more than $1.5 \cdot$ IQR from the nearest quartile. That rule would miss points, such as point A in Problem 3, that are outliers only when x and y are considered jointly. Further, a point like B in Problem 3 would not be identified as an outlier if all values of y were taken into consideration (because there is so much variability in the values of y). However, if you consider only the values of y around $x = 75$ (omitting point D), it probably would be an outlier using this rule. Thus, in this section, have students identify outliers just by sight.

1   **a.** Students should sketch an oval or elliptical cloud around the points, like those below.

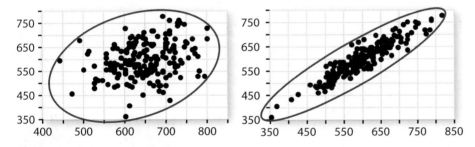

   b. The first plot has a weak positive relationship. The second plot has a strong positive relationship.

c. When the relationship is linear, you can summarize the relationship with a straight line. However, a line would not be an appropriate summary of the relationships shown below. How could you describe the shape, trend (center), and strength (spread) of these distributions?

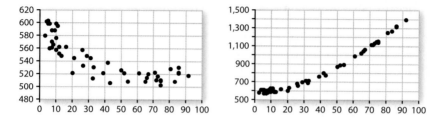

d. If the points tend to fan out at one end, the relationship is said to **vary in strength**. Both of the plots below vary in strength. Sketch a plot where the pattern varies in strength but the points cluster about a line. That is, the shape is not curved.

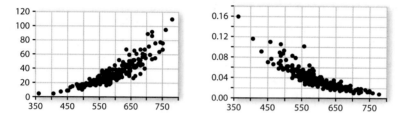

2 The scatterplot below shows the time between two consecutive eruptions of the Old Faithful geyser in Yellowstone National Park plotted against the duration of the first eruption.

Old Faithful Eruption Times

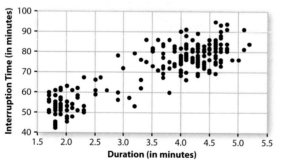

Source: Samprit Chatterjee, et al. *A Casebook for a First Course in Statistics and Data Analysis.* Wiley, 1995.

a. What is the shape of this distribution? Is it appropriate to summarize the trend with a line?

b. Is the relationship positive or negative? Is it strong, moderate, or weak? Does the strength of the relationship vary?

c. The shape of both graphs is not an oval, but curved, so the center would be a curve that arcs through the points. For the plot on the left, the strength of the relationship is moderate; but for the plot on the right, the strength is very strong.

d. One example is shown below.

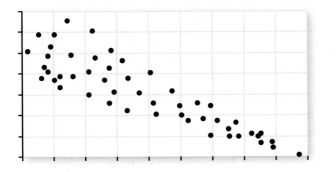

2 **a.** It is linear (roughly oval). Yes, because the relationship is linear.

b. This relationship is positive, moderate, and fairly constant in strength.

INSTRUCTIONAL NOTE

In Problem 2, you may wish to discuss the labels on the scatterplot to be sure that all students know what is being plotted.

Unit 4

c. Can you give a reason why the duration of the first eruption might have an effect on the time until the next eruption?

d. When examining a scatterplot, you should also look for *clusters* of points and for *outliers* that lie away from the main cloud of points. Do you see clusters or outliers in the scatterplot of the geyser data?

3 The state of Alaska has the largest population of black bears in the U.S.—approximately 100,000. The scatterplot below gives the weight in pounds and length in inches of a large sample of black bears.

a. Describe the shape of this plot.

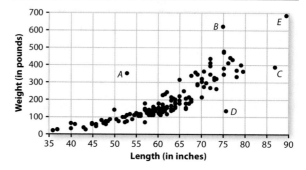

Lengths and Weights of Black Bears

b. This scatterplot illustrates the types of outliers that can occur:

- an outlier for length only

- an outlier for weight only

- both an outlier for length and an outlier for weight

- not an outlier for length and not an outlier for weight, but an outlier when length and weight are jointly considered

For each labeled point on the scatterplot, tell which type of outlier it is. Then describe the bear.

4 The plot at the top of the next page is called a **scatterplot matrix**, a matrix whose entries are scatterplots. In each scatterplot, one dot represents one of the 50 states, the District of Columbia, or Puerto Rico. The five variables are as follows:

- **Dropout%** percentage of 16 to 19 year olds who are not enrolled in school and have not graduated from high school

- **Med Age** median age (in years)

- **PerCapIn** per capita (per person) income

- **%Poverty** percentage of the population below the poverty level

- **%ColGrad** percentage of people at least 25 years old who have earned bachelor's degrees or higher

c. If an eruption lasts a long time, a lot of pressure is released so it will be longer before pressure builds up sufficiently to cause another eruption.

d. There appear to be two main clusters corresponding to shorter duration and longer duration with a few scattered points between them. There are no outliers.

3 **COMMON MISCONCEPTION** Students have the most difficulty understanding a point that is an outlier only when both variables are considered jointly. For example, on the plot below, the point at (8, 2) is an outlier. However, neither its value of x, 8, nor its value of y, 2, is unusual. What is unusual is that a relatively large value of x is paired with a relatively small value of y.

Joint Outlier of TG

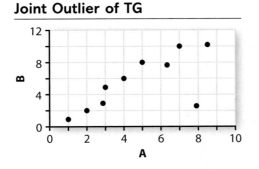

a. The plot is curved upwards. (An upward curve is what we expect in a plot of (*length, weight*) because the volume of an object increases as the cube of the length of its sides.) It fans out to the right; that is, there is more variability in the weights of long bears than short bears. There are five outliers and no distinct clusters.

b. Point A is an outlier only when length and weight are considered jointly. Neither its length alone nor its weight alone is unusual. This bear is of rather average length but is heavy for this length. This bear will look fat.

Point B is an outlier for weight only. This bear is relatively long and is unusually heavy for its length. (Best to avoid this bear.) This bear will look fat.

Point C is an outlier for length only. This bear is very long and will look thin.

Point D is an outlier only when length and weight are considered jointly. Neither its length nor its weight is unusual. This bear is fairly long as bears go but has a weight typical of a bear of more average length. This bear will look thin.

Point E is an outlier for both length and weight. This bear is unusually long and unusually heavy with a weight consistent with its length. It is a giant bear, one you definitely would want to avoid!

Unit 4

Population Characteristics

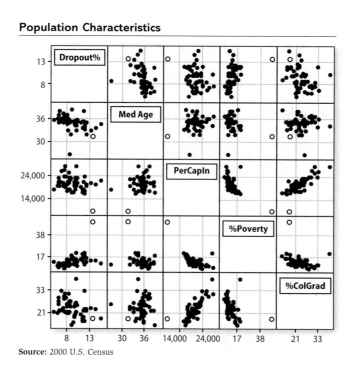

Source: 2000 U.S. Census

a. The points in the plot in the second row and fifth column have *percentage college graduate* plotted on the *x*-axis and *median age* plotted on the *y*-axis. Is there a strong positive, a strong negative, or almost no association between these two variables?

b. Describe the location(s) of the scatterplots within the matrix for which *percentage below poverty level* is the variable graphed on the *x*-axis. On the *y*-axis.

c. The state with the lowest median age is Utah. Estimate the median age in Utah. Estimate the per capita income.

d. The open circle on each plot represents Puerto Rico. The scatterplot in the first row and second column shows that Puerto Rico has a relatively high dropout percentage and a relatively low median age, but it is not an outlier. What can you tell about Puerto Rico from each scatterplot identified below? If it is an outlier, give the type of outlier.

  i. the scatterplot in the third row and fourth column

  ii. the scatterplot in the fourth row and fifth column

  iii. the scatterplot in the first row and fifth column

e. If you ignore Puerto Rico, which pair of variables has the strongest positive association?

f. If you ignore Puerto Rico, which pairs of variables have negative association?

g. Which scatterplot has a curved shape? Does it show varying strength?

Unit 4

Scatterplot Matrices The scatterplot matrix is arranged so that the plots in each row (and each column) all share a single scale. By looking across one row (or down one column), you can see one variable plotted against each of the others with the scales lined up for that variable. You can tell at a glance which variables are positively and negatively correlated with that variable. Students should expect to spend some time studying a scatterplot matrix. In this 5-by-5 scatterplot matrix, five variables are graphed; there are 20 scatterplots; each scatterplot has 52 points on it; and each point represents 2 numbers. This is a tremendous amount of information displayed in a small area.

The scatterplot matrix is a recent invention. The first written discussion of the idea appeared in the early 1980s. For a longer discussion of the scatterplot matrix, see William S. Cleveland, *The Elements of Graphing Data* (Monterey, CA: Wadsworth, 1985). A revised edition was published by Hobart Press of Summit, NJ in 1994.

 4 **a.** Almost no association

b. The percent below poverty level is graphed on the *x*-axis in the fourth column and on the *y*-axis in the fourth row.

c. Utah's median age is about 27 years. Utah's per capita income is about $18,000.

d. **i.** Puerto Rico has the lowest per capita income and the highest percentage in poverty. In fact, it is an outlier in both variables.

ii. Puerto Rico has a relatively low percentage of college grads and the highest percentage in poverty. It is an outlier in percentage in poverty, but not in percentage of college grads.

iii. Puerto Rico has a relatively high percentage of dropouts and a relatively low percentage of college grads. It is not an outlier in this scatterplot.

e. The variables of per capita income and percentage of college graduates have the strongest positive association.

f. The scatterplots showing (*per capita income, percentage in poverty*), (*dropout percentage, median age*), and (*percentage of college graduates, percentage in poverty*) have obvious negative association.

	Dropout%	Med Age	PerCapIn	%Poverty
Med Age	−0.338			
PerCapIn	−0.166	0.115		
%Poverty	0.490	−0.109	−0.489	
%ColGrad	−0.285	−0.050	0.827	−0.371

NOTE The table at the left gives all of the correlations (with Puerto Rico excluded).

g. The two plots that show per capita income and percentage below poverty level are the most curved. There is a slight variation in strength: as per capita income increases, the percentage in poverty decreases, but also has wider spread than for states with smaller per capita income.

5 Look back at the scatterplot matrix in Problem 4.

    a. Why are the scatterplots down the main diagonal of the matrix not included? What would they look like if they were included?

    b. Which pairs of scatterplots give the same information?

Summarize
the Mathematics

In this investigation, you learned how to describe the pattern in a scatterplot.

a When describing the cloud of points on a scatterplot, what information should you give?

b What are the types of outliers that you may see on a scatterplot?

c When would a scatterplot matrix be useful?

Be prepared to share your ideas and reasoning with the class.

✔Check Your Understanding

Each point on the scatterplot below represents a state or the District of Columbia. The variables are the percentage of ninth graders who graduate from high school four years later and the percentage of people who are unemployed. (Two states are missing because their graduation rate was not available.)

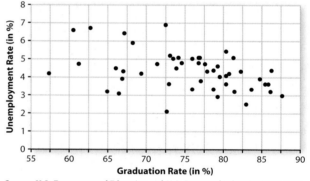

Source: U.S. Department of Education and U.S. Bureau of Labor Statistics, 2006

    a. Describe the shape of this distribution. Include the direction of the relationship, the strength, and whether the strength varies.

    b. Do you see any unusual features?

    c. Nebraska has the highest graduation rate. Estimate this rate from the plot. Is Nebraska's unemployment rate about what you would expect, given its graduation rate?

    d. Michigan has the highest unemployment rate. Estimate this rate from the plot. Is Michigan clearly an outlier?

5 **a.** The same variable would be plotted on the *x*-axis as on the *y*-axis. All points would lie on the line $y = x$.

b. Scatterplots that are reflections across the line from the bottom-left to the top-right corners of the scatterplot include the same two variables, with the horizontal and vertical scales reversed.

Summarize
the Mathematics

a Tell whether the basic shape is linear (oval) or curved; whether any relationship is positive or negative and whether it is weak, moderate, or strong; and whether there are any clusters or outliers.

b Outliers may be an outlier in the variable on the *x*-axis only, in the variable on the *y*-axis only, in both variables, or only when both variables are considered jointly.

c When you have a moderate (say 3 to 10) number of variables and you want to see the scatterplots for all possible pairs, a scatterplot matrix is useful.

MATH TOOLKIT Sketch a scatterplot that will help explain the 4 different types of outliers examined in this investigation. Also, list the information you should consider when describing the cloud of points shown on a scatterplot.

✓Check Your Understanding

a. This distribution is linear with most of the states clustered in an elliptical cloud with graduation percentages between 73% and 88% and unemployment rates between 2.5% and 5.4%. The relationship is moderately strong with a negative trend—the higher the graduation rate, the lower the percentage of unemployed tends to be. There is a slight decrease in the spread of the percentage unemployed as the graduation rate increases.

b. The only unusual feature is the wider scattering in unemployment rate of the dozen or so states with graduation rates below 73%.

c. Nebraska's graduation rate is about 88%. Although Nebraska has a high graduation percentage, its relatively low unemployment rate is about what you would expect from the general pattern.

d. Michigan's unemployment rate is about 6.9%. Although the employment rate is somewhat high compared to what you would expect from the graduation rate, Michigan is not clearly an outlier.

Applications

(1) Which are the best steel roller coasters in the United States? The rankings below are from an *Amusement Today* annual survey of roller-coaster riders.

The table and scatterplot show the top ten roller coasters from the 1999 survey and the order that those same coasters appeared in the 2006 survey.

Roller Coaster Rankings

Roller Coaster	1999 Rank	2006 Relative Rank
Magnum XL-200, Cedar Point, OH	1	1
Montu, Busch Gardens, FL	2	2
Steel Force, Dorney Park, PA	3	5
Alpengeist, Busch Gardens, VA	4	6
Kumba, Busch Gardens, FL	5	8
Raptor, Cedar Point, OH	6	4
Desperado, Buffalo Bill's Resort, NV	7	10
Mind Bender, Six Flags Over Georgia, GA	8	7
Mamba, Worlds of Fun, MO	9	9
Superman, Ride of Steel, Six Flags Darien Lake, NY	10	3

Source: *Amusement Today,* August 2000; www.amusementtoday.com/2006gtasteel.html

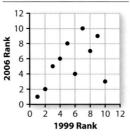

Steel Coasters

a. Why might the ranks change from year to year?

b. Is the relationship positive or negative? Strong or weak? Estimate the rank correlation by examining the scatterplot.

c. Calculate the rank correlation. Compare it to your estimate.

Applications

(1) **INSTRUCTIONAL NOTE** The term "relative rank" is used for the 2006 ranking because some of the roller coasters in the top ten in 1999 were not in the top ten in 2006. The relative rank for 2006 gives the ordering of the top ten roller coasters from 1999 as if no other roller coasters existed in 2006.

Note that Superman, Ride of Steel, may be considered an outlier if you consider both the 1999 and 2006 ranks together.

a. Different people were surveyed in 1999 and in 2006, and different people have different preferences. Further, it is unlikely that very many people have ridden all 10 roller coasters, so each person in the survey should have been asked to rate only those he or she has ridden. That will add additional variability from year to year.

b. The association is positive and moderate. A good estimate of the rank correlation would be between about 0.3 and 0.7.

c. The rank correlation is 0.515. Comparisons to estimates will vary.

2 The following are the 10 consumer products that emergency room patients in the United States most often say are related to the cause of their injuries.

Bathtubs and showers
Beds
Bicycles
Cabinets, racks, and shelves
Chairs
Containers and packaging
Knives
Ladders
Sofas
Tables

a. Ask a friend or member of your family to rank the products from 1 to 10, assigning 1 to the product he or she thinks causes the most emergency room visits in the United States, 2 to the product that he or she thinks causes the second largest number, and so on.

b. The actual ranking is given below. Make a scatterplot comparing these rankings to those collected in Part a.

Product	Rank
Bathtubs and showers	8
Beds	2
Bicycles	1
Cabinets, racks, and shelves	6
Chairs	5
Containers and packaging	7
Knives	3
Ladders	9
Sofas	10
Tables	4

c. Compute the rank correlation between your friend's or family member's ranking and the actual ranking. Was your friend or family member relatively successful or relatively unsuccessful in matching the actual ranks?

2 **INSTRUCTIONAL NOTE** If you choose to do this application as a class, do it before students read this task. Hand out a copy of the alphabetized list. Have each student rank the products according to how many emergency room visits they could cause.

a–c. All answers to this task will vary depending on the ranking given. The source for these data is the 2002 National Safety Council *Annual Injury Facts,* Table 175 (www.nsc.org/lrs/statstop.htm). Here are the numbers of injuries in one year, nationwide:

Product	Number
Saws (hand or power)	92,384
Hammers	36,894
Household containers and packaging	216,498
Bottles and jars	76,487
Knives	441,250
Tableware and flatware	106,852
Drinking glasses	86,909
Beds	495,050
Tables	307,843
Chairs	298,234
Household cabinets, racks, and shelves	261,622
Bathtubs and showers	216,221
Ladders	163,417
Sofas, couches, davenports, etc.	135,190
Televisions	42,811
Footwear	114,454
Wheelchairs	95,228
Jewelry	73,943
Lawn mowers	72,480
Bicycles	521,328
All-terrain vehicles	113,900
Skateboards	113,192
Trampolines	89,393
Swimming pools	82,304
Playground climbing equipment	81,745

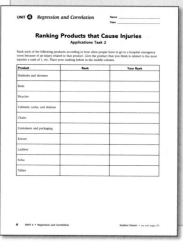

Teaching Resources

Student Master 6.

UNIT ❹ *Regression and Correlation*

Ranking Products that Cause Injuries
Applications Task 2

3 The population ranks for the 10 largest countries in the world for the year 2000 are given in the table below. Also given is the projected rank for each country, relative to the other ten countries, for the years 2025 and 2050.

Population Rankings, Largest Countries in 2000

Country	2000 Population (in millions)	2000 Population Rank	2025 Projected Relative Rank	2050 Projected Relative Rank
Bangladesh	129.2	8	8	8
Brazil	170.1	5	6	7
China	1,277.6	1	1	2
India	1,013.7	2	2	1
Indonesia	212.1	4	4	6
Japan	126.7	9	10	10
Nigeria	111.5	10	7	5
Pakistan	156.5	6	5	3
Russia	146.9	7	9	9
United States	273.8	3	3	4

Source: *The New York Times 2001 Almanac*. New York, NY: The New York Times, 2000.

a. Examine this scatterplot for the (*2000*, *2050*) rankings. Write two observations that you can make from looking at the scatterplot.

b. What is your estimate of the rank correlation for the (*2000*, *2050*) rankings? Check your estimate by computing the rank correlation.

c. Would you expect the correlation between the 2000 ranking and the projected 2025 ranking to be larger or smaller than the one you computed in Part b? Explain. Compute this correlation to see if you were correct.

Population Rankings

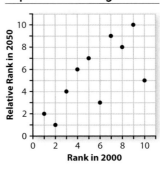

(3) **a.** There is a moderate positive association; that is, if one country had a larger population than another country in 2000, it tends to be projected to have a larger population in 2050.

The country that sticks out on the scatterplot is Nigeria, which was 10th in 2000 and is projected to move up to 5th in 2050. No other country's rank is projected to change that much.

b. The rank correlation is 0.697. Comparisons to estimates will vary.

c. You would expect the correlation between the 2000 ranking and the projected 2025 ranking to be larger than that between 2000 and 2050 because there is less time for population patterns to change. For example, the four largest countries maintained the same rank from 2000 to 2025 but are expected to change by 2050.

The rank correlation between the 2000 ranking and the 2025 projected ranking is 0.903.

4 The table and scatterplot below show data for 25 countries. The variables are a measure of the carbon dioxide emissions (in metric tons) per person and the number of years a newborn can expect to live.

Country	Carbon Dioxide Emissions (in metric tons) per Person	Life Expectancy at Birth
Australia	5.2	80.3
Brazil	0.5	71.4
Canada	5.0	80.0
China	0.7	72.0
France	1.9	79.4
Germany	2.8	78.5
India	0.3	64
Indonesia	0.4	69.3
Iran	1.5	69.7
Italy	2.2	79.5
Japan	2.6	81
Korea, South	2.6	76.7
Mexico	1.0	74.9
Netherlands	4.4	78.7
Poland	2.0	74.7
Russia	3.0	66.8
Saudi Arabia	3.4	75.2
South Africa	2.5	44.1
Spain	2.3	79.4
Taiwan	3.3	77.1
Thailand	0.8	71.7
Turkey	0.8	72.1
Ukraine	2.0	68.8
United Kingdom	2.6	78.3
United States	5.4	77.4

Source: *2006 and 2007 Statistical Abstract of the U.S.* Tables 1318 and 1325.

Life Expectancy and Carbon Dioxide Emissions by Country

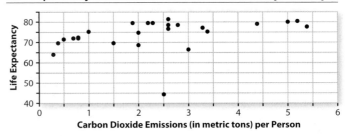

Teacher Notes

a. What is the shape of the distribution? Describe the association between the two variables. Can you use Spearman's r_s to quantify the strength? Why or why not?

b. Do you think the value of one of the two variables causes or otherwise influences the value of the other? Explain your reasoning.

c. Are there any outliers? If so, which type?

5 The *Places Rated Almanac* ranks metropolitan areas according to a variety of categories including:

- crime—violent crime and property crime rates
- health care—the supply of health care services (such as number of specialists or breadth of hospital services)
- education—the number of available educational opportunities beyond high school

Some characteristics of the 15 largest metropolitan areas in the United States are ranked in the table and following scatterplot matrix. For crime, health care, and education, a rank of 1 is best.

Philadelphia

Los Angeles

Boston

Rankings of Metropolitan Areas

Metro Area	Population	Crime	Health Care	Education
Los Angeles, CA	1	14	9	12
New York, NY	2	15	4	5
Chicago, IL	3	13	7	2
Philadelphia, PA	4	4	5	7
Washington, DC	5	5	1	3
Detroit, MI	6	9	13	14
Houston, TX	7	7	10	13
Atlanta, GA	8	11	11	9
Boston, MA	9	3	2	1
Dallas, TX	10	12	14	6
Riverside, CA	11	10	15	15
Phoenix, AZ	12	8	12	8
Minneapolis, MN	13	1	3	4
San Diego, CA	14	6	8	10
Orange County, CA	15	2	6	11

Source: Savageau, David and Ralph D'Agostino. *Places Rated Almanac*, Millennium Edition. New York: Macmillan, 2000.

4 **a.** The shape is approximately linear. There is a very slight, positive relationship with one outlier. You cannot use Spearman's r_s unless you convert the scores and percents to rankings. That is, you would give the country with the highest rate of carbon dioxide emissions a rank of 1, and so on, and do the same for the life expectancy. In addition, students may notice that there would be a tie in the rank for the carbon dioxide emissions between France and South Africa and in the expectation of life at birth between Spain and France. (These could be broken at random or by reporting more decimal places.)

 b. There is probably no direct causation between the two variables, but the amount of affluence (or degree of development of the country) causes both. (Students learn the term "lurking variable" in Lesson 2.)

 c. South Africa is an outlier. It is an outlier only in expectation of life. The carbon dioxide emissions per person is fairly typical of other countries.

Rankings of Metropolitan Areas

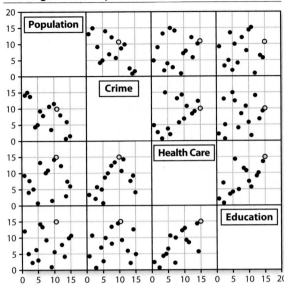

a. Examine the scatterplot matrix shown above. Describe the location(s) of the scatterplots for which *health care* is the variable graphed on the *x*-axis. On the *y*-axis.

b. The open circle on each plot represents the same city. Which city is this? For which variables does this city tend to be ranked toward the best? Toward the worst?

c. Which pair of variables appears to have the strongest positive correlation? Suggest some reasons why this correlation might be so strong.

d. Find a pair of variables with an obvious negative correlation. Write a sentence that describes this relationship.

e. Find the missing values of the rank correlation r_s in the rank correlation matrix below.

	Population	Crime	Health Care	Education
Population	1.000	____	0.168	0.161
Crime	____	1.000	0.475	0.154
Health Care	0.168	0.475	1.000	0.700
Education	0.161	0.154	0.700	1.000

f. Why are the entries along the diagonal of the rank correlation matrix in Part e all 1s?

g. How is this rank correlation matrix related to the scatterplot matrix?

Unit 4

5 **a.** Health care is the variable graphed on the *x*-axis in the third column. It is the variable graphed on the *y*-axis in the third row.

b. This city has the largest rank in health care and in education (it is the worst), so it must be Riverside, CA. Riverside is ranked towards the best only in population (if you think a smaller population is better). It is ranked towards the worst in crime, health care, and education.

c. Education and health care have the strongest positive correlation. Some possible reasons: Cities that fund education as a high priority may also fund health care more generously. People who are better educated have the money to pay for better health care. People who are better educated insist on better health care.

d. Crime and population clearly are negatively correlated. Larger cities tend to have higher crime rates. (It is not just that they have more crime overall, they have a larger number of crimes per person.)

e. Both missing values are −0.589.

f. The entries along the main diagonal all are 1 because each variable is perfectly correlated with itself. In the formula, Σd^2 will be equal to 0.

g. The entry in row *i* and column *j* of the correlation matrix gives the rank correlation between the two variables graphed in the scatterplot matrix in row *i* and column *j*.

POSSIBLE MISCONCEPTION
You may need to remind students that the city with lowest crime rate, Minneapolis, has the rank of 1 and the city with the highest crime rate, New York, has the rank of 15. This rank of 1 does not necessarily mean that Minneapolis has the least number of crimes, only that it has the lowest crime *rate*. The crime rate is usually measured in number of crimes per 100,000 inhabitants.

Connections

6 If $r_s = 1$ or $r_s = -1$, all points fall on a line. Write equations for these two lines.

7 Bianca and Pearl each throw a dart at a larger version of the grid shown here. Bianca's dart lands at the point with coordinates (3, 4). Pearl's dart lands at the point (−5, 1).

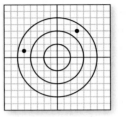

a. Use the distance formula to determine how far Bianca's dart is from Pearl's dart.

b. Whose dart is farther from the center?

c. How is the distance formula like the formula for Spearman's rank correlation?

8 Are the two expressions Σd^2 and $(\Sigma d)^2$ equivalent? Give an example to support your answer.

9 How many scatterplots are there on a scatterplot matrix with 3 variables? With 4 variables? With 5 variables? With k variables?

Reflections

10 Alicia made a scatterplot of two sets of rankings (*set A, set B*) and calculated the rank correlation. Mario made a scatterplot of (*set B, set A*) rankings and calculated the rank correlation.

a. Are there any cases when the scatterplots will be the same? Explain.

b. Will Alicia and Mario find the same correlation? Explain why or why not.

11 Write a conclusion that can be drawn from the following situations.

a. Two reporters ranked the 7 candidates for mayor according to the number of votes they thought the candidates would get in the primary election. The correlation between the rankings of the two reporters was 0.8.

b. Two judges ranked 10 skaters according to their performance. The correlation between the rankings of the two judges was −0.2.

c. Two managers ranked a set of employees on job effectiveness. The correlation between their rankings was 0.5.

d. The two managers in Part c ranked the same employees on efficiency. The correlation between their rankings was −0.7.

Connections

6 If $r_s = 1$, the points fall on the line $y = x$.
If $r_s = -1$ and there are n items being ranked, all points fall on the line between the two points $(1, n)$ and $(n, 1)$ or $y = -x + (n + 1)$.

7 **a.** $\sqrt{(3 - (-5))^2 + (4 - 1)^2} = \sqrt{8^2 + 3^2} \approx 8.54$ units

b. Bianca's dart is $\sqrt{(3 - 0)^2 + (4 - 0)^2}$ or 5 units from the center. Pearl's dart is $\sqrt{(-5 - 0)^2 + (1 - 0)^2}$ or approximately 5.1 units from the center. Pearl's is farther from the center.

c. Both involve a sum of squared differences. Both are meant to measure distance—one between two points in the plane and one between two rankings.

8 Σd^2 is not equivalent to $(\Sigma d)^2$. To compute Σd^2, the numbers are squared and then added; to compute $(\Sigma d)^2$, the numbers are added first, then the sum is squared.

For example, $1^2 + 2^2 + 3^2 = 14$ but $(1 + 2 + 3)^2 = 36$. In general, $(x + y)^2 \neq x^2 + y^2$.

> **COMMON ERROR** Task 8 offers an opportunity to address the error students often make that $(x + y)^2 = x^2 + y^2$.

9 With three variables, there are $3^2 - 3 = 6$ plots (subtracting the 3 that would be on the main diagonal). With four variables, there are $4^2 - 4 = 12$ plots. With five variables, there are $5^2 - 5 = 20$ plots. With k variables, there are $k^2 - k$ or $k(k - 1)$ plots.

Reflections

10 **a.** In general, the scatterplots will not be the same. They will be the same when the rankings are exactly the same or the exact opposites. They will also be the same for paired rankings such as this one: (1,2), (2,1), (3,4), (4,3), (5,6), (6,5), (7,8), (8,7). Mario's scatterplot will be the reflection across $y = x$ of Alicia's scatterplot.

b. The correlations will always be the same. You can see this by looking at the formula. Although a given value of d for (*set A*, *set B*) will have the opposite sign of that of (*set B*, *set A*), the value of d^2 will be the same.

11 **a.** The two reporters felt almost the same way about the order the seven candidates would finish in the election.

b. The judges not only did not have agreement in their rankings, they disagreed slightly.

c. The managers were somewhat alike in how they ranked the employees.

d. The managers were almost opposite in how they ranked the employees. Those employees ranked high by one manager tended to get a low rank from the other manager.

Unit 4

12 Sketch a scatterplot that shows:

a. a strong negative linear relationship.

b. a moderate positive curved relationship.

c. a weak negative linear relationship.

13 How is the word "linear" used differently in algebra and in statistics?

Extensions

14 The more things there are to rank, the larger the number of possible ways to rank them.

a. Suppose that four soccer teams are to be ranked on goals scored for a season. How many possible ways can such a ranking be done?

b. Make a chart that shows how many different rankings are possible if there are 1, 2, 3, 4, and 5 soccer teams to be ranked.

c. Describe any patterns in your chart.

d. If there are k soccer teams, how many different rankings are possible?

15 Give an example to illustrate that, for a given number n of items ranked by two people, the largest possible value of Σd^2 is $\frac{n(n^2 - 1)}{3}$. What does this imply about the rank correlation?

16 Suppose you are given two rankings of five items as shown below.

Item	First Ranking	Second Ranking
1	p	v
2	q	w
3	r	x
4	s	y
5	t	z

a. What is the sum $p + q + r + s + t$ equal to? What is the sum $v + w + x + y + z$ equal to?

b. Use your answer from Part a to show that $\Sigma d = 0$, no matter what the rankings are.

c. Do you think a similar argument could be given to show that for two sets of rankings of 10 items, $\Sigma d = 0$? Why or why not?

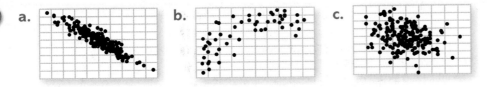

12 **a.**   **b.**   **c.**

13 In statistics, "linear" means the points tend to fall within an oval-shaped cluster. In algebra, "linear" means the points all lie exactly on a line.

Extensions

14 **a.** The ranking can be done in $4 \cdot 3 \cdot 2 \cdot 1 = 24$ ways.

b.

Number of Items	Number of Rankings
1	1
2	2
3	6
4	24
5	120

c. To get from the number of rankings in a row to the number in the next row, you multiply by the number of rankings in that row by the number of items in the next row.

d. $k \cdot (k - 1) \cdot (k - 2) \cdot \cdots \cdot 2 \cdot 1$, or $k!$

15 Opposite rankings will give the maximum value of Σd^2. For example, for 5 items, the maximum occurs when the paired ranks are $(1, 5)$, $(2, 4)$, $(3, 3)$, $(4, 2)$, and $(5, 1)$. Then,

$$\Sigma d^2 = (-4)^2 + (-2)^2 + (0)^2 + (2)^2 + (4)^2 = 40.$$

This is equal to

$$\frac{n(n^2 - 1)}{3} = \frac{5(25 - 1)}{3} = 40.$$

This implies that the rank correlation is always greater than or equal to -1:

$$\Sigma d^2 \leq \frac{n(n^2 - 1)}{3}$$
$$3\Sigma d^2 \leq n(n^2 - 1)$$
$$\frac{3\Sigma d^2}{n(n^2 - 1)} \leq 1$$
$$-\frac{6\Sigma d^2}{n(n^2 - 1)} \geq -2$$
$$1 - \frac{6\Sigma d^2}{n(n^2 - 1)} \geq 1 - 2$$

The expression on the left is the definition of r_s, so $r_s \geq -1$. This means that when ranks are opposite, the rank correlation is -1.

NOTE The solution for Task 16 is on page T277.

17 Maurice Kendall, a British statistician (1907–1983), developed an alternative method to measure the strength of association between two rankings. **Kendall's rank correlation r_k** is given by the formula

$$r_k = 1 - \frac{2c}{\frac{n}{2}(n-1)}.$$

Here, n is the number of items being ranked. To find c, write the ranks for each item side-by-side and connect the ranks as shown below for $n = 4$.

Item	First Ranking	Second Ranking
A	1	2
B	2	4
C	3	3
D	4	1

The number of crossings of the lines is c. Here, $c = 4$.

a. Does a large number of crossings indicate general agreement or general disagreement in the ranks?

b. Find Kendall's rank correlation for the roller coaster data in Applications Task 1 (page 269).

c. Compute Kendall's correlation when there is perfect agreement between the ranks 1 to 5. Compute Kendall's correlation when there is completely opposite ranking of five items.

d. Are Spearman's and Kendall's rank correlations equivalent? That is, do they always give the same value? Explain your answer.

e. Investigate whether r_k always lies between -1 and 1.

Review

18 The table below gives some information about various fast-food hamburgers.

Company	Name	Fat (in grams)	Protein (in grams)
Hardee's	Hamburger	12	14
	Thickburger	57	30
Wendy's	Jr. Hamburger	9	15
	Classic Single	20	25
Burger King	Hamburger	12	15
	Whopper	39	28
McDonald's	Hamburger	9	13
	Quarter Pounder	18	24
	Big Mac	30	25
Carl's Jr.	Kid's Hamburger	18	25
	Famous Star	32	24

Source: www.wendys.com; www.mcdonalds.com; www.burgerking.com; www.hardees.com; www.carlsjr.com (December 2006).

LESSON 1 • Bivariate Relationships **277**

16 **a.** Both $p + q + r + s + t$ and $v + w + x + y + z$ are equal to the sum of the ranks. So, each is equal to $1 + 2 + 3 + 4 + 5 = 15$.

b. $\Sigma d = (p - v) + (q - w) + (r - x) + (s - y) + (t - z)$
$ = p - v + q - w + r - x + s - y + t - z$
$ = p + q + r + s + t - v - w - x - y - z$
$ = (p + q + r + s + t) - (v + w + x + y + z)$
$ = 15 - 15$
$ = 0$

c. Yes. The argument is similar. For ten items, the sum of the ranks is 55. The proof for the general case of n ranks is parallel.

17 **a.** A large number of crossings means the same number tends to be at opposite ends of the rankings, so there is general disagreement.

b.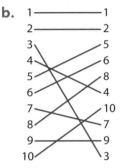

Here, there are thirteen crossings, so $c = 13$ and
$$r_k = 1 - \frac{2(13)}{\frac{10}{2}(10 - 1)} \approx 0.422.$$

c. For perfect agreement, there are no crossings, so $c = 0$ and
$$r_k = 1 - \frac{2(0)}{\frac{5}{2}(4)} = 1.$$
For a completely opposite ranking, there are ten crossings, so $c = 10$
and $r_k = 1 - \dfrac{2(10)}{\frac{5}{2}(4)} = -1$.

d. No. For example, for the roller coaster data, $r_s = 0.515$, while $r_k = 0.422$.

e. The smallest possible number of crossings is 0, which occurs when the rankings are identical. In this case,
$$r_k = 1 - \frac{2(0)}{\frac{n}{2}(n - 1)} = 1$$
for $n > 1$. The largest possible number of crossings is
$1 + 2 + 3 + \cdots + (n - 1) = \dfrac{n(n - 1)}{2}$ and occurs when the rankings
are opposite. In this case,
$$r_k = 1 - \frac{2\left(\frac{n(n - 1)}{2}\right)}{\frac{n}{2}(n - 1)} = -1$$
for $n > 1$. Thus, $-1 \leq r_k \leq 1$.

a. Make plots to compare the distribution of fat with the distribution of protein.

b. Describe the shape of the distribution of the number of grams of fat.

c. Using the *more than 1.5 • IQR from the nearest quartile* rule, are there any outliers in the distribution of the number of grams of fat?

d. Is the mean number of grams larger for fat or for protein? Can you tell from the plots or do you need to compute? Is the mean a suitable measure of center for either distribution?

19 Suppose you have a piece of cloth that has an area of 2 square yards.

a. Give two different possible dimensions for this piece of cloth.

b. How many square feet of material do you have?

c. How many square inches of material do you have?

20 Match each equation with the correct graph. All graphs are drawn using the same scales on the axes. Be prepared to explain how you can do this without using your calculator.

a. $y = -x^2 + 4$ b. $y = -x^2 + 4x$ c. $y = -x^2 + 4x - 4$

d. $y = x^2 + 4$ e. $y = -x^2 - 4x$

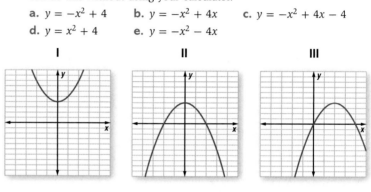

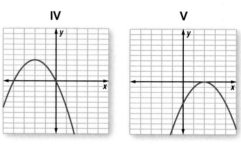

21 Rewrite each expression without parentheses.

a. $(a + 5)(a - 5)$

b. $a(18 - 4a) + 3a^2$

c. $6a^2 + 4a - (2a + 4)(a + 6)$

d. $5(2a + 10) - 6(12 - a)$

e. $(a + 9)^2$

Unit 4

Review

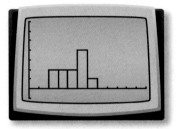

Just in Time

TECHNOLOGY NOTE The fast food data are in *CPMP-Tools*. These data are used again in Review Tasks 22 and 25 and in Investigation 2 of Lesson 2. If students use calculators, they will want to leave the numbers in their lists.

18   **a.** There are only 11 hamburgers, so students might see the most detail by making dot plots or histograms. Note that a box plot obscures the gap in the distribution of protein.

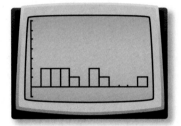

Protein (in grams)   Fat (in grams)

```
WINDOW
Xmin=0
Xmax=60
Xscl=5
Ymin=-1
Ymax=7
Yscl=1
Xres=1
```

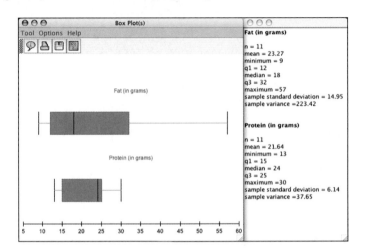

b. The distribution of grams of fat is skewed right.

c. There are no outliers in this distribution. The quartiles for fat are 12 and 32, so $1.5 \cdot IQR = 1.5(32 - 12) = 30$. Thus, any outlier would have to lie above $32 + 30 = 62$, or below $12 - 30 = -18$, which is not possible.

d. The mean number of grams is larger for fat. This is difficult to estimate from the plots. The mean number of grams of fat is about 23.3 and of the mean number of grams of protein is about 21.6. The mean is not very informative for either distribution because of the skewness in the number of grams of fat and the gap in the number of grams of protein.

19   **a.** Two possible dimensions for the cloth are 2 yards by 1 yard, or 0.25 yards by 8 yards.

b. There are $2(3^2) = 18$ square feet of material.

c. There are $2(3^2)(12^2) = 2{,}592$ square inches of material.

20   **a.** II   **b.** III   **c.** V   **d.** I   **e.** IV

21   **a.** $a^2 - 25$ **b.** $18a - a^2$ **c.** $4a^2 - 12a - 24$

     d. $16a - 22$ **e.** $a^2 + 18a + 81$

22 Refer back to the fast-food hamburger data in Review Task 18.

   a. Which hamburger has the largest deviation (in absolute value) from the mean for fat? Find and interpret that deviation.

   b. Which hamburger has the largest deviation (in absolute value) from the mean for protein? Find and interpret that deviation.

   c. Is the standard deviation of the number of grams larger for fat or for protein? Answer this question in two ways: by looking at the plots you made in Review Task 18 and also by computing the standard deviations.

23 Three vertices of square *ABCD* are $A(-2, 10)$, $B(10, 6)$, and $C(6, -6)$.

   a. Find the coordinates of the center of the square.

   b. Find the coordinates of vertex *D*.

   c. Find the reflection image of square *ABCD* across the *y*-axis. How are square *ABCD* and its image related by shape and size?

   d. Find the image of square *ABCD* under a size transformation of magnitude $\frac{1}{2}$ with center at the origin. How are square *ABCD* and its image related by shape and size?

24 In 2006, the number of students enrolled at Mission Hills High School was 1,500. By 2008, the number of students enrolled had increased to 1,815.

   a. By what percentage did the student enrollment increase between 2006 and 2008?

   b. If the percentage growth was the same in each of the two years, by what percent did the student enrollment increase each year?

25 Rewrite each expression in an equivalent form by using the distributive property and combining like terms.

   a. $\frac{1}{4}(3x + 5) + \frac{2}{3}(6x - 10)$

   b. $-15(x^2 + 4) - 11(2x + 3x^2)$

   c. $(6 - 4x)^2$

   d. $x(2x + 7) + 3(8x - 9) - 15$

26 Using the fast-food hamburger data in Review Task 18, make a scatterplot and graph the regression line for predicting protein from fat.

   a. How many grams of protein are predicted for a hamburger with 20 grams of fat?

   b. Interpret the slope of the regression line.

   c. Does a line appear to be a good summary for these data?

Unit 4

Just in Time

22 **a.** The Thickburger has the largest absolute deviation from the mean for fat. Its deviation is $57 - 23.3 = 33.7$, which means that the Thickburger had 33.7 more grams of fat than the average hamburger.

b. McDonald's hamburger had the largest absolute deviation from the mean for protein. Its deviation is $13 - 21.6 = -8.6$, which means that the McDonald's hamburger had 8.6 fewer grams of protein than the average hamburger.

c. The standard deviation is clearly much larger for *fat;* you do not need to compute to see that. The standard deviation for *fat* is about 14.95 grams and for *protein* is about 6.14 grams, less than half as large.

23 **a.** The center of the square is at the midpoint of $\overline{AC}$ (2, 2).

b. $(-6, -2)$

c. Students may draw the reflection image of square *ABCD* and record the image vertices as $A'(2, 10)$, $B'(-10, 6)$, $C'(-6, -6)$, and $D'(6, -2)$, or they may record the image using

a matrix $\begin{bmatrix} 2 & -10 & -6 & 6 \\ 10 & 6 & -6 & -2 \end{bmatrix}$.

Square *ABCD* and its image have the same shape and size.

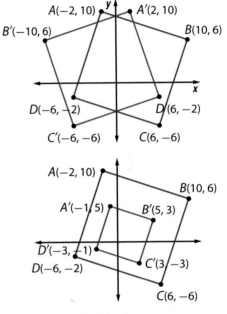

d. Students may draw the transformed image of square *ABCD* and record the image vertices as $A'(-1, 5)$, $B'(5, 3)$, $C'(3, -3)$, and $D'(-3, -1)$, or they may record the image using

a matrix $\begin{bmatrix} -1 & 5 & 3 & -3 \\ 5 & 3 & -3 & -1 \end{bmatrix}$. Square *ABCD* and its image are

similar with the image side lengths half as long as the side lengths of square *ABCD* (a scale factor of 0.5).

24 **a.** 21% **b.** 10% since $1,500(1.10)^2 = 1,815$

25 **a.** $\frac{19}{4}x - \frac{65}{12}$ **b.** $-48x^2 - 22x - 60$

c. $16x^2 - 48x + 36$ **d.** $2x^2 + 31x - 42$

COMMON MISCONCEPTION
The yearly growth rate is not half of the two-year growth rate.

Just in Time

26 See the scatterplot at the right. The regression equation is $y = 0.34x + 13.7$.

a. 20.5 grams of protein

b. The slope of 0.34 means that if one hamburger has 1 more gram of fat than another, we would expect it to have 0.34 more grams of protein.

c. Not really, because the points appear somewhat curved rather than linear.

Fat and Protein in Hamburgers

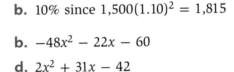

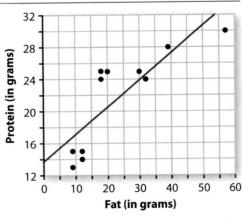

Teaching Resources

Assessment Masters 7–13.

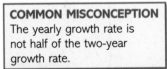
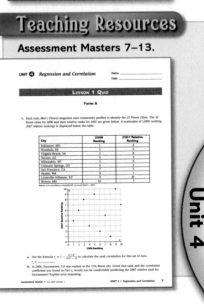

Unit 4

Least Squares Regression and Correlation

Leonardo da Vinci (1452–1519) was both an artist and a scientist. During the period 1484–1493, he combined these skills in the analysis of human proportion. As part of this work, he wrote instructions for other artists on how to draw the human body. One of his rules was that the kneeling height should be three-fourths of the span of the outstretched arms. Explore this idea by collecting measurements from the students in your class. Save the data as you will need it later in this lesson.

Complete a table like that below. Measure to the nearest inch.

Student	Arm Span	Kneeling Height

Unit 4

Least Squares Regression and Correlation

In Course 1 Unit 2, *Linear Functions,* students learned that the regression line is the line of best fit for a set of data that is linear in shape. If the points form an (noncircular) elliptical cluster—no matter how fat—a regression line is an appropriate way to model the bivariate relationship. In much the same way that the mean is a summary of single-variable data, the regression line is a summary of bivariate data. In the first investigation of this lesson, students consider some properties of the regression line and see how it is computed. The effect of outliers and influential points on the regression line is explored.

Rank correlation was investigated in Lesson 1 so that students would get a sense of the meaning of correlation. The primary objective of the third investigation of this lesson is to develop students' abilities to interpret Pearson's correlation r, the correlation commonly used for either bivariate data. Spearman's rank correlation is a special case of the more general Pearson's correlation. They give the same value for rankings with no ties.

After some initial investigation of scatterplots and the formula for Pearson's correlation, students learn to find the value of r on a calculator or computer software. Pearson's r can be interpreted in the same way as Spearman's r_s. It is again the case that $-1 \leq r \leq 1$. The correlation is 1 for a perfect positive linear relationship and -1 for a perfect negative linear relationship. If the linear association is weak, r is close to 0.

In the fourth investigation, students explore the fact that a high correlation does not necessarily mean that one variable causes the other.

Throughout this lesson, it will help students see the importance of this topic if they are on the lookout for articles and claims in the media about regression, correlation, or causation. Ask students to bring such examples so the class can discuss how strong the evidence is for a cause-and-effect relationship. It is easy to find them by searching the Internet for news articles using keywords such as "regression" and "correlation." Also see page T280B.

Limits on Extrapolation While teaching this lesson, watch for opportunities to discuss whether it is reasonable to use the regression equation for values outside of the range of values of x used to compute it. For example, the linear regression equation for the class (*arm span, kneeling height*) data may not be useful for young children with arm spans of 2 feet. Depending on the context, the domain sometimes does not include negative values. These conversations will foreshadow the more extended introduction of theoretical and practical domain and range in the next unit *Nonlinear Functions and Equations.*

Lesson Objectives

- Understand that a linear model is appropriate when the points form an elliptical cloud
- Compute errors in prediction and residuals, and locate residuals on the plot
- Understand that for the regression equation the sum of the residuals is 0
- Understand the regression line as the line that minimizes the sum of the squared residuals
- Determine whether an outlier is an influential point
- Compute and interpret Pearson's r as a measure of how closely the points cluster about the regression line
- Interpret Pearson's r as the rescaled sum of the products $(x - \bar{x})(y - \bar{y})$
- Know that adding a constant to each value or multiplying by a positive constant does not change the correlation
- Understand that association does not mean that one of the variables causes the other
- Identify possible explanations (cause-and-effect, lurking variable) for an association, and illustrate with a directed graph
- Identify the explanatory variable and the response variable

TECHNOLOGY NOTE Given the many data sets in this unit, you may wish to show students how to name lists in TI calculators as follows. Place the cursor on the list title (e.g., L5). Then, press [2nd] [DEL] to choose INS. Type in a name of your choice. Then press [ENTER]. To choose the named list for calculating or plotting, place the cursor at the location and select [2nd] [STAT], and scroll down to the named list or choose its number.

Lesson Launch

To gather the data for the Think About This Situation, you will need several yardsticks marked in inches, preferably at least one for each group of students. Students will use the (*arm span, kneeling height*) data again in Investigation 2, so ask students to keep a copy of the measurements.

This Think About This Situation takes a bit longer than others because of the data collection. If students enter the data into *CPMP-Tools* using a class computer, you will save considerable time here as well as in the investigation. These data should be saved to use on page 293. Data sets in *CPMP-Tools* for this unit are listed in the unit overview.

Articles from the Media While working on Investigation 4, you may want to have students look for an article in the media that uses the concept of correlation or association. Then after completing the investigation, they can be asked to write a paragraph describing the use of correlation in the article. Students should include whether there is any suggestion of cause-and-effect and, if so, whether they think it is reasonable. They should discuss what additional information about the situation would help them to understand better the correlation and its causes. Students can find articles by searching the Internet for news articles using keywords such as "regression" and "correlation."

Encourage students to share their results. They can report on the article, or they can produce an overhead highlighting the main points. To make the reporting more efficient, each student in a group can bring an article, then the group can determine which of the articles they would like to present to the class.

Many students will bring in examples of association involving categorical variables. For example, "men are taller than women" is an example of the categorical variable of gender (male or female) associated with the numerical variable of height (number of inches). Point out to students that you cannot compute a correlation unless you have numerical variables (quantitative variables that you can plot on a scatterplot).

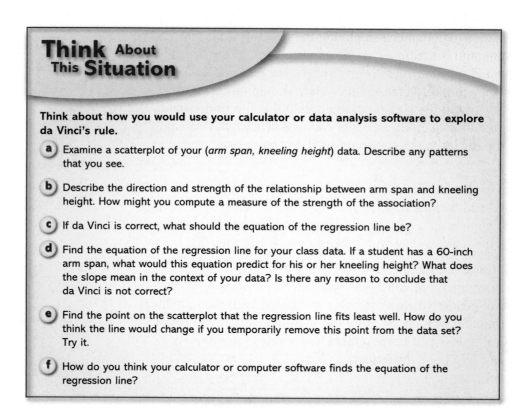

Think About This Situation

Think about how you would use your calculator or data analysis software to explore da Vinci's rule.

a Examine a scatterplot of your (*arm span, kneeling height*) data. Describe any patterns that you see.

b Describe the direction and strength of the relationship between arm span and kneeling height. How might you compute a measure of the strength of the association?

c If da Vinci is correct, what should the equation of the regression line be?

d Find the equation of the regression line for your class data. If a student has a 60-inch arm span, what would this equation predict for his or her kneeling height? What does the slope mean in the context of your data? Is there any reason to conclude that da Vinci is not correct?

e Find the point on the scatterplot that the regression line fits least well. How do you think the line would change if you temporarily remove this point from the data set? Try it.

f How do you think your calculator or computer software finds the equation of the regression line?

In previous units, you used your calculator or computer software to find a regression line to summarize the linear relationship between two variables. In this lesson, you will investigate some properties of the regression line and learn how its equation is calculated. You will also learn to describe the *strength* of an elliptical cloud of points by computing a new type of correlation that can be used even if the variables are not ranks.

Investigation 1 How Good Is the Fit?

There are several possible criteria you could use to determine which line through an elliptical cloud of points is the "best-fitting" line. You might choose the line passing through the most points, or you might choose the one with the smallest average distance from the points. In this investigation, you will further explore the method used by most calculators and data analysis software—the method of least squares. As you work on the following problems, look for answers to this question:

How is the least squares regression line determined?

Think About This Situation

a) Make the scatterplot of (*arm span*, *kneeling height*) large enough for the whole class to see. The data can be entered into the *CPMP-Tools* data analysis software.

b) The relationship will be positive and strong. The arm spans and kneeling heights each could be ranked and the correlation between the ranks measured using Spearman's rank correlation from Lesson 1. Encourage students to offer other ideas for computing a correlation without resorting to converting the values to ranks, which results in the loss of much information.

c) If Leonardo is correct, the equation would be close to *kneeling height* = 0.75(*arm span*).

d) Regression lines and prediction will vary. If the slope is, say, 0.72, this means that if one student has an arm span that is 1 inch longer than another student's, then his or her kneeling height is predicted to be 0.72 inches more. If the *y*-intercept is far from 0 or the slope is far from 0.75, students should suspect that Leonardo is not correct, at least for high school students. This conclusion also assumes that your students are a representative sample of high school students.

e) How well a point fits the line is measured by the difference between the actual kneeling height and the predicted kneeling height (a vertical distance on the scatterplot). This question introduces students to the idea of an influential point.

f) Students may suggest the following methods of finding the regression line, which are in increasing order of sophisticated thinking:

- The regression line is the line with the largest number of points on it.
- Find the distance from each line to the point that is farthest away from it. The regression line is the line with the smallest maximum distance.
- If you sum up all of the distances from the points to the line, the regression line is the line with the smallest sum.
- If you sum up all of the *squared* distances from the points to the line, the regression line is the line with the smallest sum.

As students will learn in this lesson, the last idea is how the regression line actually is computed. Occasionally, a student who has internalized the idea of the sum of squared differences as the measure of variability in statistics will suggest this. (Or, the student may get this idea from the title of the lesson!)

INSTRUCTIONAL NOTE
If students are not already familiar with entering data into *CPMP-Tools*, use this TATS as an opportunity to show them.

COLLABORATION SKILL
Use technology in a way that supports collaboration among group members.

1 With the high price of gasoline in the U.S., motorists are concerned about the gas mileage of their cars. The table below gives the curb weights and highway mileage for a sample of 2007 four-door compact sedans, all with automatic transmissions.

Compact Cars

Car	Curb Weight (in lbs)	Highway mpg
Audi A4	3,450	32
Chevrolet Cobalt	3,216	32
Ford Focus	2,636	34
Honda Civic	2,690	40
Honda Civic Hybrid	2,875	51
Hyundai Accent	2,403	36
Kia Spectra	2,972	35
MAZDA3	2,811	34
Mercedes-Benz C280	3,460	28
Nissan Sentra	2,897	36
Saturn ION	2,805	32
Subaru Impreza	3,067	28
Suzuki Aerio	2,716	31
Toyota Corolla	2,595	38
Toyota Yaris	2,326	39
Volkswagen Rabbit	2,911	30

Source: www.edmunds.com

a. What is the weight of the Kia Spectra in *hundreds of pounds*? Of the Toyota Yaris?

b. Use data analysis software or your calculator to make a scatterplot of the points (*curb weight, highway mpg*). Enter each weight in 100s of pounds, so the slope will not be so close to 0. Does a line appear to be an appropriate summary of the relationship?

c. Find the regression equation and graph the line on the scatterplot.

d. Select the best interpretation of the slope of the regression line from the choices below. Explain your choice.

- If the weight of a car is increased by 100 pounds, then we predict that the car's highway gas mileage will decrease by about 0.75 mpg.

- If one model of car is 100 pounds heavier than another model, then we predict that its highway gas mileage will be 0.75 mpg less.

Unit 4

In this investigation, students will:

- review how to use a regression line to make a prediction.
- learn the difference between an error in prediction (the error for a point that was not used to compute the regression equation) and a residual (the error for a point that was used to compute the regression equation). Usually, it is impossible to find the error in prediction because we do not know the true value of y. We can always compute a residual. See additional clarification in Problem 3 on pages 283–284.
- learn that the least squares regression equation is the one that minimizes the sum of the squared residuals.

1 **TECHNOLOGY NOTE** These data are used throughout this investigation and the next; so if using calculators, students will want to leave the numbers in their calculators. These data are in *CPMP-Tools*. Be sure students understand that the weights are given in hundreds of pounds in the student text and also in *CPMP-Tools*.

a. 29.72 hundred pounds; 23.26 hundred pounds

b. See the plot in Part c. Except for one point, the points form an elliptical cloud, and so a line is an appropriate summary. The Honda Civic Hybrid is different from the other cars, and so you should consider moving it to a data set with other hybrid cars when predicting gas mileage from weight. (Students will learn more about this in the next investigation.)

c.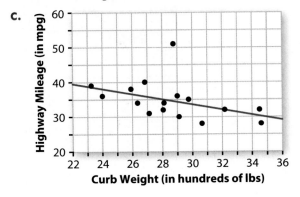

$y = -0.746x + 56.131$, where x is the curb weight in hundreds of pounds and y is the highway mpg. Note that if the weights had been entered in pounds, the slope would be -0.00746.

d. INSTRUCTIONAL NOTE Be sure students understand the importance of the phrase "we predict." The regression line provides a summary of the general trend and should not be expected to give the exact gas mileage for a given weight. Listen for this as you observe groups. You may wish to discuss this at the STM.

The second sentence is the best interpretation. The first sentence is not good because the points represent different models, not one model with changing weight. That is, the regression line was computed from different models, not from taking one car and repeatedly adding 100 pounds and seeing how the gas mileage changes.

e. A compact car that is not in the table, the Acura TSX, has a weight of 3,345 lbs. Use each of the following to predict the highway mpg for the Acura TSX.

    i. the regression line on the scatterplot

    ii. the equation of the regression line

2 For a car, like the Acura TSX, that *was not used* in calculating the regression equation, the difference between the actual (*observed*) value and the value predicted by the regression equation is called the **error in prediction**:

    error in prediction = observed value − predicted value

a. The Acura TSX has highway mpg of 31. What is the error in prediction for the Acura TSX?

b. The Volkswagen Jetta has a curb weight of 3,303 lbs.

    i. Use the regression equation to predict the highway mpg for the Jetta.

    ii. The Jetta actually has highway mpg of 32. What is the error in prediction for the Jetta?

3 For a car that *was used* in calculating the regression equation, the difference between the observed value and predicted value is called the **residual**:

    residual = observed value − predicted value

a. Estimate the residual from the plot and then compute the residual for the Honda Civic Hybrid. For the Subaru Impreza.

Compact Cars

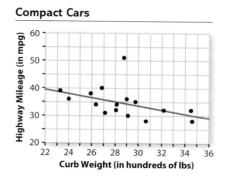

b. Are points with negative residuals located above or below the regression line?

c. Find a car with a negative residual that is close to zero. What does that residual tell you about the predicted highway mileage?

e. **i.** Approximately 31 highway mpg

    ii. $-0.746(33.45) + 56.131 \approx 31.18$ mpg

2 **a.** The error in prediction is almost zero: $31 - 31.18 = -0.18$ mpg.

  b. **i.** $-0.746(33.03) + 56.131 \approx 31.49$ mpg

     ii. The error in prediction is again very small, approximately $32 - 31.49 = 0.51$ mpg.

3 **POSSIBLE MISCONCEPTION** The distinction between residual and error in prediction is straightforward: If the car was used in the calculation of the regression equation, then the difference between observed and predicted values is a residual. If the car was not used, the difference is an error of prediction.

We are rarely able to compute errors of prediction. To compute the error of prediction, we need to know the actual value of y. If we know the actual value, then we would not need to predict it. Sometimes, errors of prediction eventually can be found. For example, if you use a regression line to predict a person's adult height from his or her height as a six-year-old, when the child grows up, you will be able to compute the error in this prediction.

a. Honda Civic Hybrid residual:
$51 - [-0.746(28.75) + 56.131] \approx 16.32$ mpg
Subaru Impreza residual: $28 - [-0.746(30.67) + 56.131] \approx -5.25$ mpg

b. The points with negative residuals are located below the regression line.

c. Cars with negative residuals close to zero are the MAZDA3 and Chevrolet Cobalt, which is the closest to zero. The actual highway mpg for these cars was slightly lower than predicted for their weight. (If the regression equation is rounded to $y = -0.75x + 56$, the Cobalt will have a very small positive residual.)

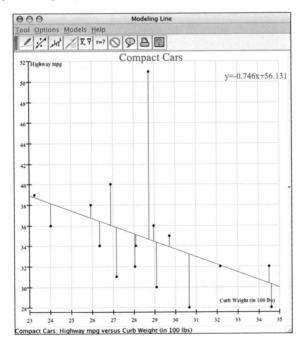

④ The equation of the regression line for the three points in the table below is $y = 2x - \frac{4}{3}$.

x	1	2	3
y	1	2	5

a. Graph this line on a scatterplot showing the three points. Draw line segments that show the size of the residuals.

b. Complete a copy of the table below using the equation of the regression line. What do you notice about the sum of the residuals? (This is always true about the sum of the residuals from the least squares regression line.)

x	y	Predicted y	Residual	Squared Residual
1	1			
2	2			
3	5			
	Total			

c. The line that goes through the points (1, 1) and (2, 2) also fits these three points reasonably well.

  i. Write the equation of this line.

  ii. Graph this line on a scatterplot showing the three points. Draw in the residuals for this line.

  iii. Complete a copy of the table above using this new equation to predict values of y.

d. Find the equation of a third line that fits these three points reasonably well. Graph this line on a scatterplot showing the three points. Draw in the residuals. Complete another copy of the table using your new equation to predict values of y.

e. Which of the three equations gave the smallest sum of squared residuals?

f. Compare your answer with that of others who may have used a different equation for the third line. What appears to be true about the regression line?

Your work in Problem 4 illustrates a general rule: The **regression line** or **least squares regression line** is the line that has a smaller **sum of squared errors** (residuals), or **SSE**, than any other line.

(4) INSTRUCTIONAL NOTE There are several techniques that can be used to fit a line to data. However, the least squares method is the one most commonly used. It gives the line that minimizes the sum of the squared errors (residuals), hence the name "least squares."

Students may ask why the residuals are squared after you find the "difference" between the points and the line. In Connections Task 12, students explore the fact that it is always the case with the least squares regression line that the sum of the residuals is 0. However, the sum of the residuals can be 0 with other lines, too, so this criterion does not define a unique line. You may wish to remind students that they learned in *Patterns in Data* in Course 1 that the sum of the deviations from the mean also is always 0. This is one reason why we square deviations when computing measures of variation.

Students are easily convinced that they cannot find a unique regression line by just minimizing the sum of the residuals. However, they may wonder why they cannot minimize the sum of the absolute values of the residuals. That does not give a unique line either. For example, consider the points $(0, 0)$, $(0, 1)$, $(1, 1)$ and $(1, 2)$. For each of these lines, $y = 2x$, $y = 1$, and $y = x + \frac{1}{2}$ (the regression line), the sum of the absolute values of the errors is equal to 2. Also see Connections Task 12 on page 314.

Statisticians have chosen the sum of the squared errors over others for many reasons. One is because of its relationship to the Euclidean distance formula, which uses a sum of squared differences. Another is that formulas that contain absolute values are difficult to manipulate. (For example, compare taking the derivative of $y = x^2$ to taking the derivative of $y = |x|$.)

The sum of squared errors is used throughout statistics as a measure of distance. Students have now seen the idea of a sum of squared differences with the standard deviation, the Euclidean distance formula, Spearman's rank correlation, and least squares regression.

In this problem, students explore the idea of minimizing the sum of the squared residuals. It may be helpful to draw the class together after groups have finished with this problem, to have students show a few of the lines that were tried.

Actually sketching the "square errors"—squares that touch the line, with side length equal to the residual—helps students to visualize how adjusting the line can make the total area of these squares as small as possible. This idea is investigated further in Problem 2 of the following investigation where students use *CPMP-Tools* and also in Connections Task 10 on page 313.

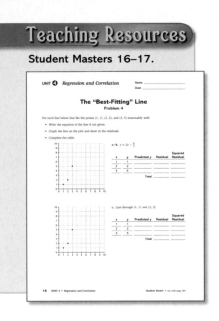

a.

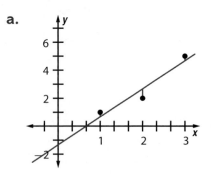

b.

x	y	Predicted y	Residual	Squared Residual
1	1	$\frac{2}{3}$	$\frac{1}{3}$	$\frac{1}{9}$
2	2	$\frac{8}{3}$	$-\frac{2}{3}$	$\frac{4}{9}$
3	5	$\frac{14}{3}$	$\frac{1}{3}$	$\frac{1}{9}$
		Total	0	$\frac{6}{9}$ or $\frac{2}{3}$

c. **i.** $y = x$

ii.

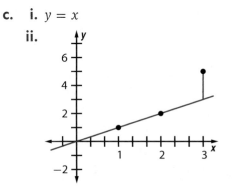

iii.

x	y	Predicted y	Residual	Squared Residual
1	1	1	0	0
2	2	2	0	0
3	5	3	2	4
		Total	2	4

d. Results will depend on which equation the student picks. One example of a line that fits the points fairly well (and goes through the centroid) is the line through $(1, 1)$ and $\left(2, \frac{8}{3}\right)$. This line has equation $y = \frac{5}{3}x - \frac{2}{3}$. The sum of the squared residuals (errors) is $0.\overline{8}$.

e. Students will find that the regression equation, $y = 2x - \frac{4}{3}$, gives the smallest sum of squared errors.

f. The regression equation appears to give the smallest sum of squared residuals. (Students will explore this idea further in Extensions Task 23.)

Summarize the Mathematics, *page 285*

Students have considered the questions in their groups, and the teacher is leading a whole group discussion.

Teacher: There are a couple of ways to find the residual. How can you find the residual visually from the scatterplot? Any ideas from your group, Emma?

Emma: Yes. After you draw the regression line, you draw from a point straight up or down to the regression line. It is the vertical distance from the point to the regression line.

Ava: I thought distance was always positive, but sometimes residuals are negative.

Madison: The negative happened when the point was below the line.

Ava: Yeah, the ones above are positive, and the ones below are negative. And that helps explain why when you add them up, the sum is always zero.

Teacher: Great discussion. It looks like the scatterplot gave you a good visual representation to help you understand how to find residuals. When trying to understand problems, do not forget about the power of the picture. Now, consider how can you find the residual from the equation of the regression line. Patrick …

Patrick: You plug in the x value of one of the data points into the regression equation to find the y value on the line. Then, get the y value of the actual data point with the same x value. Then, subtract them. *(The teacher wonders if Patrick does not know the order of subtraction or is just using sloppy wording.)*

Teacher: Let's connect this finding the difference between the y values to our description using a scatterplot and regression line. *(Teacher displays a scatterplot of data and the regression line using a transparency or CPMP-Tools.)* Patrick, come up here and explain your thinking about using the equation to find the residual. Assume that the equation of this regression line is $y = 2x$. Use the point (3, 7) to show us what you would do. *(Patrick explains. Teacher notices the vagueness about the subtraction order again in Patrick's language.)*

Teacher: Okay, now how does that connect to the vertical line drawn to the regression line from (3, 7)? Delania, what do you think?

Delania: The residual that Patrick found is the length of the segment that we drew.

Teacher: A few moments ago, we were discussing positive and negative residuals. How does that come into play here with our subtraction process, Delania?

Delania: I guess when you are looking at the plot, you can just assign a positive or negative value distance between the two points

without worrying about the order of subtraction. But if you are just looking at the two y values, you should subtract the y value of the point on the regression line *from* the y value of the actual data point.

Teacher: What did we call those two values during the investigation? Sam?

Sam: We said the residual was the observed value minus the predicted value (the one from the line).

Teacher: Great job, class. Brenon, what did your group have down for the difference between error in prediction and residual? Show us your thinking using this scatterplot.

Brenon: They are both determined by subtracting the predicted y value (from the equation) from the observed y value. When the point off the line you are considering was used to compute the equation of a regression line, like this one, we call the difference a residual. If the point was not used in calculating the regression line, like a new point here, we call the difference an error in prediction.

Teacher: Why does it make sense to call that difference an "error in prediction"?

Paige: Well, when you use a new data point, like the different car, the line only gives you a prediction of the weight. If you can look up the actual weight, then you can find how far off your prediction was—the error in the prediction.

Teacher: Okay, we have talked about parts a and b of the STM. Now, let's consider Part c. How is the idea of a sum of squared differences important to least squares regression?

Palmer: If the SSE was smaller for one line than for another line, then the line with the smaller SSE seemed to be a better fit for the data.

Teacher: What is the meaning of the term "least squares"?

Chael: That meant the smallest sum of squared errors. The regression line has the smallest sum of squared errors of any line we would suggest for the data.

Teacher: Okay, let's take a look at how the idea of residuals and sum of squared differences is shown visually using the *CPMP-Tools* software. Chauncey, would you please use our computer and display here to access the car data again? Okay, now place the regression line on the plot and select the icon showing the residuals. Remember how you found the SSE information? Let's see that, and then talk us through what you notice by selecting the squares icon on the menu bar. *(The class discusses what these features mean and also places a drawn line on the plot to visually compare the squares produced when using this line to the regression line squares.)*

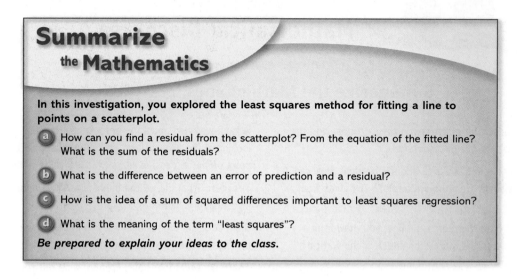

Summarize
the Mathematics

In this investigation, you explored the least squares method for fitting a line to points on a scatterplot.

a How can you find a residual from the scatterplot? From the equation of the fitted line? What is the sum of the residuals?

b What is the difference between an error of prediction and a residual?

c How is the idea of a sum of squared differences important to least squares regression?

d What is the meaning of the term "least squares"?

Be prepared to explain your ideas to the class.

✔Check Your Understanding

The data below come from a study of nine Oregon communities in the 1960s, when nuclear power was relatively new. The study compared exposure to radioactive waste from a nuclear reactor in Hanford, Washington, and the death rate due to cancer in these communities.

Community	Index of Exposure	Cancer Deaths (per 100,000 residents)
Umatilla	2.5	147
Morrow	2.6	130
Gilliam	3.4	130
Sherman	1.3	114
Wasco	1.6	138
Hood River	3.8	162
Portland	11.6	208
Columbia	6.4	178
Clatsop	8.3	210

Source: *Journal of Environmental Health*, May–June 1965.

Summarize
the Mathematics

(a) To find a residual from the scatterplot, find the vertical distance on the scatterplot from the point to the line, given a positive sign if the point is above the line and a negative sign if the point is below the line.

You can use the equation by subtracting the value of *y* predicted from the equation from the observed value of *y*.

The sum of the residuals always is 0.

(b) A residual is the difference between the observed value and the predicted value for one of the points used to compute the regression line. An error of prediction is the difference between the observed value and the predicted value for a point that was *not* used to compute the regression line.

(c) When fitting a line to real data, the points will not all lie on a line. The difference between the actual (observed) value of *y* and the value predicted by the equation is called the residual. The least squares regression line is the line that makes the sum of the squared residuals as small as possible.

(d) "Least squares" is an abbreviated term that means "the smallest possible sum of the squares of all of the errors/residuals." In other words, "least" means "minimum" in this phrase.

✔ *Check Your Understanding*

DIFFERENTIATION These data are in *CPMP-Tools*, which students can use to find the SSE. If you want to be sure students know how to compute the SSE, have them do this using the list functions on their calculators or spreadsheets so they can show they know the process without spending a lot of time computing.

BACKGROUND INFORMATION There is a lot of information on the Hanford studies on the Internet. For example, see the background information at tis.eh.doe.gov/ohre/new/findingaids/epidemiologic/hanford/.

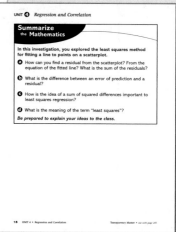

PROMOTING MATHEMATICAL DISCOURSE
See page T284B.

Teaching Resources

Transparency Master 18.

UNIT 4 *Regression and Correlation*

Summarize the Mathematics

In this investigation, you explored the least squares method for fitting a line to points on a scatterplot.

(a) How can you find a residual from the scatterplot? From the equation of the fitted line? What is the sum of the residuals?

(b) What is the difference between an error of prediction and a residual?

(c) How is the idea of a sum of squared differences important to least squares regression?

(d) What is the meaning of the term "least squares"?

Be prepared to explain your ideas to the class.

18 UNIT 4 • Regression and Correlation   Transparency Master • use with page 285

MATH TOOLKIT To explain the difference between a residual and an error of prediction, create a scatterplot and draw in the line of regression and a residual. Then, add another point in a different color and draw the segment representing the error in prediction. Add notes to clarify as needed.

COLLABORATION PROMPT We collaborated using technology by … . We could improve our collaboration by … .

Unit 4

Radioactive Waste Exposure

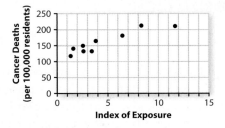

a. Describe the direction and strength of the relationship.

b. Find the equation of the regression line. What does the slope mean in the context of these data?

c. Use the equation to predict the cancer death rate for Hood River. Find and interpret the residual for Hood River.

d. What is the sum of the squared residuals? Can you find a different line that gives a smaller sum? Explain.

Investigation 2 **Behavior of the Regression Line**

You have seen that the least squares regression line makes the sum of the squares of the residuals as small as possible. The regression line has other important properties. As you work on the following problems, look for answers to this question:

What are some of the properties of the least squares regression line?

1 The point with coordinates $(\bar{x}, \bar{y})$ can be thought of as the balance point for bivariate data. This point is called the **centroid**. The regression line always goes through the centroid.

a. Shown below are the three points in Problem 4 of Investigation 1. Calculate $\bar{x}$ and $\bar{y}$. Then verify that the point with coordinates $(\bar{x}, \bar{y})$ is on the regression line.

x	1	2	3
y	1	2	5

b. Refer back to the table of data on compact car highway mileage in Problem 1 of Investigation 1 (page 282).

  i. Calculate the mean curb weight in 100s of pounds and the mean highway mpg of that group of cars.

  ii. Verify that the point (*mean curb weight, mean highway mpg*) lies on the regression line.

NOTE See page T285 for other information related to this task.

a. The relationship is positive and quite strong.

b. The equation of the regression line is $y = 9.27x + 114.68$. The slope of 9.27 tells you that if one town has 1 unit more in the index of exposure than another town, we predict that it would have 9.27 more cancer deaths per 100,000 residents.

c. For Hood River, the prediction is $y = 9.27(3.8) + 114.68 = 149.906$. The residual for Hood River is $162 - 149.906 = 12.094$. This means that there are about 12 more cancer deaths per 100,000 residents in Hood River than we would predict by using the regression line.

d. The sum of the squared residuals is computed below in the table. No line will give a smaller sum of squared errors than 1,359.2. (This SSE is quite a bit larger than others students have seen for data with about the same correlation because the cancer death rates are larger numbers to begin with.)

ASSIGNMENT NOTE These data are used again in the CYU for the next investigation and in Extensions Task 24. Students who are not using *CPMP-Tools* will want to leave the numbers in their calculators.

Community	Exposure	Cancer Death Rate	Fit	Residual	Squared Residual
Umatilla	2.5	147	137.866	9.1337	83.425
Morrow	2.6	130	138.794	−8.7937	77.329
Gilliam	3.4	130	146.213	−16.2128	262.854
Sherman	1.3	114	126.738	−12.7376	162.248
Wasco	1.6	138	129.520	8.4802	71.914
Hood River	3.8	162	149.922	12.0777	145.871
Portland	11.6	208	222.258	−14.2585	203.303
Columbia	6.4	178	174.034	3.9656	15.726
Clatsop	8.3	210	191.655	18.3453	336.550
			Total	0	1,359.2

Investigation 2 · Behavior of the Regression Line

In the previous investigation, students learned that the sum of the residuals is always 0. In this investigation, students learn that:

- the least squares regression line always goes through the point $(\bar{x}, \bar{y})$.
- an influential point is one where, if it is removed from the data set, the equation of the regression line (or the correlation) changes significantly.

An outlier can dramatically affect the least squares regression line. An outlier tends to pull the regression line towards it, especially if its value of x is far away from those of the other points. The impact is less dramatic if the outlier lies directly above or below the rest of the points.

An influential point is a special type of outlier. It is defined as a point where, if it is removed from the data set, the equation of the regression line or the correlation changes significantly. Although there are ways of formally defining a "significant" change, those methods are very advanced and ultimately must give precedence to the real-life context. So, for now, have students use their best judgment as to whether the change would matter in the actual situation.

When an influential point is identified, it is common to report the analysis both with it and without it.

NOTE The solution to Problem 1 is on page T287.

Unit 4

2 Now, use data analysis software to examine the idea of finding the line on a scatterplot that minimizes the sum of squared errors (residuals), or SSE.

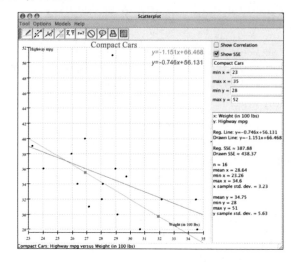

Compact Cars: Highway mpg versus Weight (in 100 lbs)

a. Using the moveable line capability of the software, visually find a line that you think best fits the compact car (*curb weight in hundreds of pounds, highway mpg*) data.

b. Compare the line you found visually and its equation with the regression line and its equation.

c. The Honda Civic Hybrid is an outlier and so may have a large effect on the location of the regression line. To investigate the effect of this point, first remove from the plot the lines you found in Part a.

   i. Delete the point for the Honda Civic Hybrid from the data set. How do the regression line and equation change?

   ii. Replace the point for the Honda Civic Hybrid and then delete the point for the Mercedes-Benz C280, which is the second heaviest car. How do the regression line and equation change in this case?

   iii. Does the Honda Civic Hybrid or the Mercedes-Benz C280 have more influence on the regression line and equation?

An **influential point** is a special type of outlier. It strongly influences the equation of the regression line or the correlation. When such a point is removed from the data set, the slope or y-intercept of the regression line changes quite a bit. The interpretation of "quite a bit" depends on the real-life situation. You will further examine the idea of an influential point in the next two problems.

1 a. $\bar{x} = 2$; $\bar{y} = 2\frac{2}{3}$; $2\frac{2}{3} = 2(2) - \frac{4}{3}$

  b. i. $\bar{x} = 28.64$; $\bar{y} = 34.75$

  ii. You can verify by showing that (28.64, 34.75) satisfies the regression equation. (The value of y is not exactly equal to $\bar{y}$ because of rounding of the regression coefficients.)

2 a. **TECHNOLOGY NOTE** The Draw Line icon ✎ in *CPMP-Tools* allows students to move a line around by dragging the points on the green line. Selecting the Show Plot Options and Information icon 🅘 provides the equation of the green line. Select the Show SSE checkbox to see the sum of squared errors for the green line as shown in the student text.

  b. Students should compare their line and its equation to the regression equation from Problem 1 on page 282: $y = -0.746x + 56.131$.

  c. i. Delete Honda Civic Hybrid: $y = -0.758x + 55.382$
      The slope and y-intercept do not change much at all. (This happens because the Honda Civic Hybrid lies right above the center of the distribution.) See the plot on the left below.

  ii. Delete Mercedes-Benz C280: $y = -0.623x + 52.796$
      In this case, the line is a little less steep (downhill) and the y-intercept is lower. But again, there is little change. See the plot on the right below.

  iii. Deleting the Mercedes-Benz C280 had more effect on both the slope and the y-intercept of the regression line.

INSTRUCTIONAL NOTE
The Compact Car data are available in *CPMP-Tools*. If you get the class together to use *CPMP-Tools* on this problem, students can learn how to delete points so they can explore Problems 3 and 4 on their own or in pairs. Students should record each regression equation as it appears in the information window so as to not lose track of this information.

INSTRUCTIONAL NOTE
From Problem 2, students should recognize that just because a point is away from other points in the plot, does not mean the point is an influential point. Neither the Mercedes-Benz C280 nor the Civic Hybrid strongly influence the regression equation. In Problems 3 and 4, students further examine this idea.

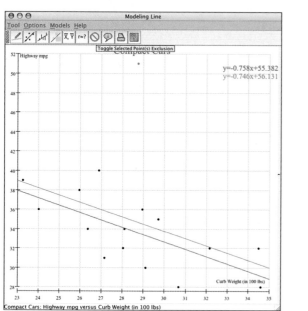

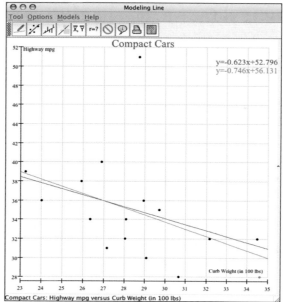

3 The data in the following table and scatterplot are from a larger set of data collected by a student for a science fair project. The student measured characteristics of a sample of horses because she wanted to see how various measurements were related to the length of the horse's stride.

Horse	Height (in hands)	Hip Angle While Running (in degrees)
Charm	16.1	47.7
Hugs	16.2	48.8
Otis	16.2	51.1
Cosmo	16.2	51.0
Gaspe	16.3	39.4
Sam	16.1	47.1
Pi	16.1	50.6
Binky	16.0	43.7
Bella	16.1	48.8
Prima	16.1	48.7
Bandit	16.0	44.8
Blackie	16.1	48.9

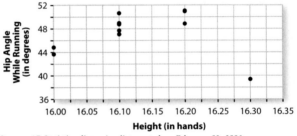

Source: AP Statistics discussion list, posted on February 03, 2006, www.mathforum.org/kb/forum.jspa?forumID=67

a. Which horse is the outlier?

b. What do you think will happen to the slope and intercept of the regression line if this horse is removed from the data set?

c. Do the computations needed to check your conjecture.

d. Is this horse influential?

3 **a.** Gaspe

b. The slope should increase a lot, and the *y*-intercept should decrease a lot.

c. The regression equation with Gaspe is
hip angle = −1.758*height* + 75.891.
Without Gaspe, the slope becomes positive and the intercept negative:
hip angle = 28.741*height* − 414.696.

d. Yes, Gaspe would be very influential in any real-life context for which you would want a regression equation.

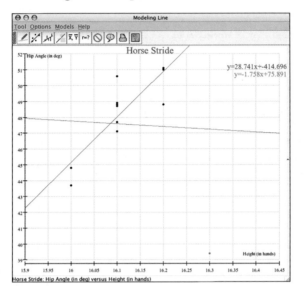

(4) The most famous scandal in baseball history occurred at the 1919 World Series. Eight players for the Chicago White Sox were accused of throwing the series to the Cincinnati Reds. The players were acquitted of criminal charges but banned from professional baseball for life.

The 1919 season and World Series batting averages for the nine White Sox players who had 10 or more at bats in the World Series are given in the following table and scatterplot. These include five of the accused players. The equation of the regression line for predicting the World Series batting average from the season batting average is $y = 1.99x - 0.36$.

Chicago White Sox

Player	Season Batting Average	World Series Batting Average	Accused? N=no/Y=yes
Eddie Collins	.319	.226	N
Shano Collins	.279	.250	N
Happy Felsch	.275	.192	Y
Chick Gandil	.290	.233	Y
Shoeless Joe Jackson	.351	.375	Y
Nemo Leibold	.302	.056	N
Swede Risberg	.256	.080	Y
Ray Schalk	.282	.304	N
Buck Weaver	.296	.324	Y

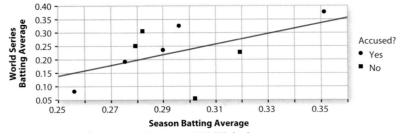

Source: www.baseball-reference.com/postseason/1919_WS.shtml

a. Which player did the worst in the World Series, compared to what would be predicted? Was he one of the accused players?

b. Do the accused players appear to have a different pattern than the players who were not accused?

c. Select the three players who you think might have influential points on the scatterplot. For each player, predict how the regression line would change if he were removed from the data set.

d. Remove one of the three players you identified in Part c, and recompute the equation. Put that player back, remove the second player, and recompute the equation. Put that player back, remove the third, and recompute the equation. Which player was most influential on the slope of the regression line?

Unit 4

④ **INSTRUCTIONAL NOTE** These data are in *CPMP-Tools*. For Part c, you may wish to decide as a class on the three players most out of the general pattern. Then, assign one player to each group of students and have the groups compare changes in the regression equation.

BACKGROUND INFORMATION According to the Chicago Historical Society, "The controversy surrounding the 1919 World Series is most confusing in regards to Shoeless Joe Jackson. The facts (the conspirators' recollections and Jackson's World Series statistics) indicate that Jackson had no involvement with the fix other than being aware that it was going on." On the other hand, according to Wikipedia, "he batted far worse in the five games that the White Sox lost, totaling only one RBI, from a home run in game 8 once the game was 5-0 for the Reds." (en.wikipedia.org/wiki/Shoeless_Joe_Jackson).

The Chicago Historical Society's Web site also explains how Shoeless Joe got his name: "Over the years, many stories circulated as to why he was tagged 'Shoeless' Joe. According to Jackson, it happened after he played ball wearing a new pair of shoes. They blistered his feet. The next day when the team was short on players, the manager told Jackson to play despite the blisters. Jackson tried his old shoes, but when those hurt, he played in his socks. In the seventh inning, Jackson hit a triple. The bleachers were close to the field, and as he ran for third base, a fan noticed his socks and yelled, 'You shoeless sonofagun you!' Shoeless never played in socks again, but the name stuck."

For more information, see www.chicagohs.org/history/blacksox.html and www.blackbetsy.com.

a. Nemo Leibold did the worst in the World Series compared to what was predicted, with a batting average of only .056 compared to a prediction of about .241. He was not one of the accused players.

b. The points of the accused players fall a little closer to the line. That is, they batted just about as predicted. (Could the accused players have planned this?)

c. The players whose points are most out of the general pattern and so may be the most influential are Shoeless Joe Jackson, Nemo Leibold, and Swede Risberg. If Shoeless Joe is removed, the line should flatten out quite a bit. If Nemo is removed, the line should be a bit higher, but keep about the same slope. If Swede is removed, the line should flatten out a bit. Students might select Buck Weaver or Ray Schalk since the residuals for those points are large. Even though these are not influential points, it is fine for students to investigate the effect of their deletion.

d. The equation of the regression line is $y = 1.99x - 0.36$. Without Shoeless Joe, the equation is $y = 1.09x - 0.105$. Although the y-intercept does not change too much, the slope is cut almost in half. Without Nemo, the equation is $y = 2.25x - 0.41$. Neither the slope nor the y-intercept changed very much. (However, the correlation does increase quite a bit. This is typical of a point that has an unusual value of y but has a value of x not far from the mean.) Without Swede, the equation is $y = 1.31x - 0.147$, which is a smaller change in the slope than when deleting Shoeless Joe. The point for Shoeless Joe is the most influential. See the three plots below. An influential point tends to pull the regression line towards it.

Without Shoeless Joe

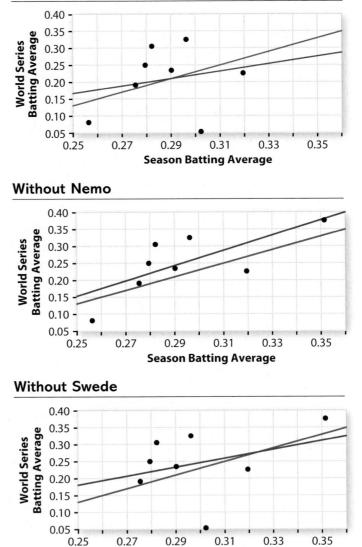

Without Nemo

Without Swede

e. If students did not select all of the players mentioned in Part d, they can investigate their effect at this point. Students should notice that the effect of removing Nemo (the point with the largest residual) was not as large as the effect of removing the players on the far left or far right.

f. **i.** There is little relationship between season batting average and World Series batting average for these players, and, in fact, the relationship is slightly negative. We would expect that if a player had a higher season batting average than a second player, he would tend to have a higher World Series batting average. That is not the case even for the players who were not accused, which seems quite strange.

    ii. If Shoeless Joe is removed from the data set, the slope of the regression line will be much more strongly negative.

g. Here is the case in favor of Shoeless Joe: Shoeless Joe hit quite well in the World Series. Comparing him to the players who were not accused, he hit much better than you would predict. His World Series batting average was .024 points higher in the World Series. According to the plot in Part f, only three non-accused players managed to have higher batting averages in the World Series than they did in regular season play. Further, according to the data in the student text, only one other accused player had a higher batting average in the World Series than he did in regular season play. In other words, Joe was well above the regression line's prediction in both cases.

Shoeless Joe Jackson

e. How is the effect of removing the point for Nemo Leibold different from the effect of removing either Shoeless Joe Jackson or Swede Risberg?

f. The scatterplot below shows all Cincinnati Reds players who had 10 or more at bats in the Series (none were accused) along with the four White Sox players who had 10 or more at bats and were not accused. It also includes Shoeless Joe Jackson who was accused (circular dot).

    i. Describe the relationship between *season batting average* and *World Series batting average* for these players. Is this about what you would expect?

    ii. How would the slope of the regression line change if the point for Shoeless Joe were removed from this data set?

Batting Averages

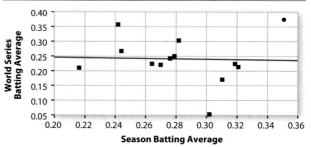

g. The Shoeless Joe Jackson Society is "devoted to the goal of seeing Joe claim his rightful place in the Baseball Hall of Fame." From the evidence that you have seen here, make a case for Shoeless Joe that the Society could use toward their goal.

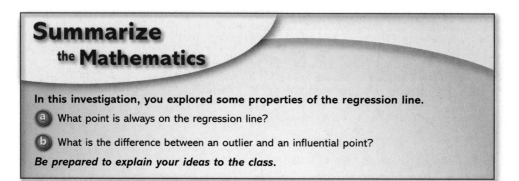

Summarize
the Mathematics

In this investigation, you explored some properties of the regression line.

a What point is always on the regression line?

b What is the difference between an outlier and an influential point?

Be prepared to explain your ideas to the class.

Summarize
the Mathematics

NOTE Solutions to Problem 4, Parts e–g are on page T289B.

ⓐ The least squares regression line passes through the centroid, $(\bar{x}, \bar{y})$.

ⓑ An outlier is a point that lies out of the pattern of the rest of the points. It can have an unusual value of x, an unusual value of y, an unusual value of both, or does not have an unusual value of either yet is separated from the rest of the points. An influential point is a special type of outlier. To find out if an outlier is an influential point, remove it from the set of data and see if the regression equation changes by an appreciable amount. If so, the outlier is an influential point.

✔ Check Your Understanding

a. The mean index of exposure is 4.61 and the mean cancer death rate is 157.4. When you substitute a value of x of 4.61 into the regression equation, you get $y = 9.27(4.61) + 114.68 = 157.41$, verifying, subject to round-off error, that the point $(4.61, 157.4)$ lies on the regression line.

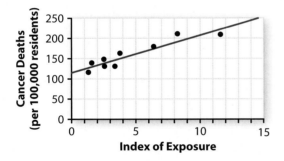

b. Portland is the only obvious potential influential point because it has an unusually large value of x. When Portland is removed, the regression equation becomes $y = 12.0x + 106$. The slope is more positive, but the y-intercept remains about the same. Overall, the line does not change much, showing that Portland is not very influential. Compare the plots.

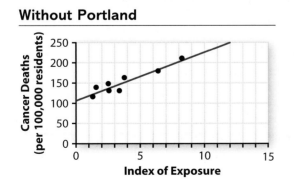

Without Portland

MATH TOOLKIT Explain the difference between an outlier and an influential point. Provide a sketch if it helps your explanation.

COLLABORATION PROMPT We collaborated using technology by … . We could improve our collaboration by … .

Unit 4

Karl Pearson

✔ Check Your Understanding

Refer to the Check Your Understanding on page 285 of the previous investigation.

a. Find the mean index of exposure and the mean cancer death rate. Then verify that the centroid is on the regression line.

b. Which community is a potential influential point? Remove this point, find the new regression line, and describe how the regression line changes.

Investigation 3 — How Strong Is the Association?

In previous investigations, you have learned how to describe the *shape* of a scatterplot and how to use the regression line as the *center* of an elliptical cloud of points. In this investigation, you will explore a way of describing the *strength* of an elliptical cloud of points by computing a correlation.

A formula for calculating a measure of linear association between pairs of values (x, y) that are ranked or unranked was developed by British statistician Karl Pearson (1857–1936). The resulting correlation, called Pearson's r, can be interpreted in the same way as Spearman's rank correlation, r_s. The correlation indicates the direction of the association between the two variables by whether it is positive or negative. It indicates the strength by whether it is near 1 or −1 versus near 0. For ranked data with no ties, Pearson's and Spearman's formulas give the same value.

As you work on the problems in this investigation, make notes of answers to this question:

How can you compute and interpret Pearson's correlation?

① Since Pearson's r can be used with either ranked or unranked data, you might expect the formula to be more complex than Spearman's formula. You would be right! The formula for Pearson's correlation r is

$$r = \frac{\Sigma(x - \bar{x})(y - \bar{y})}{(n - 1)s_x s_y}.$$

Here, $\bar{x}$ is the mean of the x values, $\bar{y}$ is the mean of the y values, s_x is the standard deviation of the x values, s_y is the standard deviation of the y values, and n is the number of data pairs.

a. Examine the formula. To use it, how would you proceed?

b. Now, examine the plot shown at the right. Which has the larger mean, the values of x or the values of y? Which has the larger standard deviation? What value of r would you expect for these points?

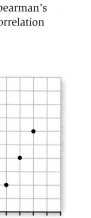

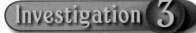

Investigation 3 How Strong Is the Association?

NOTE The solutions to Check Your Understanding are on page T290.

In this investigation, students:

- learn to use the formula for Pearson's correlation r and to find it using their calculators or computer software.
- learn that Pearson's formula can be used with ranked or unranked data, the new formula also results in numbers between 1 and −1, and it should be computed only when the data have a linear relationship—that is, the points form an elliptical cluster.
- examine why Pearson's formula works by recentering the origin at $(\bar{x}, \bar{y})$.
- explore the effect of influential points on a correlation and learn that the correlation may be 0 even if the points are very strongly associated (as with a quadratic relationship).
- learn that the size of the correlation is not an indication of whether a linear model is appropriate.

As with all summary statistics, students should get in the habit of looking at a plot of the data before computing the correlation. By the end of this lesson, students should recognize that:

- data that have a weak correlation can be linear.
- one influential point in data that are nonlinear can result in a value of r that is close to 1 or −1.
- nonlinear data can have a high correlation even with no influential points.
- data that otherwise have a strong linear relationship can have a small value of r because of one influential point.

1 **INSTRUCTIONAL NOTE** If your students need help using this formula, you may want to lead a class discussion. Begin by reviewing what each symbol represents. Students should have reviewed the standard deviation in Lesson 1, Review Task 22.

a. • First, compute the mean and standard deviation of the values of x and of y: $\bar{x}$, $\bar{y}$, s_x, and s_y.

- Subtract the mean $\bar{x}$ from each value of x and the mean $\bar{y}$ from each value of y, multiply the paired differences, and then add the products.

- Finally, divide the sum by $(n-1)s_x s_y$.

b. The values of y have both the larger mean and the larger standard deviation. The value of r should be 1 because the points all fall on a line with positive slope.

Teaching Resources

Student Master 20.

UNIT ❹ *Regression and Correlation* Name _____
Date _____

Pearson's Correlation Coefficient—Finding *r*
Problem 1

$$r = \frac{\sum(x-\bar{x})(y-\bar{y})}{(n-1)s_x s_y}$$

Compute: $\bar{x} = $ _____ $\bar{y} = $ _____

x	y	$x-\bar{x}$	$y-\bar{y}$	$(x-\bar{x})(y-\bar{y})$
1	2			
2	4			
3	6			

Sum (Σ)

Compute: $n-1 = $ _____ $s_x = $ _____ $s_y = $ _____

Calculate: $r = $ _____

20 UNIT 4 • Regression and Correlation   Student Master • Use with page 291–292

c. When using complex formulas, it is often helpful to organize intermediate calculations in a table.

   i. Compute $\bar{x}$ and $\bar{y}$. Then complete a copy of the table below.

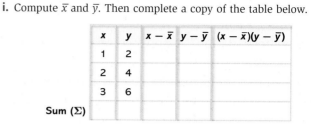

x	y	$x - \bar{x}$	$y - \bar{y}$	$(x - \bar{x})(y - \bar{y})$
1	2			
2	4			
3	6			
Sum (Σ)				

   ii. Compute $n - 1$, s_x and s_y.

   iii. Calculate r by substituting the appropriate sums in the formula. Compare the value you calculated with your prediction in Part b.

d. What value of r would you predict for the points on the scatterplot at the right? Check your prediction by computing the value of r and comparing it to your prediction.

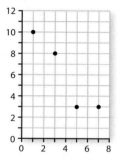

e. What value do you get for r if you reverse the coordinates of each point in Part d? Why does this make sense?

f. Create a set of six points that have correlation -1. Create a set of six points that have correlation close to 0.

(2) In this problem, you will explore how Pearson's formula works. Examine the formula for the correlation r.

$$r = \frac{\Sigma(x - \bar{x})(y - \bar{y})}{(n - 1)s_x s_y}$$

a. Recall that $(x - \bar{x})$ is called a *deviation from the mean*. What is $\Sigma(x - \bar{x})$? What is $\Sigma(y - \bar{y})$? Is this necessarily true of $\Sigma(x - \bar{x})(y - \bar{y})$? Explain.

b. As long as the values of x are not all the same and the values of y are not all the same, the denominator of the formula for r gives a positive number. Explain why this is true.

c. On the scatterplot at the right, horizontal and vertical lines are drawn through $(\bar{x}, \bar{y})$. For the points in region A:

   • Is $(x - \bar{x})$ positive or negative?

   • Is $(y - \bar{y})$ positive or negative?

   • Is $(x - \bar{x})(y - \bar{y})$ positive or negative?

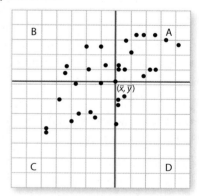

c. **i.** $\bar{x} = 2, \bar{y} = 4$

x	y	$x - \bar{x}$	$y - \bar{y}$	$(x - \bar{x})(y - \bar{y})$
1	2	−1	−2	2
2	4	0	0	0
3	6	1	2	2
Sum (Σ) 6	12	0	0	4

ii. $n - 1 = 2$; $s_x = 1$; $s_y = 2$

iii. $r = \dfrac{4}{2 \cdot 1 \cdot 2} = 1$; students should compare this value of r with their prediction in Part b.

d. For these points, $\bar{x} = 4$, $\bar{y} = 6$, $s_x \approx 2.58199$, $s_y \approx 3.55903$, and $n - 1 = 3$.

x	y	$x - \bar{x}$	$y - \bar{y}$	$(x - \bar{x})(y - \bar{y})$
1	10	−3	4	−12
3	8	−1	2	−2
5	3	1	−3	−3
7	3	3	−3	−9
Sum (Σ) 16	24	0	0	−26

$$r = \frac{-26}{3 \cdot 2.58199 \cdot 3.55903} \approx -0.943$$

e. You still get $r = -0.943$ because the formula is symmetric with respect to x and y; that is, if you reverse x and y in the formula, r does not change. Further, if you look at the graph of the transformed points, their relative positions have not changed.

f. Answers will vary. Points have a correlation of −1 when they lie on a line with negative slope. Students will not be able to use points on a horizontal line for an example of zero correlation because the correlation for points that lie on a horizontal line is undefined as you would be dividing by $s_y = 0$. (However, some calculators give a value of zero.)

2 **a.** $\Sigma(x - \bar{x}) = 0$ and $\Sigma(y - \bar{y}) = 0$. This is not necessarily the case with $\Sigma(x - \bar{x})(y - \bar{y})$ as seen in the computations in Problem 1 Parts c and d.

b. A standard deviation is always positive when not all values are equal. The sample size must be 2 or greater before computing a correlation makes sense and so $n - 1$ is also positive. So, the denominator of the formula for r is the product of 3 positive numbers, which is also positive.

c. For the points in region A, both x and y are larger than their means, so $(x - \bar{x})$ and $(y - \bar{y})$ are both positive. Thus, $(x - \bar{x})(y - \bar{y})$ is positive.

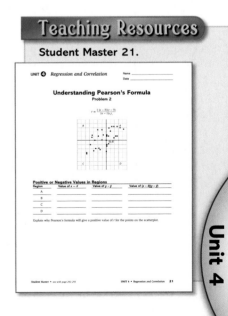

Teaching Resources

Student Master 21.

Unit 4

d. Fill in each space on a copy of the table below with "positive" or "negative."

Region	Value of $x - \bar{x}$	Value of $y - \bar{y}$	Value of $(x - \bar{x})(y - \bar{y})$
A			
B			
C			
D			

e. Explain why Pearson's formula will give a positive value of r for the points on the scatterplot in Part c.

f. Explain why Pearson's formula will give a negative value of r for the points on the scatterplot below.

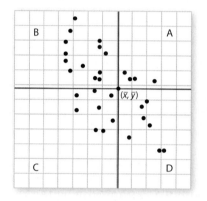

3 For most sets of real data, calculation by hand of Pearson's r is tedious and prone to error. Thus, it is important to know how to calculate r using your graphing calculator or data analysis software.

a. Refer to the scatterplot of arm span and kneeling height for the members of your class that you collected in the Think About This Situation for Lesson 2. Estimate the correlation.

b. Learn to use your calculator or data analysis software to find the value of r for these data and check your estimate in Part a.

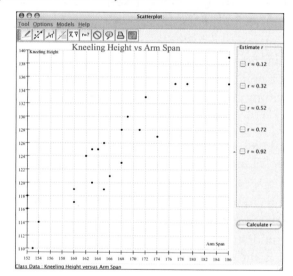

Unit 4

d.

Region	Value of $x - \bar{x}$	Value of $y - \bar{y}$	Value of $(x - \bar{x})(y - \bar{y})$
A	positive	positive	positive
B	negative	positive	negative
C	negative	negative	positive
D	positive	negative	negative

e. The points in regions A and C will contribute positive values to the sum in the numerator of the formula for r. The points in regions B and D will contribute negative values. There are more points in regions A and C than in B and D and the values of $(x - \bar{x})$ and $(y - \bar{y})$ tend to be larger in regions A and C. Thus, the sum in the numerator will be positive. Since the denominator is always positive, the value of r will be positive. Note that points close to $(\bar{x}, \bar{y})$ or to the lines $x = \bar{x}$ or $y = \bar{y}$ will contribute a smaller product than a point farther away.

f. The points in regions A and C will contribute positive values to the sum in the numerator of the formula for r. The points in regions B and D will contribute negative values. There are more points in regions B and D than in A and C and the values of $(x - \bar{x})$ and $(y - \bar{y})$ tend to be larger in regions B and D. Thus, the sum in the numerator will be negative. Since the denominator is always positive, the value of r will be negative.

3 **a.** Estimates will vary, but for most classes the correlation will be quite strong.

b. On many calculators, the value of r will appear when you compute the regression equation.

TECHNOLOGY NOTE On the TI-83/84, if r does not appear, go to **CATALOG**, scroll down to **DiagnosticOn** and hit **ENTER** twice.

4 Match each correlation with the appropriate plot. Then write a sentence that describes the association between the two variables in the plot.

a. $r = -0.4$

b. $r = 0.5$

c. $r = -0.8$

d. $r = 0.94$

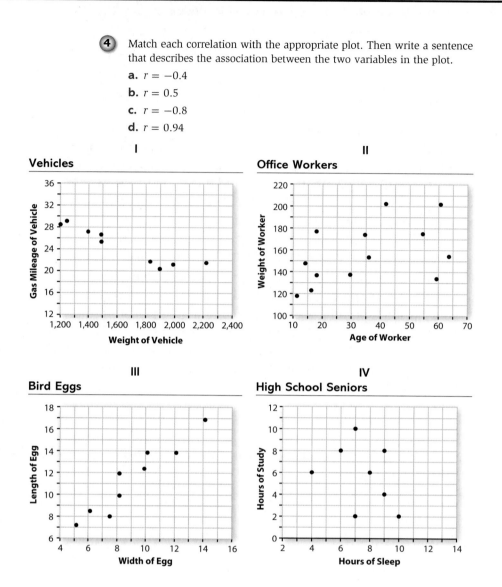

I

Vehicles

II

Office Workers

III

Bird Eggs

IV

High School Seniors

4 **a.** $r = -0.4$ matches **IV** (*hours of sleep, hours of study*)

There is a weak to moderate negative correlation between the number of hours seniors sleep and the number of hours they study. Students who sleep more tend to study less.

b. $r = 0.5$ matches **II** (*age of worker, weight of worker*)

There is a moderate positive correlation between the age and weight of the office workers. The older the office worker, the more he or she tends to weigh.

c. $r = -0.8$ matches **I** (*weight of vehicle, gas mileage of vehicle*)

Weight of vehicles has a strong negative correlation with gas mileage. The heavier the vehicle, the worse the gas mileage tends to be.

d. $r = 0.94$ matches **III** (*width of egg, length of egg*)

There is a very strong positive correlation between the width and length of bird eggs. The wider the egg, the longer it tends to be.

5 In this problem, you will explore the effect of a change of scale on the correlation, r. Shown below is nutritional information on fast-food hamburgers.

How Hamburgers Compare

Company	Burger	Calories	Fat (in grams)	Protein (in grams)	Sodium (in mg)
Hardee's	Hamburger	310	12	14	560
	Thickburger	850	57	30	1,470
Wendy's	Jr. Hamburger	280	9	15	590
	Classic Single	420	20	25	880
Burger King	Hamburger	290	12	15	560
	Whopper	670	39	28	1,020
McDonald's	Hamburger	260	9	13	530
	Quarter Pounder	420	18	24	730
	Big Mac	560	30	25	1,010
Carl's Jr.	Kid's Hamburger	520	18	25	1,040
	Famous Star	590	32	24	910

Source: www.wendys.com; www.mcdonalds.com; www.burgerking.com; www.hardees.com; www.carlsjr.com (December 2006).

A scatterplot matrix of these data is shown below.

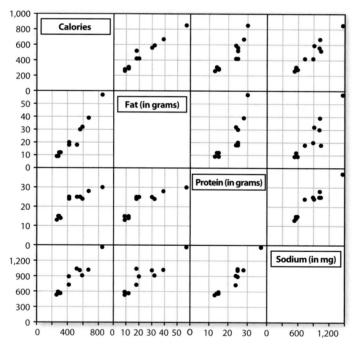

a. Find and interpret the correlation between sodium and calories. Why might this correlation be so strong?

a. The correlation is about 0.961. This is a very strong positive correlation. If one hamburger has more sodium than another, it also tends to have more calories and vice-versa. Further, if you know the number of grams of sodium in a hamburger, you can predict the number of calories quite precisely and vice-versa. This correlation might be so strong because both variables tend to increase with the size of the hamburger.

b. Transform the amounts of sodium by converting them to grams. (Recall there are 1,000 milligrams in a gram.) Find r for calories and the transformed values of sodium. What do you notice? Explain why your observation makes sense.

c. Now, transform the numbers of calories by subtracting 200 from each value. Find r for sodium and the transformed values of calories. What do you notice? Explain why your observation makes sense.

 As with the regression equation, you can tell if an outlier is influential on the correlation by temporarily removing it from the data set and seeing how much the correlation changes.

a. Which hamburger is an outlier in the (*sodium, calories*) data set? Is this outlier an influential point with respect to the correlation? With respect to the slope of the regression line?

b. For each of the plots below, identify the outlier. Indicate whether removing the point will make the correlation stronger, weaker, or unchanged.

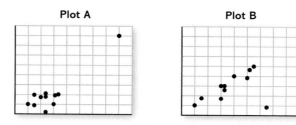

 Belinda conjectured that "a high correlation between two variables means that the variables are linearly related."

a. Use your calculator to find the correlation for the following points. From your calculated value, would you expect the scatterplot to have a linear pattern?

x	0	8	1	7	3	6	5	4	2	−2	−1
y	0	65	2	50	8	35	25	15	4	3	1

b. Produce the scatterplot on your calculator. Are the points linear? How would you respond to Belinda?

c. How well does $y = 0.97x^2 + 0.2x + 0.5$ model the pattern in the points?

d. Create a set of points that has a parabolic shape, but the correlation is 0.

b. To convert to grams, divide each value by 1,000. The correlation remains the same, about 0.961. This transformation shrinks the sodium values but does not change the relationship between the points. (It is difficult to see from the formula, but the decrease in the deviations from the mean is exactly offset by the decrease in the standard deviation.)

c. The correlation remains the same, about 0.961. If you subtract 200 from each number of calories, it does not change the deviations from the mean or the standard deviation. On the scatterplot, the relationship between the points remains the same after a slide 200 units to the left.

6 **a.** The Thickburger is an outlier in both sodium and calories. If you remove this point, the correlation changes from 0.961 to 0.928, which is a relatively small change. The slope of the regression line changes from 0.626 to 0.644, also a small change. The Thickburger is not greatly influential because it lies along the same pattern as the rest of the points and is not all that far from them.

b. Plot A: The outlier is the point in the upper right-hand corner of the plot. If it is removed, the correlation will drop close to 0, making the correlation weaker.

Plot B: The outlier is the point in the lower right-hand corner. If it is removed, the correlation will become stronger.

7 **a.** The correlation is about 0.904. It is likely that most students will say that such a high correlation must indicate that the points are linear.

b. The plot at the right shows that the points are not linear. They follow a distinct curve, which appears to be quadratic. Belinda should be asked to look at the plot of these data to help recognize that a high correlation does not imply linearly-related variables.

c. It fits very well. All of these points fall near the graph of $y = 0.97x^2 + 0.2x + 0.5$.

d. For example, these points all lie on the graph of $y = x^2$, with $r = 0$: $(-3, 9)$, $(-2, 4)$, $(-1, 1)$, $(0, 0)$, $(1, 1)$, $(2, 4)$, and $(3, 9)$.

8 **a.** The correlation is approximately 0.5, only moderate.

b. No, a linear model is a good one for these data. Although the points do not cluster closely about a line, the cloud of points is elliptical and so the data follow a linear trend. Even though there would be a lot of error in predicting the son's height from that of the father, it is appropriate to compute a regression equation and Pearson's r.

TECHNOLOGY NOTE
In *CPMP-Tools*, copy and paste commands (in the Edit menu) can be used to copy data from the "Hamburger Nutrition" spreadsheet to a new "Data Sheet 1." Usual spreadsheet commands can be used to convert these data from milligrams to grams.

INSTRUCTIONAL NOTE
In Problems 6, 7, and 8, students find that the value of r should be interpreted cautiously. They see that data can have a high correlation even though they are not linear; they also see that a single point can have a large influence on the correlation and regression equation.

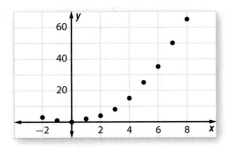

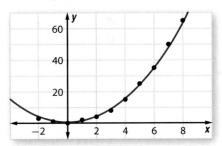

8 The scatterplot below shows the heights of 1,078 fathers and their sons. Karl Pearson collected the data around the year 1900.

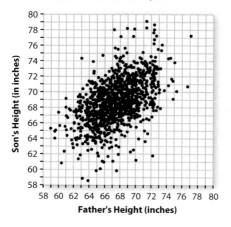

a. Make an estimate of the correlation. Would you say this is a strong correlation?

b. Does this correlation mean that a linear model is not appropriate for these data? Explain your reasoning.

9 Write a summary of what you can conclude from Problems 7 and 8. Compare your conclusions with that of others and resolve any differences.

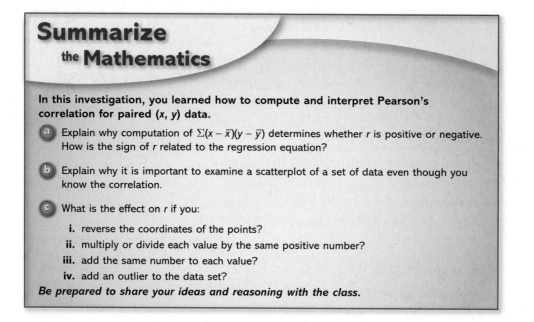

Summarize
the Mathematics

In this investigation, you learned how to compute and interpret Pearson's correlation for paired (x, y) data.

a Explain why computation of $\Sigma(x - \bar{x})(y - \bar{y})$ determines whether r is positive or negative. How is the sign of r related to the regression equation?

b Explain why it is important to examine a scatterplot of a set of data even though you know the correlation.

c What is the effect on r if you:
   i. reverse the coordinates of the points?
   ii. multiply or divide each value by the same positive number?
   iii. add the same number to each value?
   iv. add an outlier to the data set?

Be prepared to share your ideas and reasoning with the class.

9 In Problems 7 and 8, students learned that the strength of the correlation is no indication of whether a linear model is appropriate. A high correlation does not necessarily mean a linear equation is the best type of equation to model the data. As seen in Parts a and b of Problem 7, a strong correlation does not necessarily mean that the points form a cluster of points that is linear in shape (an elliptical cloud). Although these points cluster somewhat closely to a line, there is a pronounced curve that indicates a nonlinear equation would be more appropriate than a linear equation. When points follow a curved pattern, a measure of linear association, like Pearson's r, is not appropriate. Part d of Problem 7 shows that you should not say that just because the correlation is 0 or near 0 that there is no association. You should say that there is no *linear* association because there may be nonlinear association. The scatterplot in Problem 8 shows that data can be linear even though the correlation is not high. For these data, regression and correlation are appropriate summaries. The moral is that it always pays to look at the plot before deciding what summary statistics are appropriate and how to interpret them.

NOTE The solution to Problem 8 is on page T296.

Summarize
the Mathematics

a Because the other parts of the formula for r are always positive, the sign of r is determined by $\Sigma(x - \bar{x})(y - \bar{y})$. Computing $\Sigma(x - \bar{x})(y - \bar{y})$ is like moving the axes so the origin is at $(\bar{x}, \bar{y})$. If a point is in the upper-right or lower-left quadrant, $(x - \bar{x})(y - \bar{y})$ has a positive sign. If a point is in the other two quadrants, $(x - \bar{x})(y - \bar{y})$ has a negative sign. Thus, the sign of r depends on whether the sum of the positive products or the sum of the negative products is larger in absolute value. The sign of r is the same as the sign of the slope in the regression equation. Further, if $r = 0$, then the slope of the regression line is 0. (In the special case where all points lie on a horizontal line, r is undefined because $s_y = 0$, but the slope is 0.)

b Scatterplots should be examined to be sure the points are linear. You should compute a regression equation and Pearson's r only for linear (elliptical) data. A high correlation does not necessarily mean that the data follow a linear pattern. A low correlation does not necessarily mean the basic model is not linear. You also need to look at a scatterplot to make sure an influential point is not affecting the correlation.

c **i.** Reversing x and y has no effect on the correlation.
  ii. Multiplying or dividing each value by the same positive number has no effect on the correlation.
  iii. Adding the same number to each value has no effect on the correlation.
  iv. The answer depends on where the outlier is placed. It can increase (as in Plot A of Problem 6) or decrease the correlation significantly (as in Plot B of Problem 6), or it can have very little effect on the correlation (which would be the case for the outliers in the upper right of the scatterplot in Problem 8. There are so many points here that removing one would not have much effect.).

✓ Check Your Understanding

The table and scatterplot below give the marriage rates and divorce rates for the countries listed in the *Statistical Abstract of the United States*. Marriage and divorce rates are the number per 1,000 people aged 15–64.

Country	Marriage Rate	Divorce Rate
United States	11.7	6
Canada	6.8	3.3
Japan	8.8	3.4
Denmark	10.4	4.3
France	7.2	3.3
Germany	7.1	3.7
Ireland	7.6	1
Italy	6.9	1.1
Netherlands	7.7	3
Spain	7.4	1.5
Sweden	6.6	3.7
United Kingdom	7.3	4.1

Source: *Statistical Abstract of the United States*, 2006, Table 1320.

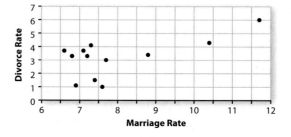

a. Estimate the correlation, and then compute the regression equation and correlation for (*marriage rate, divorce rate*).

b. Interpret the slope of the regression line in the context of this situation.

c. Which country appears to be an influential point? How will the regression equation and correlation change if this country is removed from this data set?

d. Remove this country, and recompute the correlation and regression equation. How influential is this country?

e. Convert the marriage and divorce rates for the United States to the rates per 1,000,000 people. If you do this for all countries and then recompute the regression equation and correlation, will they change?

✓ Check Your Understanding

a. The correlation is $r = 0.623$ and the regression equation is *divorce rate* $= 0.567$*marriage rate* $- 1.316$.

b. The slope of 0.567 means that if one country has 1 more marriage per 1,000 people than another country, we predict that there will be 0.567 more divorces per 1,000 people.

c. The United States appears to be an influential point because it has a relatively high divorce rate given its marriage rate. It is far away from the nearest point, representing Denmark. If it is removed from this data set, the slope of the regression line should be closer to 0 and the correlation should drop.

d. With the United States removed, the regression equation becomes *divorce rate* $= 0.336$*marriage rate* $+ 0.383$, which is a large change in the slope. The correlation drops to 0.310. The United States is quite influential. If the U.S. and Denmark were not included in the set of countries, there would be no relationship between marriage and divorce rates.

e. The new table is given below.

Country	Marriage Rate per Million	Divorce Rate per Million
United States	11,700	6,000
Canada	6,800	3,300
Japan	8,800	3,400
Denmark	10,400	4,300
France	7,200	3,300
Germany	7,100	3,700
Ireland	7,600	1,000
Italy	6,900	1,100
Netherlands	7,700	3,000
Spain	7,400	1,500
Sweden	6,600	3,700
United Kingdom	7,300	4,100

The correlation remains the same as does the slope of the regression equation. However, the y-intercept of the regression equation becomes $-1,316$ because it will be multiplied by the same amount, 1,000, as are the rates.

TECHNOLOGY NOTE
These data are in *CPMP-Tools*.

Association and Causation

Reports in the media often suggest that research has found a cause-and-effect relationship between two variables. For example, a newspaper article listed several "weird" things that are associated with whether or not a student graduates from college. The following excerpt is about one of them.

Five Weird Ways to College Success

Don't smoke.

[Alexander] Astin and [Leticia] Oseguera [of UCLA] examined the graduation rates of 56,818 students at 262 colleges, a huge sample, and reported that smoking had one of the largest negative associations with degree completion.

Source: Jay Mathews, *The Washington Post*, June 13, 2006, www.washingtonpost.com/wp-dyn/content/article/2006/06/13/AR2006061300628.html

As you work on the problems in this investigation, look for answers to the following question:

> *When you have an association between two variables, how can you determine if the association is a result of a cause-and-effect relationship?*

1 The 12 countries listed below have the highest per person ice cream consumption of any countries in the world. As shown in the following table and scatterplot, there is an association between the number of recorded crimes and ice cream consumption.

Country	Ice Cream Consumption per Person (in liters) per Year	Recorded Crimes per 100,000 Inhabitants per Year
New Zealand	26.3	12,591
United States	22.5	9,622
Canada	17.8	8,705
Australia	17.8	6,161
Switzerland	14.4	4,769
Sweden	14.2	13,516
Finland	13.9	7,273
Denmark	9.2	1,051
Italy	8.2	4,243
France	5.4	6,765
Germany	3.8	8,025
China	1.8	131

Unit 4

Investigation 4 ▸ Association and Causation

In this investigation, students learn that a strong correlation does not necessarily mean that one variable causes the other in the sense that if you change the value of the first variable, it causes a change in the value of the second variable. Data on ice cream consumption and recorded crimes in 12 countries of the world is used as an example to show that two variables may have a strong correlation without there being any reason to suspect that when one variable changes, it "causes" a change in the other variable. Students practice hypothesizing lurking variables that might, instead, explain the association.

For many problems in this investigation and the On Your Own tasks, students are asked to consider possible lurking variables. There is no "right" answer for some of the situations. How much insight students are able to show will depend on their general knowledge of the world. Ask students to back up their opinions with evidence, which should not be merely anecdotal—"My uncle never went to college, and he earns a lot of money." This type of statement reveals a misunderstanding of what it means for two variables to be associated.

(1) **INSTRUCTIONAL NOTE** You may want to point out to your students that they should not take inferences from small data sets too far. The conclusions they will be tempted to draw may not be correct for all countries in the world. In fact, this data set was constructed by "data snooping." The author tried many variables until she found one that is positively correlated with ice cream consumption (at least for the 12 countries with highest per capita ice cream consumption).

Teachers have begun this investigation by telling their students that they would like to give them ice cream but cannot because it will make them criminals. When the students say, "huh?" the teacher tells them they will see the statistical "evidence" in this investigation.

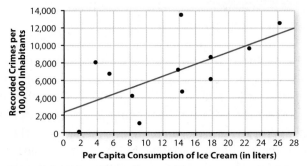

Per Capita Consumption of Ice Cream (in liters)

Source: United Nations Office on Drugs and Crime www.unodc.org/unodc/
crime_cicp_surveys.html and www.foodsci.uoguelph.ca/dairyedu/icdata.html.
Their source: *The Latest Scoop*, 2000 Edition, Int. Dairy Foods Assn.

a. For the data above, the regression line is $y = 343x + 2,500$, and the correlation is 0.637. Interpret the slope of the regression line in the context of this situation.

b. Do these data imply that if a country wants to decrease the crime rate, it should ask people to eat less ice cream? Explain your reasoning.

c. The following scatterplot shows the variables reversed on the axes. The regression equation is now $y = 0.00118x + 4.77$. Interpret the slope of this regression line. Can you now say that if the crime rate increases, then people will eat more ice cream?

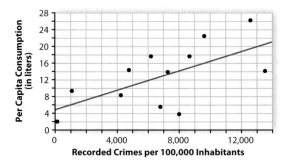

Recorded Crimes per 100,000 Inhabitants

d. A **lurking variable** is a variable that lurks in the background and affects *both* of the original variables. What are some possible lurking variables that might explain this association between crime rate and consumption of ice cream?

There are several reasons why two variables may be correlated:

- The two variables, *A* and *B*, have a **cause-and-effect relationship**. That is, an increase in the value of *A*, called the **explanatory** (or **independent**) **variable**, tends to cause an increase (or decrease) in the value of *B* called the **response** (or **dependent**) **variable**.

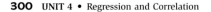

$A \bullet\!\longrightarrow\!\bullet B$

Unit 4

a. If one country has an average per capita consumption of ice cream that is one liter more than another country's consumption, it tends to have 343 more recorded crimes per 100,000 inhabitants.

b. No, asking people to eat less ice cream should have no effect on the crime rate.

c. If one country has 1 more recorded crime per 100,000 inhabitants than another country, then the people tend to eat 0.00118 more liters of ice cream per capita. No, you still cannot conclude that there is any cause-and-effect.

d. Students may suggest that the lurking variable may be the temperature in the country. In places where it is warmer, people may be outside more and so there tends to be both more ice cream consumption and more crime. They may also suggest that the association may be explained by how prosperous the country is. If people are prosperous, they may eat more ice cream and they may be more likely to insist that crimes be recorded. (That is, it is not that there is more crime in these countries, it is that more crimes are recorded.)

- The two variables, *A* and *B*, have nothing directly to do with each other. However, an increase in the value of a lurking variable *C* tends to cause the values of each of the two variables to increase together, to decrease together, or one to increase and the other to decrease.

- Even though the correlation between the two variables is actually zero or close to zero in the entire population, you get a nonzero correlation just by chance when you have a small number of observations.

$$A \bullet \qquad \bullet B$$

2 The association for each pair of variables below is strong. Decide which of the three reasons above best explains the association. Then, where appropriate, draw a directed graph to indicate the relationship between the two variables.

 a. Number of hours of studying each week and GPA

 b. Reading ability of a child and his or her shoe size

 c. Value of a car and its age

 d. Degree of baldness of a man and probability of a heart attack in the next year

 e. The median household income in the U.S. and skin cancer rate over the years

 f. Number of people attending a movie and income from ticket sales

 g. Number of letters in first name and age for a group of three adult women

3 Suppose you ask everyone in your community who has a phone for the number of letters in his or her last name and for the sum of the last four digits of his or her phone number.

 a. Should there be positive association, negative association, or no association? Why?

 b. Collect the information above from five members of your class or from a local telephone book, and compute the correlation *r* between *number of letters in last name* and *sum of last four digits of phone number*.

 c. Did you get the correlation that you predicted in Part a? Explain why this should or should not be the case.

4 Look back at the article excerpt from the *Washington Post* on page 299.

 a. What variables are said to be associated in the article? Which is considered the explanatory variable and which is the response variable?

 b. What are some possible reasons for the association that are not mentioned in the article?

2 **INSTRUCTIONAL NOTE** You probably will need to remind students that to be a lurking variable, a change in the lurking variable must cause a change in both of the other variables and not in just one of them.

a. Cause-and-effect: As the number of hours of studying increases, the GPA is likely to increase.

Number of Hours Studying •———►• GPA

(Not all studies show a positive correlation between GPA and number of hours of studying. Better students have to study less than weaker students. In a school of heterogenous students, then, you do not get a positive correlation.)

b. Lurking variable of the child's age: A child's reading ability and shoe size both increase with age.

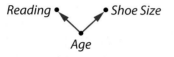

c. Cause-and-effect: As a car gets older, people are not willing to pay so much for it as they would for a newer car, even one with the same number of miles on it.

Age •———►• Value

d. Lurking variable of the man's age: As men get older, they usually lose some hair and their probability of a heart attack increases.

e. Lurking variable of time: Over time, inflation has caused most monetary values, such as median income, to go up, and environmental changes have caused increases in various diseases, such as skin cancer.

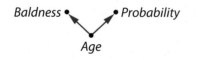

An alternative explanation might be that the increase in the median income has meant that people take more vacations (particularly to sunny climates), which in turn cause more skin cancer.

Other intermediate causes may include an increase in playing outdoor sports or using tanning booths.)

f. Cause-and-effect: Every additional person who attends a movie contributes to the income from ticket sales.

Number of People •———►• Income

g. Just by chance: Any relationship is purely coincidental.

Number of Letters in First Name •   • Age

(3) **INSTRUCTIONAL NOTE** This problem is an introduction to the principle of statistical inference that you do not always get a good estimate of the population value when the sample size is small. In this case, the correlation in the population is 0, but a sample of size 5 can give a value quite different from that.

Some teachers collect the data for Part b by having students use five last names and phone numbers stored in their cell phones. If there may be a student in your class who does not have a phone number, bring in a phone book and randomly select five names and corresponding numbers from it.

a. There should be no association because phone numbers usually are assigned at random, without any regard to the number of letters in the person's last name.

b. Students probably will get a correlation that is moderate or weak, but not exactly 0.

c. The correlation probably will be farther from 0 than students expected. Even though the correlation in the entire population between *number of letters in last name* and *sum of last four digits of phone number* is probably 0, it is unlikely to get a correlation of exactly 0, or even very close to 0, in such a small sample of people.

(4) **INSTRUCTIONAL NOTE** In this problem, students see two examples of a correlation that was found in an observational study. Unfortunately, there is no way to tell from an observational study if A causes B, if B causes A, if the correlation is due to a lurking variable, or, if the sample is small, the correlation is nonzero just by chance.

When discussing cause-and-effect, do not let students use anecdotal evidence. Remind them that they are looking for a general trend, not at just one case which may or may not closely follow the general trend of the other cases.

a. The researchers found an association between smoking/not smoking and graduating/not graduating from college. Smoking or not is considered the explanatory variable and graduating from college or not is the response variable. (These variables are not quantitative, so you could not compute a correlation.)

b. The lurking variable here may be the amount of partying (or maybe drinking) that the student does. Students who party are likely to smoke more and do not put the same amount of time into studying that other students are able to do. Another possibility is that students who smoke have other bad habits that affect their grades, such as not sleeping enough.

Teacher Notes

c. Answer the questions in Parts a and b for the following *Los Angeles Times* article.

> ### Tall Men Display Greater Risk of Skin Disease
>
> A poll conducted by University of Washington researchers in Seattle found that men taller than 6 feet, 1 inch had almost $2\frac{1}{2}$ times the risk of developing melanoma, an often fatal form of skin cancer, as those who were shorter than 5-foot-8.

Source: *Los Angeles Times*, January 14, 2002, page S2.

5 In the following study, the researchers tried to "control" for lurking variables by taking them into account.

> ### Mind Games May Keep the Brain Sharp
>
> An absorbing book or a challenging crossword puzzle may keep your mind more than busy. It may keep it healthy, too, according to a 21-year study of mental breakdown in old age. ...
>
> In the Einstein College study of 469 elderly people, those in the top third in mental activity had a 63 percent lower risk of dementia than the bottom third. Taking part in a single activity one day a week reduced the risk by 7 percent.
>
> The use-it-or-lose-it notion is not a new idea. Other researchers have discovered evidence that mental activity may guard against dementia. But it is hard to prove since early dementia without obvious symptoms may cause people to slack off their hobbies. If this is so, dementia affects hobbies—and maybe not the reverse.
>
> The researchers tried to minimize that possibility by considering only those who were dementia-free for seven years after joining the study. They also tried to eliminate the potential role of education and intelligence in guarding against dementia.
>
> The study also took physical exercise into account. Nearly all physical activities, including stair climbing and group exercises, appeared to offer no protection against dementia. The only exception was frequent dancing, perhaps because dance music engages the dancer's mind, suggested lead researcher Joe Verghese, a neurologist at Einstein College.

Source: www.cnn.com/2003/HEALTH/conditions/06/19/avoiding.dementia.ap/index.html

a. Identify the explanatory and response variables.

b. Name the lurking variables that the researchers considered.

c. Describe how the lurking variables might be taken into consideration.

d. Give at least one other possible lurking variable that is not mentioned.

c. • The researchers found a positive correlation between a man's height and his probability of getting melanoma. Height is considered the explanatory variable and getting melanoma or not is the response variable.

   • Taller men have more skin, so the amount of skin may be the lurking variable. It is also possible that taller men played more sports where they spent time in the sun.

5 a. The explanatory variable is amount of mental activity such as working crossword puzzles or reading and the response variable is whether the person got dementia or not. (However, the author realizes that it could also be the other way around: early symptoms of dementia can cause a person to stop doing mental activities.)

  b. The lurking variables considered were physical exercise, education, and intelligence.

  c. To eliminate the possibility that early symptoms of dementia cause a person to stop doing mental activities, they considered only people who had no symptoms of dementia for at least seven years after joining the study. To eliminate the potential role of physical exercise, education, and intelligence, they would divide the people up into groups with similar physical exercise, education, and intelligence and see if there was an association between mental activity and dementia within each group.

  d. One possible lurking variable not mentioned is income level. People with lower incomes may not have the money for books or newspapers or going dancing and may be prone to dementia for some reason related to poverty such as poor nutrition. Another possible lurking variable is crowded living conditions. When living conditions are crowded, a person may not have the opportunity to read or do other activities that require concentration and crowded living conditions might contribute to dementia for reasons such as exposure to more sickness.

6 By now, you may be wondering how anyone could ever know whether an association means that one variable causes the other or whether there is a lurking variable that causes both. The only way to find out for sure is to conduct an **experiment**. In an experiment, volunteer subjects are **randomly assigned** to two or more different **treatments**.

For example, suppose you want to decide if a cup of tea causes reduction in pain from a tension headache. You cannot just give a cup of tea to people with a tension headache and see if it goes away because some headaches go away over time without any treatment at all. So, you randomly divide your group of volunteers into those who get a cup of tea and those who get a cup of hot water. By randomizing, you hope to balance the people whose headaches go away quickly without any treatment at all between the two treatment groups. So if the headaches of those with tea tend to go away more quickly, you will know that it is the tea that caused it, not just sitting awhile to have a drink or not just the extra hot liquid.

a. For the study "Mind Games May Keep the Brain Sharp" from Problem 5, describe how you could conduct an experiment to decide whether one variable actually causes the other.

b. For each of these studies, explain why it is impossible to do an experiment to determine cause-and-effect.

   i. "Five Weird Ways to College Success" from page 299

   ii. "Tall Men Display Greater Risk of Skin Disease" from Problem 4 Part c

Summarize the Mathematics

In this investigation, you learned how to distinguish between correlation and cause-and-effect in situations that involved an association between two variables.

a Describe a situation involving two variables for which the correlation is strong, but there is no cause-and-effect relationship.

b Describe a situation involving two variables for which the correlation is strong and where a change in one variable causes a change in the other variable.

c Explain what is meant by the often-repeated statement, "Correlation does not imply causation."

d When you make a scatterplot, on which axis should you put the explanatory variable?

e How can you be certain whether an association means that there is a cause-and-effect relationship between two variables?

Be prepared to share your ideas and examples with the class.

(6) **INSTRUCTIONAL NOTE** There is only one tried-and-true way to tell whether a nonzero correlation means that there is a cause-and-effect relationship between two variables: run an experiment. Such an experiment should compare two or more treatments and be randomized. "Compare two or more treatments" means that, for example, to determine if tutoring increases SAT scores, there should be a group that gets tutoring and a control group that does not. "Randomized" means that whether a person goes into the tutored group or the control group is determined by chance.

The purpose of randomizing the treatments to the subjects is to balance the treatment groups so that they look as much alike as possible, except for which treatment they get. (In Course 3 Unit 1, *Reasoning and Proof*, students learn about these types of experiments and how to analyze them.)

a. You could take a group of volunteers, aged 65, and randomly divide them into a "mental activity" group and a "no mental activity group." After 15 years, you would assess what proportion of each group had dementia. It would be very difficult to be sure the volunteers stuck to their treatment. Further, it probably would be impossible to design such an experiment in an ethical manner.

b. i. You cannot randomly assign the treatments of smoking or not smoking to college students. It would be unethical to ask people to smoke. And, again, it would be very difficult to be sure the volunteers stuck to their treatment.

ii. There is no way to randomly assign the treatments "tall" or "not tall" to a group of men.

Summarize
the Mathematics

a For example, two highly correlated variables for which there is no cause-and-effect relationship are the two test averages in two different courses for each student who is taking both courses. (The lurking variables are the student's ability and study habits.)

b Examples of a cause-and-effect relationship are the number of years of schooling and salary for each worker in the U.S. and the number of people in a household and the amount of money spent on food for each household in the U.S.

c Two variables can be highly correlated even though if you change the value of one, it would not trigger a change in the value of the other.

d When a scatterplot is made, the explanatory variable should go on the horizontal or *x*-axis.

e The only way to be certain is to conduct a randomized experiment where the subjects are randomly assigned to the different treatments to be compared.

Unit 4

✓ Check Your Understanding

The following study compared state voter turnout rate to 12 social, economic, and government policy indicators.

> **Voter Turnout Correlates to Quality of Life**
>
> A new study suggests that your vote may count after all, even if every candidate you favor goes down to defeat on Election Day.
>
> A study by the Durham-based Institute for Southern Studies reveals that states with the highest rates of voter turnout also have higher rates of employment and a smaller gap in incomes between the rich and poor.
>
> "Very clearly, it pays to vote," said study author Bob Hall. "There's more reasons to vote than you may think. It may actually influence the quality of life in a broad way."

Source: *The Charlotte Observer*, October 29, 1996.

a. What are the explanatory and response variables implied by this article?

b. Do you think it could just as well be the other way around? Explain.

c. The article goes on to say that some people believe this study may not have considered enough of the variables that determine whether voters go to the polls. What are some possible lurking variables in this situation?

d. Describe an experiment that would determine if higher voter turnout improves the quality of life.

✓Check Your Understanding

a. The explanatory variable is voter turnout in a state and the response variables are employment rate and gap in income between rich and poor.

b. It could well be the other way around. In a state with a low unemployment rate and a small gap in income between rich and poor, the people may be more likely to vote and otherwise engage in civic affairs.

c. One possible lurking variable is how good a government the state has. A good state government may help reduce the unemployment rate and decrease the gap in income between rich and poor and may also encourage people to go out and vote. Another possible lurking variable is the age of people in the state. Older people are more likely to vote and are more likely to be employed than younger people. A third possible lurking variable is how good the educational system is in the state. More highly educated people are more likely to vote and are more likely to be employed.

d. You would have to randomly divide the states into two groups. In one group of states, you would work directly on increasing the voter turnout. The other group should be left as a control. The experiment must be prolonged over several years, perhaps decades, to give any economic changes the opportunity to occur. After waiting, you would see if the unemployment rates were down and the gap between rich and poor had narrowed in states with higher voter turnout, compared to the control group of states. Of course, this experiment is unrealistic, expensive, and possibly unconstitutional.

Applications

1. The following table and *plot over time* (years in this case) give the hippopotamus population on the Luangwa River in Zambia for various years between 1970 and 1984.

Year	Number of Hippos
1970	2,815
1972	2,919
1975	2,342
1976	4,501
1977	5,147
1978	4,765
1979	5,151
1981	4,884
1982	6,293
1983	6,544

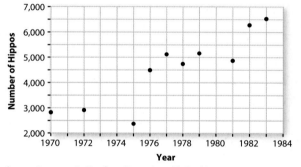

Source: Lawrence C. Hamilton, *Regression with Graphics*, page 179.

   a. Find the equation of the regression line and graph it on a copy of the scatterplot.

   b. What is the slope of the regression line? Interpret this slope in the context of these data.

   c. For which year is the residual largest in absolute value? Estimate this residual using the scatterplot. Then find the value of this residual using the regression equation. Finally, interpret this residual.

   d. Use the regression equation to predict the hippopotamus population for the current year. How much faith do you have in this prediction?

LESSON 2 • Least Squares Regression and Correlation **305**

On Your Own

Applications

1 **a.** The equation of the regression line is $y = 301.3x - 591,231$.

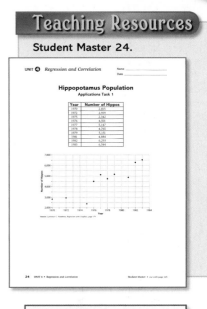

Teaching Resources

Student Master 24.

b. The slope is 301.3. This means that there tended to be an increase of 301.3 hippos per year between 1970 and 1983.

c. The residual is largest in absolute value for 1975. A good estimate of the residual from the scatterplot is about $2,300 - 3,800 = -1,500$. Using the equation, the residual is $2,342 - (301.3 \cdot 1975 - 591,231) \approx -1,495$. This means that there were 1,495 fewer hippos in 1975 than would be predicted by the regression line.

d. Substitute the current year for x into the equation $y = 301.3x - 591,231$. You would have very little faith in this prediction because the current year is so far after the years used to compute the regression equation and conditions have likely changed. In fact, since these data were collected, conservation projects have been put into effect. Further, there will be a limit to how large the hippo population can grow along this river.

TECHNOLOGY NOTE
These data are in
CPMP-Tools.

2 The age of a tree can often be determined by counting its rings. However, in tropical forests, annual tree rings do not always exist. Researchers measured the diameter of 20 large trees from a central Amazon rain forest and found their ages using carbon-14 dating. The results appear in the following table and scatterplot. The regression equation for predicting the age of a tree from its diameter is $y = 4.39x - 19$.

Diameter (in cm)	Age (in years)	Diameter (in cm)	Age (in years)
180	1,372	115	512
120	1,167	140	512
100	895	180	455
225	842	112	352
140	722	100	352
142	657	118	249
139	582	82	249
150	562	130	227
110	562	97	227
150	552	110	172

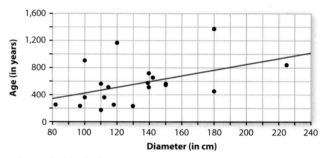

Source: *Statistics for the Life Sciences, 3rd Ed.*, Myra L. Samuels and Jeffrey A. Witmer, pages 575–576, 2003. Their source: Jeffrey Q. Chambers, Niro Higuchi & Joshua P. Schimel. Ancient trees in Amazonia, *Nature, 391* (1998) 135–136.

a. Interpret the slope of the regression line in the context of these data.

b. Use the regression equation to predict the age of a tree that is 125 cm in diameter.

c. For which tree diameter is the residual largest? Estimate the value of this residual from the scatterplot. Then find the value of this residual using the regression equation. Finally, interpret this residual.

d. Does it appear that the age of a tree can reasonably be predicted from measuring its diameter?

Unit 4

2 **a.** The slope is 4.39. This means that if one tree has a diameter that is 1 cm larger than another tree's diameter, we predict that it will be 4.39 years older.

b. A tree that is 125 cm in diameter is predicted to have an age of $4.39(125) - 19 = 529.75$ years.

c. The residual is largest for the tree with diameter 120 cm and age 1,167 years. From the plot, a good estimate of this residual is $1,190 - 530 = 660$. Using the regression equation, the residual is $1,167 - (4.39 \cdot 120 - 19) = 1,167 - 529.75 = 659.2$. This residual means that the tree is 659.2 years older than predicted by the regression equation.

d. The predictions are not very good in more than half of the cases. For only 9 trees out of 20 was the prediction correct to within 100 years. The regression equation gave a prediction for 8 trees that was off by more than 200 years. For two trees, the prediction was off by more than 600 years. The residuals are given in the table below.

Diameter (in cm)	Age (in years)	Residual	Diameter (in cm)	Age (in years)	Residual
180	1,372	600.175	115	512	25.667
120	1,167	658.706	140	512	−84.138
100	895	474.550	180	455	−316.825
225	842	−127.474	112	352	−121.156
140	722	125.862	100	352	−68.450
142	657	52.078	118	249	−250.509
139	582	−9.745	82	249	−92.390
150	562	−78.060	130	227	−325.216
110	562	97.628	97	227	−180.273
150	552	−88.060	110	172	−292.372

TECHNOLOGY NOTE
These data are in *CPMP-Tools*.

Unit 4

(3) The following table and scatterplot show the average gestation periods (length of pregnancy) and average life spans of various mammals. The regression equation for predicting *average longevity* from *gestation* is $y = 0.0425x + 6.2$.

Gestation and Life Span of Some Mammals

Mammal	Gestation (in days)	Average Longevity (in years)	Mammal	Gestation (in days)	Average Longevity (in years)
Baboon	187	20	Goat	151	8
Black Bear	219	18	Gorilla	258	20
Beaver	105	5	Horse	330	20
Bison	285	15	Leopard	98	12
Cat	63	12	Lion	100	15
Chimpanzee	230	20	Moose	240	12
Cow	284	15	Rabbit	31	5
Dog	61	12	Sheep	154	12
African Elephant	660	35	Squirrel	44	10
Fox (red)	52	7	Wolf	63	5

Source: *World Almanac and Book of Facts 2001*. Mahwah, NJ: World Almanac, 2001.

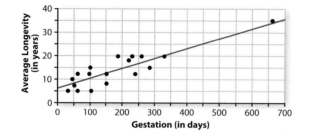

a. Does a line appear to be an appropriate model of this situation?

b. What is the slope of the regression line? What does the slope indicate in the context of these data?

c. Use the regression line to predict the average life span of elk that have a gestation time of 250 days. How much faith would you have in the prediction?

d. Domestic pigs have a 112-day gestation period and live for an average of 10 years. Find and interpret the error of prediction for the domestic pig.

e. Verify that the regression line contains the centroid $(\bar{x}, \bar{y})$.

f. Identify a potential influential point in these data and determine how influential it is with respect to the regression equation.

LESSON 2 • Least Squares Regression and Correlation **307**

3

a. Yes, the points cluster in an elliptical pattern about the regression line. The only worry is the influence of the outlier.

b. The slope is 0.0425. This means that if one species has a gestation period that is 1 day longer than that of another species, you would predict it to live 0.0425 years (about 15.5 days) longer.

TECHNOLOGY NOTE
These data are in *CPMP-Tools.*

c. The predicted lifespan of elk is $y = 0.0425(250) + 6.2 = 16.825$ years. You would have quite a bit of faith in this prediction because the points cluster closely to the regression line. In fact, the average lifespan of elk is 15 years.

d. The predicted lifespan of the domestic pig is $y = 0.0425(112) + 6.2 = 10.96$ years. The error in prediction is $10 - 10.96 = -0.96$ years. The regression line estimates a longevity that is about a year too long.

e. The centroid is $(\bar{x}, \bar{y}) = (180.75, 13.9)$. To check if this lies on the regression line, compute $y = 0.0425(180.75) + 6.2 = 13.88$. This is equal to $\bar{y}$ except for round-off error so, the centroid lies on the regression line.

f. The African elephant is potentially influential. If it is removed from the data set, the regression equation becomes $y = 0.0404x + 6.5$, which is hardly any change at all. The African elephant is not influential, even though it is an outlier in both x and y.

4 The following table and plot over time give the federal minimum wage in dollars in the United States for the years when Congress passed an increase in the minimum wage. The regression equation for predicting the minimum wage given the year is $y = 0.1027x - 200.26$.

Year	Federal Minimum Wage (in dollars)
1955	0.75
1956	1.00
1961	1.15
1963	1.25
1967	1.40
1968	1.60
1974	2.00
1975	2.10
1978	2.65
1979	2.90
1980	3.10
1981	3.35
1990	3.80
1991	4.25
1996	4.75
1997	5.15
2007	5.85

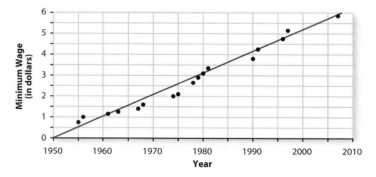

a. Is a line a reasonable model for these data?

b. Verify that the regression line contains the centroid $(\bar{x}, \bar{y}) \approx (1977.53, 2.77)$.

c. What is the slope of the regression line? What does it mean in the context of these data?

d. Check that the sum of the residuals is 0. Then find the sum of the squared residuals.

e. Use the regression line to predict the minimum wage for the current year. What was your error in prediction?

4 **NOTE** These are time series data where the variable on the *x*-axis is the year. As is characteristic of time series data, there is a cyclical pattern of points above, then below, then above the regression line.

TECHNOLOGY NOTE
These data are in *CPMP-Tools*.

a. The points appear to follow a pattern that is curved slightly upward and a nonlinear model might be best for modeling purposes. However, the curve is slight and the points cluster closely to the line and so using a line for prediction may be reasonable. There are no outliers to investigate.

Note that if the rate of inflation stayed constant from year to year and the minimum wage was adjusted each year for inflation, the data would fit an exponential equation. An exponential model does appear to be more appropriate for the years before 1981.

b. To check if $(\bar{x}, \bar{y}) = (1977.53, 2.77)$ lies on the regression line, compute $y = 0.1027(1977.53) - 200.26 = 2.83$. This is equal to $\bar{y}$ except for round-off error, so the centroid lies on the regression line.

DIFFERENTIATION If your students do not need additional practice computing the SSE, the value can be obtained directly from the information button of the *CPMP-Tools* data analysis software.

c. The slope is 0.1027. This means that the minimum wage has tended to increase about 10.3 cents per year.

d. The SSE is 1.05. Students can use calculator lists or the data analysis in *CPMP-Tools* to compute the SSE.

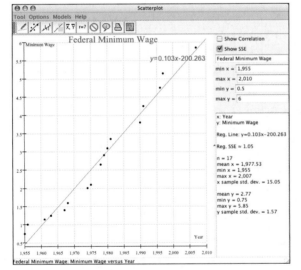

e. Answers will vary depending on the current year.

⑤ A table and scatterplot showing the amount of fiber and the number of calories in one cup of various kinds of cereal are shown below.

Cereal Nutrition Information

Cereal	Calories	Fiber (in gm)	Cereal	Calories	Fiber (in gm)
Alpha-Bits	133.5	1.5	Honey Graham Oh's	149	1
Apple Jacks	115.5	0.5	Honey Nut Cheerios	114.5	1.5
Cap'n Crunch	143	1	Kix	85.5	0.5
Cheerios	109.5	2.5	Lucky Charms	116	1
Cocoa Puffs	119	0	Product 19	110	1.5
Corn Chex	113.5	0.5	Puffed Rice	53.5	0
Corn Flakes	102	0.5	Raisin Bran (Kelloggs)	196.5	8
Froot Loops	117.5	0.5	Rice Krispies	99.5	0.5
Frosted Mini-Wheats	186.5	6	Special K	114.5	6.5
Golden Grahams	154	1	Total	140.5	3.5
Grape Nuts	389	11	Trix	122.5	0.5
Grape Nuts Flakes	144.5	4	Wheaties	110	2

Source: www.cereal.com/nutrition/compare-cereals.html

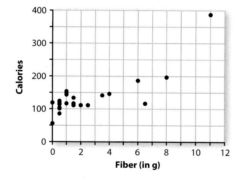

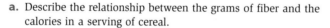

a. Describe the relationship between the grams of fiber and the calories in a serving of cereal.

b. Which of the following do you estimate is closest to the correlation?

$$r = -0.8 \qquad r = -0.3 \qquad r = 0.5 \qquad r = 0.8$$

c. Which cereal is a potential influential point? What will happen to the slope of the regression line if it is removed from the data set?

5 **a.** There is a moderate positive association between amount of fiber and number of calories in a serving of cereal. Grape Nuts, (11, 389), is an outlier in both fiber and calories.

b. The correlation is 0.81, so 0.8 is the best estimate.

c. Grape Nuts is potentially influential. If it is deleted, the slope drops much closer to 0, from 17.554 to 8.965. (Note that the correlation actually decreases somewhat from 0.808 to 0.649.)

6 The average length and weight of five different kinds of seals are given below.

Seal Sizes

Seals	Length (in ft)	Weight (in lbs)
Ribbon Seal	4.8	176
Bearded Seal	7.0	660
Hooded Seal	8.0	880
Common Seal	5.2	220
Baikal Seal	4.2	187

Source: *Grzimek's Encyclopedia, Mammals* V4. New York: McGraw-Hill, 1990.

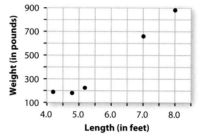

a. Estimate the correlation between the average length and weight of the seals.

b. Calculate the correlation. How close is *r* to your estimate?

c. If you include the Northern Elephant seal at 14.4 feet long and 5,500 pounds, how do you think the correlation will be affected? Check your conjecture.

d. Do you think a line is a good model of the data? Why or why not?

e. Suppose in the table above, you converted each length to meters and each weight to kilograms. (A foot is 0.3048 meters, and a pound is about 0.454 kg.) What would be the correlation? Explain.

7 Consider the following two situations involving possible lurking variables.

a. Examine the following plots of mean earnings and years of schooling for men and women who are year-round, full-time workers, 25 years and older.

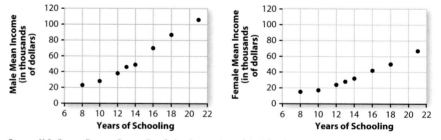

Source: U.S. Census Bureau, Current Population Survey, Annual Social and Economic Supplement. www.census.gov/hhes/www/income/histinc/p22.html

Unit 4

6   **a.** A good estimate would be between 0.8 and 0.99.

    b. For these data, $\bar{x} = 5.84$, $\bar{y} = 424.6$, $s_x = 1.596$, $s_y = 325.161$, and $n = 5$. The correlation is 0.981.

    c. The point for the Northern elephant seal does not lie on the line that the other points cluster around so you might suspect that the correlation will be smaller. (See the plot below.) On the other hand, you have seen that an influential point such as that for the elephant seal can often increase the correlation when it has a much larger or smaller value of x than the other points. In fact, the new value of r is 0.968, just a bit lower.

TECHNOLOGY NOTE
These data are in *CPMP-Tools*. To add the Northern elephant seal data to the spreadsheet provided in *CPMP-Tools*, choose Enable in the Edit menu and enter the additional data values.

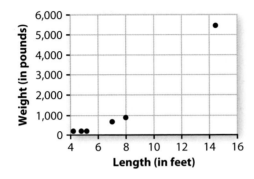

    d. From the plot, it is clear that a curve, not a line, would be a better model for the sizes of seals. This makes sense as, from the geometry of the situation, you would expect the relationship to be cubic because seals are somewhat similar in shape and linear measures are related by a cubic equation to measures depending on volume, such as weight.

    e. Students should recognize that the correlation remains 0.981 under these transformations. Some students may do the transformation and recognize, after the fact, that the correlation remains the same.

7   **a.**   **i.**   *Schooling* $\longrightarrow$ *Income*   or $S \longrightarrow I$

       ii. $S \nwarrow \quad \nearrow I$
               P

i. As you can see, for people in the United States, there is a high correlation between number of years of schooling *S* and yearly income *I*. One theory is that the correlation is high because jobs that pay well tend to require many years of schooling. Model this theory by a directed graph.

ii. Some people have suggested that there is a lurking variable *P*, which is the economic status of the person's parents. That is, a person whose parents have more money tends to have the opportunities to earn more money. He or she also tends to be able to stay in school longer. Model this theory by a directed graph.

b. Examine the following report of research in which some possible lurking variables have been controlled.

Schooling Pays Off on Payday

Workers earn more from their investment in education than had been thought, a new study says. Students can increase their future income by an average of 16% for each year they stay in school, the study reports. Researchers Alan Krueger and Orley Ashenfelter, both of Princeton, based their estimate on interviews with 250 sets of twins. They correlated differences in wages and years of schooling within sets of twins.

Source: Todd Wallack, *USA Today*, September 1993.

i. How have the researchers controlled for some lurking variables? Which lurking variables have been controlled by this method?

ii. What lurking variable(s) has not been controlled?

8 The following article appears to claim that unemployment allows people to live longer.

Study Links Job Loss, Longer Life

As the economy enters another year of expansion and low unemployment, new research suggests that loss of a job may actually contribute to a healthier, longer life for at least some Americans. Christopher Ruhm, a professor of economics at the University of North Carolina at Greensboro, has concluded in a study that higher unemployment may lead to lower overall mortality rates and reduce fatalities from several major causes of death. The new study, which looks at state-level data compiled between 1972 and 1992, suggests that a 1 percentage point rise in the unemployment rate lowers the total death rate by 0.5 percent.

Source: *San Diego Union-Tribune*, January 27, 1997. Reprinted by permission of Reuters.

a. What variable is said to be the explanatory variable? The response variable?

b. i. The researchers chose twins for the study. The twins in the study probably grew up in the same household and so had identical economic status. By comparing the income of the twin with more education to that of the twin with less education, researchers can eliminate the effect of the parent's economic status. Lurking variables controlled include such things as quality of parenting, quality of local schools, number of siblings, and other variables, as well as economic status.

ii. Differences between the twins have not been controlled. For example, motivation to "succeed" by having more schooling and by earning more money has not been controlled nor has the differences in ability between the twins.

8 a. The last sentence says, "the new study … suggests that a … rise in the unemployment rate lowers the total death rate … ," so the explanatory variable is the unemployment rate and the response variable is the total death rate.

b. Suppose you were to graph these data on a scatterplot.

    i. What would each point represent?

    ii. What variable would go on the *x*-axis? On the *y*-axis?

    iii. What would be the slope of the regression line?

c. Name a lurking variable that might explain the relationship between higher unemployment rates and lower death rates.

9 In each of the following news clips, a study is reported that revealed an association between two variables. Comment on the validity of the conclusion and whether or not you think there is a cause-and-effect relationship between the two variables.

a. *USA Today* (June 14, 2001) reported a study by researcher Lilia Cortina of the University of Michigan-Ann Arbor that rudeness in the workplace is damaging mental health and lowering productivity. "As encounters with uncivil behavior rose, so did symptoms of anxiety and depression. … Incidents of rude behavior were tied to less job satisfaction for the employee and lower productivity.

b.

Study Links Parental Bond to Teenage Well-Being
by Judy Foreman

A study published in the Journal of the American Medical Association finds that strong emotional connection to a parent is the factor most strongly associated with teenagers' "well-being", as measured by health, school performance, and avoidance of risky behavior. The correlations were found to hold regardless of family income, education, race, and the specific amount of time a parent spends with a child or family structure.

From an initial 1995 survey of 90,000 students in grades 7 through 12, the study focused on 12,000 teenagers, who were interviewed individually at home in 1995 and again in 1996. The study was praised for its breadth and depth, and the data are expected to be a continuing source of material for investigation.

Among the findings already reported here are the following. High parental expectation for school performance were associated with lower incidence of risky behavior. Feeling that at least one adult at school treats them fairly was associated with lower risk in every health category studied except for pregnancy. Students with easy access to guns, alcohol, tobacco at home were more likely to use them or to engage in violence.

Source: *The Boston Globe*, 10 September 1997, A1.

b. i. Each point would represent a state in a particular year.

    ii. Unemployment rate would go on the *x*-axis and death rate on the *y*-axis.

    iii. The slope of the regression line is −0.5 because if one state has an unemployment rate that is 1% higher than that of another state, it tends to have a death rate that is 0.5% lower.

c. These data were collected by state, so one lurking variable might be the age of people in the state. Younger people tend to have a higher unemployment rate than older workers and they are certainly less likely to die, so states with high percentages of young people are going to have a relatively high unemployment rate and a low death rate. Another possible lurking variable is the type of industry in the state. Perhaps states with more polluting industries tend to have a higher unemployment rate and a higher death rate.

9 a. This is probably not a cause-and-effect relationship. Rudeness and symptoms of anxiety/depression and less job satisfaction/productivity are probably all caused by a lurking variable such as bad management. Other possible lurking variables that would cause these three things are dangerous working conditions, boredom on the job, difficulty in commuting to the location, or other poor working conditions.

b. It is quite plausible that emotional connection to a parent causes general well being in a teenager and that higher parental expectations cause less risky behavior.

> **INSTRUCTIONAL NOTE**
> The context in Task 9 Part b may be sensitive for some students.

c.

> ### Why Your Credit History Affects Your Insurance Rates
> *by Carrie Teegardin and Ann Hardie*
>
> By shuffling a customer's debt and bill-paying records through a complicated computer program, insurers believed they could predict with amazing accuracy which customers were most likely to get into an auto accident and file a claim.
>
> The computer program boiled each customer's history down to a new version of a credit score and called it an "insurance score." Customers with bad scores were bigger risks than customers with good scores, insurers said, so it was only fair that their policies cost more.
>
> Like most people, Golick couldn't then—and can't now—explain the connection. Why would information about credit card bills and mortgage payments predict someone's driving habits?
>
> "I work in this business. It is not obvious to me," said Golick, who in addition to his legislative job is an attorney for Allstate Insurance Co. "I do know that the data is conclusive that there is absolutely a correlation."
>
> The mysterious correlation was so strong that it prompted Golick, who handles regulatory matters for Allstate's Southeast region, to take action. In 2003, he sponsored legislation that allows insurers to use credit information when pricing auto and homeowners insurance—but keeps the formulas they use secret from consumers.

Source: *Atlanta Journal-Constitution*, December 12, 2006, www.ajc.com/business/content/business/stories/2006/12/09/1210bizcreditmain.html

Connections

10 Make a scatterplot of the points $(1, 1)$, $(2, 2)$, and $(3, 5)$. Plot the regression line $y = 2x - \frac{4}{3}$. Draw line segments on your graph to show the residuals for each point. Illustrate the geometry of the term *squared residuals* by drawing on the graph an appropriate square for each residual.

11 Consider the set of points $(1, 3)$, $(2, 2)$, $(3, 5)$, and $(6, 5)$.

  a. Using the equation $y = x + 0.75$, find the sum of the residuals and the sum of the squared residuals.

  b. Using the equation $y = 0.5x + 2.25$, find the sum of the residuals and the sum of the squared residuals.

  c. One of the two equations is the regression equation. Tell which one it is and how you know.

c. This is probably not a cause-and-effect relationship. Both a bad credit history and bad driving habits may be caused by the lurking variable of how responsible the person is.

Connections

10 The sum of the squared residuals is the sum of the areas of the squares below on the graph.

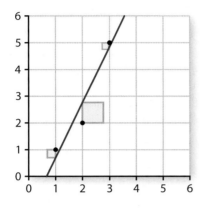

11 a. The sum of the residuals is 0 and the SSE is 6.75, as computed below in the table.

x	y	Predicted y = x + 0.75	Residual	Squared Residual
1	3	1.75	1.25	1.5625
2	2	2.75	−0.75	0.5625
3	5	3.75	1.25	1.5625
6	5	6.75	−1.75	3.0625
		Total	0	6.75

b. The sum of the residuals is 0 and the SSE is 3.25, as computed below in the table.

x	y	Predicted y = 0.5x + 2.25	Residual	Squared Residual
1	3	2.75	0.25	0.0625
2	2	3.25	−1.25	1.5625
3	5	3.75	1.25	1.5625
6	5	5.25	−0.25	0.0625
		Total	0	3.25

c. The second equation must be the regression equation because it has the smaller sum of squared errors. Note that in both cases, the sum of the residuals is 0. (That will happen with any line that goes through the centroid. See Connections Task 12.)

12 In this task, you will discover one reason why the sum of the *squared* residuals and not the sum of the *absolute values* of the residuals is used in defining the regression line.

a. Find the centroid of the points below.

x	y
0	0
0	1
1	0
1	1

b. Find the equations of three different lines that go through the centroid.

c. For each of your three lines in Part b:

i. find the sum of the residuals.

ii. find the sum of the absolute values of the residuals.

iii. find the sum of the squared residuals.

d. Which of your three lines has:

i. the smallest sum of residuals?

ii. the smallest sum of absolute residuals?

iii. the smallest sum of squared residuals?

e. What is one helpful result of squaring the residuals when finding the regression line?

13 Imagine a scatterplot of points (x, y) and a second scatterplot of the transformed points $(-x, y)$. Make conjectures about answers to the questions in Parts a–c.

a. How do the plots of (x, y) and $(-x, y)$ differ?

b. How are the correlations related?

c. How are the regression lines related?

d. Test your conjectures with a set of ordered pairs (x, y) and a transformed set $(-x, y)$.

14 Create a set of five ordered pairs (x, y) for which the values of y are all even, positive integers and the points are not all collinear.

a. Plot your points.

b. Find the correlation, the regression line, and the sum of the squared errors.

c. Transform the values using the rule $(x, y) \rightarrow (x, 0.5y)$. Make a scatterplot of the transformed values. Then find the regression line and recalculate the correlation and the sum of the squared errors.

d. Compare and explain the results of Parts b and c.

Unit 4

12 **a.** The centroid is (0.5, 0.5).

b. Several such lines are $y = x$, $y = 0.5$, $y = 1 - x$, $y = \frac{3}{4} - \frac{1}{2}x$.

c. **i.** In each case, the sum of the residuals will be 0. Any line that goes through the centroid has the sum of the residuals equal to zero.

ii. The sums of the absolute value of the residuals will vary.

iii. The sums of the squared residuals will vary.

d. **i–iii.** Answers will vary depending on the line the students choose. The line with the smallest SSE is $y = 0.5$, the regression line.

e. Minimizing the sum of the squared errors gives a horizontal line, which is the most reasonable summary line because it shows that there is no relationship between x and y; that is, knowing the value of x does not help you predict the value of y. Each line through the centroid has the same sum of residuals and many of these are not reasonable summary lines. It is also interesting that the equations $y = x$, $y = 1 - x$, and $y = 0.5$ each have the same sum of absolute errors. Yet, $y = 0.5$ is clearly the best summary line.

13 **a.** Each plot is a reflection across the y-axis of the other plot.

b. The correlations will be the same in absolute value but will have opposite signs.

c. They have the same y-intercept and slopes that are the same in absolute value, but they have opposite signs.

d. Examples will vary.

14 **a.** One example is shown.

b. $r \approx 0.740$, $y = 1.8x + 1$, SSE = 26.8

c. $r \approx 0.740$, $y = 0.9x + 0.5$, SSE = 6.7

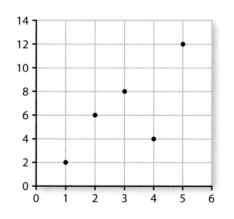

d. All distances in the y direction have been halved, so coefficients of the regression equation also will be halved (every point is half as high as it was before). Each error also is halved. Squaring these errors makes the sum of the squared errors one-fourth as large as before. The correlation is the same, as multiplying by a constant does not change the value of r.

15 For a project, Diana is examining the question of whether she can use linear regression to predict the height of a daughter from the height of the mother. She did all of her measurements in inches and has computed the mean height of the mothers, the mean height of the daughters, the value of r, and the equation of the regression line. Her science teacher suggested that she report her results in centimeters rather than in inches. (Recall there are approximately 2.54 centimeters in an inch.)

   a. How can Diana most easily find the mean height in centimeters of the mothers and the daughters?

   b. If Diana reports her results in centimeters rather than in inches, how is the value of r affected?

   c. If Diana reports her results in centimeters rather than in inches, how does the equation of the regression line change?

   d. If the heights of the mothers are left in inches but the heights of their daughters are reported in centimeters, how is the value of r affected?

16 In this task, you will compare Pearson's correlation and Spearman's rank correlation for two sets of data.

   a. Compute Pearson's correlation for the roller coaster rankings in Applications Task 1 on page 269 in Lesson 1. Spearman's rank correlation was 0.515. Compare the two correlations.

   b. Refer to the sizes of seals in Applications Task 6, page 310. Rank the seals according to length. Rank the seals according to weight. Using the ranks, compute and compare Pearson's correlation and Spearman's rank correlation. Then, compare these with the correlation computed using the actual lengths and weights in Applications Task 6 Part b.

   c. When might you want to rank data before computing a correlation? When would you not want to rank data before computing a correlation?

Reflections

17 What can you say about the shape of a cloud of points:

   a. if the points tend to be above the regression line on the left and right and below it in the middle?

   b. if the points tend to be below the regression line on the left and right and above it in the middle?

15 a. Multiply each mean height by 2.54.

b. The value of r does not change if values are all multiplied by the same constant.

c. The y-intercept is multiplied by 2.54, but the slope does not change.

d. The value of r does not change, even if the values of just one variable are multiplied by the same constant.

16 a. Pearson's correlation is the same as Spearman's, 0.515. This is always the case in rankings where there are no ties.

b. Fortunately, there are no ties in the measurements, so they can be ranked easily, as in the table below. (If there were ties, you could break them at random, or give each amount the average of the tied ranks.) Using the ranks, the values of Pearson's correlation and Spearman's rank correlation are equal, 0.9. However, using the actual lengths and weights, the value of Pearson's correlation is 0.981. For these data, the points are clustered more closely to the regression line with the original measurements than with the ranks.

Seals	Length (in ft)	Weight (in lbs)	Length Rank	Weight Rank
Ribbon Seal	4.8	176	4	5
Bearded Seal	7.0	660	2	2
Hooded Seal	8.0	880	1	1
Common Seal	5.2	220	3	3
Baikal Seal	4.2	187	5	4

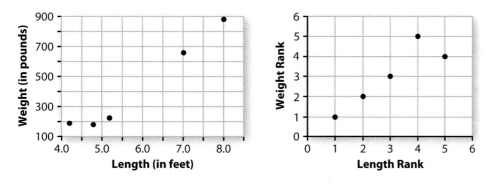

c. You might want to rank the data if the numerical values had been approximated in the first place and you did not have much faith in them. You might want to rank the data if there is an outlier in the data set that would be too influential. You would not want to rank the data if you did not want to lose the extra information that you get from the actual values.

Reflections

17 a. The points follow a pattern that is curved up.

b. The points follow a pattern that is curved down.

18 The eighth and ninth grade point averages (GPAs) for a sample of 25 students are given in the scatterplot. The line on the scatterplot is the regression line. Its equation is $y = 0.58x + 1.33$.

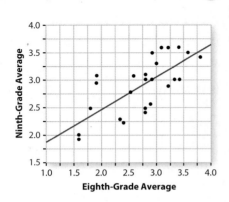

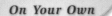

a. Which of the following is the best interpretation of the slope of the regression line? Explain your reasoning.

- If a student raises his or her eighth-grade GPA by 1 point, then we expect the student to raise his or her ninth-grade GPA by 0.58.
- If a student has an eighth-grade GPA of 1, then we expect the ninth-grade GPA to be 1.58.
- If one student has an eighth-grade GPA that is 1 point higher than another student's, then his or her ninth-grade GPA tends to be only 0.58 higher.

b. Roughly how large would you expect the error of prediction to be in the case of a student with an eighth-grade GPA of 2.2?

19 Many formulas in statistics are based on just a few fundamental ideas. Think about how the formulas in the following pairs are similar.

a. In what way is the formula for the standard deviation similar to the formula for the sum of squared residuals (errors)?

b. The formula for Spearman's rank correlation r_s involved a sum of squared differences. Does the formula for Pearson's correlation r include any sums of squared differences? Explain.

c. The formula below gives the slope of the regression line (see also Extensions Task 25, page 318). How is this formula similar to the formula for Pearson's correlation?

$$b = \frac{\Sigma(x - \bar{x})(y - \bar{y})}{\Sigma(x - \bar{x})^2}$$

20 The following data were collected in an experiment in which students threw a ball straight up in the air and measured the height of the ball over a series of time intervals.

Time (in seconds)	0.0	0.2	0.4	0.6	0.8	1.0	1.2	1.4
Height (in meters)	1.1	2.3	3.2	3.6	3.7	3.5	2.7	1.6

a. Calculate the correlation for these data.

b. As you saw in the Course 1 *Quadratic Functions* unit, you can predict the height h of an object at time t if you know its initial height h_0 at time 0 and the velocity v_0 at which it was initially thrown straight up using the rule:

$$h = h_0 + v_0t - 4.9t^2$$

In this rule, height is in meters, time is in seconds, and velocity is in meters per second.

i. What is h_0 for the data collected by these students?

ii. Use this value and one other point in the table above to estimate v_0.

18 **a.** The third sentence in the best interpretation. The first sentence is not good because the points represent different students, not one student over time. The second sentence has an incorrect interpretation of the slope of a line.

b. Looking at the scatterplot, residuals are about the same size for all values of x and a typical residual is about ± 0.3, so you would expect to have an error in the prediction of around 0.3.

19 **a.** Each is made up of a sum of squared differences from the "center." In the case of the standard deviation, the center is the mean. In the case of the SSE, the center is the regression line. Further, for both the standard deviation and the SSE, the sum of the deviations from the center (the mean or the regression line) is equal to 0.

b. Yes, in the denominator of Pearson's formula the standard deviation of the values of x and the standard deviation of the values of y both involve sums of squared differences.

c. The numerators are exactly alike. The denominators are somewhat different, although both involve $\Sigma(x - \bar{x})^2$. Both denominators are always positive so do not affect the sign. This means the slope and the correlation always will have the same sign, determined by the numerator. If the correlation is 0, the slope will be 0. However, for points that fall on a horizontal line, the correlation is undefined because $s_y = 0$, but the slope will be 0 because $y - \bar{y} = 0$ for all y.

20 **a.** $r \approx 0.195$

b. **i.** When $t = 0$, the height is 1.1 meters, so $h_0 = 1.1$.

ii. Using the point $t = 1.0$ and $h = 3.5$, the equation gives $v_0 = 7.3$ meters per second.

INSTRUCTIONAL NOTE
Reflections Task 20 again serves as a warning to always plot the data first.

iii. Write a rule that describes the pattern in these data using your estimated coefficients.

iv. How well does your rule model the students' data?

c. What might explain why there is a low correlation in Part a but fairly good agreement with your rule in Part b?

21 Each year, hundreds of thousands of people come to see the blooming of the cherry trees around the Jefferson Memorial in Washington, D.C. The *Peak Bloom Date* is defined as the day in which 70 percent of the blossoms of the Yoshino Cherry trees are open. The date when the Yoshino cherry blossoms reach peak bloom varies from year to year, depending on weather conditions.

The plot over time below shows the days after March 1 when the cherry trees hit peak bloom for the years beginning in 1980.

Peak Cherry Tree Blooming

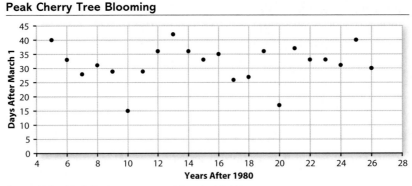

Source: National Park Service. www.nps.gov/cherry/updated.htm

a. Estimate the correlation between day of peak bloom and year.

b. Should a line be fit to these data?

c. As is typical of plots over time, there is a pattern in these data, apart from any linear trend. How would you describe it?

Extensions

22 Experiment with data analysis software and sets of ordered pairs (x, y) to create the following examples.

a. An example where a line is a good model for the scatterplot even though there are relatively large residuals

b. An example where a line is not a good model for the scatterplot even though there are relatively small residuals

iii. $h = 1.1 + 7.3t - 4.9t^2$

iv. The predictions from the rule and the data agree fairly closely.

c. As time increases, the height increases, reaches a maximum, then decreases. The equation is quadratic and the pattern on the graph at the right is parabolic. The correlation is very weak because it only indicates the degree to which points cluster about a line; it gives no indication of the degree to which they follow another relationship. There is no reason to expect a high correlation using a formula that measures how closely the points cluster about a line rather than about a parabola.

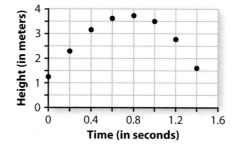

21 **NOTE** These are time series data, where the variable on the x-axis is the year. As is characteristic of time series data, there is a cyclical pattern of points above, then below, then above the regression line.

TECHNOLOGY NOTE
These data are in
CPMP-Tools.

a. The correlation is very close to 0.

b. No, the points do not form an elliptical cluster.

c. Although the general trend is somewhat linear, there are cycles. The points decrease, increase, decrease, increase, and then decrease. (This is one type of autocorrelation—a pattern within the pattern.)

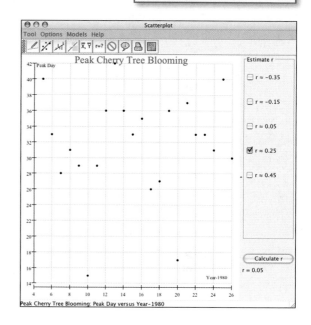

Extensions

22 **a.** An example of an elliptical cloud with a large number of points (similar to the father and son heights data) would have some large residuals, but a line would be a good model.

b.

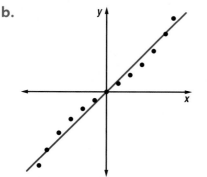

23 In this task, you will explore the relationship between the slope of a line through the centroid and the sum of squared residuals.

   a. Find the centroid of the four points $(1, 1)$, $(2, 3)$, $(3, 4)$, and $(6, 8)$.

   b. Find the equation of the line that goes through the centroid and has a slope of 0. Compute the sum of squared residuals (SSE) for that line.

   c. Repeat Part b using the slopes in the table below. Fill in the values of the SSE.

Slope	0	0.5	1	1.5	2	2.5
SSE						

   d. Plot the pairs (*slope, SSE*). What do you observe?

   e. Estimate the slope that will give the smallest SSE.

   f. Check your answer to Part e by finding the equation of the regression line.

24 In this task, you will explore why the regression line is sometimes called the "line of averages." Shown below is a plot of the data from the Check Your Understanding on page 285 of the exposure to radioactive waste from a nuclear reactor in Hanford, Washington, and the rate of deaths due to cancer in these communities. The vertical lines divide the set of data points into thirds.

Radioactive Waste Exposure

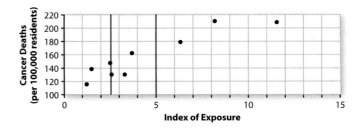

   a. Compute the centroid of the points in each of the three vertical strips using the data given on page 285 and plot them on a copy of the plot.

   b. Draw in the regression line.

   c. How close are the three centroids to the regression line? Could you have done a good job of approximating the regression line just by drawing in a line that goes almost through the three centroids?

25 Formulas that can be used to find the slope b and y-intercept a of the regression line $y = a + bx$ are

$$b = \frac{\Sigma(x - \bar{x})(y - \bar{y})}{\Sigma(x - \bar{x})^2} \quad \text{and} \quad a = \bar{y} - b\bar{x}.$$

   a. Use these formulas to find the equation of the regression line for the points $(1, 1)$, $(2, 2)$, and $(3, 5)$. Check your computations by finding the regression equation using your calculator or data analysis software.

   b. What fact is reflected in the formula for a?

23 **a.** $(3, 4)$

b. $y = 4$; SSE $= 26$

c.

Slope	0	0.5	1	1.5	2	2.5
Equation	$y = 4$	$y = 0.5x + 2.5$	$y = x + 1$	$y = 1.5x - 0.5$	$y = 2x - 2$	$y = 2.5x - 3.5$
SSE	26	10.5	2	0.5	6	18.5

d. The points lie on a parabola.

e. The equation of the regression line is the one that goes through the centroid and has the smallest SSE. That is, the slope of the regression line would be the value of x at the vertex of the parabola because the vertex represents the smallest SSE. This appears to be at approximately 1.4.

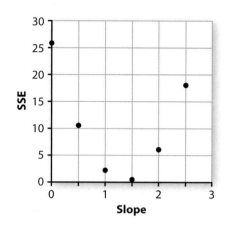

f. The equation of the regression line is $y = 1.36x - 0.07$. The slope of the regression line is 1.36, close to the approximation found using the graph.

24 **a.** The centroids are $(1.8, 133)$, $(3.27, 140.7)$, $(8.77, 198.7)$. The centroids are represented by Xs in the plot below.

b. The regression equation is $y = 9.27x + 115$.

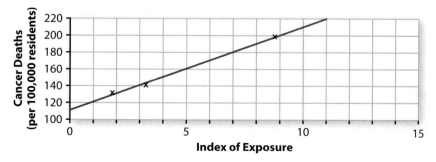

c. Each of the centroids lies very close to the regression line, so you could have done a good job of approximating the regression line by drawing in the line that just about goes through these three points as shown on the following plot. The equation of this line is $y = 9.73x + 112.6$, which is quite close to the equation of the regression line.

NOTE The solution to Task 25 is on page T319.

26 Examine these four sets of points and their scatterplots.

Set 1		Set 2		Set 3		Set 4	
x	**y**	**x**	**y**	**x**	**y**	**x**	**y**
10	8.04	10	9.14	10	7.46	8	6.58
8	6.95	8	8.14	8	6.77	8	5.76
13	7.58	13	8.74	13	12.74	8	7.71
9	8.81	9	8.77	9	7.11	8	8.84
11	8.33	11	9.26	11	7.81	8	8.47
14	9.96	14	8.1	14	8.84	8	7.04
6	7.24	6	6.13	6	6.08	8	5.25
4	4.26	4	3.1	4	5.39	19	12.5
12	10.84	12	9.13	12	8.15	8	5.56
7	4.82	7	7.26	7	6.42	8	7.91
5	5.68	5	4.74	5	5.73	8	6.89

Source: Anscombe, F.J., Graphs in Statistical Analysis, *American Statistician, 27*, 17–21.

Set 1

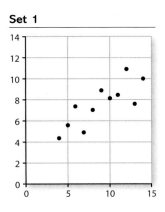

Set 2

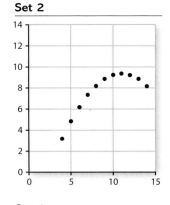

Set 3

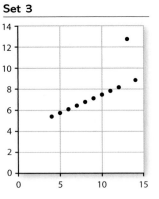

Set 4

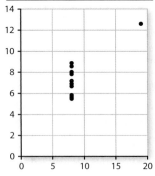

25 **a.** For these points, $\bar{x} = 2$ and $\bar{y} = \frac{8}{3}$, so

$$b = \frac{(1-2)\left(1-\frac{8}{3}\right) + (2-2)\left(2-\frac{8}{3}\right) + (3-2)\left(5-\frac{8}{3}\right)}{(1-2)^2 + (2-2)^2 + (3-2)^2} = \frac{4}{2} = 2.$$

Then, $a = \frac{8}{3} - 2(2) = -\frac{4}{3}$. The equation is $y = 2x - \frac{4}{3}$.

b. The formula for a is equivalent to the fact that the centroid lies on the regression line:

$$\bar{y} = b\bar{x} + a$$
$$\bar{y} - b\bar{x} = a$$
$$a = \bar{y} - b\bar{x}$$

26 **a.** Student predictions will vary.

b. Each of the four data sets has the same correlation $r = 0.82$ and the same regression equation $y = 3.0 + 0.5x$.

c. This situation illustrates that it is necessary to look at the plot before computing a regression equation or correlation. A linear regression equation is appropriate only for Set 1, which is clearly linear. The second set looks quadratic, concave down. The third set has an influential point, which should be examined because it may be a mistake as the remaining 10 points are collinear. The fourth set is different from the remaining three as there are only two different values of x. The single point (19, 12.5) is highly influential because it alone determines the slope of the regression line.

> **INSTRUCTIONAL NOTE**
> Extensions Task 26 should convince students that it is always important to examine the plot.

a. Which scatterplot do you predict would have the largest correlation? Which would have the regression line with the largest slope?

b. Check your predictions in Part a by computing the correlations and slopes.

c. What does this analysis illustrate?

27 Not surprisingly, the correlation is related to the slope of the regression line and to the SSE. Verify that the formulas in Parts a and b hold for the points (1, 1), (2, 2), and (3, 5) and the regression line $y = 2x - \frac{4}{3}$. (Refer to your work in Problem 4 of Investigation 1.)

a. The following formula can be used to find r if you know the SSE, the values of y, and whether the trend is positive or negative.

$$r^2 = 1 - \frac{SSE}{\Sigma(y - \bar{y})^2}$$

b. A relationship among the slope b, the correlation r, the standard deviation of the values of x, and the standard deviation of the values of y is expressed by the formula:

$$b = r\frac{s_y}{s_x}$$

c. Interpret the formula in Part b for the case when the values of x and the values of y have the same standard deviation.

Review

28 The vertices of a quadrilateral *PQRS* are given in the matrix below.

$$\begin{array}{cccc} P & Q & R & S \\ \begin{bmatrix} 0 & 2 & 8 & 1 \\ 4 & 6 & 3 & -1 \end{bmatrix} \end{array}$$

a. Find the coordinates of the image if quadrilateral *PQRS* is reflected across the line $y = x$. Draw a sketch of quadrilateral *PQRS* and this image.

b. Find the coordinates of the image if quadrilateral *PQRS* is rotated 180° about the origin. Draw a sketch of quadrilateral *PQRS* and this image.

c. Find the coordinates of the image if quadrilateral *PQRS* is first reflected across the *y*-axis and then size transformed with center at the origin and scale factor of 3. Draw a sketch of quadrilateral *PQRS* and this image.

29 Consider the graphs of $y = 4x - 40$ and $2x + y = 18$.

a. Describe the shape of these graphs, and explain why the graphs intersect.

b. Find the coordinates of the point of intersection of these two graphs. Show your work.

27 **a.** For these points, SSE $= \frac{2}{3}$ and $\bar{y} = \frac{8}{3}$, so

$$r^2 = 1 - \frac{\frac{2}{3}}{\left(1 - \frac{8}{3}\right)^2 + \left(2 - \frac{8}{3}\right)^2 + \left(5 - \frac{8}{3}\right)^2} \approx 1 - 0.0769 = 0.9231.$$

NOTE The solution to Task 26 is on page T319.

Taking the square root, $r \approx \pm 0.961$, which is what you get if you use the usual formula.

b. For these points, $r = 0.961$, $s_x = 1$, and $s_y = 2.082$.

$$b = r\frac{s_y}{s_x} = (0.961)\frac{2.082}{1} = 2$$

This is what you get if you use the usual formula for the slope.

c. If the two variables have the same nonzero standard deviation, then the slope is equal to the correlation.

Review

28 **a.** $\begin{bmatrix} 4 & 6 & 3 & -1 \\ 0 & 2 & 8 & 1 \end{bmatrix}$ **b.** $\begin{bmatrix} 0 & -2 & -8 & -1 \\ -4 & -6 & -3 & 1 \end{bmatrix}$

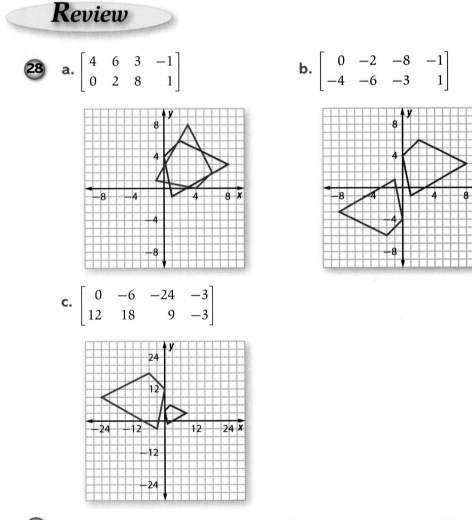

c. $\begin{bmatrix} 0 & -6 & -24 & -3 \\ 12 & 18 & 9 & -3 \end{bmatrix}$

29 **a.** Two lines with different slopes will intersect in one point. The slopes of the lines are 4 and −2.

b. Students might solve using substitution or linear combinations.
$\left(9\frac{2}{3}, -1\frac{1}{3}\right)$

30 Factor the following expressions.

a. $x^2 + 4x$

b. $5x^2 - 25x$

c. $-6x^2 + 4x$

d. $18x - 12x^2$

e. $15x^2 + 27x - 90$

31 Answer the following questions about percent change.

a. Mr. and Mrs. Reyes bought a house for $150,000. Three years later, it was sold for $165,000. By what percent did the house increase in value?

b. If all recording companies agree to lower the average price of compact discs from $15 to $12, by what percent will the average price be marked down?

c. The membership fee at the Sierra Vista Community Recreation Center is expected to increase by 4% per year for the next several years. If the membership fee is $253 this year, what will it be in three years?

32 Without using your calculator, determine if the numbers in each pair are equivalent.

a. $5\sqrt{5}$ and $\sqrt{125}$

b. $\sqrt{288}$ and $12\sqrt{2}$

c. $6\sqrt{5}$ and $2\sqrt{45}$

d. $\sqrt{8}\,\sqrt{10}$ and $\sqrt{16}\,\sqrt{5}$

e. $\sqrt[3]{16}$ and $2\sqrt[3]{2}$

f. $\sqrt[3]{12}\,\sqrt[3]{18}$ and 6

33 Draw a graph of each quadratic function, and identify the coordinates of the vertex of each parabola.

a. $y = -x^2$

b. $y = x^2 + 3$

c. $y = -x^2 + 4x$

d. $y = (x - 2)(x - 8)$

Just in Time

30 a. $x(x + 4)$

b. $5x(x - 5)$

c. $-2x(3x - 2)$

d. $6x(3 - 2x)$

e. $3(5x^2 + 9x - 30)$

31 a. $1 - \dfrac{150{,}000}{165{,}000} \approx 0.10$, or 10% profit

b. $1 - \dfrac{12}{15} = 0.2$, or 20% markdown

c. $253(1.04)^3 \approx \$284.59$

Just in Time

32 a. Equivalent

b. Equivalent

c. Equivalent

d. Equivalent

e. Equivalent

f. Equivalent

Just in Time

33 a.
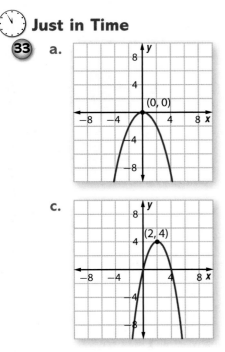

b.
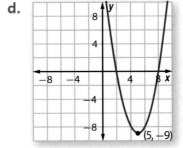

c.

d.

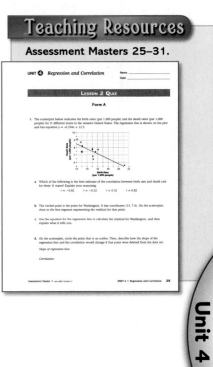

Looking Back

I n this unit, you learned how to interpret
scatterplots and how to describe their shape, their
center using the regression line, and their strength
(spread from the regression line) using Pearson's
correlation coefficient. You learned that the regression
line is the line that minimizes the sum of the squared
residuals. You discovered that influential points, which can
be detected visually on a scatterplot, can make a marked
difference in the correlation coefficient and the regression line.
You also examined why a high correlation between two variables
does not imply that a change in one of the variables tends to
cause a change in the other. The tasks that follow give you an
opportunity to pull together the important ideas and methods
of this unit.

1 A study was conducted to determine if babies bundled in warm
clothing learn to crawl later than babies dressed more lightly. The
parents of 414 babies were asked the month their child was born
and the age that the child learned to crawl. The table below and
the scatterplot on the next page give the average daily outside
temperature when the babies were six months old and the average
age in weeks at which those babies began to crawl.

Crawling Age

Birth Month	Average Outside Temperature at Age 6 Months (in °F)	Age Began to Crawl (in weeks)
January	66	29.84
February	73	30.52
March	72	29.70
April	63	31.84
May	52	28.58
June	39	31.44
July	33	33.64
August	30	32.82
September	33	33.83
October	37	33.35
November	48	33.38
December	57	32.32

Source: Benson, Janette. *Infant Behavior and Development*, 1993.

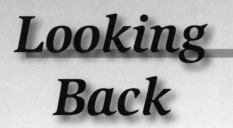

Looking Back

TECHNOLOGY NOTE The crawling age data are in *CPMP-Tools*.

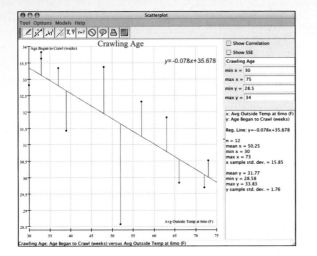

Crawling Age

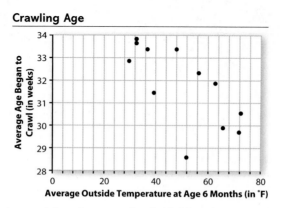

Average Age Began to Crawl (in weeks)

Average Outside Temperature at Age 6 Months (in °F)

a. Does it appear from the scatterplot that babies who are six months old during cold months of the year learn to crawl at a later age on average than babies who are six months old during warmer months?

b. Approximately how many babies are represented by each point on the scatterplot?

c. What is the shape of the cloud of points?

d. Find the least squares regression line for predicting age from temperature, and graph it on a copy of the scatterplot.

e. Interpret the slope of the regression line in the context of these data.

f. Find the point that has the largest residual (in absolute value).

   i. In what month were these babies born?

   ii. Estimate the residual for that point from the scatterplot.

   iii. Compute this residual using the regression equation and the data in the table.

   iv. Is this point an outlier in terms of x, in terms of y, in terms of both x and y, or only in terms of x and y jointly? Explain.

g. Is the point you identified in Part f an influential point? Explain your reasoning.

2 Respond to the following questions in the context of the baby-crawling study.

a. What variable is suggested as responsible for the association between temperature at six months and the age the babies began to crawl?

   i. Is this a lurking variable? If so, in what sense?

   ii. Make a directed graph to illustrate how this variable operates.

b. What other explanations might be given for this association? Make a directed graph to illustrate each of your possibilities.

1
a. Yes. The only birth month that does not follow this trend is May, where babies begin to crawl earlier than expected.

b. About $\frac{414}{12}$, or 34.5, babies are represented by each point, assuming the births were evenly distributed throughout the year.

c. The shape is elliptical with one outlier, the point for May.

d. The least squares regression line is $y = -0.078x + 35.7$.

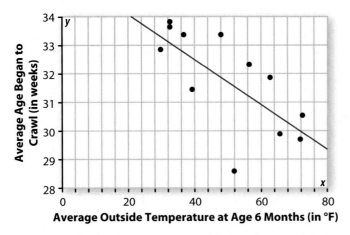

e. Every one degree increase in average temperature tends to reduce the average time to learn to crawl by 0.078 weeks.

f. **i.** May

   ii. A good estimate would be about −3.

   iii. The residual is $28.58 - [-0.078(52) + 35.7] = -3.064$.

   iv. This point is an outlier only in terms of x and y together. The value of x is not unusual and the value of y is not much smaller than the others. It is the two together that make the point stand out.

g. The regression equation changes from $age = -0.078temp + 35.7$ to $age = -0.076temp + 35.8$. This is only a slight change and so May is not influential on the regression equation.

2
a. When the weather is cold, children are bundled up in warm clothing and the extra clothing is what delays crawling.

   i. This is not a lurking variable in the sense that the amount of clothing causes temperature as well as age when crawling began.

   ii. The directed graph would look like this:

Temperature •———▶•———▶• Age at Crawling
Amount of
Clothing

b. Another possibility is that when it is cold, parents keep children off of the floor and so they do not have time to practice crawling. The directed graph would look like this:

Temperature •———▶•———▶• Age at Crawling
Time Spent
on Floor

3 Refer again to the baby-crawling study in Task 1.

    a. Estimate the correlation.

    b. Compute the correlation using the list capabilities of your calculator and the formula

$$r = \frac{\Sigma(x - \bar{x})(y - \bar{y})}{(n - 1)s_x s_y}.$$

    c. Compute the sum of the squared residuals (SSE).

    d. Explain the relationship of the SSE to the regression equation.

    e. Is the month of May influential with respect to the correlation? Explain.

4 Suppose you transform the data in the baby-crawling study by converting the temperature in Fahrenheit to temperature in Celsius and the age the babies began to crawl to days rather than weeks. This formula may be used to convert the temperatures to degrees Celsius:

$$C = \frac{5}{9}(F - 32)$$

    a. How, if at all, will this transformation change the correlation?

    b. How, if at all, will this transformation change the slope and intercept of the regression line?

    c. Make these transformations to check your answers to Parts a and b.

Summarize the Mathematics

In this unit, you studied regression and correlation—ways of summarizing the center and strength of an elliptical pattern of paired data.

a What does "linear" mean in statistics? Does a weak correlation necessarily mean there is no linear relationship?

b Describe how the idea of a sum of squared differences is used in statistics.

c What is an influential point?

d What transformations can you make on a set of data and not change the value of the correlation coefficient?

e Give an example to illustrate that a strong correlation does not imply a cause-and-effect relationship.

Be prepared to explain your responses to the class.

✔ Check Your Understanding

Write, in outline form, a summary of the important mathematical concepts and methods developed in this unit. Organize your summary so that it can be used as a quick reference in future units and courses.

3 **a.** A good estimate would be −0.6 to −0.8.

b. $\bar{x} = 50.25$, $\bar{y} = 31.772$, $s_x = 15.85$, $s_y = 1.761$, $n = 12$

$$r = \frac{\Sigma(x - \bar{x})(y - \bar{y})}{(n - 1)s_x s_y} = \frac{-214.73}{11(15.85)(1.761)} \approx -0.699$$

With no rounding, the correlation is −0.700.

c. SSE = 17.403

d. The regression equation is the equation that makes the sum of the squared errors as small as possible. In this case, no line will make the SSE smaller than 17.403.

e. If May is removed from the data set, the strength of the correlation increases from −0.700 to −0.829. The month of May is influential only on the correlation, which is what you would expect as it lies below the center of the other points.

4 **a.** The correlation will remain −0.700.

b. Both the y-intercept and the slope change in complicated ways.

c. The new y-intercept is 232, and the new slope is −0.980. The original y-intercept was 35.7, and the original slope was −0.078.

Summarize
the Mathematics

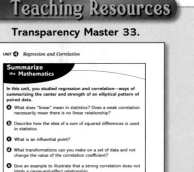

a Linear means that the points form an elliptical cluster, which may be either fat or skinny. A weak correlation does not mean that there is no linear relationship. For example, see the scatterplot of fathers and sons heights in Problem 8 on page 297.

b A sum of squared differences is used as a measure of distance in statistics, just as it is in Euclidean geometry. Thus, a sum of squared differences appears in the formula for the standard deviation as $\Sigma(x - \bar{x})^2$; in Spearman's rank correlation coefficient as Σd^2; in Pearson's correlation coefficient in the standard deviations in the denominator; in the definition of the least squares regression line (minimize $\Sigma(observed\ y - predicted\ y)^2$); and in the denominator of the formula for the slope of the regression line as $\Sigma(x - \bar{x})^2$.

c An influential point is an outlier that has the property that when it is removed from the data set, the coefficients of the regression equation or the correlation change significantly.

d If you add (or subtract) the same constant to each value of one or both variables or if you multiply or divide each value of one or both variables by the same positive number, it does not change the correlation.

e Students have seen many examples of two variables with a strong correlation but with no cause-and-effect relationship. Examples often occur when time is a lurking variable; many things tend to increase over time, such as a child's reading level and shoe size.

Student Masters 34–36.

UNIT ❹ Regression and Correlation   Name _____
Date _____

UNIT SUMMARY

In the *Regression and Correlation* unit, you investigated both visually and numerically the strength of the association between paired variables. You used scatterplots, least square regression lines, and correlations to help you identify and talk about the pattern of association between a pair of variables and the strength of the association.

In this unit, you began by looking at scatterplots.

• Explain why you should always look at a scatterplot before computing a regression line or interpreting a correlation.

• What does it mean when a scatterplot is called "linear"?

The summary line that you computed is called the least squares regression line.

• Give two reasons that you might want to find a regression line for a set of paired data.

• What is the meaning of "least squares"?

• Explain what a residual is and how it can be estimated from the scatterplot.

• Explain how a residual can be found from the regression equation.

Assessment Masters 37–52.

Student Masters 53–54.

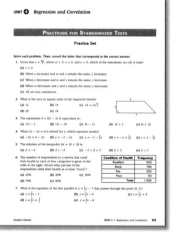

✓ Check Your Understanding

You may wish to have students use the Teaching Master, *Regression and Correlation* Unit Summary, to help them organize the information. Above all, this should be something that is useful to the individual student.

Practicing for Standardized Tests

Each Practicing for Standardized Tests master presents 10 questions in the multiple-choice format of test items similar to how they often appear in standardized tests. Answers are provided below.

Answers to Practice Set 4

1. (e)	**2.** (a)	**3.** (c)	**4.** (d)	**5.** (d)
6. (e)	**7.** (a)	**8.** (b)	**9.** (c)	**10.** (a)

Midterm Assessments

A bank of assessment tasks from which to construct a midterm exam that fits your particular class needs and emphases are provided in the Unit 4 Resource Masters and the TeacherWorks CD. In addition to problems similar in form to those on quizzes and tests, these assessment banks include several multiple-choice tasks for each unit.

Teacher Notes

Glossary/Glosario

Math Online A mathematics multilingual glossary is available at www.math.glencoe.com/multilingual_glossary. The Glossary includes the following languages:

Arabic	English	Korean	Tagalog
Bengali	Hatian Creole	Russian	Urdu
Cantonese	Hmong	Spanish	Vietnamese

English	Español

(A)

Addition Rule Formula for the probability that event A occurs, or event B occurs, or both events occur: $P(A \text{ or } B) = P(A) + P(B) - P(A \text{ and } B)$.

Regla de adición Fórmula para encontrar la probabilidad que el evento A ocurra o que el evento B ocurra, o que ambos eventos ocurran: $P(A \text{ ó } B) = P(A) + P(B) - P(A \text{ y } B)$.

Addition Rule for Mutually Exclusive Events Simplified form of the Addition Rule that can be used only when event A and event B are mutually exclusive: $P(A \text{ or } B) = P(A) + P(B)$.

Regla de adición para eventos mutuamente excluyentes Forma simplificada de la Regla de adición que puede usarse solamente cuando el evento A y el evento B son mutuamente excluyentes: $P(A \text{ ó } B) = P(A) + P(B)$.

Additive identity matrix (p. 134) An $m \times n$ matrix E such that $B + E = B = E + B$, for all $m \times n$ matrices B. (Also called a *zero matrix*, since every entry in an additive identity matrix is 0.)

Matriz identidad aditiva (pág. 134) Una E matriz $m \times n$ de modo que $B + E = B = E + B$, para todas las B matrices $m \times n$. (También se le llama *matriz cero*, debido a que cada entrada en una matriz de identidad aditiva es 0.)

Additive inverse matrix (p. 134) The matrix which when added to a given matrix yields the zero matrix.

Matriz inversa aditiva (pág. 134) Matriz que al sumarla a una matriz dada da como resultado la matriz cero.

Adjacency matrix for a digraph (p. 93) Matrix representation of a digraph in which the vertices are used as labels for the rows and columns of a matrix and each entry of the matrix is a "1" or a "0" depending on whether or not there is a directed edge from the row vertex to the column vertex. (Sometimes an adjacency matrix is constructed such that each entry is the *number* of directed edges from the row vertex to the column vertex, thus an entry could be larger than 1.)

Matriz de adyacencia para un dígrafo (pág. 93) La representación de una matriz de un dígrafo en el cual los vértices se usan como rótulos para las filas y columnas de una matriz y cada entrada de la matriz es un "1" o un "0" dependiendo de si hay o no una arista dirigida de la fila del vértice hacia la columna del vértice. (Algunas veces una matriz de adyacencia se construye de tal manera que cada entrada es el *número* de aristas dirigidas de la fila del vértice a la columna del vértice, por lo tanto una entrada puede ser mayor que 1.)

Algorithm (p. 167) A list of step-by-step instructions, or a systematic step-by-step procedure.

Algoritmo (pág. 167) Lista de instrucciones detalladas o procedimiento detallado.

Angle in standard position (p. 461) A directed angle with vertex at the origin of a rectangular coordinate system and initial side the positive x-axis.

Ángulo en posición estándar (pág. 461) Un ángulo dirigido con vértice en el origen de un sistema rectangular de coordenadas y lado inicial del eje x positivo.

Angle of depression (p. 476) The acute angle between the line of sight and the horizontal when sighting from one point downward to a second point.

Ángulo de depresión (pág. 476) Ángulo agudo entre la línea de visión y la horizontal cuando se aprecia de un punto hacia abajo a un segundo punto.

Angle of elevation (also called *angle of inclination*) (p. 481) The acute angle between the line of sight and the horizontal when sighting from one point upward to a second point.

Ángulo de elevación (también llamado *ángulo de inclinación*) (pág. 481) Ángulo agudo entre la línea de visión y la horizontal cuando se aprecia de un punto hacia arriba de un segundo punto.

Glossary/Glosario

English	Español

Association (p. 299) A relationship between two variables. Association can be positive or negative, weak or strong, curved or linear. Compare with *correlation*.

Asociación (pág. 299) Una relación entre dos variables. La asociación puede ser positiva o negativa, débil o fuerte, curva o lineal. Comparar con *correlación*.

· **B** ·

Bivariate data (p. 257) Data consisting of ordered pairs that are responses for two variables for each person or object of study, such as age and height for each tree in a park.

Datos covariantes (pág. 257) Datos que constan de pares ordenados que son las respuestas para dos variables para cada persona u objeto de estudio, tales como edad y altura para cada árbol de un parque.

Brute-force method (p. 409) A problem-solving method that involves finding and checking all possibilities.

Método de la fuerza bruta (pág. 409) Método de resolución de problemas relacionado con hallar y comprobar todas las posibilidades.

· **C** ·

Cause-and-effect relationship (p. 299) A change in the value of one variable (called the *explanatory* or *independent variable*) tends to cause a change in the value of a second variable (called the *response* or *dependent variable*).

Relación de causa y efecto (pág. 299) Un cambio en el valor de una variable (llamada la *variable explicativa* o *independiente*) tiende a causar un cambio en el valor de una segunda variable (llamada *variable de respuesta* o *dependiente*).

Centroid (p. 286) On a scatterplot of points (x, y), the point $(\bar{x}, \bar{y})$, where $\bar{x}$ is the mean of the values of x and $\bar{y}$ is the mean of the values of y. (In a polygon, the point that is the "center of gravity.")

Centroide (pág. 286) En una gráfica de dispersión, de los puntos (x, y), el punto $(\bar{x}, \bar{y})$, donde $\bar{x}$ es la media de los valores de x, y $\bar{y}$ es la media de los valores de y. (En un polígono, el punto que es el "centro de gravedad.")

Circle The set of all points in a plane that are a fixed distance r, called the *radius*, from a given point O, called the *center* of the circle.

Círculo Conjunto de todos los puntos de un plano que están a una distancia dada r, llamada *radio*, de un punto O dado, denominado *centro* del círculo.

Circuit (p. 403) A route through a vertex-edge graph that starts and ends at the same vertex and does not repeat any edges.

Circuito (pág. 403) Una ruta a través de un grafo que empieza y termina en el mismo vértice y no repite ningún vértice.

Closed interval A continuous interval of real numbers that includes the endpoints of the interval; the interval from a to b, including a and b, is denoted $[a, b]$ or $\{x: a \leq x \leq b\}$.

Intervalo cerrado Intervalo continuo de números reales que incluye todos sus puntos límite; el intervalo de a a b, incluyendo a y b, se denota como $[a, b]$ ó $\{x: a \leq x \leq b\}$.

Column matrix (p. 119) A matrix consisting of one column. (Also called a *column vector* or a *one-column matrix*.)

Matriz columna (pág. 119) Matriz formada por una columna. (También llamada *vector de columna* o *matriz de una columna*.)

Column of an $m \times n$ matrix (p. 76) A vertical array of m numbers in the matrix.

Columna de una matriz $m \times n$ (pág. 76) Matriz o conjunto vertical de m números en la matriz.

Column sum of a matrix (p. 81) The sum of all numbers in a column of a matrix.

Suma de columna de una matriz (pág. 81) La suma de todos los números en la columna de una matriz.

Glossary/Glosario

English	Español

Complementary angles (p. 481) Two angles whose measures sum to 90°.

Components of a translation (p. 199) The horizontal and vertical directed distances (left or right, up or down) through which all points in the plane are moved by the translation.

Composition of transformations (p. 213) The result of applying two transformations in succession. The transformation that maps the *original preimage* to the *final image* is called the *composite transformation*.

Conditional probability (p. 528) The probability that an event A occurs given that another event B occurs, written $P(A \mid B)$. When $P(B) > 0$,
$P(A \mid B) = \dfrac{P(A \text{ and } B)}{P(B)}$.

Congruent figures Figures that have the same shape and size, regardless of position or orientation. (For angles: having the same measure; for segments: having the same length.)

Connected graph (p. 406) A vertex-edge graph that is all in one piece; that is, from each vertex there is at least one path to every other vertex.

Correlation (p. 257) A measure, usually Pearson's r, of the linear association between two variables. A number between -1 and 1 that tells how closely the points on a scatterplot cluster about the regression line.

Cosine function (p. 457) If $P(x, y)$ is a point (not the origin) on the terminal side of an angle θ in standard position and $r = \sqrt{x^2 + y^2}$, then $\cos \theta = \frac{x}{r}$. If A is an acute angle in a right triangle, then $\cos A = \dfrac{\text{length of side } adjacent\ to\ \angle A}{\text{length of } hypotenuse}$.

Critical path (p. 434) A path through a *project digraph* that corresponds to the earliest finish time for the project.

Ángulos complementarios (pág. 481) Dos ángulos cuyas medidas suman 90°.

Componentes de una traslación (pág. 199) Distancias dirigidas horizontal y vertical (izquierda o derecha, arriba o abajo) por las cuales se mueven todos los puntos en un plano por una traslación.

Composición de transformaciones (pág. 213) Resultado de aplicar dos transformaciones en sucesión. La transformación que traza la *figura geométrica original* (o preimage) a la *imagen final* se llama *transformación compuesta*.

Probabilidad condicional (pág. 528) La probabilidad que un suceso A ocurra a condición de que otro suceso B ocurra, de manera escrita es $P(A \mid B)$. Cuando $P(B) > 0$, $P(A \mid B) = \dfrac{P(A \text{ y } B)}{P(B)}$.

Figuras congruentes Figuras de la misma forma y tamaño, sin importar su posición u orientación. (Para los ángulos: tener la misma medida; para los segmentos: tener la misma longitud.)

Grafo conexo (pág. 406) Un grafo que es de una sola pieza, o sea, de cada vértice hay por lo menos un camino a cada uno de los otros vértices.

Correlación (pág. 257) Una medida, usualmente la r de Pearson, de la asociación lineal entre dos variables. Un número entre -1 y 1 que indica qué tan cerca los puntos en una gráfica de dispersión se agrupan acerca de la línea de regresión.

Función de coseno (pág. 457) Si $P(x, y)$ es un punto (no el origen) en el lado terminal de un ángulo θ en posición estándar y $r = \sqrt{x^2 + y^2}$, entonces coseno $\theta = \frac{x}{r}$. Si A es un ángulo agudo en un triángulo rectángulo, entonces $\cos A = \dfrac{\text{medida del cateto } adyacente\ a\ \angle A}{\text{medida de la } hipotenusa}$.

Trayectoria crítica (pág. 434) Una trayectoria a través de un *dígrafo de proyecto* que corresponde al tiempo más temprano del final para el proyecto.

Glossary/Glosario

English	Español

Critical Path Method (CPM) (p. 437) A method using critical path analysis to optimally schedule large projects consisting of many subtasks; developed at about the same time as and similar to the Program Evaluation and Review Technique (PERT).

Método de Trayectoria Crítica (CPM por sus siglas en inglés) (pág. 437) Método que emplea un análisis crítico de trayectoria para programar de manera óptima proyectos grandes compuestos de muchos subproyectos; desarrolladas aproximadamente al mismo tiempo y similares a la Evaluación de Programa y Técnica de Revisión (PERT por sus siglas en inglés).

Critical task (p. 440) A task on a *critical path*.

Tarea crítica (pág. 440) Tarea o trabajo en una *trayectoria crítica*.

• **D** •

Dart A nonconvex quadrilateral with two pairs of congruent consecutive sides.

Dardo Cuadrilátero no convexo con dos pares de lados consecutivos congruentes.

Degree of a vertex The number of edges touching the vertex. If an edge loops back to the same vertex, that counts as two edge-touchings.

Grado de un vértice Número de aristas que concurren en el vértice. Si un extremo se regresa al mismo vértice, eso cuenta como dos veces.

Dependent variable (p. 3) A variable whose value changes in response to change in one or more related independent variables. (Also called a *response variable*.)

Variable dependiente (pág. 3) Variable cuyo valor cambia en respuesta a cambios en una o más variables independientes relacionadas. (También llamada *variable de respuesta*.)

Diagonal of a polygon A line segment connecting two vertices that are not adjacent.

Diagonal de un polígono Un segmento de recta que conecta dos vértices que no son adyacentes.

Digraph (p. 93) A vertex-edge graph in which all the edges are directed, that is, the edges have arrows indicating a direction. (Also called a *directed graph*.)

Dígrafo (pág. 93) Grafo en el cual todas las aristas están dirigidas, es decir, las aristas tienen flechas que indican una dirección. (También se le llama *gráfico dirigido*.)

Direct variation (p. 1) If variables x and y are related by an equation in the form $y = kx$ or $\frac{y}{x} = k$, then y is said to vary directly with x, or be directly proportional to x.

Variación directa (pág. 1) Si las variables x y y están relacionadas por una ecuación en la forma $y = kx$ o $\frac{y}{x} = k$, entonces se dice que y varía directamente con x, o que es directamente proporcional a x.

Directed edge (p. 93) An edge in a vertex-edge graph with a direction indicated.

Arista dirigida (pág. 93) Arista de un grafo en que se indica la dirección de la misma.

Directed graph See *digraph*.

Grafo dirigido Véase *dígrafo*.

Distance Formula (p. 171) Formula for calculating the distance between two points in the coordinate plane.

Fórmula de distancia (pág. 171) Fórmula para calcular la distancia entre dos puntos en un plano de coordenadas.

Distance matrix (p. 414) A matrix representation of a weighted graph in which the vertices are labels for the rows and columns and each entry is the length of a shortest path between the corresponding vertices.

Matriz distancia (pág. 414) Representación de una matriz de un gráfico cargado en el cual los vértices son rótulos para las filas y columnas y cada entrada es el largo de la trayectoria más corta entre los vértices correspondientes.

Glossary/Glosario

English	Español

Domain of a function (p. 330) For a function f, all values of the independent variable x that have corresponding $f(x)$ values. (Also called *input values* for the function.)

Dominio de una función (pág. 330) Para una función f, todos los valores de la variable independiente x que tienen valores $f(x)$ correspondientes. (También llamados *valores de entrada* para la función.)

E ·

Earliest Finish Time (EFT) (p. 438) The minimum amount of time needed to complete a large project that consists of numerous subtasks.

Tiempo mínimo de resolución (EFT por sus siglas en inglés) (pág. 438) La cantidad mínima de tiempo necesario para terminar un proyecto grande compuesto por varios subproyectos.

Elimination method (p. 55) A method used to solve a system of linear equations. One or both of the equations may be multiplied by a nonzero constant so that the coefficient of one of the variables is the same in both equations, subtracting the equations eliminates that variable.

Método de eliminación (pág. 55) Método que se utiliza para resolver un sistema de ecuaciones lineales. Una o ambas ecuaciones se pueden multiplicar por una constante no-cero para que el coeficiente de una de las variables sea el mismo en ambas ecuaciones, restar las ecuaciones elimina esa variable.

Equally likely outcomes (p. 562) Outcomes that all have the same probability of occurring.

Resultados equiprobables (pág. 562) Resultados que tienen la misma oportunidad de ocurrir.

Equation of a line An equation that can be expressed as $ax + by = c$ where a and b are not both 0.

Ecuación de una línea Una ecuación que puede expresarse como $ax + by = c$ en donde a y b no son ambas 0.

Error in prediction (p. 283) For points not used to calculate the regression equation, the difference between the observed value of y and the value of y predicted by the regression equation.

Error en la predicción (pág. 283) Para aquellos puntos no utilizados para calcular la ecuación de regresión, la diferencia entre el valor observado de y y el valor de y predicho por la ecuación de regresión.

Euler circuit A route through a connected graph such that (1) each edge is used exactly once, and (2) the route starts and ends at the same vertex.

Circuito de Euler Camino en un grafo conexo de modo que (1) cada arista se recorre sólo una vez y (2) el camino empieza y termina en el mismo vértice.

Expected value or expectation (p. 525) The mean, or average, of a probability distribution.

Valor previsto o de expectativa (pág. 525) Media, o promedio, de una distribución de probabilidad.

Experiment (p. 4) A research study in which subjects are randomly assigned to two or more different treatments in order to compare how the responses to the treatments differ.

Experimento (pág. 4) Estudio de investigación en el cual se asignan sujetos al azar a dos o más tratamientos diferentes para comparar cómo se diferencian las respuestas a los tratamientos.

Explanatory variable See *independent variable*.

Variable explicativa Véase *variable independiente*.

Exponential function A function with rule of correspondence that can be expressed in the algebraic form $f(x) = a(b^x)$ $(a, b > 0)$.

Función exponencial Función con regla de correspondencia que se puede expresar en forma algebraica $f(x) = a(b^x)$ $(a, b > 0)$.

Glossary/Glosario

English	Español

(F)

Fair price (p. 546) The price that should be charged to play a game so that, in the long run, the player wins the same amount that he or she pays to play.

Precio justo (pág. 546) Precio que se debe cobrar para jugar un juego de modo que, a la larga, el jugador gane la misma cantidad que éste paga por jugar.

Function (p. 161) A relationship between two variables in which each value of the independent variable x corresponds to exactly one value of the dependent variable y. The notation $y = f(x)$ is often used to denote that y is a function of x.

Función (pág. 161) Una relación entre dos variables en la cual cada valor de la variable independiente x corresponde exactamente a un valor de la variable dependiente y. La notación $y = f(x)$ comúnmente se usa para denotar que y es una función de x.

(G)

Glide-reflection (p. 224) A rigid transformation that is the composition of a reflection across a line and a translation in a direction parallel to the line.

Reflexión del deslizamiento (pág. 224) Transformación rígida que es la composición de una reflexión en una recta y una traslación en dirección paralela a esa recta.

Graph See *vertex-edge graph*.

Gráfica Véase *grafo*.

(H)

Half-turn (p. 229) A 180° rotation about a point.

Media vuelta (pág. 229) Rotación de 180° con relación de un punto.

Hamilton circuit (p. 408) A route through a vertex-edge graph that starts at one vertex, visits all the other vertices exactly once, and ends at the starting vertex.

Circuito de Hamilton (pág. 408) Camino a través de un grafo que empieza en una vértice, visita todas las demás vértices exactamente una vez y termina en el vértice inicial.

(I)

Identity matrix (p. 135) An $n \times n$ square matrix I such that $A \times I = I \times A = A$ for all $n \times n$ matrices A. (Also sometimes called a *multiplicative identity matrix*.)

Matriz identidad (pág. 135) Una matriz I cuadrada $n \times n$ de modo que $A \times I = I \times A = A$ para todas las matrices A $n \times n$. (También llamada en ocasiones una *matriz multiplicativa de identidad*.)

Identity transformation A rigid transformation that maps each point of the plane onto itself.

Transformación de identidad Transformación rígida que traza cada punto de un plano en sí mismo.

Immediate prerequisite table (p. 436) A table showing the immediate prerequisites for each task within a large project.

Tabla de prerrequisitos inmediatos (pág. 436) Tabla que muestra los prerrequisitos inmediatos para cada tarea dentro de un proyecto grande.

Independent events (p. 523) Two events A and B are independent if the occurrence of one of the events does not change the probability that the other event occurs. That is, $P(A \mid B) = P(A)$. Alternatively, events A and B with nonzero probabilities are independent if $P(A \text{ and } B) = P(A) \cdot P(B)$.

Eventos independientes (pág. 523) Dos eventos A y B son independientes si el que uno ocurra no afecta la probabilidad de que el otro ocurra. Es decir, $P(A \mid B) = P(A)$. Igualmente, los eventos A y B con probabilidad no-cero son independientes si $P(A \text{ y } B) = P(A) \cdot P(B)$.

Glossary/Glosario

English	Español

Independent variable (p. 3) Variables whose values are restricted only by the context of the problem or by mathematical restrictions on allowed values. These variables influence the values of other variables called *dependent variables*. (Also called an *explanatory variable*.)

Variable Independiente (pág. 3) Variable cuyos valores están restringidos solamente por el contexto de un problema o por restricciones matemáticas sobre los valores permitidos. Estas variables influyen en los valores de otras variables, las llamadas *variables dependientes*. (También llamada *variable explicativa*.)

Influential point (p. 287) On a scatterplot, an outlier such that when it is removed from the data set, the slope or *y*-intercept of the regression line changes quite a bit, where "quite a bit" must be determined by the real-life situation.

Punto influyente (pág. 287) En una gráfica de dispersión, un valor atípico dado que cuando se elimina del conjunto de datos, la pendiente o intersección *y* de la línea de regresión cambia un poco, situación en la cual "un poco" debe determinarse de acuerdo con la situación real.

Initial side of an angle (p. 461) The position of a ray that is one side of the angle before it rotates about the angle's vertex to the terminal side.

Lado inicial de un ángulo (pág. 461) Posición de una semirrecta que está en un lado del ángulo antes de rotar en el vértice de un ángulo al lado terminal.

Inscribed angle (p. 178) An angle whose vertex is on the circumference of a circle and whose sides are segments connecting the vertex to two other points on the circumference.

Ángulo inscrito (pág. 178) Ángulo cuyo vértice está en la circunferencia de un círculo y cuyos lados son segmentos que conectan el vértice con otros dos puntos en la circunferencia.

Inverse matrix (p. 137) For a given square matrix A, the matrix denoted A^{-1} (if it exists) that satisfies $A \times A^{-1} = A^{-1} \times A = I$, where I is the identity matrix. (Also called *multiplicative inverse matrix*.)

Matriz inversa (pág. 137) Para una matriz cuadrada dada A, la matriz denominada A^{-1} (si existe) que satisface $A \times A^{-1} = A^{-1} \times A = I$, donde I es la matriz identidad. (También llamada *matriz inversa multiplicativa*.)

Inverse variation (p. 42) If variables x and y are related by an equation in the form $y = \frac{k}{x}$ or $yx = k$, then y is said to vary inversely with x, or be inversely proportional to x.

Variación inversa (pág. 42) Si las variables x y y están relacionadas por una ecuación en la forma de $y = \frac{k}{x}$ o $yx = k$, entonces se dice que y está inversamente con x, o que es inversamente proporcional a x.

Isosceles triangle A triangle with at least two congruent sides. The side that joins the congruent sides is called the *base*, and the angles that lie opposite the congruent sides are called the *base angles*.

Triángulo isósceles Triángulo con por lo menos dos lados congruentes. El lado que une a los lados congruentes se llama *base* y los ángulos opuestos a los lados congruentes se llaman *ángulos basales*.

· **K** ·

Kite A convex quadrilateral with two distinct pairs of congruent consecutive sides.

Deltoide Cuadrilátero convexo con exactamente dos pares de lados congruentes consecutivos.

Kruskal's Algorithm (p. 405) An algorithm for finding a minimum spanning tree in a connected graph.

Algoritmo de Kruskal (pág. 405) Algoritmo para hallar un árbol de expansión en un grafo conectado.

Glossary/Glosario

English	Español

L

Law of Cosines (p. 457) In any triangle ABC with sides of lengths a, b, and c opposite $\angle A$, $\angle B$, and $\angle C$, respectively: $c^2 = a^2 + b^2 - 2ab \cos C$.

Ley de cosenos (pág. 457) En cualquier triángulo ABC con longitudes de sus lados a, b, y c opuestos $\angle A$, $\angle B$, y $\angle C$, respectivamente: $c^2 = a^2 + b^2 - 2ab \cos C$.

Law of Large Numbers In a simulation, the more runs there are, the closer the probability determined by the simulation tends to the theoretical probability.

Ley de números grandes En una simulación, si el número de repeticiones es mayor, más cercana a la probabilidad teorética tiende a ser la probabilidad determinada por la situación

Law of Sines (p. 457) In any triangle ABC with sides of lengths a, b, and c opposite $\angle A$, $\angle B$, and $\angle C$, respectively: $\frac{\sin A}{a} = \frac{\sin B}{b} = \frac{\sin C}{c}$.

Ley de senos (pág. 457) En un triángulo ABC con longitudes de sus lados a, b, y c opuesto $\angle A$, $\angle B$, y $\angle C$, respectivamente: $\frac{\sin A}{a} = \frac{\sin B}{b} = \frac{\sin C}{c}$.

Least squares regression line (p. 257) The line on a scatterplot that has the smallest sum of squared residuals (SSE). (Also called the *regression line*.)

Línea de regresión de cuadrados mínimos (pág. 257) La línea en una gráfica de dispersión que tiene la menor suma de residuos cuadrados (SSE por sus siglas en inglés). (También llamada *línea de regresión*.)

Line reflection (p. 201) A rigid transformation which associates with each point P in a plane an image point P' such that the "mirror line" (or line of reflection) is the perpendicular bisector of the segment $\overline{PP'}$ if P is not on the line of reflection. A point on the line of reflection is its own image.

Línea reflexión (pág. 201) Una transformación rígida que se relaciona con cada punto P en un plano con un punto de imagen P' de modo que la "línea de espejo" (o línea de reflexión) es el bisector perpendicular del segmento $\overline{PP'}$ si P no está en la línea de reflexión. Un punto en la línea de reflexión es su propia imagen.

Linear data (p. 264) The points on a scatterplot are called "linear" if they form an elliptical cluster so that a line is an appropriate summary.

Datos lineales (pág. 264) Los puntos en una gráfica de dispersión se llaman "lineales" si forman un grupo elíptico para que una recta sea un resumen apropiado.

Linear function A function with rule of correspondence that can be expressed in the algebraic form $f(x) = mx + b$.

Función lineal Función con regla de correspondencia que puede expresarse en la forma algebraica $f(x) = mx + b$.

Linear scale (p. 388) A scale for which the difference between equally spaced scale points is a constant.

Escala lineal (pág. 388) Escala para la cual la diferencia entre los puntos de la misma están separados por igual.

Logarithm (p. 325) If $y = 10^x$ then x is the common or base-10 logarithm of y. This relationship is often indicated by the notation $y = \log x$ or $y = \log_{10} x$.

Logaritmo (pág. 325) Si $y = 10^x$ entonces x es el logaritmo común o de base 10 de y. La notación $y = \log x$ ó $y = \log_{10} x$ usualmente indica esta relación.

Logarithmic function (p. 381) A function with rule of correspondence that can be expressed in the form $f(x) = \log x$.

Función logarítmica (pág. 381) Función con regla de correspondencia que puede expresarse en la forma $f(x) = \log x$.

Glossary/Glosario

English	Español

Logarithmic scale (p. 388) A scale for which the ratio between consecutive scale points is a constant.

Escala logarítmica (pág. 388) Escala para la cual el radio entre puntos consecutivos de la escala es constante.

Lurking variable (p. 300) When explaining the association between two variables, a third variable that affects both of the original variables.

Variable latente (pág. 300) Al explicar la asociación entre dos variables, una tercera variable que afecta a ambas variables originales.

· (M) ·

Main diagonal of a square matrix (p. 80) The entries in the matrix that run from the top-left corner of the matrix to the bottom-right corner.

Diagonal principal de una matriz cuadrada (pág. 80) Entradas de una matriz que van de la esquina superior izquierda de la matriz a la esquina inferior derecha.

Matrix (p. 73) A rectangular array of numbers (plural: *matrices*).

Matriz (pág. 73) Arreglo rectangular de números (plural: *matrices*).

Matrix addition (p. 134) Two matrices A and B, having the same size, are combined by adding their corresponding entries to produce the sum matrix, $A + B$.

Adición de la matriz (pág. 134) Dos matrices A y B, que tienen el mismo tamaño, se combinan al sumar sus entradas correspondientes para producir la suma de la matriz, $A + B$.

Matrix multiplication (p. 105) An $m \times k$ matrix A and a $k \times n$ matrix B are multiplied to produce the $m \times n$ product matrix, $A \times B$, in which the entries of $A \times B$ are computed by a specific method of combining rows of A with columns of B.

Multiplicación de la matriz (pág. 105) Una matriz A $m \times k$ y una matriz B $k \times n$ se multiplican para producir el producto $m \times n$ de matriz, $A \times B$, en el cual las entradas de $A \times B$ se computan con un método específico de combinación de filas de A con columnas de B.

Matrix of coefficients of a system of linear equations (p. 133) A matrix whose entries are the coefficients of the variables in the system of linear equations.

Matriz de coeficientes de un sistema de ecuaciones lineales (pág. 133) Matriz cuyas entradas son los coeficientes de las variables en el sistema de ecuaciones lineales.

Midpoint (p. 163) The point on a segment that is equidistant from the endpoints of the segment.

Punto medio (pág. 163) El punto en un segmento que está a la misma distancia de los extremos del segmento.

Midpoint Formula (p. 169) Formula for calculating the coordinates of the midpoint of the segment connecting two points in the coordinate plane.

Fórmula de punto medio (pág. 169) Fórmula para calcular las coordenadas de un punto medio de los segmentos que conectan dos puntos en el plano de coordenadas.

Minimum spanning tree (p. 403) A spanning tree in a vertex-edge graph that has minimum total weight.

Árbol de expansión mínima (pág. 403) Árbol que atraviesa en un grafo que tiene peso total mínimo.

Multiplication rule (p. 532) If A and B are two events, $P(A \text{ and } B) = P(A)P(B \mid A)$.

Regla de multiplicación (pág. 532) Si A y B son dos eventos, $P(A \text{ y } B) = P(A)P(B \mid A)$.

Multiplication Rule for Independent Events (p. 523) When events A and B are independent, the multiplication rule simplifies to $P(A \text{ and } B) = P(A) \cdot P(B)$.

Regla de multiplicación para eventos independientes (pág. 523) Cuando los eventos A y B son independientes, la regla de multiplicación se simplifica a $P(A \text{ y } B) = P(A) \cdot P(B)$.

Glossary/Glosario

Multiplicative inverse matrix See *inverse matrix.*

Matriz inversa multiplicativa Véase *matriz inversa.*

Multiply a matrix by a number (p. 85) Multiply each entry in a matrix, A, by the same number, k, to generate the entries in a new matrix, kA. (Also called *scalar multiplication.*)

Multiplicar una matriz por un número (pág. 85) Multiplicar cada entrada en una matriz, A, por el mismo número, k, para generar las entradas en una nueva matriz, kA. (También conocida como *multiplicación escalar.*)

Mutually exclusive events (or *disjoint events*) (p. 523) Events that cannot occur on the same outcome.

Eventos mutuamente excluyentes (disjuntos) (pág. 523) Eventos que no pueden ocurrir en el mismo resultado.

— **N** —

Negative correlation (p. 264) The points on a scatterplot have a downwards trend from left to right and so the slope of the regression line is negative.

Correlación negativa (pág. 264) Los puntos en un diagrama de dispersión tienden a bajar de izquierda a derecha y por lo tanto la pendiente de la línea de regresión es negativa.

— **O** —

One-to-one function (p. 354) A function f for which each value of $f(x)$ in the range of f corresponds to exactly one value of x in the domain of f.

Función biunívoca (pág. 354) Función f para la cual cada valor de $f(x)$ en el rango de f corresponde exactamente al valor de x en el dominio de f.

Orientation of a figure (p. 212) Can be determined by clockwise or counterclockwise labeling of consecutive vertices of a figure.

Orientación de una figura (pág. 212) Se puede determinar por los rótulos de los vértices consecutivos de una figura en dirección de las manecillas del reloj o contrario a éstas.

Outlier on a scatterplot (p. 77) A point that does not follow the trend of the other points and so lies outside the main cluster of points.

Valor atípico (o Dato aberrante) en una gráfica de dispersión (pág. 77) Punto que no sigue la tendencia de los demás puntos y queda fuera del grupo principal de puntos.

— **P** —

Parallel lines Lines that are coplanar and do not intersect.

Rectas paralelas Rectas coplanarias que no se intersecan.

Parallelogram (p. 154) A quadrilateral with opposite sides congruent.

Paralelogramo (pág. 154) Cuadrilátero de lados opuestos congruentes.

Perfect correlation (p. 260) All points on a scatterplot fall on the regression line so that the correlation is 1 or -1.

Correlación perfecta (pág. 260) Todos los puntos en una gráfica de dispersión recaen en la recta de regresión de modo que la correlación es biunívoca.

Perpendicular lines Lines that intersect at right angles.

Rectas perpendiculares Rectas que se intersecan en ángulos rectos.

Point matrix (p. 233) A one-column matrix whose entries are coordinates of a point in the plane. (See also *column matrix.*)

Matriz punto (pág. 233) Matriz de una columna cuyas entradas son coordenadas un punto en el plano. (Véase también *columna de matriz.*)

Glossary/Glosario

English	Español

Positive correlation (p. 264) The points on a scatterplot have an upwards trend from left to right and so the slope of the regression line is positive.

Correlación positiva (pág. 264) Los puntos en un diagrama de dispersión muestran una tendencia hacia arriba de izquierda a derecha y por lo tanto la inclinación de la línea de regresión es positiva.

Power function (p. 10) A function with rule of correspondence that can be expressed in the algebraic form $f(x) = ax^r$ $(r \neq 0)$.

Función exponencial (pág. 10) Función con regla de correspondencia que puede expresarse con la forma algebraica $f(x) = ax^r$ $(r \neq 0)$.

Preimage (p. 199) If point A' is the image of a point A under a transformation, then point A is the preimage of point A'.

Preimagen (pág. 199) Si el punto A' es la imagen de un punto A después de una transformación, entonces el punto A es la preimagen del punto A'.

Probability distribution A description of all possible quantitative (numerical) outcomes of a chance situation, along with the probability of each outcome; the distribution may be in table, formula, or graphical form.

Distribución probabilística Descripción de todos los resultados posibles de una situación aleatoria, junto con la probabilidad de cada uno; la distribución puede estar en forma de tabla, fórmula o gráfica.

Program Evaluation and Review Technique (PERT) (p. 435) A technique using critical path analysis to optimally schedule large projects consisting of many subtasks; developed in the 1950s to help create military defense systems. (See also *Critical Path Method*.)

Técnica de Evaluación y Revisión de Programa (PERT, por sus siglas en inglés) (pág. 435) Técnica que utiliza el análisis de trayectoria crítico para programar de manera óptima proyectos grandes compuestos de muchos subproyectos; desarrollado en la década de 1950 como ayuda para crear sistemas de defensa militar. (Véase también *Método de trayectoria crítica*.)

Project digraph (p. 437) A digraph representing a large project, in which the vertices represent the subtasks of the project and the directed edges show the immediate prerequisite(s) for each task.

Dígrafo del proyecto (pág. 437) Grafo que representa un proyecto grande, en el cual los vértices representan los sub-proyectos del proyecto y las aristas dirigidas muestran los prerrequisito(s) para cada trabajo.

• **Q** •

Quadratic equation An equation that can be expressed in the form $ax^2 + bx + c = 0$ $(a \neq 0)$.

Ecuación cuadrática Ecuación que puede expresarse en la forma $ax^2 + bx + c = 0$ $(a \neq 0)$.

Quadratic formula (p. 340) A formula for the solutions of a quadratic equation in the form $ax^2 + bx + c = 0$: $x = \frac{-b}{2a} \pm \frac{\sqrt{b^2 - 4ac}}{2a}$.

Formula cuadrática (pág. 340) Fórmula para las soluciones a una ecuación cuadrática que puede expresarse en la forma $ax^2 + bx + c = 0$: $x = \frac{-b}{2a} \pm \frac{\sqrt{b^2 - 4ac}}{2a}$.

Quadratic function A function with rule of correspondence that can be expressed in the algebraic form $f(x) = ax^2 + bx + c$ $(a \neq 0)$.

Función cuadrática Función con regla de correspondencia que puede expresarse en la forma algebraica $f(x) = ax^2 + bx + c$ $(a \neq 0)$.

Glossary/Glosario

Random digit A digit selected from 0, 1, 2, 3, 4, 5, 6, 7, 8, 9 in a way that makes each of the digits equally likely to be chosen (has probability $\frac{1}{10}$); successive random digits should be independent, which means that if you know what random digits have already been selected, each digit from 0 through 9 still has probability $\frac{1}{10}$ of being the next digit.

Range of a function (p. 330) For a function f, the values of the dependent variable y corresponding to values of x in the domain of f. (Also called *output values* of the function.)

Rank correlation (p. 259) A correlation based on two different rankings of the same items. Two types of rank correlation are Spearman's and Kendall's.

Rare event (p. 566) In a waiting-time distribution, an event that falls in the upper 5% of the distribution.

Rectangle A quadrilateral with opposite sides congruent and four right angles.

Regression equation (p. 282) The equation of the least squares regression line for the points on a scatterplot.

Regression line See *least squares regression line.*

Regular polygon A polygon in which all sides are congruent and all angles are congruent.

Residual (error) (p. 283) For points used to calculate the regression equation, the difference between the observed value of y and the value of y predicted by the regression equation, $y - \hat{y}$.

Response variable See *dependent variable.*

Rhombus A quadrilateral with all four sides congruent.

Rigid transformation (p. 196) A transformation of points in the plane that repositions figures without changing their shape or size.

Dígito aleatorio Dígito escogido de 0, 1, 2, 3, 4, 5, 6, 7, 8, 9 de modo que cada uno tenga la misma probabilidad de elegirse que cualquier otro (tiene probabilidad $\frac{1}{10}$); los dígitos aleatorios consecutivos deben ser independientes, o sea, se conocen los dígitos aleatorios ya escogidos, cada dígito de 0 a 9 aún tiene $\frac{1}{10}$ de escogerse cono el dígito siguiente.

Rango de una función (pág. 330) Para una función f, los valores de las variables dependientes y que corresponden con los valores de x en el dominio de f. (También llamada *valores de salida* de la función.)

Correlación de rango (pág. 259) Correlación basada en dos diferentes rangos del mismo objeto. Dos tipos de rangos son los de Spearman y de Kendall.

Evento raro (pág. 566) En una distribución de espera de tiempo, un evento que está en el 5% superior de la distribución.

Rectángulo Cuadrilátero con lados opuestos congruentes y cuatro ángulos rectos.

Ecuación de regresión (pág. 282) Ecuación de la recta de regresión de los mínimos cuadrados para los puntos en una gráfica de dispersión.

Recta de regresión Véase *línea de regresión de mínimos cuadrados.*

Polígono regular Polígono cuyos lados y ángulos son todos congruentes.

Residuo (error) (pág. 283) Para puntos que se usan para calcular la ecuación de la regresión, la diferencia entre el valor observado de y y el valor y predicho por la ecuación de la regresión, $y - \hat{y}$.

Variable respuesta Véase *variable dependiente.*

Rombo Cuadrilátero con cuatro lados congruentes.

Transformación rígida (pág. 196) Una transformación de puntos en un plano que vuelve a colocar figuras sin cambiar su forma o tamaño.

Glossary/Glosario

English	Español
Rotation (p. 161) A rigid transformation of points in the plane that rotates (or turns) figures about a specified point, called the *center of rotation*, through a specified angle, called the *directed angle of rotation*.	**Rotación** (pág. 161) Transformación rígida de puntos en un plano en la que una figura gira en torno a un punto fijo, llamado *centro de rotación*, y a través de un ángulo especificado, llamado *ángulo dirigido de rotación*.
Rotation matrix (p. 232) A matrix, which when multiplied on the right by a point matrix, has the effect of rotating the point about the origin through a specified angle.	**Matriz rotación** (pág. 232) Matriz que al multiplicarse a la derecha por un punto de matriz tiene el efecto de rotar el punto del origen a través de un ángulo dado.
Row matrix (p. 105) A matrix consisting of one row. (Also called a *one-row matrix* or a *row vector*.)	**Matriz fila** (pág. 105) Matriz que consta de una fila. (También llamada *matriz de una fila* o *vector fila*.)
Row of an $m \times n$ matrix (p. 76) A horizontal array of n numbers in the matrix.	**Fila de una matriz $m \times n$** (pág. 76) Arreglo horizontal de n números en la matriz.
Row sum of a matrix (p. 81) The sum of all the numbers in a row of a matrix.	**Suma de fila de una matriz** (pág. 81) Suma de todos los números de la fila de una matriz.

· (S) ·

English	Español
Sample space A list of all possible outcomes of a chance situation.	**Espacio muestral** Lista de todos los resultados posibles de un suceso.
Scalar multiplication See *multiply a matrix by a number*.	**Multiplicación escalar** Véase *multiplicar una matriz por un número*.
Scale factor of a size (or similarity) transformation (p. 215) The ratio of the distance between any two image points and the distance between their preimages under the transformation.	**Factor de escala de una transformación de tamaño (o similitud)** (pág. 215) Radio de distancia entre cualquiera dos puntos de una imagen y la distancia entre sus preimagenes bajo la transformación.
Scatterplot matrix (p. 266) A matrix where each entry is a scatterplot formed using a pair of variables from a set of multivariate data.	**Matriz de gráfica de dispersión** (pág. 266) Matriz en la cual cada entrada es una gráfica de dispersión formada usando un par de variables de un conjunto de datos multivariados.
Similar figures (p. 215) Figures that are related by a similarity transformation. These figures have the same shape, regardless of position or orientation, but may be of different scales.	**Figuras semejantes** (pág. 215) Figuras que se relacionan por una transformación de similitud. Estas figuras tienen la misma forma, sin importar la posición u orientación pero pueden ser de diferentes escalas.
Similarity transformation (p. 196) Composition of a size transformation and a rigid transformation (possibly the *identity transformation*). Such a transformation resizes a figure in the plane without changing its shape.	**Transformación de similitud** (pág. 196) Composición de una transformación de tamaño y una transformación rígida (posiblemente la *transformación de identidad*). Tal transformación cambia de tamaño en el plano sin cambiar su forma.
Simulation Imitating a real-life situation by creating a mathematical model that captures the situation's essential characteristics.	**Simulación** Imitación de una situación real al crear un modelo matemático que captura las características esenciales de la situación.

Glossary/Glosario

English	Español

Sine function (p. 457) If $P(x, y)$ is a point (not the origin) on the terminal side of an angle θ in standard position and $r = \sqrt{x^2 + y^2}$, then $\sin \theta = \frac{y}{r}$. If A is an acute angle in a right triangle, then $\sin A = \frac{\text{length of side } opposite \angle A}{\text{length of } hypotenuse}$.

Función de seno (pág. 457) Si $P(x, y)$ es un punto (no el origen) en el lado terminal de un ángulo θ en posición estándar y $r = \sqrt{x^2 + y^2}$, entonces $\sin \theta = \frac{y}{r}$. Si A es un ángulo agudo en un triángulo rectángulo, entonces $\sin A = \frac{\text{medida del cateto } opuesto\ a \angle A}{\text{medida de la } hipotenusa}$.

Size of a matrix (p. 76) The number of rows and columns in a matrix, denoted by (*number of rows*) × (*number of columns*).

Tamaño de una matriz (pág. 76) Número de filas y columnas en una matriz, indicado por (*número de filas*) × (*número de columnas*).

Size transformation (or *dilation*) (p. 205) A transformation that moves each point P in the plane along a ray through P from a specified point O, called the *center of the transformation*, according to the rule $OP' = kOP$, where P' is the image of P and $k \neq 0$ (k is called the *scale factor* or *magnitude* of the transformation).

Transformación de tamaño (o *dilatación*) (pág. 205) Transformación que mueve cada punto P en el plano a lo largo de una semirrecta a través de P del punto dado O, llamado *centro de la transformación*, según la regla $OP' = kOP$, donde P' es la imagen de P y $k \neq 0$ (k se llama el *factor de posicionamiento* o *magnitud* de la transformación.

Slope of a line Ratio of change in y-coordinates to change in x-coordinates between any two points on a nonvertical line; $\frac{change\ in\ y}{change\ in\ x}$ or $\frac{\Delta y}{\Delta x}$; indicates the direction and steepness of a line.

Pendiente de una recta Radio de cambio en las coordenadas y para cambiar en las coordenadas x entre dos puntos cualesquiera en una recta no vertical; $\frac{cambio\ en\ y}{cambio\ en\ x}$ o $\frac{\Delta y}{\Delta x}$; indica la dirección e inclinación de una recta.

Square matrix (p. 138) A matrix with the same number of rows and columns.

Matriz cuadrada (pág. 138) Matriz con el mismo número de filas y columnas.

Spanning tree (p. 403) A tree in a vertex-edge graph that includes all the vertices of the graph.

Árbol de expansión (pág. 403) Árbol en un grafo que incluye todos los vértices de la gráfica.

Strength of a correlation (p. 260) The association between two variables is strong if the points cluster closely to the regression line and weak if the distances from the regression line to the points tend to be large.

Fuerza de una correlación (pág. 260) La asociación entre dos variables es fuerte si los puntos se agrupan cerca de la recta de regresión y débil si las distancias de la recta de regresión a los puntos tiende a ser grande.

Subscript notation (p. 189) A letter or number displayed slightly below a variable. Subscripts are used to discriminate between variables that have the same letter symbol.

Notación de subíndice (pág. 189) Una letra o número que aparece ligeramente debajo de una variable. Las notaciones de subíndice se usan para discriminar entre variables que tienen el mismo símbolo de la letra.

Substitution method (p. 51) A method used to solve a system of linear equations. Two equations with two variables are combined into a single equation with only one variable by *substituting* an expression for a variable from one equation into the other.

Método de substitución (pág. 51) Método que se utiliza para resolver un sistema de ecuaciones lineales. Dos ecuaciones con dos variables se combinan en una sola ecuación con únicamente una variable al *sustituir* una expresión por una variable de una ecuación a la otra.

Glossary/Glosario

English	Español

Sum of squared errors (SSE or sum of squared residuals) (p. 285) The sum of the squared residuals, $SSE = \Sigma(y - \hat{y})^2$.

Suma de cuadrados debido al error (SSE, por sus siglas en inglés, o suma de residuales cuadrados) (pág. 285) La suma de residuos cuadrados, $SSE = \Sigma(y - \hat{y})^2$.

Symmetric matrix (p. 92) A square matrix that exhibits reflection symmetry about its main diagonal.

Matriz simétrica (pág. 92) Matriz cuadrada que muestra simetría de reflexión de su diagonal principal.

System of equations A set of two or more equations with two or more variables for which common solution(s) are sought.

Sistema de ecuaciones Conjunto de dos o más ecuaciones con dos o más variables para las cuales se buscan solución(es) en común.

· (T) ·

Tangent (p. 180) A line is *tangent* to a given curve at a point, called the *point of tangency*, if the line touches the curve at that point, but does not cross the curve at that point.

Tangente (pág. 180) Una recta es *tangente* de una curva dada en un punto, llamado *punto de tangencia*, si la recta pasa a través de la curva en sólo un punto pero no cruza la curva en ese punto.

Tangent function (p. 462) If $P(x, y)$ is a point (not the origin) on the terminal side of an angle θ in standard position and $r = \sqrt{x^2 + y^2}$, then $\tan\theta = \frac{y}{x}$ ($x \neq 0$). If A is an acute angle in a right triangle, then $\tan A = \frac{\text{length of side } opposite \angle A}{\text{length of side } adjacent \text{ to } \angle A}$.

Función de tangente (pág. 462) Si $P(x, y)$ es un punto (no el origen) en el lado terminal de un ángulo θ en posición estándar y $r = \sqrt{x^2 + y^2}$, entonces $\tan\theta = \frac{y}{x}$ ($x \neq 0$). Si A es un ángulo agudo en un triángulo rectángulo, entonces, $\tan A = \frac{\text{la medida del cateto } opuesto \text{ a } \angle A}{\text{la medida del cateto } adyacente \text{ a } \angle A}$.

Taxi-distance (p. 191) The shortest distance between two locations following a path along the edges of a square grid (or parallel to those edges).

Distancia taxi (pág. 191) La menor distancia entre dos posiciones seguida de un camino a lo largo de las aristas de una cuadrícula cuadrada (o paralela a esas aristas).

Terminal side of an angle (p. 461) The position of a ray that is the side of an angle after rotating about the angle's vertex from the initial position.

Lado terminal de un ángulo (pág. 461) La posición de una semirrecta que es el lado de un ángulo después de rotar en torno al vértice del ángulo de una posición inicial.

Transformation (p. 161) A one-to-one correspondence (function) between points of a plane.

Transformación (pág. 161) Correspondencia (función) biunívoca entre dos puntos de un plano.

Translation (p. 197) A rigid transformation that shifts all points in the plane a specified distance and direction, determined by the *translation vector*.

Traslación (pág. 197) Transformación rígida que cambia todos los puntos en el plano a una distancia y dirección dadas, determinadas por el *vector de traslación*.

Transpose of a matrix (p. 126) The matrix obtained from a given matrix A by interchanging the rows and columns of A. Denoted by A^T.

Trasposición de una matriz (pág. 126) Matriz que se obtiene de una matriz dada A al intercambiar las filas y columnas de A, la cual se denomina A^T.

Glossary/Glosario

<table>
<tr><th>English</th><th>Español</th></tr>
<tr><td>

Traveling Salesperson Problem (p. 407) A problem related to vertex-edge graphs stated informally as follows: A sales representative wants to visit several different cities, each exactly once, and then return home. Among the possible routes, which will minimize the total distance traveled? (Also called the *Traveling Salesman Problem* or the *TSP*.)

Tree (p. 403) A connected graph that has no circuits.

Trial (or sometimes *run*) One repetition of a simulation.

Trigonometric functions (p. 457) The sine, cosine, and tangent functions and (to be defined in a later course) their reciprocals.

TSP See *Traveling Salesperson Problem*.

</td><td>

Problema del vendedor viajero (pág. 407) Problema relacionado informalmente con grafos de la siguiente manera: un vendedor quiere visitar diferentes ciudades, solamente una vez cada una, y después regresar a casa. De entre los resultados posibles, ¿cuál minimizará la distancia total que se viaja? (También conocido como *TSP*, por sus siglas en inglés.)

Árbol (pág. 403) Gráfica conectada que no tiene circuitos.

Prueba Repetición de un simulacro.

Funciones trigonométricas (pág. 457) Funciones de seno, coseno y tangente y (se definirán en un curso posterior) sus recíprocos.

TSP Véase *Problema del vendedor viajero*.

</td></tr>
</table>

···············(V)···············

<table>
<tr><td>

Venn diagram A diagram where mutually exclusive events are represented by non-overlapping circles and events that are not mutually exclusive are represented by overlapping circles.

Vertex-edge graph (p. 68) A diagram consisting of points (called *vertices*) along with segments or arcs (called *edges*) joining some of the points. (Also simply called a *graph*.)

</td><td>

Diagrama de Venn Diagrama en el cual los eventos mutuamente excluyentes se presentan por círculos no sobrepuestos y los eventos que no son mutuamente excluyentes se presentan por círculos sobrepuestos.

Grafo (pág. 68) Diagrama que consta de un conjunto de puntos (los *vértices*) junto con segmentos o arcos (las *artistas*) que unen algunos de los puntos. (También llamada simplemente una *gráfica*.)

</td></tr>
</table>

···············(W)···············

<table>
<tr><td>

Waiting-time (geometric) distribution (p. 525) A probability distribution of the number of independent trials required to get a specified outcome called a "success." The probability that a success will occur must be the same on every trial.

Weighted graph (p. 403) A vertex-edge graph with numbers (*weights*) on its edges.

Weights (p. 403) Numbers that are placed on the edges (or vertices) of a vertex-edge graph.

With replacement Selecting a sample from a set so that each selection is replaced before selecting the next; thus, a member of the set can be selected more than once.

</td><td>

Distribución (geométrica) del tiempo de espera (pág. 525) Distribución probabilística del número de pruebas independientes requeridas para obtener un resultado especificado llamado "éxito." La probabilidad de que un éxito suceda debe ser la misma en cada prueba.

Gráfico cargado (pág. 403) Grafo con números (*pesos*) en sus aristas.

Pesos (pág. 403) Números que se colocan en las artistas (o vértices) de un grafo.

Con devolución Selección de una muestra de un conjunto de modo que cada selección se devuelve antes de elegir la siguiente; así cada miembro del conjunto puede escogerse más de una vez.

</td></tr>
</table>

Glossary/Glosario

English	**Español**

Without replacement Selecting a sample from a set so that each selection is not replaced before selecting the next; no member of the set can be selected more than once.

Sin devolución Selección de una muestra de un conjunto de modo que cada selección no se devuelve antes de elegir la siguiente; así cada miembro del conjunto no puede escogerse más de una vez.

- - - - - - - - - - - - - - - (X) - - - - - - - - - - - - - - -

x-intercept(s) of a graph The point(s) where the graph intersects the *x*-axis.

Intersección(es) *x* de una gráfica El punto o los puntos en que una gráfica interseca el eje *x*.

- - - - - - - - - - - - - - - (Y) - - - - - - - - - - - - - - -

y-intercept(s) of a graph The point(s) where the graph intersects the *y*-axis.

Intersección(es) *y* de una gráfica El punto o los puntos en que una gráfica interseca el eje *y*.

- - - - - - - - - - - - - - - (Z) - - - - - - - - - - - - - - -

Zero matrix (p. 134) A matrix in which every entry is 0. See *additive identity matrix*.

Matriz cero (pág. 134) Matriz en la cual cada entrada es cero. Véase *matriz identidad aditiva*.

Index of Mathematical Topics

Index of Mathematical Topics (continued)

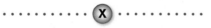

Index of Contexts

Index of Contexts (continued)

Index of Contexts (continued)

Index of Contexts (continued)

Index of Contexts (continued)

Index of Contexts *(continued)*

Index of Contexts (continued)

Index of Contexts (continued)

Index of Contexts (continued)

Photo Credits